Under the Editorship of

GARDNER MURPHY

Principles of Abnormal Psychology

Principles of Abnormal Psychology:

The Dynamics of Psychic Illness

REVISED EDITION

A. H. MASLOW, Ph.D.
BROOKLYN COLLEGE
and
BÉLA MITTELMANN, M.D.
NEW YORK UNIVERSITY-BELLEVUE MEDICAL CENTER

Harper & Brothers Publishers New York

PRINCIPLES OF ABNORMAL PSYCHOLOGY:
THE DYNAMICS OF PSYCHIC ILLNESS, REVISED EDITION

Printed in the United States of America

C-A

Contents

Foreword to the First Edition

This book attempts to present an integrated picture of what we know of the psychologically disturbed individual. In this attempt we have used contributions from a wide variety of sources—from clinical, experimental, hypnotic, comparative, psychoanalytic, and psychobiological observations. Our aim was to avoid polemics and to utilize and synthesize whatever good material was available. We have brought to this task two traditions that are certainly ready for fusion, namely, the experimental-academic and the clinical-medical.

We found that this synthesis could be accomplished best in terms of dynamic psychology. This word has several meanings for us. For one thing, it means greater stress on the motivational or conative aspects of psychic life, and, more particularly, on motivations of which the individual is not fully aware. Secondly, in the study of psychopathology it means an emphasis on the meanings and motivational roles of symptoms. Most important of all, perhaps, it means that every psychic state is, by definition, also a motivating state. For example, a state of fear always leads to further reactions, i.e., flight, submission, attack. We are interested not only in what special state the individual is in, but also what he does about it. Thus our emphasis is directed away from the purely static description, listing, and analysis of psychic states to the study of the dynamic interplay, interdependence, and motivational roles of these states. We emphasize the interrelation between the various responses of the individual, the broad patterns that are observable in his reactions—in other words, the integrated features manifested in his experiences and total behavior.

The concepts and terminology used have been derived from the study of abnormal psychological phenomena. Operationally, however, we have utilized and adopted observations and concepts from other fields of psychology. For example, conditioned responses mean to us not only a linear connection between stimulus and response, but a reaction pattern of the individual in response to situations, on the basis of previous experience, depending on his immediate state, and involving broad needs and goals such as complex physiological drives and needs for safety. Similarly, disturbances of conditioned reactions involve disturbances in the state of the individual and in the condition of his drives and needs.

We have been constantly influenced in our thinking by the methodology and, concepts of Gestalt psychology; all data have to be considered and evaluated in terms of interrelated patterns which can be described as smaller and larger configurations and as varying relationships of the individual with the environment.

We have attempted to bring into this structure the psychological implications of modern anthropology and sociology. One of the authors has done psychological field work with a so-called "primitive" society. This ever-present contrast with our own culture has, we hope, helped us to be more sophisticated about the role of culture in the psychic life of the individual.

Pedagogically we have attempted to make this book not only intelligible but plausible to the average college student who is willing to read it carefully. We have used case material generously, a good deal of it from our own case files. A survey of the Table of Contents will show that this book differs considerably from other texts. It is our hope that this is an improvement.

We have tried to make the book less forbidding by having as few footnotes as possible, and by removing from the text as many bibliographical interruptions as we dared. We hope that the scientists, upon whose work we have built, will not feel this to be a lack of gratefulness; it is done for the student's sake. The bibliography is fairly full.

Our work received considerable stimulus from the conference on the problems of interrelation between psychological and physiological disturbances called by Dr. Howard S. Liddell at Cornell University in Ithaca and sponsored by the Josiah Macy, Jr., Foundation. The participants were: Drs. F. Alexander, M. Altman, O. D. Anderson, C. Binger, F. Deutsch, H. F. Dunbar, S. Dworkin, J. Eisenbud, J. Finesinger, L. K. Frank, F. Fremont-Smith, H. Gantt, D. M. Levy, H. S. Liddell, B. Mittelmann, N. S. Moore, R. Parmenter, L. Saul, G. E. Sutherland, W. P. Van Wagenen, H. G. Wolff, and other members of Dr. Liddell's staff.

We have had the benefit of discussion with many leading representatives of the various points of view which have been influencing us. We wish to thank Drs. Ruth Benedict, Margaret Mead, Ralph Linton, Gregory Bateson, and the many other anthropologists with whom we have discussed the cultural aspects of our joint problems. Drs. Benedict and Mead were also good enough to read and criticize preliminary drafts of certain parts of the manuscript.

In addition to the writings of Freud and the many other authors quoted, we have utilized for this synthesis the recent psychoanalytic contributions, both verbally communicated and printed, of Drs. Erich Fromm, Karen Horney, Abram Kardiner, David M. Levy, and Sandor Rado, as well as the published contributions of Franz Alexander and other members of the Chicago Institute for Psychoanalysis.

We have also extensively drawn on the field of psychobiology as evolved in the writings of Adolf Meyer and the other authors quoted, particularly the books by Dr. Oskar Diethelm and Dr. Wendell Muncie. These contributions have become an integral part of psychiatric thinking.

One of the authors (B. M.) has collaborated with Dr. Harold G. Wolff at the Cornell University Medical College for several years in psychosomatic research, and has applied the results and formulations evolved in that investigation to the present synthesis.

We have been strongly influenced by the methods of Dr. Max Wertheimer and Dr. Kurt Lewin. Those who are familiar with their profound thinking will detect their influence in many pages of this book. The influence of Dr. Kurt Goldstein's important book, *The Organism,* is also to be noted.

One of the authors (A. H. M.) has benefited greatly by discussions with Dr. Alfred Adler, and has attempted to give proper emphasis to his contributions to psychopathology.

Dr. Clark Hull and his many collaborators are chiefly responsible for the understanding of the role that the Pavlovian conditioning theory may eventually play in abnormal psychology.

For reading various portions of the manuscript and for various helpful suggestions, we wish to thank Drs. Ruth Munroe, Frank Fremont-Smith, David M. Levy, Miss Jane Belo, and Drs. Walter Briehl, Eugene C. Milch, Jon Eisenson, and Gerald Lawlor.

We are especially grateful to Dr. Abram Kardiner, for his suggestions and formulations in the section on traumatic neuroses, and to Dr. David Rapaport and Dr. Ruth Munroe for their valuable aid with the section on projective methods of examination.

Finally, we wish to thank Dr. Gardner Murphy, the editor of this series, for his encouragement and his suggestions. Discussions with him have been most stimulating in achieving an adequate synthesis between "social" and "biological" considerations.

We are deeply grateful to Miss Ida Kramer and Miss Evelyn Green, our secretaries and assistants, for their many hours of untiring work and their many useful suggestions. We also wish to thank Miss Irma Grable for her typing and clerical assistance, Miss Frances Corn for her research and helpful suggestions, Miss Ruth Ritzman for typing, and Mr. John Honiggman for his help in preparing the index.

We wish to express our extreme gratitude to Miss Dorothy Thompson, of Harper & Brothers, for her indispensable help in determining the form of this book. We feel that her suggestions have made our thoughts much more lucid and understandable.

A. H. M.
B. M.

Foreword to the Revised Edition

As stated in the Foreword to the First Edition, this book attempts to present an integrated picture of what we know of the psychologically disturbed individual, utilizing clinical, experimental, psychoanalytic, psychobiological, comparative, sociological, and anthropological observations.

This revised edition contains some entirely new sections: on the nature and form of psychological disturbances in infants, children, adolescents, and old age; on character disturbances and psychopathy; on reactions to conditions of war; on somatic methods of treating mental disorders; on psychotherapy of children; and on guidance in occupational settings, schools, industry, and social work. All other topics have been brought up to date and, as a result, changes have been made in all chapters of the book except in the first one. Particularly extensive were the revisions in the sections on social and cultural aspects of the etiology of psychopathological reactions, on schizophrenia, on psychosomatic syndromes, and on psychotherapy of adults. The chapter on animal neurosis has been omitted, and the material from it, with many new additions, has been integrated throughout the text.

We hope that the new edition, as a whole, represents a more successful attainment of our original aims of integration of the many sources of information.

This revision was undertaken by one of the authors, Béla Mittelmann, in consultation with A. H. Maslow. Miss Laura Malkenson surveyed new developments in some of the fields of abnormal psychology and prepared the index. She is responsible for some of the new material, particularly in the section on projective tests.

We want to express our appreciation to Ruth Munroe and to Gardner and Lois Murphy for many stimulating discussions on topics in the book, to Dr. Paul Hoch for reading the manuscript and offering many valuable suggestions, and to Dr. Archie Silver for reading and commenting on the sections dealing with infants and children.

BÉLA MITTELMANN

January, 1951

PART I

Introductory Concepts

1 Introductory Survey: A Typical Case

Before we go into the complexities and specific details of abnormal psychology, let us see if it is not possible to get some preliminary notion of the *whole* of the material. We are, after all, aiming in this book at a better understanding of human nature, of the total personality, in so far as this can be obtained through the study of psychopathology. The following case is typical enough so that we can draw from it some idea of the kind of phenomena with which we have to deal, of the difficulties we shall meet, and of the paths over which we shall travel toward better understanding. After this bird's-eye survey, the student may find it easier to enter the maze of problems and questions through which he must pass before arriving at his goal, a better understanding of himself and of the people about him.

A woman twenty-eight years old developed attacks of heart palpitation, difficulty in breathing, choking sensation, dizziness, and trembling of the hands. The attacks were accompanied by an acute fear of dying. At times, she felt that the walls were closing in on her, or that she was alone on a great height, or that she was a small thing in the mesh of gigantic circumstances. The patient was examined by a physician, who found her physically healthy. The psychological examination revealed that the attacks started about two months previously, under the following conditions: She had been married three years. When she married, an unusual agreement was made at her husband's suggestion: if either of them should wish to dissolve the marriage, the other would make no objection. About two months earlier, that is, just before the patient's attacks began, her husband announced that he was leaving to work permanently in South America. With this, he suggested that they dissolve the marriage. The patient was sad and was disturbed by this, but she raised no objections, according to their agreement. Not long after, she had her first attack of palpitation, accompanied by the fear of dying.

During the past two months, the patient's work as supervisor in a library suffered. She frequently felt tired, or preoccupied and tense. On such occasions, she made mistakes in her work, found it difficult to concentrate, and was easily exhausted. She became irritable, and had frequent disagreements with her colleagues. She did not sleep well. She lost her appetite. She was still living with her husband but derived no pleasure from sex relations.

Previous Difficulties. About eight years before these attacks, the patient had had severe attacks of anxiety under the following circumstances: She went to the hospital for a minor operation which was not at all dangerous. In the hospital, however, she became terror-stricken, was afraid that she would die, and had palpitation and difficulty in breathing. During this period, she was much disturbed and frightened by the fact that she had to stay in bed for several days. Her discomfort continued after she left the hospital, but subsided in about a month.

The Patient's Condition Between Periods of Attack. The patient was an efficient worker and had advanced in her position. She had some friendships of long duration. She enjoyed going to the theater, reading books, seeing friends, eating good food. A careful survey of her reactions and mode of living, however, showed that some difficulties were present practically all the time. She was often possessive and over-sensitive with her friends. She was tense in her work, and she was apt to be upset by any mistake or criticism. She was occasionally moody and worrisome; she did not quite know why. At times she felt exhausted and had difficulty in carrying on her work. Her husband was the first man with whom she had been in love; she had never before been able to be close to men, even though she had longed for such closeness.

The circumstances of her attachment to him were also interesting. The people who introduced him to her told her that he was "flighty." He himself agreed with that statement. He pursued her ardently and praised her because of her appearance, her tastes, and her interests. He told her, even before proposing, that he wanted to have an affair with her. She, however, wanted to get married, but had not made up her mind whether she wanted to marry him. He later made the suggestion of their liberty to dissolve their possible marriage, and soon thereafter she fell in love with him. The marriage was a happy one, for they had many interests in common. He was jocular, gay, and complimentary. He was, however, often busy with his work in the evening; this troubled her at first. As far as she knew, he had always been faithful to her. She usually reached an orgasm, but with some difficulty.

Childhood History. The patient was the older of two siblings. She had pneumonia when she was four years old; she herself did not remember this. Her father, a warm and affectionate person, died when she was six years old. She had been more attached to him than to her mother. Her mother, who was still alive, was emotionally unapproachable, never demonstrative, but worrisome and rather exacting in discipline. She (the mother) preferred the patient's sister. The mother was over-solicitous and rather strict about the patient's eating habits and excretory functions as a child. She was always strict in moral questions. The patient remembered being unhappy about her sister, and having quarrels with her. She was unhappy also when thinking about her father. As a child she was irritable, was afraid of the dark, and at one period was panicky if she was alone in the room, even for a short period. When she was seven years old, she wet her bed for a period of time.

Treatment and Outcome of Her Condition. The patient received mental hygiene treatment. She came twice a week for interviews. At these interviews, the information given above was obtained and discussed with her. After two visits, the patient's condition began to improve; she was permanently freed of her attacks of anxiety after six weeks of treatment. She separated from her husband and stood the separation well. The patient was seen by the therapist at six-month intervals for four years. It is significant that, after her acute symptoms and complaints subsided, she had the same difficulty in finding a man to whom she could be attached as she had had before she met her husband. Minor difficulties with her work and relationships with her friends likewise remained. The type of treatment administered to her does not, as a rule, correct such character difficulties.

GENERAL DISCUSSION

This case has been chosen purposely. It is not a very severe case. We may say that the woman suffers from a moderately severe neurosis. She seeks the same things that every other person seeks—happiness, love, and self-respect. But she does this in a rather peculiar way. Furthermore, we from the outside can see clearly that her technique of seeking love and happiness is "bad," for it almost guarantees the opposite of what she is seeking.

Why does she behave in such a way? What peculiar logic forces her to feel and behave as she does? We shall make a few broad generalizations and then take up a few of the more technical aspects of this case.

First, let us say that in general the study of such patients will *always* show that the symptoms are the ways in which a certain kind of personality will react to the fact of frustration or conflict, which is precipitated by an external situation and which threatens the loss of gratification or love or self-respect. These symptoms are meaningful and logical—even if the logic is private, personal, and peculiar—in the sense that most frequently they serve a purpose or fulfill a function. These processes guard the individual against further loss or hurt; or they serve to get revenge, to change the situation, to retrieve what was lost, to make some integration or compromise that gives partial satisfaction to all the conflicting elements in the situation, etc.

METHODS OF ANALYSIS

Since the character structure is very important in this picture, we first try to get some idea of what sort of person we are dealing with. There are two good ways of doing this, both necessary and both used simultaneously. First, we try to understand the development of the personality. The question here is, "How did she get to be the way she is?" Usually the patient's childhood relationships to her parents are studied, for the chances are that the whole pattern of her personality, her attitude toward life, and the general trend of her style of adjustment to life were acquired in early life (not always, but usually).

Second, we analyze the personality as we find it actually existing, in all its internal interrelationships and structures, and in all its relationships and reactions to the current problems set for the individual by the world she is living in. The first type of analysis we may call "genetic analysis"; the second type, "character analysis."

Now let us turn back to our patient. The outstanding fact on the genetic side is that she did not get enough love as a child (rejection). Her mother was not affectionate, and she preferred the sister (leading to sibling rivalry). Her father, who was affectionate, died when she was young. People who are starved of love when they are children usually grow up to be what we call "insecure personalities."

We know a good deal about such people and can describe their symptoms with fair accuracy. However, just putting a label on this patient and describing her symptoms does not help much. This is what is called *static*, descriptive psychology. If we want to understand her character to the point where we can help her, we must understand her *dynamically*. That is, we need to understand how she feels about her symptoms, how she reacts to and against them, what their function is, what they lead her to do. In a word, we wish to understand how these symptoms act as motives or drives to further processes.

Our patient's reaction to rejection and her consequent insecurity were a kind of defensiveness, a tendency to keep up her guard *always* so that she would not be hurt again as she had been in childhood. Mostly, this meant isolation from men, and a refusal to fall in love. She was afraid of love, because that meant letting her defenses drop and becoming vulnerable to hurt. When she sought for love as a youngster, she was hurt; and she will tend to go through life with this habitual expectation. It is for this reason that it becomes difficult for her to let herself go, to fall really in love without any reservations. In a word, she is forced by her character, which is a creation of her past, to make reservations and restrictions, all of which indicate fundamental mistrust and expectations of hurt. She does this to guard against further hurt; but while these guards defend her against hurt, they also make love impossible or difficult.

We do not wish to paint too black a picture. Many such people have been gradually weaned from this mistrustful attitude toward life by a psychologically good marriage in which they were loved over a long period of time. In such cases, as the defenses are slowly found to be unnecessary, they are dropped and may disappear completely; the individual may become trusting, affectionate, and loving. For our patient there was no such fortunate outcome because her husband left her. The person who is lifted slowly from the bottom of a deep well and is then suddenly dashed to the bottom again may be more hurt and more embittered than one who is not lifted at all. So with our patient, who had had a taste of how good life might be. Her symptoms were worse than any she had ever experienced before, and it did her little good to realize that they were made possible only by her own reservations and initial mistrust.

THE MEANING OF THE SYMPTOMS

Such symptoms serve many purposes. In the first place, they represent in part a sheer defeat and discouragement reaction, sheer response to pain and suffering. But even this is complex, for this patient's suffering is in turn much intensified by her feeling of wounded self-esteem, with its consequent sense of helplessness, and her feeling of greater insecurity resulting from this horrible rejection. Peculiarly enough, the symptoms are also an expression of the conflict which disturbed her initially, of simultaneously wanting love and being afraid of it. Of course, she is hurt by losing her husband; but at the same time there is still a remnant of her original feeling that a husband is dangerous, so that deep down she even feels a little relieved at his loss and the removal of all the problems he represented.

The symptoms have still another meaning. It is as if they said, "See how helpless I am when you leave. I need you. Have pity and come back. I cannot do without you. I throw myself on your mercy. I am completely dependent on you."

DISCUSSION OF SOME TECHNICAL POINTS

The foregoing paragraphs give a general picture, a bird's-eye view. Now, point by point, we shall go over the case history from the standpoint of each of the various chapters in the book, to show how all the subjects discussed in them are necessary in understanding any individual case.

WHAT IS "ABNORMAL" (SICK) IN THIS PATIENT

The symptoms of sickness or disturbance in our patient discussed up to this point were as follows: (1) certain specific manifestations called symptoms, which are not present in healthy individuals—e.g., attacks of palpitation, overwhelming fear of death; (2) suffering and unhappiness; (3) impaired ability to enjoy life—e.g., less pleasure in work, in food, in sexual activity; (4) impaired efficiency—e.g., difficulties in work; (5) excessive defensiveness, chiefly in the form of isolation from men and from love, with great fear of being hurt and of being dependent. All these symptoms are important; however, as usually happens, this patient came because of the first group, which were obvious and disturbing.

THE RELATION OF HER DIFFICULTIES TO HER PERSONALITY

Careful examination of this patient's outlook on the world, on herself, on her work, and on her relationships with people shows that many features which are more easily observable during the acute period are also present during calm periods and persist after the acute symptoms subside. These reaction patterns are relatively permanent; such permanent attitudes toward the world, people, etc., may be called an aspect of her personality or character. Thus our patient had more or less permanent, even though mild, difficulties with her work, in her relationships with friends, in her attitude toward herself, and particularly in her relationships with men. The question may be asked, why are more acute manifestations of these difficulties observable during certain periods? The answer is that they occur in response to particularly difficult or acute or threatening situations. Thus the patient's severe difficulties began when she was threatened with separation from her husband. Similar symptoms had been observed once before, in the hospital episode, but they were not as severe.

THE PERSONALITY AS A WHOLE; VITAL NEEDS AND THE CONCEPT OF CONFLICT

The student must have felt by now that neurotic symptoms are not to be considered as foreign bodies within an individual's psyche but rather are closely interrelated with vital needs, with aims in life, and with attempts at solving life's problems. In other words, they have to do with the "total personality." It is also obvious from the above case that an individual's vital needs may be at cross purposes. This patient, for example, had a strong need for love, but was at the same time so afraid of it that she tried to put it out of her life. This clash of vital interests is called "conflict." The student should observe, however—and this is an extremely important point—that both of these conflicting desires really represented one and the same goal, namely, happiness, or, at any rate, comfort. There was never any question about the desirability of this goal; the only question was as to which was the best path to happiness or lack of pain. One of the most common misconceptions of the beginning student of abnormal psychology is to think of the personality as if it were made up of several different parts which are absolutely incompatible and at war with each other. This is not so, except possibly for certain very sick people. All human beings want the same things. The trouble is that there are many possible paths to these ultimate goals. When we are presented with a choice of paths, we frequently choose foolishly because of poor attitudes toward the world, usually acquired in unfortunate experiences in childhood and usually carried about unconsciously.

LIMITING THE CONCEPT OF NEUROSIS

For other reasons also, the personality of the individual with neurotic symptoms should not be considered as completely different from the personality of a healthy person. All individuals with neurosis show strength, health, and normal functioning in many respects. In many situations they behave to all intents and purposes in a healthy fashion; it is only in certain other situations that they show severe disturbances. For example, the work of our patient was good, as a whole. When she was not working under the stress of disappointment and frustration in other spheres of life, and when her work was not exposed to any criticism, she enjoyed it thoroughly and was almost perfectly efficient. When her friends showed adequate interest, were congenial, and flattered her enough, her relations with them were entirely satisfactory, at least externally.

Even here, if we examine behind the façade of the patient's functioning well in some situations, we see that there are impulses which represent certain measures she takes to function well by making the best of a bad situation. Thus she was very good in her library work and had written several scientific essays on the subject. But even in this best aspect of her work there was a factor that, by stretching the point, might be said to have a neurotic aspect. She relied on it too much; the satisfactory functioning of her personality was based almost exclusively on it; it might be said to be too important for her. Thus she had fantasies, not only that her publications would be very successful, but also that they were the most wonderful ones that had ever been printed. At times she pursued these grandiose daydreams with intense and elated emotions. We may say that they served the purpose of compensating her for her feelings of rejection and her lack of self-confidence in the rest of her life. Nevertheless, it was clear that in this aspect of her work she showed much less "neuroticism" than, for example, when her work was criticized. Then she grew highly emotional; if she was able to argue the point at all, she became illogical and incoherent, and either would not see the meaning of the criticisms or would distort them. She had to consider herself flawless and perfect in her work, and she elaborated various defenses to safeguard this picture of herself. This was the one way she had of consoling herself for other pleasures and satisfactions, which she missed, and it was the main basis for building up her self-esteem, since she allowed no one to love her.

PSYCHOSOMATIC RELATIONSHIPS

Viewing the material from another angle, the student will see that no line has been drawn in this case history between the "mind" and the "body." This patient's symptoms were a fusion of psychic and somatic symptoms. For instance, in her anxiety attacks there were both somatic manifestations—heart palpitation, disturbed respiration, tenseness, and trembling of the muscles—and psychic manifestations—the thought of dying, feelings of panic, and various fears. In short, the whole person was involved. For a full understanding of such a case, we shall have to comprehend clearly the relationships between "psychological" and "bodily" manifestations in psychopathology.

ETIOLOGY

It is not only desirable but necessary to understand the historical development that lay behind the patient's symptoms. It is true that a difficult problem, a terrifying situation, or a chronic frustration will precipitate a neurotic outbreak; but it is just as true that the reason why the individual cracks under the strain can be understood only if we understand the personality as it has been formed through his life. Thus we find ourselves, again and again, going back to the patient's earlier life for several reasons—so that we can understand the symptoms better ourselves, so that the patient may acquire insight into the meaning of his behavior, and so that we may know what specific therapeutic measures are necessary in addition to the general therapy which is used in practically all cases.

But there are two other aspects of the etiology of the personality. First, the individual is a biological organism, born into the world with certain strengths and weaknesses, with such and such a nervous system and glandular system. His biological equipment has an important bearing upon any understanding of his personality. We need not discuss the most obvious examples, such as innate feeble-mindedness or birth injuries to the brain. The fact that, because of hereditary factors, he may be four inches shorter than the average man or have too large a nose—these are biological factors that will influence the personality. We must also remember that the human animal, like every other animal, is equipped with certain innate drives, such as hunger, sex, and thirst. Deprivation in these spheres may be tremendously important psychologically.

In one way the human animal is different from all other animals, for he is the only one that has a complicated culture, passed on from generation to generation, a culture that he begins to acquire from the moment of his birth. The particular kind of culture which he "interiorizes" will determine in large part the nature of his conflicts, lay out for him the ways in which he is permitted to satisfy his desires, allow certain defense processes and forbid others, etc. Our patient, living in a competitive, relatively insecure society, naturally tends to be competitive and relatively insecure. Our society has created certain gaps between the sexes; in general, it is also characterized by an ambivalent attitude toward sex. It is natural, therefore, that in a large proportion of neurotic patients we should find conflict and ambivalence in sexual life. Thus, in order to understand our patient, we must also understand her cultural background.

PSYCHOTHERAPY

It is only on the basis of all these types of knowledge that a discussion of psychotherapy becomes possible and understandable. Psychotherapy is fundamentally different from all other forms of therapy, and it cannot be grasped until adequate psychological knowledge is acquired. It is therefore impossible to say much about it at this point.

RÉSUMÉ

In the case cited above, we specified just why the patient was considered maladjusted or sick. We also saw in this case the intimate relations between psychic and bodily manifestations in motivation and emotion as well as in appearance of symptoms. It was shown briefly that the essential part of the picture was a subsurface phenomenon, almost entirely unconscious. The patient did not realize what her conflicts were; she was totally unaware of the unconscious defensive processes which she had automatically elaborated to handle the situation; she did not realize that her self-esteem and security were being attacked and that, in various ways, she was attempting to defend them. Some sources of her trouble were found in the immediate situation, and others in her character structure, which in turn was found to be a product of her life history. A certain type of therapy was used which relieved the severest symptoms. The particular disturbance from which she suffered is called "anxiety hysteria."

Thus we see that if we attempt to understand any case of maladjustment, we must bring to bear upon it all the resources of modern psychology.

SUGGESTED READINGS

Probably the best introduction to the study is a popularization by George Preston, *Psychiatry for the Curious* (742). We recommend also such popular treatments as Menninger's *The Human Mind* (639), Hendrick's *Facts and Theories of Psychoanalysis* (403), and Zweig (1015). Case readings are desirable. Some may be found in Menninger. A good collection is Burton and Harris, *Case Histories in Clinical and Abnormal Psychology* (140). Of course, there are always a few in any textbook of abnormal psychology or psychiatry. For different approaches to the problems raised, see White's textbook (973) and Cameron (147). Interesting and instructive reading is Zilboorg and Henry, *A History of Medical Psychology* (1013).

II The Meaning of "Healthy" ("Normal") and of "Sick" ("Abnormal")

Adjustment of a person may be defined as a characteristic way in which he perceives, reacts to, and solves the main problems of life. For the sake of simplicity, we may classify the main problems of life into three categories: (1) problems set by external reality in its biological and physical aspects (we must get food to eat, and we must have shelter); (2) problems set by the culture in which the person lives—its demands and prohibitions, its habits and taboos, its internal conflicts and inconsistencies; (3) the problems set by internal psychological demands; these in turn may be put under three heads: (a) the need for comfort, gratification, and the avoidance of pain; (b) the need for self-esteem, independence, achievement, and adequacy; (c) the need for security, the love of our fellow men, and a feeling of belongingness.

The words "healthy" and "sick," "normal" and "abnormal," have been used in three senses.

1. The pathological approach: We have mentioned that disturbances and conflicts in the manner of satisfying these needs may produce acute symptoms as well as habitual long-range modes of reaction. The latter we call character disturbances. Such problems are stinginess, the need to produce flawless work, and stubbornness. For example, the patient described in the first chapter worked well as a librarian, but she needed self-aggrandizing attitudes to overcome her feeling of inadequacy and helplessness in the situation. In the history of psychopathology, the extension of the investigation of psychological problems to habitual modes of reaction was a very important enlargement, but it also diminished the sharp delineation between health and sickness, between normal and abnormal. In this respect, even those individuals who did not break down in normal situations of stress, in the face of severe threat had reaction patterns similar to those of the people who did break down. In spite of this, the whole emotional

life of the individuals who did break down could not be understood and fully appreciated without taking into account their habitual modes of reaction. Conversely, the individuals who did not break down showed nevertheless a peculiar rigidity and vulnerability as regards some of the habitual modes of reaction mentioned. The recognition of the similarities in some of the dynamics of sick and healthy individuals is of great psychological importance. It implies, however, in some respects, the definition of pathology as representing only quantitative differences. In other words, an individual may be more or less "sick."

2. The statistical approach: Most psychological traits are assumed to fall into a "normal" distribution, with most of the cases in the middle and a few at the extremes. These extremes, which constitute only a small percentage of the total population, are arbitrarily lopped off and labeled "abnormal" or "pathological" or "deviant," and the far larger percentage clustering around the middle is arbitrarily called "normal" (279). This approach is of value if we recognize its limitations. Much of what lies at the extremes—delusions, anxiety attacks—is pathological; genius is not. Further, many children show an unreasonable fear between the ages of four and seven. Slight fear of harmless animals is common in women. These traits which appear in a great number of individuals are minor "sicknesses," the same way as the common cold is. (See also Morlan [685].)

3. The cultural approach: It is impossible, in many respects, to understand "abnormality" without reference to the cultural background. Some societies expect the individual to show no strong ambition, to refrain from becoming emotionally or physically violent, and to coöperate with other members of the group (Zuñi). Other societies put a premium on boasting, on ambition, on accumulation of wealth, on surpassing and vanquishing others, on certain states of violence, and on killing (Kwakiutl). Each of these two societies strongly disapproves of the "deviant" mode of behavior. It has been suggested that all concepts of normal or abnormal should be considered in terms of conformity to the cultural norms. The facts mentioned pose difficult problems which have not yet been adequately solved, but the following general statements can be made: The "dynamics" of a reaction pattern occurring in a group in which it is accepted has only partial identity with the "dynamics" of the same pattern occurring in individuals living in a society where it is not. This applies even to such phenomena as dream states and hallucinations—including hearing supernatural voices. Occurring in harmony with cultural norms, they may imply, although possibly representing conflict solutions, a desire to develop in a certain direction and to advance one's career—e.g., to become a medicine man. In the group which rejects such phenomena they represent a near-catastrophic solution of conflicts, a state of helplessness—in a word, a state of psychic illness.

In addition, we may add that normality is also relative to social status, age, and sex. Behavior that is healthy in an individual ten years of age may be unquestionably unhealthy in an individual of thirty.

MANIFESTATIONS OF PSYCHOLOGICAL HEALTH ("NORMALITY")

1. *Adequate Feelings of Security.* The feeling that one is safe in contact with fellow beings in the occupational, social, and family settings.

2. *Adequate Self-Evaluation.* This includes (a) adequate self-esteem—a feeling of value proportionate to one's individuality and achievements; (b) an adequate feeling of worth-whileness—feeling morally sound, with the feeling of no severe guilt and the ability to recognize some socially and personally unacceptable common human desires which will always be present as long as one lives in a society.

3. *Adequate Spontaneity and Emotionality.* This involves ability to form strong and lasting emotional ties, such as friendships and love relations; the ability to give adequate expression to resentment without losing control; the ability to understand and to share other people's emotions; the ability to enjoy oneself and laugh. Everyone is unhappy at times, but this must have valid reasons.

4. *Efficient Contact with Reality.* This has at least three aspects: the physical, the social, and the internal world. This implies (a) an absence of excessive fantasy; (b) a realistic and broad outlook on the world, with the ability to withstand the ordinary shocks of life, such as illness and reversals; and (c) the ability to change if external circumstances cannot be modified. A good phrase for this is "coöperation with the inevitable."

5. *Adequate Bodily Desires and the Ability to Gratify Them.* This includes (a) a healthy attitude toward bodily functions in terms of accepting them but not being preoccupied with them; (b) ability to derive pleasure from the physical things in life, such as eating and sleeping, and to recover well from fatigue; (c) sexual adequacy—healthy desire and the ability to gratify it without fear and guilt; (d) ability to perform the excretory functions adequately without shame or conflict; (e) ability to work; (f) absence of an excessive need to indulge in any of these activities, and the ability to stand, at least temporarily, a fair amount of deprivation.

6. *Adequate Self-Knowledge.* This includes (a) adequate knowledge of one's own major motives, desires, goals, ambitions, inhibitions, compensations, defenses, inferiority feelings, etc.; (b) realistic appraisal of one's own assets and liabilities. Honest self-appraisal is based on the ability to accept oneself as natural and not to repudiate any important desires or thoughts even if some of them may be socially or personally unacceptable. These will always be present as long as one lives in a society.

7. *Integration and Consistency of Personality.* This means (a) fairly

rounded development, versatility, interest in several activities; (b) morals and conscience which are not too inflexible from the group's point of view; (c) ability to concentrate; (d) no major conflicting trends within the personality, and no dissociation of personality.

8. *Adequate Life Goals.* These involve (a) achievable, realistic, and compatible goals; (b) reasonable persistence of efforts to achieve them; (c) goals which involve some good to society.

9. *Ability to Learn from Experience.* The ability to learn from experience includes not only accumulation of knowledge and acquisition of skills through practice, but also an elasticity and receptiveness and therefore absence of rigidity in the approach to handling occupational tasks. Even more important are the ability to learn spontaneously—in the muscles and bones and without the need of elaborate meditation—one's own strength, the dangers of certain situations, the possibility or certainty of success, and the carrying over of this knowledge, which is a knowledge in feeling, action, and evaluation, into reaction and behavior in the fields of interpersonal relations, the gratification of bodily needs, and pursuit of life goals. Equally important is the resultant avoidance of methods that have failed when the risk is not worth taking or better methods are available.

10. *Ability to Satisfy the Requirements of the Group.* The individual must be (a) not too unlike the other members of his group in ways that the group considers important; (b) adequately informed and essentially accepting of the folkways of his group; (c) willing and able to inhibit the drives and desires tabooed by his group; (d) able to show the fundamental strivings expected by his group: ambition, promptness, friendliness, sense of responsibility, loyalty, etc.; (e) interested in the recreational activities favored by his group.

11. *Adequate Emancipation from the Group or Culture.* This involves (a) at least some originality, individuality, the ability to consider some things good, others bad; (b) some independence of group opinions; (c) the absence of an excessive need for flattery, reassurance, or group approval; (d) some degree of tolerance and appreciation of cultural difference.

TWO EXAMPLES

Now let us see, first, what a "healthy" or "normal" individual is like in flesh and blood.

The subject is the middle of three siblings, with a sister four years younger than he and a brother three years older. His father is quick-tempered, although he does not go into rages. His mother is calm and somewhat on the submissive side. Both are affectionate and allowed the children much freedom when they were young—for instance, allowing them to take trips by themselves.

At the age of five, the subject had a nightmare in which a large animal was chasing him. He started to bite his nails at about the same time. He still does so under stress.

He was always very athletic, while his brother was more intellectual. They used to fight a lot. At that time the subject was quick-tempered, "like my father," whenever his brother said to him, "That's silly."

He got along well with his sister and treated her better than his brother did, against whom he would defend her.

When he reached a point where he equaled his brother in strength, he became calm, "like my mother." Thus there was mixed identification.

He always did good average work in school, while his brother was above average.

At the age of sixteen, he met a girl whom he courted for five years. They had frequent quarrels because of her jealousy, which, in turn, would arouse his jealousy. They broke up on an average of twice a year. However, they married after he finished college. Now they have three children, to whom he is much attached.

He went into business, in which he was successful. He makes plans covering broad outlines but is impatient with even important details. His wife is systematic, often scolds him, and gets worked up. He laughs it off.

He was a member of one of the political organizations in his community. There was corruption in the organization which he fought against unsuccessfully. Finally he decided to resign from the organization despite the fact that to do so was disadvantageous for his business.

During the war he enlisted in the service and quickly became an officer. He was in the North African campaign. He experienced some anxiety during action, but did not break down.

After the birth of his sister he saw her in the nude and learned about the difference between the sexes. He did some masturbating during puberty. He started having sexual relations at the age of sixteen and a half with friends, but not with his future wife. He now has intercourse about twice a week. While in the army, he stood the sexual frustration well, although he did not like it, and had occasional relations with other women.

He is a good mixer, with lasting friendships.

This man has engaged successfully in all important activities that his culture has a pattern for. He went through school, got married, had children, is on good terms with his family, is interested in community affairs, and even went through harrowing experiences without breakdown. Had he lived in a different place, as among the Chinese or among the Mohammedans in periods of predominant polygamy, his relationship to his parents would have been quite different, and he would have had many wives instead of one; if he had lived among the Marquesans he would have been one husband among several married to the same woman. Thus the outlook and patterns he developed are very intimately connected with the cultural environment. He went through several periods of stress, with which he coped successfully. The first one occurred around the age of five. Apparently the birth of his sister meant to him the coming of another rival, besides his brother, for the love of his parents. It is also likely that his attachment to his mother at that time was particularly intense and that he feared his father's temper. The anxiety was expressed in the nightmare of being chased by an animal and in the nail-biting. He solved this crisis, because of the persistent affection of his parents, by kindness and playfulness toward his sister. He had a continual stress situation with his brother, who very likely considered him (the subject) a rival. This struggle was fairly well resolved about puberty, when the subject came into his own. There was a situation of stress with his wife also, as witnessed by the recurrent breakups before the marriage.

Is this subject "absolutely normal"? Obviously not. Apart from the history of the nightmare, of the quarrels with his brother, the breakups with his future wife, there is also the recurrent nail-biting when he is in situations of stress. One can further ask: Is there a guarantee that this subject will never have more serious disturbance? The answer to that is, no, there is no guarantee. It is not likely that he will, but he may. For instance, if his wife became seriously disturbed (she is obviously more vulnerable than he); if at the same time, let us assume, in a national economic crisis he lost his business and had to work for a high-handed boss who insisted, let us say, on details, this man might very well break down. There is no absolute dividing line between normality and abnormality, or between emotional health and emotional illness, and it depends not only on the individual, but also on the circumstances, whether he stays well or becomes sick.

The difference between "healthy" and "sick" is so gradual that one might be tempted to say that there is no such thing as a normal, or an emotionally healthy, individual. Practically, however, the difference is very important, and there are figures available on a national scale about the percentage of the population that has been emotionally healthy up to early or middle adulthood. It was found during Selective Service examinations that approximately 10 percent of the unselected male population was suffering from a severe enough emotional disturbance to make them, in the opinion of the examining psychiatrist, unfit for military service (641). Fifteen percent of the population was suffering from a moderate emotional disturbance so that the psychiatrist had to weigh the individual's assets and liabilities in order to decide whether he was fit for military duty.[1] Seventy-five percent of the male adult population presented no problem worthy of consideration. It may be added here that only a small fraction (1 or 2 percent of the population or less) was incapacitated for civilian work by emotional disturbance.

The breakdown of a person may occur in a situation which in the past he has unwittingly avoided. A brief illustration will show this point.

A man of sixty-six developed attacks of palpitation, together with a sinking sensation in his stomach and loss of appetite. These symptoms were accompanied

[1] This figure is based upon the personal observations of one of the authors.

by fear of death. His present complaints were the first serious emotional disturbance he ever had. He had been married for thirty years, and, although there had never been any children because of his wife's sterility, there was no unhappiness about this.

He had always had counseling jobs in youth organizations. Six months before his symptoms appeared, however, he was made head of the central office of another organization. He was required to attend conferences with the members of the board of directors. These conferences always took place during lunch, and it was usually before or during lunch that he developed his symptoms. It thus became clear that his fears represented reactions to meeting these individuals. He had always had an undercurrent of anxiety concerning people who were his equals or his superiors, but he had never been seriously put to the test until, at the age of sixty-six, he received his present appointment.

REACTIONS TO STRESS SITUATIONS

We will now proceed to discuss two kinds of stress situations and enlarge our concept of the relationship between "healthy" and "sick." One of these situations (the reactions of the brain-injured patient) is definitely pathological; the other (reactions to extreme situations of stress) is on the borderland of pathology.

REACTIONS OF THE BRAIN-INJURED PATIENT

"Here is a man with a lesion of the frontal lobe, to whom we present a problem in simple arithmetic. He is unable to solve it. . . . He looks dazed, changes color, becomes agitated, anxious, starts to fumble, his pulse becomes irregular; a moment before amiable, he is now sullen, evasive, exhibits temper, or even becomes aggressive. It takes some time before it is possible to continue the examination. Because the patient is so disturbed in his whole behavior, we call situations of this kind *catastrophic situations*."[2]

Some patients may react even more severely and lapse into complete unconsciousness. Such patients may try to defend themselves against the onslaught of any task or stimulus with which they cannot cope. As a result, they may shun the company of other people, they may constantly engage in self-chosen activities, and they may develop excessive orderliness so that they will not get confused by the problem of where to find things and how to utilize them.

Other aspects of the reactions of brain-injured patients will be discussed later. (See Chapters III and XXXV.) The following points should be made here. One may describe the mentioned reactions in negative terms by saying that a patient wants to avoid failure, frustration, helplessness, and anxiety; or one may put them in positive terms and say that the patient wants to

[2] K. Goldstein, *Aftereffects of Brain Injuries in War*, Grune & Stratton, New York, 1942, p. 71.

retain the feeling of mastery and of integration; he wants to preserve himself. This striving for self-preservation is an equally strong dynamic force in both healthy and "sick" individuals.

REACTIONS TO SITUATIONS OF EXTREME STRESS

A striking presentation of the problem is given in an account of the reactions to the tortures suffered during transportation to a Nazi concentration camp. These tortures included, apart from the physical suffering, the prisoners' being forced to curse their God, to accuse themselves of vile actions and their wives of prostitution.

"The writer recalls his extreme weariness, resulting from a bayonet wound and a heavy blow on the head. . . . He wondered that man can endure so much without committing suicide or going insane; that the guards tortured prisoners in the way it had been described in books on the concentration camps; that the Gestapo was so simpleminded as to enjoy forcing prisoners to defile themselves. It seems that he gained emotional strength from the following facts: that things happened according to expectation; that, therefore, his future in the camp was at least partly predictable from what he already was experiencing and from what he had read; and that the Gestapo was more stupid than he had expected. He felt pleased that the tortures did not change his ability to think or his general point of view. . . .

"The writer feels that he was able to endure the transportation and what followed, because he convinced himself that these horrible and degrading experiences somehow did not happen to 'him' as a subject, but only to 'him' as an object. The importance of this attitude was corroborated by statements of other prisoners. They couched their feelings usually in such terms as, 'The main problem is to remain alive and unchanged.' What should remain unchanged was individually different and roughly covered the person's general attitudes and values.

"The author's thoughts and emotions during the transportation were extremely detached. It was as if he watched things happening in which he only vaguely participated."[3]

Examining these statements, we find that the writer developed three main reactions to the tortures suffered: (1) detachment, (2) attitudes of superiority, and (3) attitudes of illusory safety (things are predictable). The latter two, under the circumstances, were entirely unrealistic, and the first one is a not uncommon symptom in psychopathology. However, the key to the meaning of these phenomena is revealed in the statement, "The main problem is to remain *alive* and *unchanged*." Both of these aspects are easily detectable in the manifestations. The detachment dulled the acuteness of the pain; the detachment and the superiority enabled the author not to turn on his persecutors, who would have killed him; the assumption of predictability gave him a feeling of security when everything was in danger. The

[3] B. Bettelheim, Individual and mass behavior in extreme situations, in T. M. Newcomb, E. L. Hartley, et al., *Readings in Social Psychology*, Henry Holt and Company, New York, 1947, pp. 231-232.

special manner in which he achieved these measures was characteristic of his whole background and personality: engaging in analysis of his reactions and of the behavior of others and accenting predictability. The author is a psychologist. In this manner of reaction he was maintaining his former personality, he was remaining "unchanged." A similar tendency to maintain the general characteristics of the personality has been found in individuals who, after varying periods of discrimination and less extreme persecution, left Germany (28).

The tendency to maintain a continuity of personality or of "character" in both healthy and sick individuals was early recognized and was termed "life style" (Adler). The phrase implies that everything that a person does, feels, and thinks is characteristic of him. Most of his artistic and intellectual products will bear the stamp of his personality, of his way of living, and of his outlook on the world; e.g., anything by Mozart is Mozartian.

These two tendencies, to preserve life and to maintain the existing interests, goals, and values, are universal psychological trends and are presented in this illustration even more dramatically than in the reactions of the brain-injured patient. One could debate whether to call the reactions described by the author healthy and normal or to say they were on the border line of abnormal and sick. If these reactions were to be sustained for a long time after the conditions eliciting them had ceased to exist, they would be considered pathological. Within the situation, however, since they were successfully adaptive, they cannot be so considered.

In the situation described above, the two aims—self-preservation and maintaining the integrity of the personality—coincided in that they both required the same type of adaptive behavior. In some situations, however, this is not so. In attempting to maintain their personality, prisoners at times found themselves risking their lives. The author cited, for example, was taking such a risk in interviewing other prisoners about their reactions. At other times the prisoners might give up the attempt to maintain their personality intact in order to be able to live with increased safety in the camp. This occurred frequently in the cases of prisoners who had been in concentration camps for several years.

Similar though less dramatic conflicts occur in less extreme life situations. Thus the individual may find it necessary to make a choice between a mode of behavior which would benefit him personally but is contrary to his ideals, and a mode of behavior which, though compatible with his ideals, would mean sacrificing personal advantage. The "normal" person described earlier in this chapter was confronted with such a choice when he resigned from the political organization. Further, conflicts may arise between ways of preserving life or ways of escaping greater pain: namely, through avoidance or through attack, through fight or through submission. The tendency to maintain former personality can also lead to a discrepancy between the realistic situation and the individual's ideals—for example, a man who, courting a woman when his funds are limited, wants to pay all the expenses even though she may have more money than he and even though she would be willing to share the expenses. These various conflicts will be discussed in further detail in the chapter (IV) on unconscious motivation and conflict. We would like to emphasize here the following: In psychopathological reactions, excessive threat is perceived to preservation of life with its various derivatives, namely integration, discomfort and pain, and ability to master situations. There is also excessive clinging to previous goals and thus to the maintenance of the personality. The reasons for this and its details will be elaborated in subsequent chapters. Here one might say that, in so far as the individual is psychologically sick, he behaves as if he were in a concentration camp when he is not in it or long after he has left it.

SUGGESTED READINGS

The best textbooks now available on the normal personality are Allport's *Personality: A Psychological Interpretation,* Stagner's *Psychology of Personality* (892), and, more complex, Murphy's *Personality: A Biosocial Approach to Origins and Structure* (702). We recommend also Shaffer, *The Psychology of Adjustment* (851).

From the cultural point of view, the best references are Ruth Benedict's book *Patterns of Culture* (78) and Mead, *From the South Seas* (635). Karen Horney's book (431) also provides good reading in this connection. For the discussion of more detailed problems see Kluckhohn and Murray (505) and Newcomb, Hartley, et al. (710).

III Psychosomatics: Motivation, Emotion, Experimental Neurosis

THE PROBLEM OF PSYCHIC-SOMATIC CORRELATION

Some of the data we obtain from sick individuals refer to observable, objective phenomena. Much, however, is of such a nature that we can know about it only if the individual chooses to tell us. Thus, in the case cited in Chapter I, an observer could note that, during an attack, the patient's facial expression was "anxious," she was breathing more deeply, her heart was beating faster; he could see her go to the window and open it. These are all observable phenomena. The following data, however, could be obtained only through her statements: During such attacks she was afraid that she might drop dead, that she might go insane; she had the feeling that she—an insignificant thing—was caught in a gigantic mesh of circumstances. In fact, her whole situation and the arrangement with her husband, while in a considerable measure referable to observable facts, represented her attitudes toward expectations of the future, and only she could tell about them.

An even more striking contrast between these types of data is furnished by such an example as the following:

The patient lies on the bed motionless; he does not react to pain, he does not answer questions, he does not attend to his wants; he remains in this condition for several weeks. His condition then changes, and he becomes communicative. He says that, while lying on the bed motionless, he was not unconscious; in fact, when he made the attempt, he knew everything that was going on around him. This statement can be verified. He can actually relate minor incidents that occurred while he was lying in the motionless state. He says that while he was lying in this state he was going through an intense and dramatic experience. He thought a gigantic battle was going on in the universe between good and evil; he, himself, was the battleground; the forces of good and evil were equally balanced. The slightest motion on his part could have decided the battle in one direction or the other. He was not sure, however, what kind of effect his movements would have on the battle; therefore, he said, he lay without moving. Obviously, this rich and dramatic and significant experience of the patient could not have been surmised simply from looking at him.

On further examination of the problem of the two types of data, we find that the division between them is not sharp, that actually in a great many instances there is considerable correlation between them. The correlation is obvious in the two cases cited. The first patient had certain feelings and thoughts which regularly occurred with her bodily complaints. The second patient's fantasy and his lying motionless have an understandable connection.

There are numerous cases in which the two kinds of data show correlation in either psychologically healthy or sick people—e.g., when the individual is in a state of strong emotion, anger, or fear. In addition to the commonly experienced subjective feelings in such emotions, there are also changes in heart rate, salivary secretion, gastric secretion, blood pressure, circulation, etc.

Another example of correlation may be found in certain studies of electric phenomena in the brain. In these experiments electrodes are placed on the scalp and connected with an apparatus that records the electric current generated in the cortex of the brain. The tracing thus obtained shows so-called alpha waves, with a rhythm of about ten per second. If the subject has his eyes closed, the alpha rhythm is very evident; but, if he suddenly opens his eyes in the light, the alpha waves disappear. Thus there is a correlation between a subjective sensory experience and the observable record of the electrical activity of the brain.

PSYCHOSOMATIC CONCEPTS

The ideal concepts would be those that refer to both introspective experiences and observable phenomena accurately correlated. Such concepts, however, are not always available, and for many important introspective data there are no observable correlates. Thus, in considering the concept of the feeling of helplessness, we should think not only of a subjective feeling, but also of changes in muscle tone, and, further, of actual situations in which the subjective and the observable phenomena appear. Many of the concepts to be discussed here will sound purely introspective; but they should be thought of in terms of widespread phenomena in the brain itself and in the periphery and interior of the body, and in terms of reactions to situations and various tasks which the individual has to face. As an illustration we may use some observations on experimental neurosis in animals by H. S. Liddell and his co-workers (568, 569, 570, 30, 31, 32).

A sheep was used as the experimental animal. Presenting it with a task which it had to solve but could not was the method of producing breakdown in its behavior ("neurosis").

The animal was trained to stand on a platform in harness. After a period of repeated struggle, it finally learned to stand quietly. The unconditioned stimulus was an electric shock to the foreleg of the animal. To this stimulus, or, in other words, whenever the electric shock was administered, the animal flexed its foreleg and then stood quietly again. The sound of a metronome beating at the rate of one beat a second was used as a conditioning stimulus in the following manner. The metronome started to beat, and when, let us say, the fifth beat was reached, the shock was administered. If this was done a certain number of times, the animal behaved in the following way. It stood quietly both when the metronome was silent and when it started to beat. As the fifth beat was approaching, the animal started to flex its foreleg until the shock actually occurred. Then it stood quietly again. The animal could be conditioned in a similar manner if the electric shock came at the tenth, fifteenth, or even at the twenty-fifth second. It stood quietly up to shortly before the shock was delivered and stood quietly again after it was delivered. If, however, the interval was thirty seconds, a profound disturbance occurred. The animal waited too long, then not long enough, before the shock came. After such experiences, the animal's behavior changed. Henceforth, it was restless on the platform. Even when the metronome didn't beat, it kept moving its foreleg. When the metronome did beat, it flexed its foreleg with each beat. But still other changes were noted in the animal. Whereas it formerly went willingly to the laboratory on collar and chain, it now vigorously resisted going there and had to be placed by force on the table. But more than that, it became more restless even in the pen both during the day and during the night. Further, the animal tended to be withdrawn, to crouch in a corner, and to be more submissive in case of attack. And, still further, the sheep's pulse became rapid and irregular as compared with that of the normal animal.

If such an animal is kept away from the laboratory for a year and a half, its condition improves. If then the tests are resumed, the sheep's "neurotic condition" will return. In one instance it persisted until the animal's death at the age of thirteen years and four months. Changes affecting the animal's total behavior were observed in a cat (Masserman) and in a dog (Gantt) made "neurotic" by the conditioning technique.

Such a "neurotic condition" did not occur if the sheep had to learn a simple maze, where, if it could not solve the problem, it could turn its attention to other matters. If the same sheep learns to stand quietly and to restrain itself on the platform, it *has* to come to grips with the problem presented by the electric shock. If the problem (in the previous example, gauging the time interval) is too great and the sheep must face it, a breakdown occurs. To quote Liddell, "It is our belief that this restraint, first imposed from without, and then imposed by the animal upon itself, is the fundamental condition favoring the development of nervous strain with resulting neurosis."[1]

The following points should be stressed in connection with the experiments on the sheep for the purpose of our discussion of human psychopathological reactions:

[1] H. S. Liddell, Nervous strain in domesticated animals and man, *Cornell Veterinarian*, 1936, 26, 107-112.

1. The "breakdown" of the sheep occurred in a *situation of stress.* The breakdown included changes in coping with and behaving in a wide variety of circumstances, and changes in the functioning of many organs of its body.

2. After the sheep in its helpless state developed a neurotic reaction and was exposed repeatedly to the traumatic situation, a permanent change occurred. It could not, even in the same situation, cope with tasks which it had been able to do previously. Its behavior altered in even different situations—for example, in the pen.

3. There were several significant aspects of the situation of stress: (a) the inability to master the problem presented by the situation; (b) the impossibility of escape from the problem; (c) "voluntary" or trained relinquishing of freedom; (d) conflict. Actually a multiplicity of conflicts is present: Thus the sheep "wants" to cope with the situation but has had the experience of being unable to do this successfully. It wants to escape but has an internal inhibition which makes it stay. It wants to run away but is forced to stay; it wants to do the inevitable task but knows that it is helpless in the face of it.

4. The concepts which explain and describe best what happens to the sheep are stated in terms of forces and of being driven. The animal is forced to face an impossible task; it is driven to run away, and simultaneously it is driven to remain. We now turn to some of these concepts.

THE CONCEPT OF DYNAMICS

As we have seen, both healthy behavior and pathological behavior are best conceived of in terms of force, desire, goal, or drive. The individual wants something, or feels driven. Even if obstacles arise, he persists in pursuing the goal. He *has* to cope with the problems that confront him. He wants to solve them, or rather he feels forced to solve them.

THE CONCEPT OF CAPABILITY AND OF HELPLESSNESS

In the healthy reaction the individual usually feels that he is able ultimately to master the task confronting him. In the pathological reaction the individual feels that he has not adequate strength to dare even to want his goal. In other words, a healthy person pursuing a goal does so actively, dynamically, with his whole personality. In the case of a pathological reaction, the feeling of helplessness assumes great dynamic importance; it becomes an urgent, threatening force, and the individual feels forced to take all sorts of measures to meet the situation. For example, when the sheep on the platform fails repeatedly to cope adequately with the electric shock, it is driven constantly to do something about the expected shock. This is why the animal jerks its foreleg spasmodically although the metronome is not yet beating and the animal has not yet received a shock.

THE CONCEPT OF CONSTELLATION; GENETIC CONSIDERATIONS

Now let us enlarge this concept of feeling helpless in a situation with which the individual has to cope. This is best accomplished if we consider an infant in his relationship with his wants, needs, and environment.

The human being is, as a child, biologically dependent on adult individuals, because of the helpless state in which he is born and in which he remains for a period of time. The term "biological dependence" here means a need for actual help and support—that is, food, clothing, and shelter—from the adult.

In addition to his biological dependence, the newborn helpless individual is also subjected to cultural dependence; that is, the degree of his dependence on the adult is regulated and determined by the customs, goals, expectations, and actualities in his environment.

This biological and cultural dependence is later invariably accompanied by certain emotional characteristics and by emotional dependence. In his actual seeking of goals, in the sphere of ideals, and in his conflicts, the dependent individual, both consciously and unconsciously, is strongly influenced by the adult on whom he is dependent and whom he loves. He adopts the goals and ideals set for him by the adult; these goals become important and significant for him, and he values them. Furthermore, for the love and approval of the adult, or because of fear of him, he gives up other goals which he had previously pursued of his own accord. In this respect the child becomes compliant and accepts restrictions on his freedom somewhat as the sheep did when it finally was willing to go to the laboratory and coöperate with the experimenter.

In these constellations and reactions, the child feels essentially safe, strong, and intact if the adult does not confront him with situations which are beyond his power to cope with. This corresponds to the stage at which the sheep could cope with the problem of the electric shock up to a certain point.

During this period of biological and cultural dependence some of the infant's most important needs are physiological, particularly his food, excretory, and genital needs, as well as the need and desire for locomotion. In addition, in our society, he needs love and respect. All these needs are ordinarily fulfilled and regulated in his relationship with the adult. If in this relationship, however, taboos are introduced which are beyond his comprehension; if he is made to feel, in direct or indirect ways, that he is unloved or worthless; if he is always threatened with abandonment; if he is constantly disapproved of and punished; if he is always requested to renounce and is not given compensation, then a deep feeling of helplessness and worthlessness arises in him. This feeling is very strong because the child is actually dependent on the help and affection of the adult and because the adult is infinitely stronger.

There is a further development. The child becomes intensely resentful and hostile toward the adult who, he feels, refuses help, threatens, punishes, and frustrates. This resentment arises again and again, whenever the child is "unfairly handled"; and it has further consequences which are likewise very important. The helpless child may become intensely hostile to individuals on whom he is dependent, who are stronger than he, whom he needs to love, and who set his goals and ideals. This in turn leads to a strong fear of retribution, the fear of abandonment, the fear of injury, the fear of complete frustration in his bodily wants. Furthermore, the child feels helpless in the face of these threats. This conflict leads to a great devaluation of the self, and to a strong feeling of worthlessness and guilt. Thus a dynamic constellation comes into existence and becomes constantly active. The child pursues a goal; but he feels helpless and worthless, is resentful of those on whom he is dependent, and is afraid of being humiliated, abandoned, considered worthless, injured, or completely denied and frustrated. Because of the child's helpless and dependent state, his fear has a potentially catastrophic intensity. This condition—feeling helpless in a potentially hostile world—has been called "basic anxiety" (Horney).

The patient who was discussed in the first chapter was biologically and culturally dependent on her parents. As we said, her mother was emotionally distant, yet over-solicitous and overbearing in her discipline and moral outlook. The patient, feeling herself dominated and rejected as well as humiliated, became resentful. Her resentment led to the feeling of abandonment, guilt, and worthlessness, and to the fear of injury. Thus, in its essential features, her later reactive constellation started in her childhood. Under these circumstances the experience of pneumonia was an additional serious threat. The loss of her father deprived her of the only source of affection that was in any way equivalent to her needs.

THE CONSTELLATION DESCRIBED IN THE CHILD SIMILAR TO THAT IN THE ADULT

The constellation described in the child has strong convincing value because his helplessness is obvious and unquestionable. In the adult, however, the situation is not quite so obvious; but it becomes clearer if we examine and observe him more carefully when he breaks down in the face of a difficulty. In such situations we have to go beyond the patient's statements, and we have to be aware of connections of which he is unaware. In other words, we have to see connections which to him are "unconscious," and we have to see evaluations, strivings, needs, and desires of which he knows nothing. If we do this, we find that in its broad outlines the constellation in the adult is very similar to that described in the child. The patient cited in the first chapter had as great an emotional need and in that sense felt as dependent on her husband as a biologically helpless and mistreated child does. She unconsciously considered him powerful and herself weak in comparison, just as the child does when he compares himself with his parent. She felt as profoundly rejected and unfairly treated and was as angry and hostile as a child. She was as much afraid of utter abandonment, of counterattack and injury, and of complete frustration as was the child we described. All this manifested itself in a compressed or telescope fashion in her attacks of anxiety.

How the general evaluation of the self and of the relationship with another individual becomes so deeply disturbed in later life will be discussed in other chapters.

FURTHER SIMILARITIES BETWEEN DYNAMICS OF ANIMAL NEUROSIS AND HUMAN BREAKDOWN

In discussing the dynamics of neurosis in the sheep, we stressed several points. There are similar ones in the dynamic constellation of a human breakdown.

1. The breakdown in the child or adult occurs in situations of stress, when he feels helpless in the face of problems with which he cannot cope.

2. There is intense conflict in such situations. For example, the helpless individual wants to escape from the situation but has to face it. He is hostile toward the "unfair" individual but is afraid of him. He wants to attack, but he needs and wants help.

3. Once the breakdown is severe enough, it tends to continue even if the external situation of stress has temporarily abated.

4. The sheep's compliance in the situation is the result of training. When obedience was first asked of him, he struggled against it. Later he gave in of his own volition.

DYNAMIC SIGNIFICANCE OF BASIC ANXIETY AND ITS DERIVATIVES

We said earlier that, in the healthy reaction, the individual as a whole is bent on reaching his goal, whereas in the case of anxiety and helplessness the individual is also constantly driven to take some action about the distressing situation and the threatening danger. He is trying to avoid anticipated pain, to maintain or reëstablish his integration, and to preserve his life. (See Chapter II.) Let us now enlarge on this statement, particularly in the light of what we have learned about the "basic anxiety" found in the sick individual (see page 27).

The individual may try in various ways to relieve or remedy his fear and at the same time pursue some of his goals. Some of the means he adopts may appear only in special situations; others may be present as a constant drive, a seeking out of some situations and an avoidance of others—all for the purpose of allaying anxiety or reaching the goal, or both. If they are present almost constantly, we can speak of them as character traits.

One of these measures may be the need to enter into a dependent relationship in which the other individual's strength is overvalued; he offers help and support to the small and helpless individual. This drive for love and attention may have a demanding quality. This desire for dependence was present unconsciously to a considerable degree in the patient described in the first chapter. It appeared in an observable form in her strong attachments to her friends and in her expectation and demand that they include her in all their plans.

Another measure which an individual may adopt is to do everything perfectly, to be flawless, to surpass everybody, to dominate and control. Here again the expectation is that this will guard him against the state of helplessness and worthlessness and will protect him against retribution. These trends also were strong and unconscious in the above-mentioned patient. They were observable in connection with her work; she felt constantly driven to do perfect work, was much disturbed by a mistake, had fantasies in which she had written the best pamphlet on library work, and was apt to be sharply critical and unreasonable when one of her subordinates made mistakes.

Another type of device which is observable in some individuals is the gratification of a bodily urge to relieve and protect against a catastrophic or distressing expectation. The function of eating, both in its self-preservatory and in its pleasure-seeking aspects, may be thus used. For example, a patient may eat whenever he is anxious, whenever he fears that he will be defeated. He may eat great amounts of sweets in an almost compulsive manner. He may eat as if he were protecting himself against starvation and as if the pleasure of eating guarded him against the catastrophic situation.

All these types of devices will be elaborated on in subsequent chapters. Here one dynamic topic which is of obvious and immediate psychosomatic significance will be discussed—namely, emotions.

EMOTIONAL REACTIONS

The student will remember, from his study of elementary psychology, the demonstrations of the relationships between consciously felt emotions and bodily changes. In fear, for instance, the tonus of the body changes, the adrenal gland becomes more active, the gastrointestinal tract and all its glands cease functioning, the heart beats faster, the breathing is rapid, the whole vasomotor system changes so that blood is withdrawn from certain areas and shifted to certain others, particularly the peripheral muscles, etc. (Cannon). A certain logic unites all these somatic responses with the individual's perceptions (of danger) and with his introspective, emotional content (fear). The individual, with all his parts, with all his capacities, with all his past experiences in such a danger situation, tends to react as a unit. He perceives a problem which his past experience tells him he cannot overcome but which may overcome him, and he prepares to do whichever has more survival value—i.e., to flee or to fight if cornered.

To avoid confusion, some discussion of vocabulary is necessary here. Today we distinguish "fear" from "anxiety." A simple differentiation is that fear is a reaction to something in the "real" world; anxiety is a reaction that seems unjustified or out of all proportion to the actual danger that is apparently involved. This description is further complicated by the fact that in anxiety, even though the emotional response itself may be conscious, the situation that arouses it may be completely unconscious. For instance, the patient described in the first chapter had attacks of anxiety that were conscious. The causes of these attacks, however, were unconscious—i.e., the fear of being abandoned after she had reached out emotionally toward her husband and had thus made herself dependent and vulnerable.

But the concept of unconscious anxiety is even broader. This unconscious anxiety is present constantly as an active dynamic factor in many pathological reactions. It always contains an anticipated helplessness, worthlessness, humiliation, or injury (431). That is, it includes a state of anticipation of disaster or catastrophe, as well as emotions of self-condemnation, guilt, worthlessness, and so on. It is this anticipation of breakdown, of the complete collapse of self-esteem, of the complete withdrawal of the respect and affection of others, that we call the fear of catastrophic breakdown. To repeat, anxiety may be described from the changes in breathing, in blood pressure, etc., from various kinds of perceptions and from certain kinds of feelings, such as helplessness or anticipated helplessness, vaguely understood or wholly unconscious feelings of incipient danger to the personality (catastrophic breakdown). But there is more than just this description, for this whole state itself acts as a motive, a drive, a cause for action. The entire organism girds itself, starts to protect itself in various ways, does something about the situation. In other words, it is a dynamic situation.[2]

[2] We can understand now why the problem of anxiety creates so much trouble for psychologists. Some think of it as a kind of by-product, an epiphenomenon that arises from the situation and floats above it like smoke over a battlefield; but in itself it has no more influence on the situation than does the smoke. It is, so to speak, caused by the battle, but has no causal influence on it. These individuals think of anxiety as a purely introspective phenomenon. But there are others who speak of anxiety in a dynamic sense, as an influence that starts things going, as a cause; but if one reads carefully, he can see that these people do not speak of anxiety, as the first group does, merely as an introspective phenomenon; they think of it in its total psychosomatic nature. That is, they include not only the introspection but also the neural and physiological processes that give rise to the anxiety. We have a choice as to how we shall use the word in this book; we shall use it as a psychosomatic concept and not merely as a psychic concept, just as we shall also imply that any feeling, any psychic state, is likewise a psychosomatic entity.

ANGER, HOSTILITY, AGGRESSION

The emotion of anger is also fairly well known in its psychosomatic relationships. Ordinarily, anger and fear are treated as if they were contraries of each other. In psychopathology, however, we shall see that they are very closely related.

As far as the somatic reactions in anger are concerned, they are very simple; on the basis of present knowledge, they are the same as the somatic reactions in fear. The introspective content of anger is, in the typical case, a feeling of wanting to attack; in fear it is usually the conscious feeling of wanting to flee. But let us analyze further. Anger of some kind is always present in every psychopathological individual; it is frequently overlooked because it is either unconscious or directed inward toward the self. The unconscious reaction of anger in its widest psychosomatic sense occurs in situations in which the individual feels disappointed in his vital expectations of help and affection, in which rejection is threatened or his self-esteem is attacked by threatened injury; it frequently is also aroused through sheer deprivation as well as frustration. (See Chapter V.) But these are the situations which we have already described as causing fear or anxiety. This is not a contradiction. The simple fact of the matter is that, where the individual's self-esteem or feeling of security is threatened, he will feel *both* afraid and angry. Introspectively or unconsciously, both will be felt; sometimes one, sometimes the other, will predominate. The somatic pattern involved is *one.*

The essential difference, however, is in overt reaction. In fear and anxiety these reactions might be flight, defensiveness, giving in; in anger or hostility we tend to find aggression. But even here there is no black and white separation. Aggression may arise from fear as well as from anger, as in the cornered animal making a desperate last stand; the individual who has psychosomatic fear and is forced to flee or defend himself is also angry and aggressive.

Generally, when one becomes angry with a more powerful or a needed individual, this will breed anxiety also because of the danger of manifesting such an impulse against a person who is so important. In psychoanalysis, when we go below the surface, we frequently find that the key here is the fear of retribution, sometimes of actual physical retribution. An example would be a person who feels threatened and who fears or anticipates catastrophic breakdown. Let us say that he is threatened with abandonment by someone whom he considers powerful, on whom he feels utterly dependent, and whose approval he needs—his father, perhaps. Because of this threat and because of his fear, he will feel angry and hostile toward the one who threatens him with so much psychic pain. But several things may happen to this hostility. For instance, it is common to project it upon the feared object

—i.e., to start feeling that his father is angry with him; this in turn increases his anxiety and fear of abandonment and retribution, which in turn increase his anger toward his father, and so on. But reactions of anger (hostility) and fear (anxiety) may also have strong effects on the patient's evaluation of his worth. Fear of the feeling of worthlessness because of condemnation by another individual gives rise to resentment against this individual, which increases the feeling of condemnation by this individual, which involves self-condemnation and guilt, which involves more anxiety, more hostility, etc.

In psychopathology, then, it is better to speak of a single entity, fear-anger or anxiety-hostility, and to speak of it in the widest psychosomatic sense. Fear-anger is a dynamic state of the total organism in which the body is prepared for either attack or flight or symbolic representations of either or both, and in which perceptions of the situation and the life history are all integrally bound together. It is not only a state of affairs (static) but also a tendency to do something (dynamic).

EXPERIMENTAL STUDY OF OBSERVABLE VEGETATIVE CHANGES DURING EMOTIONAL STRESS

We said earlier that a sick individual may continually expect a catastrophic situation and thus be under severe chronic emotional stress. We mentioned earlier that the sheep, after its breakdown in the unsolvable situation, had a continuously rapid pulse. At other times it had an irregular pulse, particularly when placed in the traumatic situation.

Disturbances in the functioning of various organs which are not under the control of the will are frequent in patients. The patient described in the first chapter had a rapid pulse rate—120 per minute—when she had an anxiety attack; under usual circumstances, when she was relaxed, her pulse rate was 72 per minute. Many such vegetative changes occurring under stress have been subjected to experimental investigation and to accurate measurement. As an example, changes in finger temperature accompanying emotional stress will be described here (Mittelmann and Wolff [674, 676]).

The subject rested on a comfortable table in a constant-temperature room; the subject's hand rested on a pillow. Next to his fingers was placed a radiometer, an instrument which measures the temperature of the fingers by measuring their heat radiation. The essential principle upon which this instrument operates is that of the thermocouple, with which the student becomes familiar in the physics laboratory.

During control periods in which the subjects were in a relaxed condition, the finger temperature ran an even course at about 33° C. In order to induce affective states experimentally, a discussion was conducted dwelling on difficulties in the individual's life situation to which he reacted with signs of emotional distress. One subject was a high-school girl in her late teens. She was an only child, whose parents had separated when she was one year old. Generally she lived with her mother, but had spent one bad summer with her father, who affected her emotionally. She was a very pretty girl, even beautiful, according to some. Yet she was convinced that she was unattractive and that she had "pop-eyes." She was sensitive to disapproval and strongly desired praise and attention. She had many acquaintances but no close friends. She was attached to her mother, whom she considered a "companion," but still she was often on bad terms with her because of criticisms and general disagreements. At such times, she would not speak to her mother for weeks, and felt bitter and helpless because she was dependent on her mother for support.

In one experiment, in which she was asked to repeat and retain a series of digits, her finger temperature dropped 4.8° C. in twelve minutes, then came back to normal afterward. Her introspective report was that during the repetition of digits she was very eager to perform well, and was disturbed over mistakes because she considered the procedure to be a test of her intelligence.

The experimenter then engaged the subject in conversation about her mother, with whom she was on bad terms at that time. Finger temperature dropped 13.2° C.! When the conversation was terminated, the finger temperature returned to normal. Her report was of anger, feelings of inadequacy and helplessness.

This typical psychosomatic experiment demonstrates various other points that we have discussed. First of all, it shows the correlation between conscious happenings and bodily happenings. It shows, furthermore, that some of the reactions which we ordinarily regard as purely psychic are in reality psychosomatic, responses of the whole individual. The function involved here is an autonomic one, not under the control of the will; but strong reaction could be experimentally induced simply by conversation about sore points in the patient's life. Finally, such experiments help us to understand how private "introspective states," continued over a long period of time, may produce widespread pathological changes in the body.

DISTURBANCES RESULTING FROM GROSS ORGANIC DAMAGE TO THE BRAIN TISSUE

Up to this point we have discussed reactions and motivations, methods of coping with difficult situations when there was no gross organic damage either to the brain or to the organs of the body—in other words, conditions in which the difficulty was primarily psychological. In many cases, however, there is an organic damage either to the brain or to some organ in the body; and, correlated with that, there are disturbances in one or another psychological function. As examples of this, some clinical observations on human beings and some experimental observations on animals will be discussed.

THE EFFECT OF THE REMOVAL OF BOTH FRONTAL LOBES

Each half of the cerebrum is divided into several lobes, one of which is called the frontal lobe. This lobe is itself divided into various parts; the hindmost part, the so-called central gyrus, contains the centers of muscular activity. If this part is removed, the patient becomes paralyzed; but if parts in front of it are removed, there is no paralysis. If the pre-motor part of one side of the frontal lobe is removed, there are as a rule no noticeable disturbances in any of the psychological functions. Sometimes, if the pre-motor area is removed from the dominant hemisphere—e.g., from the left brain in right-handed people—disturbances in some psychological functions do occur. They always appear if this area is removed from both sides.

The possible symptoms and the principles involved are illustrated in the following observations of a man whose frontal lobes (the pre-motor areas) were removed bilaterally (122).

The patient was a forty-year-old man, a successful broker on the New York Stock Exchange. He developed a tumor of the brain. During the operation large portions of his frontal lobes were removed on both sides.

The patient was not able to go back to his previous work. He talked a lot about going back, in a boastful manner, but never made any effort to do so.

In general, the outstanding features in his behavior and speech were boastfulness and the tendency to self-aggrandizement. The patient's self-aggrandizing and boastful manner showed itself also in his considering himself the best conductor and the best dancer. It showed in his statement that he could lick anybody, that nobody in the world could fool him. It further showed itself in reminiscences and stories about his boyhood, in all of which he either beat up somebody or fooled somebody. In all his stories about sexual exploits he showed the same trend. Together with that he was inclined to be facetious and euphoric (being in an elated mood). His memory for recent events was faulty. He sometimes forgot, for example, that he had gone to the movies the day before. He was incapable of logically following through a topic in thinking or in conversation if this topic was in any way complicated. Thus, at one moment he would say he did not believe in capital punishment for people who committed a crime when they did not know what they were doing; he would then say he did not believe in capital punishment for kidnapers; then he would say that kidnapers did know what they were doing. He would say he did not believe in torturing people under any circumstances as a punishment, but then he would say that torture was too mild a punishment for kidnapers. He was easily distractible.

On other occasions he behaved in a childish, angry, and abusive manner. He would refuse to get undressed in the evening and to wash his face in the morning. He would walk into a room where people were playing cards and would say, "You're all a lousy bunch of players. Do you want to start something?" An example follows of his manner of conversation, illustrating his self-aggrandizement, his boastfulness, his inconsistency in thinking, and his distractibility:

"Dr. Brickner: One thing your illness lost you is the knowledge that you're not perfect.

"The Patient: It's a damn good thing to lose.

"B: Do you really believe in your heart that you are perfect?

"Pt: Yes. Of course we all have faults. I have faults like everyone else.

"B: Name some of your faults.

"Pt: I don't think I have any.

"B: You just said you had.

"Pt: Well, they wouldn't *predominate* on the Exchange.

"B: I mean personal faults.

"Pt: Yes, I have personal faults. I never give a man an opportunity to do what he wants to do on the Exchange, if I know it.

"B: Is that a fault?

"Pt: That's being a good broker.

"B: Can you name a personal fault? Do you really believe you're perfect?

"Pt: You bet I do—pretty near perfect—they don't come much more perfect than I am."

Often when the patient conversed, his attention would suddenly be attracted by something around him.

Patient talking about himself:

"Pt: You must have a certain mentality that catches on to the knack of executing an order. (To his wife, *referring to the colored stripes on the sleeves of her dress*) The yellow is for Princeton, the green for Irish, and the blue for Navy.

"B: What's the white for?

"Pt: White is for the doctor—purity."[3]

EXPERIMENTAL INVESTIGATION OF FRONTAL-LOBECTOMIZED ANIMALS

The frontal-lobectomized chimpanzee is distinguished from the normal animal by his restlessness and distractibility and by a rather fatuous equanimity of spirit which one encounters in a good-natured drunkard, but never in a normal chimpanzee (Fulton [327]). The intellectual performance suffers. Intellectual function and also memory are tested with the stick-and-platform test and the delayed-reaction test.

In the more complex form of the stick-and-platform test, the animal has to use shorter sticks to gather in longer sticks beyond its reach, finally reaching the banana with the longest stick. In another complicated test, sticks of varying lengths are placed on two platforms. In order to get the banana, the ape has to carry the sticks from one platform to the other. The normal chimpanzee is able to do this task successfully; but, if the pre-motor areas in both sides are removed, the animal cannot do this (Jacobsen [451, 452]).

The delayed-reaction test is as follows: There are two cups in the cage, separated from the ape by the bars and a glass door. Food is placed under one of the cups. After a certain length of time, the ape is permitted to reach for the food. In order to choose correctly, he has to remember under which cup the food was placed. The normal chimpanzee can do this task correctly after intervals of as long as five minutes. After bilateral frontal lobectomy, the chimpanzee is unable to do it after an interval of five seconds.

[3] R. M. Brickner, *The Intellectual Functions of the Frontal Lobes,* The Macmillan Company, New York, 1936, pp. 45, 48. The effect of frontal-lobe operations depends in part on the amount of tissue involved. For further discussion, see Chapter XIX.

This test can be made more complicated by lowering an opaque screen after the food is put under one of the cups. The chimpanzee, of course, cannot see the cups until the screen is raised. At times, even normal animals become emotionally disturbed and fail in this form of the test. Thus an adolescent female, affectionate, coöperative, and eager to work in the problem situations, became greatly upset whenever she made an error in the delayed-reaction test. In these circumstances she flew into a temper tantrum, during which she rolled on the floor, beat the grate, defecated and urinated, and showed signs of diffuse sympathetic discharge. She finally refused to go into the problem cage. After the removal of both frontal areas, a profound change occurred in this animal. She ran eagerly into the experimental cage, did not get excited when the opaque screen was lowered, and never showed any emotional disturbance, no matter how many times she made a mistake. It was as if the animal had joined the happiness cult of the elder Micheaux and had placed its burdens on the Lord. Objectively the animal failed in the test even with only the glass door in operation (Fulton and Jacobsen).

Thus we see the similarities—intellectual and memory defects, distractibility, and euphoria—between human beings and chimpanzees following the bilateral removal of the pre-motor area of the frontal lobes.

PERSONALITY ASPECTS AND PSYCHODYNAMICS IN FRONTAL LOBECTOMY

The following data throw further light on the behavior, reactions, and emotional life of patients whose frontal lobes have been bilaterally removed. The situation is not as simple as it might seem. We cannot say simply that, if certain parts of the frontal lobes are removed, certain symptoms will then appear. In general, the following occurs: (1) the patient's ability to perform certain tasks is impaired, and his drives are altered; (2) some of his functions and emotional needs remain unchanged; and (3) he reacts to his deficiencies in terms of his altered drives.

It is obvious that in this whole process the patient's earlier personality is of paramount importance. The patient reported by Brickner had been a shy and quiet child, submissive to his dominant father and dependent on his mother. He married, but the aggressor in the courtship was his wife. After his marriage he wished to remain in his parents' home. Before his illness, he often showed a spark of facetiousness and frequently told humorous and sometimes boastful stories. In general, he was a mild and submissive individual who repressed all hostility and compensated for his feelings of inadequacy by a whimsical, humorous, and somewhat boastful manner. The one function that was good was his occupational activity. The results of the frontal lobectomy were: (1) impairment of the previously good intellectual function (memory and logic); (2) a decrease in self-criticism and self-restraint and, as a result of this, an increase in spurious self-evaluation, in the expression of previously repressed hostility, and in childish, dependent attitudes.

The functions that he retained from previous periods were some ideals of achievement, a desire for the respect and praise of others, and some self-criticism.

It was a painful experience for this patient to realize that his intellectual functions had become impaired and that he was unable to live up to the ideals which he still cherished. He reacted to these disappointments and this realization in terms of the already altered goals and reaction patterns—namely, with a further increase of self-evaluation and dependence and with hostility. This is why he becomes boastful, almost grandiose, combative, and abusive. He makes no attempt to work. He grows more dependent on his mother, who bathes him and often dresses him. He never engages in normal sexual relations with his wife, but only in autoerotic practices.

We wish to emphasize again that direct damage to the brain is not followed by a simple defect; the symptoms are determined by the direct effect of the damage and the reaction of the patient's total personality to this damage.

PERSONALITY PROBLEMS IN PRIMARY DISTURBANCES OF METABOLISM AND IN CHANGED APPEARANCE OF THE BODY

Another type of psychological problem arises in some conditions in which there is a primary disturbance in some function of the body. This will be illustrated by a condition called adiposogenital dystrophy (Fröhlich Syndrome), which is due to a glandular disturbance, particularly underfunctioning of the pituitary gland. The metabolism is usually low, and there is "general poverty of drive." The boys are stout and have small, underdeveloped genitals. Thus the appearance of the body is altered. Such boys frequently lack ordinary skills and often behave passively. They are apt to play with girls and smaller children; at times they are irritable, angry, and abusive. However, it is not as simple to explain their emotional difficulties as one might think. It could first be assumed that such boys are suffering from a glandular disturbance which *directly* influences their nervous system and with that their whole behavior; but on detailed examination the behavior is found to be determined by several factors (Mittelmann [660]), which will be discussed in connection with a case.

The patient was a stout boy with small genitals. His basal metabolism was −20. His mother was over-protective, strict, and dominant. He tried to play with other boys of his own age (about five), but was unable to compete with them effectively in sports. After a period of distress, he gave up further attempts and instead played with his sister, with other girls, and with smaller boys. He was peaceful and never fought with other children. When he was ten years old, his classmates, some of them nearing puberty, became increasingly rough and teased him about his stoutness and about his playing with girls. About the same time, while in the shower room, some other boys remarked about the smallness of his genitals. He felt bitter and inferior about this. His behavior soon underwent a considerable change. He became disobedient and abusive toward his mother; he beat his sister; he fought with the boys if they called him "sissy" and started to play games with his classmates, picking quarrels with them frequently.

The treatment of the patient at the age of thirteen consisted of the administration of thyroid gland tissue to raise his metabolism to normal, and the injection of a pituitary-like substance. He began to develop normally and lost his stoutness. Both he and his mother needed psychotherapy in addition. The patient's behavior grew normal in about six months' time.

The factors that influenced this boy's behavior at various times were these: His metabolism was always low; hence he had a constant "general poverty of drive." His mother was always over-solicitous. Both of these factors made him inclined to be passive, as did also his difficulty in competing with other boys. When he was five years old, the most painless and gratifying solution was to find pleasure and consolation in playing with girls and with younger children. His experiences at the age of ten—the attitude of the other boys in connection with the appearance of his body and his passive mode of behavior—hurt his self-esteem deeply. His reaction to this hurt was over-aggressiveness, in spite of his "poverty of drive." Thus we see that this patient's problems were caused partly by the direct influence of his disturbed metabolism and partly by the reaction of his total personality to his deficiencies.

PSYCHOLOGICAL DISTURBANCE LEADING TO PATHOLOGY IN METABOLISM

Organic factors are often important in another type of psychological problem. Exophthalmic goiter is a condition in which there are enlargement of the thyroid gland and a considerably increased metabolism (up to $+100$), bulging of the eyes, trembling of the fingers, loss of weight, rapid heart rate, excessive perspiration, and other symptoms. The main psychological symptom is marked restlessness and irritability. Many of these symptoms are due to an overfunctioning of the thyroid gland. In other words, if a healthy individual is given adequate amounts of thyroid substance continuously, he will develop similar disturbances (with the exception of the bulging of the eyes) and will become markedly restless and irritable. The psychopathological problem here, however, is not as complex as it is in the patient with an exophthalmic goiter. For example, a young married woman developed an exophthalmic goiter after her husband had recovered from an attack of pneumonia. Her thyroid gland was operated on, and she improved. Five years later this condition reappeared after her daughter's recovery from an attack of pneumonia (659).

It is clear that exophthalmic goiter developed in this patient in response to a situation of severe stress. The problem, however, does not end there. Further examination showed that her reaction to stress was not normal. This patient had had a very unhappy childhood. Her father drank and was often abusive and violent at home toward both her mother and herself. The mother suffered from attacks of anxiety and leaned heavily on the patient for support against the father. The patient felt helpless and resentful toward both parents; she felt catastrophically threatened by her father and had a strong sense of worthlessness and guilt because of resentment toward her mother. At the age of eighteen she married a man to whom she was not attached, solely in order to get away from her home. Her husband, too, turned out to be a disappointment. He was seclusive and emotionally detached, and never showed any warmth toward her. She would have left him except for the child to whom she gave birth a year after her marriage.

Her reaction to the illnesses of her husband and child can now be better understood. She unconsciously evaluated their sickness as a fulfillment of a death-wish she had toward them. This wish was the reaction of an individual who felt that all her vital needs were denied but was powerless to deal with the situation. Their death would liberate her, but at the same time deprive her of even the small amount of love she could obtain. Her conflict was intense, though unconscious. She condemned herself severely and feared retribution.

After the exophthalmic goiter developed, the patient became irritable. Previously she had never contradicted her husband, but she now expressed her resentment toward him in a rather explosive manner. This increased her fear of him. Her irritability toward her child also increased, and she condemned herself for this because it clashed with her ideals. Thus we see that the final symptoms in this patient were the result of (1) her original conflicts; (2) the over-secretion of the thyroid gland (chemical effect on the nervous tissue); (3) the personality reactions to the effects of this over-secretion, resulting in increased fear and guilt.

The patient was operated on a second time and was given psychological treatment. The husband also was interviewed several times, and the arrangement in the home was improved. The patient recovered fully, and her life became happier.

This case shows that a personality reaction may precipitate a severe organic disturbance, and that there is a further personality reaction to this disturbance.

RELATIONSHIP BETWEEN ORGANISM AND ENVIRONMENT

Certain processes occur in the organism regardless of the type of environment, although they change, depending on the environment. This applies both to physiological and to psychological processes. On the physiological side the consumption of body fuel and the elimination of waste products have to take place under any circumstances. The psychological concomitants are some experience of tension and the experience of relief. Other phenomena occur only under certain environmental conditions. The combined physiological reactions that take place at great altitudes—e.g., at 15,000 feet—naturally cannot be observed to occur at sea level because of the higher oxygen pressure. Similarly, certain physiological and psychological reactions occur in sudden transference into low oxygen pressure (elation and flightiness terminating in lethargy, mental dullness from the beginning in an atmosphere 13 percent oxygen, corresponding to an altitude of 12,400 feet).

Let us return now to the physiological processes that occur in the organism under all circumstances—e.g., the metabolic changes, which in the vertebrates always include the consumption of oxygen. These processes may vary tremendously with heat or cold, during activity and rest. One would assume that breathing movements would have to occur as long as the organism is alive. However, if the subject is placed in a chamber in which the air pressure varies ± 55 mm. of mercury around the atmospheric pressure twenty to thirty times per minute, adequate gas exchange takes place without lung movement, and the respiratory movements cease. Under different circumstances, of course, the cessation of respiratory movements would be accompanied by intense alarm. Under these circumstances, that reaction is absent (Thunberg [931], Barach [44]).

Thus one of the most consistent needs of the organism (to breathe) is dramatically eliminated by a proper manipulation of the environment. This observation brings home forcibly the fact that the organism in all its physiological and psychological reactions always has to be viewed in relation to its environment. In this book we will deal predominantly with the psychological environment. The psychological environment refers not only to physical but also to social and cultural milieu. Intricate striving for achievement, elaborate ideals, and sustained reactions of guilt, for example, are observable only in intimate, protracted contact with certain cultural environmental conditions. This approach was most forcibly expressed by the formulation that the organism always has to be viewed as behaving in its life space—the totality of facts which determine the behavior of an individual at a certain moment (Lewin [559]).

SUMMARY

1. In certain instances a definite correlation can be established between introspective "psychological" and objective observable phenomena.

2. Normal and pathological psychological phenomena are best accounted for in terms of forces—that is, psychodynamics. These drives, needs, and reactions to situations should be thought of in broad patterns comprising both introspective and observable phenomena.

3. Psychopathology may appear because of disturbances in the motivations of an individual whose body structure is essentially normal or because of primary damage and disturbance in the structure of the body.

4. The following can be said about disturbance of motivation: In the healthy reaction one of the most important dynamic factors is "I can do this." In the pathological reaction the central dynamic constellation is that of helplessness.

5. A primary "psychological" disturbance of motivation leads to disturbance in the functions of the body, particularly through the vegetative nervous system, which is correlated with the emotions of fear and anger. In a primary organic disturbance the psychological symptoms are the direct results of this defect and the reactions of the patient's personality to it.

6. The needs of the organism depend upon the environment. To put it in a different way, the environment can diminish, eliminate, or stimulate the needs of the organism. Thus the individual's psychological needs must be considered in terms of his current and past environmental experiences.

"General Adaptation Syndrome" implies that the same organismic changes occur in any type of stress: infection, physical effort, situational tension. It has three phases: alarm reaction, resistance, and exhaustion. Rats show increase in blood pressure, ulcerations in the gastrointestinal tract, enlargement of the adrenal cortex, etc., during sustained stress. (H. Selye and C. Fortier, Adaptive reaction to stress, *Psychosomatic Medicine,* 1950, 12, 149-157.)

Correspondingly, the adrenal cortical, or the adrenal corticotropic hormone of the pituitary (ACTH), is therapeutic in many disorders (arthritis, asthma, burns, etc.), many of them psychosomatic.

SUGGESTED READINGS

Psychosomatic Medicine is a journal which deals with the subject matter of this chapter. The student is also referred to the specific papers mentioned in the chapter. The serious student will be interested in the digest of all the important psychosomatic work in Dunbar's *Emotions and Bodily Changes* (226).

Two physiological classics, both by Cannon, should also be mentioned: *Bodily Changes in Pain, Hunger, Fear and Rage* (150) and *The Wisdom of the Body* (149). Significant work on the subject is that by Freeman (288, 289). A very good popular introduction to the subject of psychosomatic medicine is Hinsie, *The Person in the Body* (414). A readable and comprehensive book is Weiss and English (960). Alexander and French (22) is a more complex handling of the subject matter. On experimental neurosis we recommend Pavlov (724, 725), Gantt (330), and Anderson and Parmenter (31).

PART II

Psychodynamic Processes

IV Unconscious Psychological Processes: Conflict

UNCONSCIOUS ACTIVITIES

It has been repeatedly emphasized in the preceding chapters that the patient cannot adequately account for the complaints and symptoms from which he suffers, but that their meaningful connections can be seen if we assume, on the basis of valid evidence, that he is motivated by needs, goals, and emotions of which he is not aware; in other words, they are unconscious. The existence of unconscious psychological processes can be demonstrated experimentally and clinically by means of hypnosis and in other ways.

Conscious wishes are more controllable than unconscious wishes. The amazing difference in controllability can be seen most clearly in one of the essential aspects of psychoanalytic therapy. The first task of this therapy is always phrased as "increasing the patient's insight into his own motives, or making the unconscious conscious." How this is done will not be discussed here; we shall point merely to the fact that deep therapy is never possible without this insight into unconscious motives. Sometimes, in simpler cases, the mere baring of an unconscious impulse or thought or fantasy to consciousness may deprive it, automatically and at once, of all its pathological power. Indeed, it was with this discovery by Breuer and Freud that the history of psychoanalysis began. For instance, in hypnotic experiments, it is merely necessary to tell the patient what happened during the trance—i.e., make him conscious of it—in order for the suggestions to lose all or most of their power. We quote from an experiment by Erickson:

"I secretly made the acquaintance of his roommate and acquainted him with my intentions, securing his full cooperation; then after a period of about three months, I endeavored first by indirect and then gradually by more and more direct suggestions to induce him to read his roommate's mail surreptitiously. These letters were casually left on the bureau but were always placed in definite relationship to certain objects and various cues arranged to determine whether or not they had been touched. All efforts in this regard failed. Also, during the roommate's absence from the room I would visit the subject and put him in a trance and endeavor to get him to read one of the letters. He always resisted strongly and when finally I succeeded by urgent direct suggestions to get him to open one side of the paper, he opened it but looked at the blank side and declared that there was no writing on it. I urged him to turn it around and he did so but held it bottom side up. I had him turn it right side up and then discovered that he could not read it because he had taken his glasses off previously, the significance of which act I had not appreciated at the time. Only after much hunting were his glasses found, whereupon he declared that the writing was so difficult that he could not read it. An effort was made to help him, whereupon he developed a psychic blindness and could not see.

"Throughout this whole experiment it was very difficult to retain this subject's friendship. He tended to avoid me and he seemed distrustful of me. When he was told later of the experiment he confessed that he had disliked me intensely but that his knowledge of Dr. Hull and Hull's interest in my work had convinced him that it must be of some scientific value and that he was willing to endure his dislike of me in the hope of forwarding some scientific inquiry.

"Before he was given any understanding of my experiment I attempted another one, somewhat less drastic in nature. He had a reasonable money allowance but he knew I was extremely poverty-stricken. I built up a belief in him that unless I could secure some money of some sort I would not be able to complete my special research work. I built up this belief in both the waking and trance states, and then after having made proper arrangements with his roommate, I tried to get him to steal money from his roommate for me, making use of every possible euphemism in broaching my suggestion. He promised to cooperate, but despite carefully determined sums of money left in bureau drawers, table drawers, extra suits, no results were forthcoming, and the subject professed a complete inability to find any money. Finally he consented to pick his roommate's pocket. He was carefully drilled in the art of picking a pocket until he could pick mine easily. At the chosen time while his roommate was busy talking to me, apparently having met me for the first time, my subject in a deep somnambulistic trance state stood alongside of him slightly to the rear. He proceeded to pick his roommate's pocket but instead of doing it delicately and carefully, he merely forced his hand in it rudely and awkwardly, yanked out the pocketbook and with extreme care and secrecy handed it to me.

"I questioned him extensively about his success in picking the pocket and he seemed to believe fully that he had picked it in the best possible style. Much later when I informed the subject of the use I had made of him, he was tremendously interested, and had no recollection of either experiment; and when I enabled him by means of hypnotic suggestions to recall the entire procedure and his reactions at the time, he could give me only this explanation, 'I wanted to do what you said; I tried hard. I had an idea that it was terribly important or you wouldn't ask me to do those things, but I just couldn't do them.' After this explanation he lost all of his dislike of me and on various occasions acted as a demonstration subject for me. Subsequently, he transferred to another medical school. When I met him again a year later he was still interested in hypnosis and inquired at length about my work."[1]

The following experiments by Luria (591) illustrate how unconscious conflict is accompanied by physiological and unconscious ideational and behavioral changes:

While the subject, a medical student, was in a deep hypnotic trance, it was suggested to her that she had performed an illegal abortion. When she was awakened from the trance, she said that she felt very bad, that something disagreeable had happened but she did not know what. Prior to the hypnotic trance, the patient had been asked to free-associate. In each hand she held a bulb. She was asked to press the bulb in her right hand every time she said a word. The movements of both hands were recorded along with her breathing. The recording taken before hypnosis showed that her associations were evenly spaced, that the voluntary movements of her right hand were of equal pressure, that there was almost no involuntary movement of the left hand, and that her breathing was regular. This same experimental procedure was repeated a week after the hypnotic session. This time the voluntary movements showed marked variations in pressure, there was a good deal of involuntary movement of the left hand, and breathing was irregular. Many words relating to the suggested conflict situation appeared in her associations. Before they actually appeared, however, long pauses began to occur between associations. During the course of free-associating, she said, "I remembered what I dreamt" (the conflict situation suggested to her while she was under hypnosis). The experimenter told her to continue her free associations. No more words referring to the conflict situation occurred in her associations, and the recording of voluntary and involuntary movements and of the respiration returned to normal.

It will be noticed in these examples that both behavior and attitudes proceeded from unconscious determinants. The attitude of dislike in the first example and the physiological changes in the second disappeared dramatically when their unconscious determinants became conscious.

The following important question arises: Why is there this difference in the "controllability" of conscious and unconscious impulses? Or, to put it in another way, why is it that with insight the individual can handle his problems differently than he does when they are largely unconscious? There are two approaches to this problem: (1) the conditioned-response experiments; (2) the psychodynamics of the unconscious process, or, to express it better, understanding why a certain psychological process becomes unconscious.

CONDITIONED-RESPONSE EXPERIMENTS AND UNCONSCIOUS ACTIVITIES

Cason (154) was one of the first to demonstrate that involuntary processes could be conditioned in the laboratory. He was able to condition the con-

[1] M. H. Erickson, An experimental investigation of the possible anti-social use of hypnosis, *Psychiatry*, 1939, 2, 391-414.

striction and dilatation of the pupil of the eye to sound stimuli that were originally incapable of influencing it. This he did with the ordinary technique first used by Pavlov—presenting simultaneously an adequate stimulus (a light flashed into the eye), capable of constricting the pupil, and an inadequate stimulus (in this case, the sound of a bell), incapable of producing constriction. After many such simultaneous presentations, the sound alone would produce pupillary constriction.

Some years later, Hudgins (436) substantiated and extended Cason's results. In this experiment the subject was conditioned first to the sound of a bell, then to the sound of his own voice as it said the word "constrict," then to the whispered sound of his own voice, and finally merely to the *thought*. The result was that the subject could constrict or dilate his pupils at will.[2]

This was the first time that an involuntary, nonconscious process had ever been brought under conscious voluntary control in the laboratory. These experiments also proved that the conditioning process did not necessarily involve consciousness, for some of the subjects were not aware of the conditioned constriction and dilatation of their pupils.

Similarly, Menzies (642) found in some subjects that uttering or thinking "cold" words—e.g., ice, frost, iceberg, snow—produced a constriction of the blood vessels similar to that produced by the actual application of cold water to the subject's body. "Hot" words—fire, heat, burn, red-hot—produced in some subjects vasodilatation similar to their response to the actual application of hot water.

A recent experiment by Baker (42) seems to bear more directly on our problem. This unusual experiment, if it is confirmed by other experimenters, will open up an important path in the experimental study of unconscious activities. An involuntary response, constriction or dilatation of the pupil, was conditioned to a subliminal sensory stimulus—i.e., a sound that was not consciously heard, an electric shock not consciously felt, etc. Baker found, first, that conditioning took place with amazing rapidity (in the preliminary form in only one trial and in a final form in two trials), and, second, that this conditioning was extraordinarily persistent, for in some subjects it could be elicited months later without any further training. Throughout the experiment the subject was not conscious of what was going on; that is, he never knew that he was being conditioned, nor was he aware after the completion of the experiment that he was different in any way.

This same author has completed another experiment that goes even

[2] These and other experiments are presented here in a very schematic form; the interest is in the results rather than the methods or details. For the latter, see the bibliography, or Hilgard and Marquis (410).

farther along the path of "experimentalizing" clinical psychology. This was an experiment on what Freud originally called "catharsis," which holds that unconscious material ceases to exert its harmful influence when it has been made conscious. Can the Baker effect be destroyed if the subject is made conscious of what is going on?

In this experiment the response conditioned was emotional—specifically, the psychogalvanic skin response made when blindfolded subjects received what they falsely interpreted to be hypodermic injections. The conditioned stimulus was the very faint sound of a buzzer. The subjects could have heard this buzzer if they had attended to it, but in their preoccupation with the fearful possibility of being given a hypodermic injection they were unaware of the sound. In other words, the conditioned psychogalvanic skin response can be thought of as the "symptom" of the "unconscious" processes initiated by the buzzer.

When a conditioned response had been established in this situation, the next steps were (1) to show the subject that he had never been given a hypodermic injection, and (2) to call his attention to the buzzer and convince him that he had been responding to it quite "unconsciously." Thus the unconscious material was made conscious.

In seven out of the fifteen subjects in this experiment, the expected "catharsis" actually occurred. That is, making the subliminal stimulus supraliminal (conscious) caused the conditioned response to disappear, or making the unconscious material conscious brought about the removal of the "symptom." Of course, there is still the question why this change was not found in the other eight subjects; but the experiment shows that when unconscious processes are made conscious they may be profoundly altered. Furthermore, there is here a strong indication that the experimental worker in the laboratory is dealing with at least some of the processes dealt with by the analyst in the life situation.

These experiments, like certain older ones, prove that we can perceive unconsciously, react unconsciously, and learn unconsciously. They also indicate that unconscious processes seem to proceed in accordance with somewhat different principles than do conscious activities; i.e., they appear to be less controllable and to persist longer. In a word, they seem to be more "powerful" in various ways than when they are conscious. It is also important to remember that these experiments differ in important ways from the work of clinical students of unconscious activities. For one thing, the psychoanalysts have worked mostly with unconscious *emotional* and *conative* processes, drives, wishes, desires, etc. One important difference between conscious and unconscious processes is that the conscious processes are those that have been verbalized, the unconscious those that have not (Watson, Guthrie, Freud). This aspect, however, has its limitations. Certainly, a good many emotional reactions occur in the infant before speech age. These are almost never remembered, but many processes that have already been verbalized and have appeared in consciousness later become repressed.

EXTRASENSORY PERCEPTION AND UNCONSCIOUS PROCESSES

The status of extrasensory perception (E.S.P.) and telepathy is still controversial. Two types of evidence exist—the statistical and the anecdotal. The process involved is in part unconscious, for the subject does not know how he obtained the information. The statistical type of evidence refers mainly to the correct identification by the subject of cards specially designed for this purpose in a frequency greater than that of chance. The anecdotal evidence is the correct knowledge of a unique event which the subject could not have obtained through ordinary means of communication or perception. Psychopathological methods of investigation at times accidentally contribute to the anecdotal type of evidence. Thus a female patient may have a dream in which the therapist's wife gives birth to a child. This dream may occur at the time such an event actually takes place; the woman in the dream looks like the therapist's wife, whom the patient has never seen; and the patient had no opportunity to find out about the event. At times such material appears in the patient's fantasies or in free associations to a dream fragment. In the latter circumstance, the patient initially was not conscious of a thought indicating his knowledge of the event. This type of occurrence is most apt to take place if the event fits in with a significant dynamic trend of the patient. This type of anecdotal observation, of course, cannot be considered as conclusive evidence of telepathy or extrasensory perception (237, 231, 768).

UNCONSCIOUS AND EMOTIONAL CONDITIONING

Probably the best experimental lead is the work with emotional conditioning. We know that such conditioning can take place in early infancy, even before the age of verbalization. It may persist for a lifetime, the individual remaining unaware of the source of his emotional reaction. These conditioned responses are peculiar in that they may be established in one trial, and they apparently are not easily extinguished. Furthermore—and this is of great interest for us—they show a good deal of irradiation; that is, the same emotional response may be evoked by a stimulus which only resembles the original conditioning stimulus.

A psychologist reports the following observations upon himself. He found himself disliking intensely and beyond all reason a certain woman with whom he was thrown into social contact. He was consciously aware that she was a fine person, totally undeserving of any such dislike. The aversion went so far that he was compulsively driven to avoid her, even when this amounted almost to open insult. Quite spontaneously, it flashed upon him one day that this woman, in her body build and in her facial characteristics, resembled in a vague way an aunt who had been important in his upbringing, who had been very cruel to him, and whom he had hated intensely. He also had a "prejudice" against red-headed people. This he traced to the age of four, when he was terrorized by a red-headed bully.

Aftereffects interesting to the student are that his dislike for red-headed people seems to have disappeared, and that his dislike for the woman, although lessened, is still strong.

The idea of unconscious emotional conditioning is important; but it should not be thought of in terms of an individual being unconsciously conditioned to one stimulus and always reacting to that stimulus in terms of the conditioned emotion. The above example shows that the psychologist's becoming aware of a possible source of his dislike for a certain woman did not eliminate his reaction toward her. In all seriously "irrational" and psychopathological reactions the complexity of "unconscious emotional conditioning" is broad and multiple. The individual's whole personality, together with fundamental needs, is involved in the reaction. If we further consider what happens in a hypnotic experiment psychodynamically, and what happens when the hypnotist makes the subject conscious of the motivations, we find some important additional factors. In the hypnotic experiment, the subject's whole interpersonal relationship (to the hypnotist), in terms of his needs, attitudes, and ideals, is involved. This leads us to the second point that requires discussion—namely, what forces make a psychological process unconscious.

PSYCHODYNAMICS OF UNCONSCIOUS PROCESSES

In general, we can say that the most important unconscious processes are not unconscious by accident; they do not just happen to be unconscious. They are unconscious for a reason and a purpose. The reason may be complex, but as a rule it includes avoiding pain, danger, and hurt to self-esteem and security. For example, what were some of the reasons why the patient described in the first chapter did not see the connection between her fear and her husband's threatened departure? There are several reasons. She was reluctant, even afraid and guilty, to admit to herself that she was angry at him. She was reluctant to admit to herself that she felt utterly dependent on him; this hurt her self-esteem. She was reluctant to admit to herself that she was afraid of him; this, too, hurt her self-esteem.

When all the processes and reactions that are unconscious in a patient are considered, there are strong reasons for their being unconscious and for his shutting them out of awareness. We are discussing here not just one or two impulses, but the sum total of all the interrelated unconscious reaction patterns. We find that all of them are unconscious because they are all connected with reactions which spring from the anticipation of a catastrophic situation characterized by helplessness, abandonment, worthlessness, fear of humiliation, and injury. To put it another way, various psychological processes must be repressed in their totality by the patient because of his fear of a catastrophic breakdown; he feels that all these processes must remain unconscious; for, if they became conscious, if he had to admit them, if he had to cope with the problems they present, he would be thrown into a catastrophic state of helplessness.

We can now understand some of the qualities of unconscious processes which have been described by Freud. In unconscious reactions there is no appreciation of the limitations of reality. Thus a patient who needs absolute dependence to feel safe unconsciously can strive for this unlimited and, in reality, never attainable goal. Anger and hostility know no bounds in unconscious reactions. The patient dreams that the object of his anger dies or is killed, but would not admit such an impulse consciously. Unconscious processes often contain contradictory impulses. The patient may dream that he is completely and willingly dependent on an all-powerful person whom he loves, and next dream that this all-powerful individual is murdered. Thus attitudes of over-evaluation, love, and dependence, and attitudes of hostility toward this person exist side by side. All these qualities of unconscious processes become understandable if we realize that they represent the reactions which spring from a catastrophic fear and the devices which the patient uses in attempting to escape a catastrophic situation.

Likewise, we can now understand more clearly why the individual can handle the problem better if he can do so with full consciousness. In the process of making unconscious reaction patterns conscious, the patient's fears must be diminished, he has to see the disadvantages of using these devices, his helplessness has to be relieved. Thus, if we succeed in making important psychological processes conscious, we really enable the individual to recast his whole reaction pattern. In a sense we stop a vicious circle. Previously, in order to allay his fears, to strengthen himself, and to be able to function, the individual had to repress—that is, make unconscious—certain needs, goals, reactions. After this, by the very fact of having made them unconscious and keeping them unconscious, he loses control over them. In the reverse process the individual is strengthened. This finally enables him to become conscious of attitudes; once they are conscious, his control over them further increases.

The individual may be conscious of a great many things and still may have only illusory control over them. For example, a man may adopt an attitude of being detached and of having others do his fighting for him. This attitude, although conscious, does not cover his whole reaction pattern. Underneath it may be profound fear and an inability to assert himself, to commit himself to causes and goals. He may expect a catastrophic situation if he ever tries to assert himself. In such instances the consciousness is really purposive. He is conscious only of what he needs to be conscious of, of what his life style demands. If this is the case, he really has no control over his detached aloofness. He would acquire control over it only if after a laborious process his fear were made conscious and he were enabled to become stronger.

THE NATURE OF CONFLICT

CONSCIOUS CONFLICT

The nature of conflict will be understood more easily if we begin with the study of those innumerable and inevitable conflicts that are entirely conscious. Shall we go to the movies or stay home and listen to the radio? Shall we work or play for the next few hours? Here two impulses are in conflict because they are incompatible with each other. One cannot both go and stay, one cannot wear two outfits at the same time, one cannot work and loaf at the same time. In the healthy person, such conflicts, in spite of the fact that they occur by the thousands, are solved easily and quickly without any pathological effects. Advantages are weighed, all the factors in the situation are considered, the possible pleasures are balanced against the possible pains, and, as such processes go on, one of the two alternatives becomes stronger and wins. Even in conscious conflict, however, psychologists have discovered that a great deal of this weighing and balancing process goes on behind the scenes; that is, judgment, or the deciding process, may be largely nonconscious.

Conscious conflicts may be extremely severe. One frequent conflict is that between marriage and a career. For example, a college student who wishes to become a physician falls in love in his sophomore or junior year. Since our folkways demand that he be able to support his wife, marriage must wait until he finishes college, four years of medical school, several years of internship, and then some years of economic struggle for a sufficient income. This means a period of perhaps ten years before he can marry. There are dozens of possible half-solutions and compromises in this situation. Certainly the conflict is severe no matter what compromise is made, and many factors may be involved. Many interesting facts can be obtained from such situations; but the one of greatest interest here is that such conscious conflicts rarely breed neurosis (even though there may be some "symptom" results), whereas unconscious conflicts, even when they are apparently less severe or important than the conflict in the above example, are much more likely to eventuate in general psychic illness or character change.

UNCONSCIOUS CONFLICT

Erickson's experiment, quoted at length above, demonstrated the existence of unconscious processes and, equally convincingly, the existence of unconscious conflicts. The command called for an activity against which the subject had strong moral impulses—opening his friend's mail or stealing from him. In these experiments the subject used all sorts of devices to escape the conflict situation and somehow or other solve the conflict problem. The following discussion will concern the types and significance of unconscious conflict in psychopathology.

Various types of unconscious conflict can be distinguished. On the one hand, conflicts may arise between unconscious impulses, "forbidden" drives or needs, and, on the other hand, (1) other, incompatible wishes, (2) the limitations set by reality, or (3) those set by morals, ideals, or ethical notions. Thus there is always some kind of incompatibility between the two sides to the conflict, but this may be caused by any one of three factors that clash with the need in question. Since the effects of these types of conflict may be somewhat different, they merit a closer examination.

Conflict Between Two Incompatible Wishes or Needs. It is possible to love and to hate John Smith simultaneously, to feel superior and inferior to him at one and the same time, to wish him well and with equal strength to wish him unhappiness. A man may unconsciously need from his wife the simultaneous satisfaction of a need for dependence and for independence. (There was this conflict in the case cited in Chapter I.) Such a conflict is a common factor in the typical "adolescent" conflict. The following example is characteristic:

A student in a psychology class, the mother of a little boy whom she loved to distraction, reported the following dream and her reactions to it: "I brought little Teddie to his grandmother, sneaked in and left him there. I returned home only to find that somehow he was there again. I then brought him to an uncle, and the same thing happened. Again and again I brought him to someone else's home, left him there, and then returned to my home, and there he was. Throughout I felt more and more irritated." To her the only plausible interpretation was that she wanted to get rid of her child. But how could this be? She shivered even at the *thought* of losing her baby. Her teacher explained to her again the nature of unconscious motives, the meaning of ambivalence, and suggested that she do a little soul-searching. Her ultimate report was: "I guess deep down I keep on thinking how I could have a career if not for Teddie. My love for him is real, but my desire for a career is just as real. My dream seems to say that if only Teddie were elsewhere, I could have my career." The sequel was as interesting as the dream. She decided to go into nursery school work, where she could have both her career and her baby. Compromise is usually the outcome of conflict; but in this case, because the conflict became conscious and her wits could be brought to bear on the problem, the compromise between two incompatible desires was an unusually efficient and satisfactory one.

Conflict Between a Need and Limitations Set by Reality. The common phrase for this sort of conflict is "wishing for the moon." Usually, as we grow up, we put such unreal hopes behind us. But in our unconscious wishes we sometimes seem never to grow up. The wishes for impossible things, which are of course rejected consciously (because we are "sensible" and "realistic"), may persist permanently in unconscious form. The cripple in his dreams is a great athlete, the octogenarian is young again, and the dumpy girl looks like Greta Garbo, if only the conscious screen is ripped away. It is doubtful whether a short man *ever* gives up his unconscious hope of gaining height, even if he is consciously quite reconciled to his shortness.

As always, the overt resultant behaviors, thoughts, wishes, and general character will be in part determined by such a conflict. Close examination will always show some trace of such effects in that complex compromise formation that is our behavior and our consciousness.

Conflict Between an Impulse and the Individual's Morals, Ideals, or Code of Ethics. Conflicts of this type may and often do center about impulses other than sexual. An impulse to steal or an actual act of theft may conflict with the ideal of honesty. This was the case with the subject in Erickson's experiment. A mean, nasty, or cruel act may have been long forgotten on the surface, but deep down it may burrow about, clashing with the ideal we have of ourselves as kind, decent people. The fear of such conflict and self-punishment may be very useful for society, for it keeps John Smith and Jane Jones, who otherwise might harm society by erring, on the strait and narrow path.

"I had in my office a pretty little Italian girl who had recently developed a curious habit—a tic. Every few minutes she would draw her under lip between her teeth. The lip, extending for half an inch down her chin, had become an unsightly red. Tessa was also very depressed. Her mother said that Tessa had acted queer ever since she had been allowed to attend her first dance at school. Her mother hadn't wanted her to go in the first place—she herself had never gone out as a young girl. But the teacher telephoned especially to urge her to let Tessa attend like the other girls. Tessa's story to me, confided with tears, was that one of the boys had danced her into the coat-room, where he had soundly kissed her. And Tessa liked it! She had told no one about this episode; indeed, there was no one to tell, since she had no close girl friends in the American school, and she fancied that her mother would turn her into the street if she knew."[3]

Allied to this type of conflict is that in which there is a discrepancy between one's ideal picture of oneself and one's actual deeds, when there is worry over a lack in oneself, when one has ideals of personality which can never possibly be achieved, when one is disappointed in one's achievements or status. One process in particular, the expiation process, is extremely important in dealing with guilt feelings. As we shall see in a later chapter, this consists essentially of making up for a wrong act by paying for it in

[3] Reprinted from *The Happy Family,* by John Levy and Dr. Ruth Munroe, by permission of and special arrangement with Alfred A. Knopf, Inc., authorized publishers. Copyright 1938 by Ruth Munroe Levy. Pp. 33-34.

some way. The self-punishment process is also frequent whenever illicit wishes or actions have given rise to guilt feelings.

Unconscious Conflicts in Social Relationships. The same rules and generalizations that we have spoken of already in connection with intrapsychic conflict hold also for unconscious conflicts created by incompatible needs and demands in the relationship between two persons—parent and child, friends, husband and wife. No close relationship between two persons can ever be understood completely unless the unconscious as well as the conscious factors in the situation are known. For instance, anyone will recognize the more obvious motives for marriage; but it is less often realized that people may marry for reasons that they themselves are not conscious of. A desire for dependence or for independence, for power, for appreciation, for submission—any of these demands may be made of one's marital partner without either person's realizing it. Psychologically good marriages are often good simply because these unconscious needs dovetail with each other. Thus a man who has a strong unconscious need to be mothered and who marries a woman with a strong unconscious need to mother someone may make both himself and his wife happy. If, on the other hand, he resents being mothered as a trespass on his independence and manliness, they will both be unhappy without knowing why. The situation may be further complicated by the fact that both incompatible desires may be present unconsciously and simultaneously, the need for being mothered and the need for independence. When such conflicts are unconscious, the marital friction that ensues will be puzzling and not understandable. The husband and the wife may tend to blame each other or perhaps may feel inadequate and unworthy, and on the surface the picture may be one of conflict, like the following:

"Mr. Black, aged forty-five, enjoys cutting a bit of a figure with the ladies—in all innocence, be it said. His wife is not very attractive. She naturally resents a little his greater popularity and is slightly uneasy about her own status in his affections. Consciously, however, she repudiates any such petty jealousy. She never reproaches him for gallivanting around—but she does show an intense wifely solicitude for his lumbago, his heart condition, his figure even, which serves to remind him and his lady friends of his advancing years. Outwardly she is within her rights as a conscientious helpmate. Actually she makes constant, insidious little attacks upon him, without recognizing them as such for a moment. Mr. Black is more acute. He is beginning to be seriously annoyed by his wife. Her jealousy is indeed petty. She could handle it easily if she knew about it. So long as she conceals it from herself, this series of antagonistic, socially acceptable acts is likely to continue. A person may wreck a precious marriage to gratify an insignificant bit of vanity because his conscious efforts unwittingly reinforce an unconscious impulse of destructive nature."[4]

[4] Reprinted from *The Happy Family*, by John Levy and Dr. Ruth Munroe, by permission of and special arrangement with Alfred A. Knopf, Inc., authorized publishers. Copyright 1938 by Ruth Munroe Levy. P. 52.

SIGNIFICANCE AND NATURE OF UNCONSCIOUS CONFLICT IN PSYCHOPATHOLOGICAL PROCESSES

We have said that the conflict may be between two incompatible wishes of a similar nature, or between a need or wish and the impossibility of achieving it, or between the individual's impulse and his ideals. We said further that guilt feelings and self-condemnation may be part of the conflict and that social relationships may be involved. In the conflicts involved in psychopathological processes, as a rule, all these aspects are present. In fact, the conflicts are always multiple, although the emphasis at any particular moment may be on one special conflict. As we have seen, an individual who is driven by the expectation of catastrophic helplessness and worthlessness, by anger and fear of a stronger individual, by fear of abandonment, humiliation, condemnation, or injury, takes measures which are conflicting. He wants to be dependent, and he wants to attack and be superior; he wants to submit, and he wants to conquer. All these impulses are partly or completely conflicting. Thus conflict is part and parcel of every psychopathological reaction.

Because of his great need, the patient's longings and desires are boundless. Reality constantly disappoints him. He has to be dependent, and he needs overwhelming help to a degree that cannot be realized. Although he is sometimes aware of this, he still needs it. Here there is a conflict between an impulse and the limitations of reality. Another measure by which the patient unconsciously tries to relieve his fear and his helplessness and obtain approval is a drive for perfection and excessively strong moral ideals. These needs and impulses, however, clash with his desire for dependence and submission; they clash with his hostility, aroused by disappointments. Here there is a conflict between impulses and the ideals and ethical code.

Why can the patient never adequately solve his conflicts, why do they continue, and why do they keep him under constant tension? Because vital needs and impulses, vital desires, literally life-saving measures are always involved. The patient cannot say, "I'll submit," because his ideals are equally vital. He cannot follow his ideals alone, because he is constantly disappointed, and he is driven to be hostile or to submit. He cannot say, "I will not strive for the impossible," because he clings to unlimited goals, for only they will relieve unequivocally catastrophic expectation. All this was true of the patient described in the first chapter.

DYNAMIC REACTIONS TO CONFLICT

Every conflict *involves in its very nature automatic, persistent attempts to solve it, to get rid of it, or to avoid it.*

Conflicts are painful for several reasons. They give the individual a feeling of lack of integration and of threatening disorganization. They further lead to a feeling of hesitation and indecision. They may also represent threats to the self-esteem and to the feeling of adequacy. They are problems that we are unable to solve and they therefore represent a lack of power in us and inferiority. Further, there may be deprivation or frustration, partial or complete, of one or several vital needs involved in the conflict. In general, individuals with a measure of self-confidence tend to attack conflict situations, whereas people with little of this quality tend to avoid them and escape them. The attempt at tackling the situation may mean trying to achieve both of the desired goals. The most common reaction is compromise-formation. This will be discussed in a later section. (See Chapter VIII.) Most conflicts cannot be completely avoided or removed, and therefore some halfway measure of success is all that is possible—except, of course, healthy solutions. These are realistic measures, definite decisions that may mean partial frustration, and involve intelligence. In the case cited in Chapter I the peculiar marriage contract was a compromise solution; i.e., the woman wanted both love and independence. She got a little of both, but neither wish was fully satisfied. In contrast, the "healthy" man in Chapter II decided to step out of his political party for the time being when its corrupt leadership could not be removed.

"A . . . woman . . . believes that her husband should maintain his masculine friendships, both for his own enjoyment and as a matter of business expediency. She sees to it that he pays his dues at several clubs, that he arranges for golf . . . and squash at frequent intervals. But she is also a little sorry for herself because she lives in the suburbs and is . . . tied down to her house and baby. Moreover, she is . . . fond of her husband. She likes to have him around. Now, it often happens that she 'forgets' about his club nights. She invites guests . . . so that he finds it awkward to leave. She is apt to get a violent headache on Sunday morning. Although she urges him to go right ahead with his golf, . . . somehow [he] always stays at home. Occasionally she drops into his office for a surprise at five o'clock. . . . The day she comes turns out to be his afternoon for squash.

". . . Mrs. Wilson solved her dilemma by consciously arranging for her husband's masculine pursuits and unconsciously—'accidentally'—managing to keep him home pretty often."[5]

If the conflict is severe and long-continued, if it cannot be solved or avoided, and if compromise formations do not suffice to relieve the situation, then complete breakdown, a catastrophic breakdown, may ensue (Schulte, Maier, Liddell, Goldstein). Essentially it is a purposeless, useless, nonfunctional reaction, and the most disastrous consequence possible.

[5] Reprinted from *The Happy Family*, by John Levy and Dr. Ruth Munroe, by permission of and special arrangement with Alfred A. Knopf, Inc., authorized publishers. Copyright 1938 by Ruth Munroe Levy. Pp. 56-57.

CONFLICT AND "PERSONALITY AS A WHOLE"

From what has been said up to this point, the student has undoubtedly formed a picture of conflict as a sort of battle, of dissociation, of disintegration of the personality into two warring camps. He may then ask how it is possible to speak of the personality as a unified, integrated whole, and at the same time to speak of conflict, which is ever present in the personality.

1. The statement that the individual reacts as an integrated whole does not necessarily mean that he reacts as a harmoniously integrated whole. The term "whole" refers to a pattern in which the relations of the elements can be stated. It means that the individual's image and evaluation of himself and of others are involved in the reactions, and that various aspects and details of his reactions influence each other. Clashes may occur in these various reactions, but, even so, they do not exist side by side without positively influencing each other. Naturally, an individual will do his best work and be happiest and most secure if he acts not only as an integrated but as a harmoniously integrated whole.

2. Intrapsychic conflict occurs when two desires are incompatible with each other.

The patient in Chapter I was torn between the desire for dependence and the desire for independence. But what do these mean? What she ultimately wanted was love, affection, freedom from hurt, etc. The path of isolation was one way of achieving them (although a poor one); dropping her defenses, giving up her isolation, was another path to the same set of goals. In a sense there was no conflict in what she wanted; there was conflict only in the choice of means to these ends.

SUMMARY

In neurosis there is always a sharp conflict between two vital needs of the personality. It is obvious that the patient wants protection against an anticipated catastrophic expectation. The trouble arises from the fact that the various means (which are goals in themselves) which he feels forced to use are incompatible. It is further obvious that he wants happiness, love, affection, satisfaction of his bodily needs, achievement, pleasure. But again the means with which he wants to achieve these goals and the special coloring he gives them are contradictory. Thus there is serious conflict in the partial and intermediary goals, but often no contradiction in the patient's ultimate goals.

SUGGESTED READINGS

For an excellent general survey of the field we recommend Symonds' *The Dynamics of Human Adjustment* (919). Probably the simplest introduction to Freud is his *Psychopathology of Everyday Life.* A good book to own is *The Basic Writings of Sigmund Freud* (313) in the Modern Library edition, which includes the book cited and four others (see Bibliography). Guthrie's *Psychology of Human Conflict* (374) is useful and interesting reading, as is also Luria's *Nature of Human Conflict* (591). For a general approach to this whole system of thinking, a readable, even fascinating book is *The Happy Family* by Levy and Munroe (552).

Easily the best experimental demonstration of conflict and unconscious activities is found in Erickson's article "Experimental demonstrations of the psychopathology of everyday life," in the *Psychoanalytic Quarterly* (248). On the role of conditioning, Hilgard and Marquis (410) is useful. For a survey of experimental work see Sears's monograph (843) and Maier's book (606).

V Frustration and Its Effects

THE CONCEPTS OF FRUSTRATION AND DEPRIVATION

The concept of frustration is customarily applied to the blocking of gratification of bodily desires. By extension, it is sometimes also used to describe the impossibility of gratifying those personality needs whose importance we have already discussed—the need for dependence, prestige, self-esteem, love and affection, etc.—needs which do not center around obtaining gratification and pleasure through the use of one particular bodily organ.

If confusion is to be avoided, we must distinguish sharply between these two concepts of deprivation and frustration. For, as we shall see, their effects and their roles in psychopathology are very different. We shall define deprivation simply as the nongratification of a wish or desire or need, usually of an organic character. Frustration, on the other hand, will be defined as a deprivation which is also a threat to the personality, particularly to the self-esteem or feeling of security. The discussion to follow will amplify and explain these concepts. Since mere deprivation is usually not of great importance in the etiology of psychic illness, we shall be most concerned with frustration—that is, with threats to the personality.

The following experiments by D. M. Levy (543) on a litter of puppies illustrate the significance of bodily needs aiming at satisfaction, and the disturbances arising out of their nongratification.

In a litter of six puppies, two of the puppies were permitted to suckle at their mother's teats. The other puppies were fed by bottle. Two of the four were given milk and water from the bottle through nipples that had a moderately large hole so that it took them about five minutes to get the necessary amount of food. The other two puppies were fed through nipples which had a very large hole so that they took all the liquid within about two minutes. Within a few weeks the following situation developed: The two breast-fed puppies thrived and engaged in no suckling activity except at the mother's nipples. They played in a lively manner and then rested. The second two puppies frequently engaged in suckling activities on various objects and were more restless than the two breast-fed puppies. The last two puppies engaged in almost continuous suckling activities, very frequently on each other, so that they sucked each other's skin bloody. They were restless practically all the time, even in their sleep. If they played, or if the litter was taken for a walk, the last two puppies would pair off and go separately from the other four and would fight and snarl at the others. Thus they were irritable and combative. These puppies lost weight, although they received the same amount of nourishment as the second two puppies.

The first obvious implication of these experiments is that the dogs had a certain need for activity with their mouths which required satisfaction. This activity was separate from the need for nourishment. If this need was not satisfied while taking nourishment, it led to a continuous activity for its satisfaction. If the deprivation was even greater and the most satisfactory activity was barred, the search for satisfaction became extremely vehement and was accompanied by inability to relax adequately and by behavior disturbance.

In evaluating this development, we should not consider only the need that is satisfied through activity of the mouth. A more complete reaction of the total organism has to be considered; and in this two factors enter: (1) a continuous tension and distress, which is never fully eased, and is similar to continuous pain; (2) a helplessness in the attempt to relieve this distress. The "neurosis" of the two puppies is a result of the three factors mentioned.

In this experiment the urge that was blocked was a bodily one aiming at gratification. As a rule, at least in the human being, the problem is not as simple as it appears here. Neither in the normal nor in the pathological is a "simple urge" ever dealt with. The total process of motivation may be divided into three phases: the drive, the motivated behavior, and the goal object or goal activity. The drive may be relatively physiological—e.g., a hunger drive; but even in this case socially learned modifications are clearly apparent—for example, getting hungry three times a day. With reference to motivated behavior, it is by now a truism that the adult human being goes about achieving goal objects, whether driven physiologically or socially, along paths that are culturally determined; thus he eats with knife and fork. Finally, cultural determination is also at work in goal objects; theoretically almost any living tissue, plant or animal, might serve as food, but actually only a small proportion of them is used as food; thus we eat fish but not worms. Obviously, in considering motivation, it is impossible to limit ourselves to the purely biological and hereditary—i.e., to instincts, physiological drives. Furthermore, as has been repeatedly stated, the individual's self-confidence, his general evaluation of himself, of his body, and of other individuals, play a significant role in the dynamics of every significant activity.

SOURCES OF FRUSTRATION

SITUATIONAL FRUSTRATION

Invariably in everyone's life there are situations which are extremely depriving; it is impossible to live without going through such situations. Thus illness represents not only a threat, but also a frustration, for it may make the individual stop certain activities—such as the pleasures of eating—although he may not have lost the desire for them. The death of anyone close to him may likewise be a severe frustration apart from all other aspects. Death may mean deprivation of bodily needs, as in the case of a married couple; but there is always also a frustration of emotional needs, of the need for closeness, affection, support, and dependence. Unrequited love is likewise a frustration of both bodily and emotional needs. Furthermore, reality always sets limitations and in that sense causes at least some blocking of the individual's goals and desires. No one can succeed in everything that he aims at, although often what he aims at is very dear to him. A scientist may invest time, energy, and emotion in a piece of research and then fail. Such an experience, of course, is disappointing, and it may be frustrating. Such situations are significant because a breakdown frequently occurs when they arise; they do not, however, necessarily lead to the breakdown. Situational frustration is commonly referred to as external frustration.

INTERNAL FRUSTRATION

By the term "internal frustration" is meant the inability of the individual, for psychological reasons, to gratify an urge or a desire or a need even when he has the opportunity to do so. This factor is very important in psychopathological reactions; as a matter of fact, internal frustration is present in every patient with these reactions. We have said repeatedly that in every significant activity of the individual his evaluation of himself (self-esteem) and of other persons (feeling of security) is involved. This evaluation concerns his general strength and his body and its activities. The causes of internal frustration are conflict, inhibition, condemnation, fear. If the patient feels helpless in a situation, if he condemns and rejects a part of his body and its function, if he expects disapproval for an activity when approval is vital to him, he cannot adequately engage in that activity even if he has the opportunity. Furthermore, every activity means attitudes toward other people and assumptions regarding their attitudes toward him. Physical intimacies have the connotation of emotional intimacies. If, because of his basic character, the patient expects rejection, humiliation, and injury from the other individual, this fear will make adequate gratification impossible. The patient may have conflicting attitudes and needs in regard to the measures which he uses to save himself from a catastrophic situation. Thus he may want to be dependent but at the same time to respect himself; he may want to dominate and subjugate his partner. The result may be that he is internally frustrated in his dependency longings and experiences, as was the case with the patient described in Chapter I.

All the phenomena mentioned here may be—and, as a rule, are—largely unconscious. Thus a distinction must be made between conscious and unconscious frustrations. Even when the frustration is conscious, a great many aspects of the experience may be unconscious. Or a conscious deprivation may also be unconsciously frustrating.

EFFECTS OF FRUSTRATION

THE CONCEPT OF FRUSTRATION TOLERANCE

The effects of frustration depend on several factors: (1) the degree of frustration; (2) the nature of the impulse that is frustrated; (3) the personality structure of the individual who suffers frustration.

Frustration tolerance (Rosenzweig [801]) is the ability of a person to go through a frustrating situation without reacting to it in a "bad" way. Further, what is a frustrating situation for one individual may not be for another. For some people the feeling of frustration itself is absent from so-called frustrating situations. Within certain limits, if they perceive that they cannot obtain something, they may lose their desire for it; or they may have little desire for anything *until* it becomes available.

PERSISTENCE OF THE THWARTED WISH

An unfulfilled wish or desire is an unsolved problem. If it is conscious, it tends to attract attention to itself again and again. In such situations the individual's energy remains partly directed toward attempts at solving the problem even though this is impossible. This reduces the energy available for other tasks. Some feeling of discomfort over this state of affairs may likewise be present. But if the individual is essentially adequate, he stands the persistence of his unsatisfied wish well. He can look at it realistically, wait, persist in his attempt at solution, or relieve the tension by his sense of humor. In other words, the unsolved problem represents no threat to him.

The phenomena surrounding the persistent wish can, however, be much more serious. Such a wish may become unconscious if it represents a threat. Under such circumstances the individual does not admit even to himself that he has certain wishes because they create guilt feelings, self-condemnation, and loss of self-esteem; they are pushed out of consciousness and disappear as far as he is concerned. Actually, however, they continue to exist in an unconscious form and at times become a tremendously important factor in the psyche. He expends energy on keeping them repressed, they are accompanied by continued tension, discomfort, and feelings of threat and danger, and he may try to satisfy them in indirect and substitute ways.

PERSISTENCE OF THE THWARTED WISH AND PRIMITIVATION

Some effects of frustration will be discussed in connection with the following experiment (Barker, Dembo, Lewin, and Wright [46]):

In one experiment thirty, in another experiment seventy-eight, children, ranging in age from two to six years, were observed in order to determine the effects of frustration on intellectual and emotional behavior. In the first phase of the experiment, each child was allowed to play with some toys for a half-hour while the experimenter sat at the desk and made notes. In the second phase, the next day, the child was brought in again and this time was allowed to play in the adjoining room with some much more desirable toys. In the third phase, fifteen minutes later, the experimenter returned the child, without explanation, to the other room, where he had played the previous day, and allowed him to play with the original, much less attractive toys for a half-hour. During this period, the fine toys were in constant view of the child through a wire net that had been lowered between the two rooms. Again the experimenter sat at his desk and made notes on the behavior of the children.

In the nonfrustrating situation, one subject played continuously with the toys in a constructive manner, frequently commenting on her activities. The following is a record of her play in the frustrating situation:

"1. Subject watches experimenter lower the partition. She asks, 'I will not play on the other side again?' Experimenter answers, 'You can play here now.' Subject faces the experimenter for about 15 seconds with hands behind her neck.

"2. Subject looks around.

"3. Subject goes to Square 3 and examines sailboat and fish pole.

"4. Subject stands at Square 3 and looks at barrier.

"5. Turning to the play material on Square 3, subject takes the fish line and dangles it about sailboat.

"6. Subject goes to the barrier and reaches through the meshes of the screen.

"7. Subject turns around, looks at the experimenter, laughs as she does so."[1]

These effects and some others to be mentioned may be summarized in the following way: There was a general primitivation of the intellectual performance of an average of 17.3 months of mental age. In subjects who felt more seriously frustrated, this regression was 24 months. With this, naturally, went a reduction in the constructiveness of the play. Emotionally, there was a marked decrease in the happiness of the mood of the children (less laughing, smiling, and gleeful singing), there was an increase in motor restlessness and in general tension (more loud singing and talking, restless actions, stuttering, and thumb-sucking), and there was an increase in aggressiveness (more hitting, kicking, breaking, and destroying). Interestingly, there were changes in the social interaction. There was an increase

[1] R. G. Barker, T. Dembo, K. Lewin, and M. E. Wright, Experimental studies of frustration in young children, in T. M. Newcomb, E. L. Hartley, et al., *Readings in Social Psychology*, Henry Holt & Co., New York, 1947, p. 285.

in coöperative actions (children helping each other to achieve common goals). All the aggressive acts that took place were done by the children jointly against the experimenter; strong friends went so far as to hit the experimenter with blocks, tear his records, throw him off his chair, scratch at him, and so forth. The weak friends stopped at touching the experimenter while calling him names. In general, the friendly contact with the experimenter decreased, although still predominating over the hostile contact.

Thus we can observe from these experiments (1) primitivation of the performance, (2) persistence of the thwarted wish (see also Zeigarnik [1006] and Rosenzweig [802]), (3) increase in aggression toward the frustrator, and (4) an increase in some constructive measures, attempting to cope with the situation. The last two effects will be discussed later in detail.

FRUSTRATION AND AGGRESSION

Aggression is one of the most universal and important effects of frustration. Our analysis will follow that made by Dollard, Doob, Miller, Mowrer, and Sears in a coöperative investigation at the Institute of Human Relations (216). These men define aggression as an act whose goal is injury to someone or to whatever stands for that someone. The strength of the tendency to aggression, they believe, depends directly on the amount of frustration. The inhibition of any act of aggression depends upon the amount of punishment or pain which would ensue if the act were not inhibited; this anticipated punishment need not be direct. The greater the anticipated punishment for an act of aggression, the less likely it is to occur.

Aggression may be direct or indirect. The simplest and strongest form is that directed against a person who is the source of frustration. If this direct aggression is blocked for some reason, indirect or substitute forms of aggression may be expected. Thus, if someone frustrates an individual, the latter's primary tendency will be to revenge himself directly upon the frustrator. If this is impossible, his aggression will be displaced; that is, it will be directed toward some other person or even toward an inanimate object.

These formulations, as well as some of the subsequent ones, have been demonstrated by a variety of experiments. The previously described reaction of children in response to play frustration included aggressive acts.

Sears and Sears (844) varied the point, during bottle feeding of a six-month-old baby, at which the nipple was withdrawn from the mouth. They found that it caused angry cries. The quickness with which crying started was related to the degree of the child's hunger. If he had had little milk, the crying started almost instantly, but if he had had nearly a full ration, there was a longer latency to the reaction.

In an experiment to be described later (see pp. 161-162), it was found that in a group of children who showed general apathy in the presence of their autocratic leader, the aggression flared up to ten times its previous level with his repressive influence gone. In another autocratically led group, the aggression of four of the five members was twice focused on the remaining youngster to such a degree that the scapegoat left the group (Lewin, Lippitt, and White [562]). (See also Fredericksen [285].)

It is also possible that there may be a change in the *form* of aggression. Thus, instead of punching someone, one may gossip about him or try to hurt him financially or in any one of dozens of other ways. There are less obvious changes in form that are just as important. For instance, aggression may express itself in fantasy and dreaming, or it may even turn inward; that is, the aggression whose expression is blocked may be turned against the self in the form of self-condemnation, guilt feelings, anger with oneself, and possibly even suicide.

The final principle of aggression elaborated by this group of psychologists is that of "catharsis of aggression"—namely, that the expression of any act of aggression reduces the tendency to all other such acts. For example, if one lets himself explode in a fit of anger over a particular frustration, he is less likely to become angry over other frustrations during the same period. (See also Release Therapy, Chapter XVII.)

It is necessary to add the following remarks to these statements. Aggression in response to frustration is a widespread phenomenon. The amount and the quality of aggression depend on the structure of the personality—that is, on the individual's strength and approval of himself. If his evaluation of himself is seriously damaged, and if, as is natural in such instances, he attributes damaging motives to the frustrator, his aggression will be much more violent in both intensity and quality. It may be overt and seem to go beyond justified bounds, or it may be unconscious. If it is entirely unconscious, the individual nevertheless may show serious symptoms; he may feel frustrated, become angry but be unaware of it, and have an attack of anxiety, as did the patient described in the first chapter when she felt angry at her husband.

In the face of a serious deprivation the healthy individual may become aggressive in various ways. He may persist in the pursuit of his goal; he may insist on his rights and demand satisfaction in an emphatic, possibly sharp manner. In the pathological reaction, there is very strong hostility which the patient may express in an excessively violent way such as a temper tantrum, or he may repress it completely and show incapacitating symptoms, or he may consider his strength so low that he withdraws from the situation completely.

FRUSTRATION AS A THREAT

As we have said, the effects of a frustrating situation depend on the strength of the individual who is frustrated, on the degree of frustration, and on the nature of the need that is frustrated.

There are certain frustrations which, if severe enough, represent a serious threat to anyone, no matter how well and strong he may be at the time. We have already pointed out that two elements can be differentiated in the concept of frustration. One is the inability to attain satisfaction (deprivation). The other, as was indicated in connection with the experiments on the puppies, is the feeling of actual helplessness to do anything about the situation and to withstand this deprivation.

Experience with human infants throws further light on the problem. Levy found that if the infant was bottle-fed and the opening in the nipple was large, the baby engaged in thumb-sucking. If the opening in the nipple was made smaller and the suckling need was thus satiated, the thumb-sucking stopped (541). The thumb-sucking activity may be considered a moderate disturbance. "Nursing frustration," however, may constitute a much more serious disturbance in the human infant (769). If the nipples of the mother's breast are inverted (instead of being flat they are hollow and therefore cannot be sucked at adequately), a newborn infant first gets restless and then goes into a state similar to a deep sleep, in which he stops reacting adequately to external stimuli. This condition is very similar to the stupor or coma of the adult, and considerable nursing care is required to bring the infant out of it. When he develops this condition, he has not lost any wants and is not yet undernourished. Apparently this is a "psychological" state due to continuous frustration of the infant's most important bodily need. In this instance, as in the experiments on the puppies, we should consider not only the local need of the mouth, but also the threatening character of the continuous tension and the feeling of helplessness in trying to relieve this tension. In such a case, the human infant becomes absolutely helpless and is utterly incapable of doing anything about this problem. It is to be noted that the significance of the mouth function in an infant is very great; it is the only way in which he can master anything in the world, for skilled grasping and locomotion are as yet entirely undeveloped. Any disturbance in this function is of the most fundamentally threatening character. Under such conditions a previously healthy organism becomes seriously sick as the result of a severe deprivation.

In psychopathological reactions to frustration, the situation is more complicated, but it is similar in one important respect. The serious psychopathological reaction arises if the patient feels severely deprived of one of his vital needs. He perceives this blocking of a vital need as an extremely serious threat, one which endangers his whole existence; at least potentially, he feels catastrophically threatened. It has been repeatedly brought out that in the basic psychopathological constellation the patient feels potentially helpless and worthless; he feels afraid of and angry at individuals whom he perceives as more powerful than he, and potentially he anticipates abandonment, humiliation, condemnation, injury, and complete deprivation. To relieve this fear, he uses various devices, pursues various goals, and engages in various activities in ways which enable him to exist. For example, he may depend emotionally and actually on another individual. If this vital need is frustrated—if he is no longer permitted to depend on this person, or if his self-esteem is not constantly flattered, maintained, and raised—the patient's first reaction is that his vital device is taken away from him, and, second, he evaluates the frustrating situation as the final realization of his worst anticipations. The need and gratification that are frustrated may be largely of a psychological type. Often in such relationships more definite bodily needs are also involved, as in the case of the child-parent and the husband-wife relationship. In other cases some form of bodily gratification is the device used by the patient to maintain his whole emotional security. The device may be eating or sexual gratification or even one of the excretory functions. If then, for some reason or other, gratification in this sphere is denied, the individual reacts severely. For example, women who become stout from overeating and then begin to diet become profoundly depressed, anxious, and disturbed soon after starting the diet. When they begin eating again, they feel psychologically better. For other individuals almost every form of physiological gratification is significant to their security, often because they consider physical gratification an expression of help and support, love and affection, from others. If they cannot obtain this gratification, they not only lose their chief means of consolation, but also feel rejected and abandoned.

There is still another reason why frustration constitutes such a serious problem and initiates psychopathological reactions. In the preceding section we said that one of the most universal reactions to frustration is some degree of aggression. This leads to disturbance in two ways. The patient feels that he is threatened in a vital spot, that the gratification on which his whole existence depends has been taken away. His hostility is commensurate with the enormity of this threat. In other words, he unconsciously regards the frustrator as hostile, cruel, heartless, menacing. Since the patient does not have enough strength to tolerate even a normal amount of aggression in himself, the enormous amount which arises in a frustrating situation leads to an extremely intense expectation of counterattack, abandonment, condemnation, disapproval, which in turn leads to self-condemnation and guilt.

It was said in an earlier section that a patient with psychopathological reactions suffers a certain amount of frustration all the time, even under the best circumstances, and that "inner frustration" is part and parcel of all psychopathological pictures. This statement will be considered further at this point in connection with situations of frustration. We saw above that, while some degree of frustration is present in patients who are either actually or potentially sick, they can, under favorable circumstances, obtain enough gratification of vital needs and thus enough security to function with comfort. Frustrating situations that cause serious trouble involve radical changes in the external environment—for example, the breaking-up of a marriage, the loss of a job, or the death of someone dear to the patient. In such cases a new kind of frustration appears; it is much more severe, much greater in intensity, much more threatening. It is easily apparent that such situations are likely to occur in the lives of potential patients because their needs are so great, so unlimited.

Up to this point we have spoken mostly of unexpected, new, and dramatic occurrences in the patient's life as leading to the breakdown. In some cases the situation is chronic and develops more gradually. The patient finds himself in a difficult situation; perhaps his marriage partner is disappointing, or his child is sick, or his work presents difficulties. The situation creates a continuous, threatening problem which he manages to handle in various ways, but always with the hope that sooner or later the situation will change. But finally, after one device after another fails and one hope after another is shattered, he finds himself beaten, definitely frustrated, helpless, and without hope. Then the breakdown occurs. This general development is at times complicated by the patient's suffering another disappointment which likewise strikes at his confidence in himself and at his whole security system. Such developments are usually present in breakdowns that occur during the menopause. The fact of the menopause may lower the woman's evaluation of herself, and her hope of finding another mate or finding a new job or attaining new goals may be finally shattered.

THE EFFECTS OF THE GRATIFICATION OF IMPULSES

Let us not concern ourselves only with the negative side of the picture. If frustration of impulses has bad effects, their gratification has good effects; however, this has not as yet been adequately studied. Kardiner (483) has pointed out that, in addition to the obvious fact of the immediate sensual pleasure derived from drive satisfaction, such satisfaction also has effects on the personality. The individual who does something successfully, who carries out a wish, enhances his self-esteem thereby and, at least with relation to that particular wish, builds up his self-confidence. If such satisfactions and achievements are frequent enough and if there are not too many failures and deprivations, we should expect this self-confidence to become generalized (Kardiner). That is, instead of saying that the individual is self-confident with respect to a single field, we would say that he is in general a self-confident person.

Can gratification go too far? Probably it can. The individual who sees all his wishes gratified and who suffers no deprivations has failed to learn how to inhibit himself. (See Chapter XI on maternal over-protection.) There are even more serious possible effects. The person who has his every wish satisfied may lose all his motivation, all his reason for living, since there is nothing to look forward to, nothing to hope for. One needs only to read Suetonius'

The Lives of the Caesars to see how complete a breakdown can be when people can fully gratify all their wishes and are never deprived or frustrated.

Too much frustration and too much gratification—both have evil consequences. The individual must strike the proper balance between them. Discipline, training in hardship and in deprivation, are by no means outlawed by the psychologist.

SUGGESTED READINGS

The base line from which discussion of frustration proceeds today is *Frustration and Aggression* by Dollard, Doob, Miller, Mowrer, and Sears (216). Some experiments by this group are described in 217 and 435. A typical criticism of their work is that by Gould (362).

The Dollard book can be supplemented by Kardiner's *The Individual and His Society* (483). Look up "frustration" in the index. D. M. Levy's articles on "instinct-satiation" and his monograph on sibling rivalry (544) are also valuable sources.

Other interesting experiments are cited in 435 and 717. Rosenzweig's work in this field is also noteworthy. Characteristic are 800, 801, and 804.

VI Disturbances of the Evaluation of the Environment

THE BASIC PSYCHOPATHOLOGICAL CONSTELLATION

We have said previously that the fundamental dynamic constellation in individuals who suffer from serious psychological disturbance is characterized in part by a feeling of worthlessness and helplessness, by resentment toward more powerful individuals, and by the fear of abandonment, humiliation, disapproval, condemnation, injury, and complete deprivation—a fear which is potentially catastrophic in intensity.

It is convenient to differentiate two aspects of this constellation: (1) The individual's general attitude about the world, particularly the people in it; his assumptions as to how this world feels toward him, whether it loves him or not, whether it accepts or rejects him, whether it helps him or threatens him; if it threatens him, in what way, and how he feels toward a world that he perceives as threatening. This set of reactions we shall call *security feeling.* (2) The individual's image and evaluation of himself—his own resources, his prestige, his strength, his worth, his body, his functions. This group of feelings we shall sum up under the category of *self-evaluation* or *self-esteem.*

There are many connections between these two groups of reaction patterns which will be discussed later. However, it is both convenient and useful to discuss the two reaction patterns separately because differences in emphasis on one or the other are always observed in various patients.

RELATIVELY MILD MANIFESTATIONS OF INSECURITY

There are many individuals who function fairly well, who cannot be considered exactly sick—certainly not seriously sick—yet who are apt to be overshy or withdrawn or mistrustful, or the like. They may be tense and moody and, at times, surly or abrupt. The following excerpts are from the self-analysis of a college student who did rather well in her studies but impressed all her acquaintances in this way:

"I don't trust anybody in the world. . . . People are all selfish deep down . . . and I have decided that the best thing to do is never to be too close to anybody and to keep my secrets to myself. . . . Women are catty and jealous and all the men I have ever known have been out to get from me whatever they could. . . . Now when I go out with a man I make sure that I have the upper hand. That was the way it was with my father and mother. My mother was weak so my father took advantage of her all his life. It doesn't pay to be weak. . . . I am determined that I will be one of the strong ones. . . .

"I guess I could be called a pessimist. I am always expecting the worst to happen; and even when something nice comes about, to myself I feel that it cannot last. . . .

"Life is a hard thing. I cannot feel relaxed and happy with other people because I am always suspicious of their motives; but the trouble is, I cannot even feel relaxed when I am alone. I get the most horrible thoughts about everybody. Sometimes I think I hate everyone in the world, but I try not to show it. Even in my dreams I have these horrible thoughts and I wake up in a cold sweat.

"My parents never really wanted me or loved me, and nobody else ever has either. If I died tomorrow there would not be anybody in the world who would be sorry for more than a few minutes, and there would be a lot of people who would be glad.

"The one thing that drives me on is getting ahead in the world. I think the rich man is the one safe person. Everybody is afraid of him and doesn't dare try to pull any funny stuff. When he talks, everybody listens, no matter what he talks about. If I have a lot of money, I can get anything I want—fame, power, love, everything."

In this instance the expectation of hurt from the world was conscious. Of course, if such a person is studied carefully and over a long period, it will be found that his expectation of threat from the world is, at least potentially, much more intense than he realizes, and has aspects of which he is entirely unaware. He judges his views at their face value, without realizing that there are difficulties within him. For example, he is unaware that his behavior arouses discomfort and antagonism in people with whom he is in intimate contact. It is probable that if an individual with such an outlook faces a situation of severe stress, the breakdown will be much more severe.

The above excerpt illustrates an open and unquestionable expectation of threat from the environment. To bring out this distrust even more sharply, we cite excerpts from an autobiographical analysis by another college student, who, both subjectively and in his behavior, felt secure in the world.

"I have the feeling of being at home in the world and at home with people. I realize now that I have always assumed that a person was nice until he had proven himself to be otherwise. I like them, therefore they like me. I have always had lots of friends, and as a matter of fact, I can think of very few people whom I have ever called enemy. . . .

"One thing that amazes me . . . is that I realize that all this is true in spite of the fact that I am pretty frank in my criticisms. They do not seem to resent criticisms from me although they do from others. . . .

"You point out that secure people are generally more happy. I never realized it exactly, but in looking back, I think I can say that my life certainly has been a happy one.

"There is another thing that I now realize is related to other parts of my personality. I feel that I am a truly democratic person. I have always felt that all people are interesting, each in his different way, and that it was silly to compare people with each other. Every person is good for some things, and not good for others, and there is a place in life for everybody. It takes all sorts of people to make a world, and one kind is just as important as another kind. I have never felt that just because I was a college student I was superior to my butcher or to the street sweeper. They are doing the best they can, and essentially we are all working toward the same thing and are really partners rather than competitors. . . ."

LESS OBVIOUS EXAMPLES OF EXPECTATION OF THREAT FROM THE ENVIRONMENT

Many people behave very calmly and at first give the impression of being unusually poised and well balanced. After longer acquaintance, closer observation, or more detailed psychological study, the following points may become striking: Such persons give the impression of too much calmness; they never, or almost never, are enthusiastic about anything. They do not assert themselves even when their own interest is at stake. Further questioning may bring out the fact that they have never undertaken anything out of openly confessed ambition and initiative. Their philosophy may hold that it is best to go through life as a calm spectator, with a sort of serene lassitude, without too much wear and tear and hustle and bustle, and let others do the fighting. On still further investigation, contradictory features may appear. This man who admits no ambition is an engineer and has made a success of his life career. Yet all his associates feel that he could do more than he is accomplishing; and, in off moments, he himself is dissatisfied with his status. This unusually calm and philosophical man will say that on some occasions, for an unexplained reason, he has a mild spell of anxiety —for example, if the subway train stops for any length of time in the tunnel. He admits that at times he indulges in fantasies such as this: He is flying high in a newly invented airplane, equipped with new instruments of destruction that rain havoc on cities and death on their inhabitants. Further investigation shows that he is quite frequently domineering with his wife and becomes rude and abusive to her for trivial reasons.

We begin to realize that this individual's calmness and easygoing philosophy are not to be taken at their face value. This man feels threatened, and he tries to manage his life so that he will never be confronted with a dangerous situation. He is afraid to assert himself; he is afraid of antagonists, of rivals, of his wife, and of people to whom he is close. This fear is in a way similar to the fear and anticipation of harm which was openly expressed by the college student who called herself a pessimist and said that the world consists of weak and strong people and that everyone was her potential enemy.

Our purpose in describing this man is to show that sometimes, even when a person presents a front of comparative security—in fact, the opposite extreme of anticipation of threat—detailed examination will show that in reality he feels constantly threatened. The threat which such an individual perceives unconsciously is likewise much more intense than he would be willing to admit; it is glimpsed in his mild and fleeting anxiety when the train stops in the tunnel. If such a person faces a difficult stress situation, he often suffers a severe breakdown. Something like this occurred in the patient described in the first chapter.

There are many other apparently normal individuals in whom close examination shows an undercurrent expectation of threat from the world which they unconsciously consider potentially very severe. In this group are the people who always or frequently seem overbearing, who are too assertive, who seem to avoid situations in which they would be in an "inferior" position; and also those who always say "yes" and are extremely humble in their behavior. Needless to say, this anticipation of threat, while always present, varies considerably, depending on the situation with which the individual is confronted.

SEVERE MANIFESTATIONS

We wish now to speak of some manifestations of insecurity which are quite overwhelming, in fact, nearly catastrophic. In these manifestations is clearly apparent either the expectation or the actual experience of a profound hurt.

Some patients suffer from a so-called "delusion of persecution." They are convinced that people look at them strangely and make derogatory and hostile remarks about them. They are convinced that they have enemies who are going to hurt them, and that there are plots against them. They go through distressing experiences; they taste poison in their food and are convinced that it was put in by one of their enemies; they smell gases which their enemies have released to destroy them. They hear voices which call them obscene and abusive names and threaten them with destruction and humiliation. They experience threatening sensations in their bodies which are the result of their enemies' attacks. In short, any world event, any physiological experience, may be perceived and construed by such patients as the result of an action of their enemies and thus as a threat. Some patients of this type may be constantly in utter panic because they are always expecting a murderous attack.

It is obvious that in such instances the appreciation and evaluation of the hardest facts of reality are altered. The patient's experiences, of course, are conscious, but not entirely so; he has no insight, and sees no connections with his inner life. He takes his experiences at their face value. In other words, instead of blotting out his inner life, he alters reality. It is absolutely impossible to show him that the trouble is not with the world but with him. He is not aware of the reasons for his outlook, and his own impulses toward the world are entirely unknown to him. What we wish to show here is that the expectation or the experience of overwhelming threats from the world may be entirely open and almost catastrophic in intensity.

There are other cases in which an overwhelming threat is experienced consciously. The anxiety attacks suffered by the patient mentioned in the first chapter were such experiences. In rare instances such a state of anxiety, such expectation of physical suffering or death, may be almost continuous. Here also the patient has no true insight into his inner life. He does not see the connection between various events and his attacks of anxiety, and he is not aware of the nature or extent of his needs and of his impulses toward the world. Thus the experience of overwhelming danger may be conscious, and it is connected with the individual's attitudes toward the world.

VARIETIES OF CATASTROPHIC EXPECTATION AND EXPERIENCE

Just as disturbances of the evaluation of the environment and of oneself are always found together and are part of the serious psychopathological constellation, so the various aspects of the anticipated catastrophic hurt are usually present in the patient. The emphasis, however, may be on one or another aspect.

The varieties of catastrophic expectation are as follows: the expectation of abandonment, injury and annihilation, condemnation and disapproval, humiliation, enslavement, loss of love, and utter deprivation. It is obvious that many of these special fears overlap. Thus the perception of loss of love is very close to abandonment, and abandonment is very close to complete deprivation. In the following examples, some one aspect is emphasized.

The patient described in the first chapter was afraid, in her anxiety attacks, particularly of being hurt and abandoned by her husband; this was a counterattack against her resentment toward him. She likewise had a strong fear of being utterly deprived in all her bodily needs which aimed at gratification; this was particularly true in regard to her need of eating and her sexual needs. With certain limitations, her husband had been the only person to whom she could get really close; and she had magnified his stature and his strength so that she could be dependent on him. Thus, unconsciously, her whole existence depended on his support and love; her bodily gratifications were possible only with his help. When he told her that he was leaving, all this was threatened. Because of this threat, she became angry at him. The further consequence was an intensification of all these threats and an anticipation of bodily injury and annihilation by this infinitely stronger individual.

Utter condemnation and disapproval are the dominant notes in some forms of emotional depression. If the depression is severe enough, the patient manifests a "delusion of sin and guilt." He is utterly dejected; he condemns himself, and says that he has committed the unpardonable sin. He is convinced that the whole world considers him a sinner, that God has rejected him and will punish him, that he is more worthless than a worm before God and man. Of course, in such a state the feeling of complete loss of love and of abandonment is likewise very strong. The expectation of bodily deprivation is also present, may, in fact, be one of the dominant features. This is particularly true of depressed patients who refuse food.

The anticipation or experience of extreme injury, of annihilation, is seen in the condition described above as "delusion of persecution." The whole world is considered hostile, ready to attack and destroy. In such cases the expectation and experience of utter humiliation and enslavement may also be present. The patient feels that he is being influenced, that his activities are governed and guided by his persecutors. He is deprived of his will, of his self-determination; he is a slave, an automaton. The "voices" that he hears call him "a prostitute," "a pervert," and refer to him in excretory terms. He is utterly humiliated.

These examples are extreme and dramatic, and occur in breakdowns which are almost catastrophic in intensity. Special aspects of the catastrophic fear can also be seen in milder form in disturbances that are not as severe. For example, individuals who want exclusive attention and constant unqualified affection and who become deeply disturbed if it is not forthcoming or if anyone else shares it, are particularly afraid of a catastrophic loss of affection. Other people in any situation of stress eat a lot and may want constant sexual attention. In such cases the catastrophic fear has chiefly the quality of complete bodily deprivation.

The catastrophic hurt may be anticipated in connection with various fields, functions, or aspects of the patient's existence. Thus the expectation of injury may apply to the whole body or to special parts of it, to the genitals in particular. Humiliation may be perceived particularly in social contacts or in being thwarted in work. To repeat, there are differences in emphasis. A full understanding of a patient's special problem can be obtained only by a complete study of his whole personality and of all his problems.

SUGGESTED READINGS

There is no one best source here. The interested student will have to look through Adler's works for his various discussions of basic "inferiority feeling," in which he lumps together low self-esteem and insecurity feelings. Horney's notion of "basic anxiety" is clearer and more understandable (431). Kardiner's concept of the "security system of the individual" (483, 484) is somewhat similar, but there is more stress on what the individual does about the situation. A clear distinction between security and self-esteem is made only by Plant in Chapter V of his *Personality and the Cultural Pattern* (736). Freud's *The Problem of Anxiety* is recommended for the industrious student.

VII Disturbances of Self-Evaluation

MILD DISTURBANCES OF SELF-EVALUATION

As we found with the evaluation of the world and of people, so with the evaluation of the self: there are some mild, open, and conscious disturbances, both subjectively and in the behavior of the individual. Such people are not seriously sick, but they may be shy, uncomfortable, fretful, and moody. The following excerpt from the self-analysis of a college student is an illustration.

"The most general thing I can say about myself is that I feel inferior. I don't seem to think well of myself. My mother tells me that I have no independence at all. . . .

"I remember once going around with one of the students. He was very attentive and I liked him. But the other girls in the dormitory did not and I got so mixed up about it that I dropped him. I remember I was so anxious to hear their opinion of him, because I didn't trust my own opinion. When they did not like him he actually changed in my eyes too.

"I am often weak in many other things too. In class I look stupid because I never say anything. Even when I am sure I am right, somehow I always feel that my opinion cannot be as good as others, and I am afraid that whatever I might say would be stupid. As a result, I usually keep my mouth shut. Even at parties and on dates I say what other people want to hear, or else keep quiet. . . .

"When I go out with men I get into trouble too. They all seem to want to paw me and I hate this. I know that other girls can handle the situation, but I cannot seem to. Sometimes I just give in and sometimes I just break out crying. I don't look forward to dates at all, but all of my friends urge me to go. I don't seem to understand men. I know the girls in the dormitory like men, are even crazy about them, but they just seem sort of animal-like to me and I can never relax with them and have a good time. I wonder what I will do about marriage. I love children and certainly will have them, but why must I go through all this nasty sex business first? The only time I have ever doubted God was when I thought about this. Why is it necessary to be an animal before you can have a baby?"

The case just cited presents a picture of relative but not very extreme self-devaluation. The following excerpts from a self-analysis of a man with high self-evaluation provide a good contrast:

"In answer to your questions I can say the following: I usually feel self-confident and sure of myself and practically never bashful or shy, and I can remember only once being really self-conscious and that was in my one try at amateur acting when I had to say some awful things. . . . You could call me a strong person. At least I think you could. For instance, I have generally been the leader in my crowd and my friends come to me to settle their arguments. I feel that I can handle almost any situation and I am certainly not afraid of any of the people I know. . . .

"I have never blushed in my life. . . .

"I do not know what will happen in the future, but I am sure I can take care of myself."

LESS OBVIOUS EXAMPLES OF DISTURBANCES OF SELF-EVALUATION

Some individuals, when asked how they feel about themselves, will first say that they are well satisfied with their performance. Further conversations and observation bring out the fact that they are eager to do everything well. They are very accurate in their work; in fact, they may be extremely accurate in almost anything they do. They say that everything should be done well; and they invest considerable time, energy, and emotion in doing their tasks well. They also expect other people to do their work perfectly. This may be the first hitch. Such individuals are apt to be emotional and a bit over-emphatic when they criticize other people because of their neglect of relatively minor matters. Thus, they may wax eloquent if someone's desk is not in perfect order. If they themselves happen to make a mistake, they grow rather disturbed and find it hard to forgive themselves, or they become unusually defensive and accuse someone else of being responsible for the mistake. In all of this there is apparent their need to do things without a flaw—a need so great as to be beyond the point of reasonableness. When such an individual is carefully examined or is caught in a mood of discouragement, he will say that he is dissatisfied with himself, that he does not trust his powers and is not satisfied with his achievements. Usually he has fantasies of great achievement; but when he is moody he thinks of failure, in his fantasies others surpass him, he is unable to do his work adequately. He may also be inclined to hound other people for their imperfections, and to demand unqualifiedly good performance of them.

Still other people manifest too much sureness, even on matters about which they know nothing; they show a surprising absence of doubt of their ability to carry out any task whatsoever; situations in which most people are doubtful and worried leave them absolutely unconcerned.

Longer acquaintance with such individuals or a careful study of them sometimes shows that, behind this need for perfection, behind this over-sureness and bravado, there is actually a doubt of their ability or worth similar to that expressed consciously by the student whose self-analysis was quoted. However, these individuals may be unconscious of this evaluation of themselves most of the time; it is glimpsed only when they are off guard or after they have failed. If they have to face situations of severe stress—particularly if there is a strain on their resources or if their self-esteem is threatened—they may suffer a more serious breakdown.

SEVERE MANIFESTATIONS

In some of the conditions described in Chapter VI, severe and overt disturbance of the evaluation of the self was manifest. For example, in attacks of anxiety, patients often feel that they are small, insignificant things caught in the mesh of gigantic circumstances, that they are faced with tremendous forces although they themselves are utterly powerless and helpless, or that they are alone, thrown entirely on their own resources, which fail them completely. Individuals who suffer severe depression, with delusions of sin and guilt, may feel utterly worthless, accuse themselves of crimes, consider themselves most contemptible and loathsome creatures.

In all these conditions there is a profound and open disturbance of self-evaluation. Of course, such individuals are not conscious of the ramifications of their experiences. They take them at their face value without understanding their real meaning.

VARIETIES OF CATASTROPHIC SELF-DEVALUATION

Self-devaluation is, at least potentially, catastrophic in intensity. It has various aspects, which are commonly found in the same individual; but the emphasis is different in various patients.

The varieties of catastrophic self-devaluation are as follows: feeling and expectation of helplessness, loss of self-esteem, moral worthlessness and guilt, inability to give love, loss of strength, loss of capability. Clearly there is a considerable overlapping among them. Thus a feeling of helplessness always involves loss of self-esteem; the inability to love involves the feeling of moral worthlessness and loss of self-esteem. This is why one patient usually shows many of them. It is further obvious that in cases of self-devaluation, disturbances of the evaluation of the world are often present. If this self-devaluation is of the catastrophic variety, insecurity feelings will *always* be found.

The feeling of catastrophic helplessness was eloquently illustrated by the anxiety attacks described in Chapter I. This patient felt helpless in the face of a gigantic and hostile world; she had always considered herself helpless and poor in resources. In her frustration, her conflicts, and the anticipated abandonment and threat of attack by her husband, she anticipated utter helplessness. This case clearly indicates that helplessness is one of the most common—in fact, an ever-present—aspect of psychopathological disturbances.

Even when the obvious emphasis is on some other aspect, helplessness always plays a very significant role, and it is always potentially catastrophic in intensity. This is true of the patient's estimation of his total possibilities and strength. He always feels that a thorough and radical change in his mode of living and reactions is beyond his strength. If circumstances demand it—if, for example, it is attempted in psychoanalytic treatment—he always feels that he is not capable of it. If any of his vital needs is threatened, he anticipates the catastrophically helpless state, and he is convinced that he cannot remedy the situation. If the feeling of helplessness is further aroused by failure of one of his functions, the emphasis in the feeling of helplessness may be predominantly in the field of one particular function—for example, in the field of bodily function, such as locomotion or eating or sexual function, or in the field of intellectual or emotional function.

The anticipation of catastrophic loss of self-esteem is often disclosed in patients by deep psychological analysis. Such people are convinced that something is lacking in them, that they have fatal shortcomings, that they fall utterly below their ideals and would fail in the most dismal and humiliating fashion if they attempted to live up to them or if their true nature were revealed to other individuals and to themselves. Often this low estimation of the self, this idea of something essential being lacking, is expressed by a reference to an insignificant bodily deformity such as a slight curvature of the spine or a slight difference in the size of the breasts, or thick lips. This catastrophic undervaluation of the self is expressed in some patients in delusions about their body. Some profoundly depressed patients and some who suffer from delusions of persecution also have delusions that their brains are gone, that their lungs are shriveled, that their bowels are stopped up. Patients who hear voices calling them derogatory names likewise suffer a great loss of self-esteem.

Profound disturbance of moral self-evaluation is present in the cases of depression with delusions of sin and guilt that have already been mentioned. These patients consider themselves abject sinners, and utterly worthless. Both self-condemnation and expectation of catastrophic disapproval and condemnation may be associated with some particular function of the body; in fact, the whole image and evaluation of the body and its functions may be catastrophically disturbed. In our culture, self-devaluation is very commonly associated with the genital organs and functions.

The catastrophic fear of inability to give love and affection is likewise common in patients who have found it necessary to put other people at a distance because of anticipation of rejection. If in the course of treatment they get to the point where they want to reach out to other people with genuine emotions, and they find that they are not able to, they are of course distressed and alarmed. Near-catastrophic experience of the inability to love is also present in the profoundly depressed patient. It is particularly striking in patients who suffer from "depersonalization." These individuals see everything, perceive and understand everything, but somehow the experience lacks a genuine quality; they complain bitterly that they cannot experience genuine feeling, pleasure, or even sorrow; they feel that their emotions are dead.

INTERRELATIONS BETWEEN SELF-EVALUATION AND EVALUATION OF THE ENVIRONMENT

Although disturbances of the evaluation of the self and of the evaluation of the environment have been discussed separately, the two are always found together in the psychologically sick, and there are connections between them. Some further remarks on this point will be made.

The individual tends to assume that the world evaluates him in the same manner as he evaluates himself. Thus he who feels worthless is convinced that the world considers him worthless.

The individual tends to expect a response from the environment similar to his toward it. This is obvious in connection with the inability to give affection and love. The patient feels unable to give affection, and is convinced that the environment does not give it to him; hence he feels unloved. It is equally true that he tends to treat the environment as he assumes it treats him. If, for example, he is convinced that he will not get genuine affection from anyone and that he will be rejected, he in turn will be unwilling to reach out emotionally toward others. He becomes unable to love.

The reaction of resentment and hostility is an important connecting link between evaluations of the self and of the environment. Thus the individual feels helpless; he considers that he does not get adequate support from his environment; he becomes unconsciously angry, and then anticipates complete abandonment in an even more helpless state. Or he feels unloved and rejected by the environment, grows angry because of this, anticipates utter condemnation and disapproval from the environment, and feels himself worthless and guilty. Similarly, he looks down on himself; he evaluates and interprets some act or attitude of the environment as humiliating, becomes resentful, and is then afraid of further humiliation.

The individual evaluates himself in comparison with the environment. He who feels helpless views the environment as all-powerful. As a result, all threats which he perceives as coming from the environment become terrific in intensity, and he feels that he cannot cope with them. The individual who lacks self-esteem compares himself with others and considers himself worthless. Thereupon he tends to raise his evaluation of others and at the same time envies them. The expected hurt from the overvalued individuals is then all the more painful.

EVALUATION OF THE SELF AND OF THE ENVIRONMENT AS A TOTAL REACTION

Thus far the evaluation of the self and of the world has been discussed in introspective terms. We shall now speak of reactions of the total organism. The attitudes and reactions that have been mentioned show themselves in the individual's whole behavior and vegetative reactions. The posture, the demeanor, the mien of the "threatened" person and the "secure" person tend to differ in subtle ways. The two even tend to have different tastes in food and literature, to behave differently to their friends, and to reveal a difference in practically everything they do. (For experimental work, see W. Wolff [993] and P. Eisenberg [232, 233, 235], among others.)

Another way of emphasizing the broader concept of self-evaluation is to study other people's impressions of the individual in question. Since this is, in large part, based upon behavior both obvious and subtle, we can thus learn much about the self-evaluation. The secure individual is likely to be described by his friends and neighbors as easy, natural, relaxed, affectionate, and friendly (if they approve of him), or as smug, bovine, unambitious, self-satisfied, easygoing, and lazy (if they disapprove of him). The threatened or insecure person is usually first described by other people as tense and nervous. He is often characterized as suspicious, envious, fearful, unpredictable, unstable, or introspective. Or he may be described as *extremely* pleasant or overbearing. For example, the forced laughter of a threatened individual is different from the relaxed and easy laughter of someone who has confidence in other people's affection for him.

The individual's involuntary functions are also correlated with evaluation of the self, particularly if his actual reaction to a definite situation is included. For example, a person is shy; his hands are cold and his pulse is rapid. Even when he apparently behaves in an easy manner, his hands may be cold and his heart may beat rapidly. The general appearance of the individual and the conditions of his vegetative functions in severe reactions may of course be very striking. A depressed patient has a dejected facial expression, his eyes lack luster, the action of his bowels is sluggish, his hands are cold.

FURTHER DYNAMIC CONSEQUENCES OF CATASTROPHIC EVALUATION OF THE SELF AND OF THE ENVIRONMENT

The constellations which have been described are of dynamic significance not only because they contain the element of drivenness, but because the individual reacts further in response to the initial pattern. These further reactions also have an intense element of drivenness.

Every patient who feels catastrophically threatened always has a never-dying longing for restoration and safety. This may be conscious or unconscious, or both. The special form of restoration sought depends on the situation, on his hurt, and on the threat he perceives, as well as on the environment and on his notions of what will be most valuable for the purpose. All these problems will be discussed in the next chapter; here certain forms of this longing and of attempts at remedying the situation will be considered.

Intense Longing for Support and Dependence. It was stated above that the feeling of helplessness almost automatically carries with it an overvaluation of the strength of other individuals. Thus the patient may seek his restoration by dependence on a stronger person.

There is a still further development in this reaching out for unqualified support. The patient feels that the person from whom he expects and wants undivided support must realize his helplessness and will thereby be convinced of his real need of support. The patient's helplessness that is manifest in an actual situation of stress is thus a phenomenon which has several factors. One factor is the kind of helplessness he felt when he first reached out for dependence; he in no way wanted this helplessness, it had no goal. But after he reached out and thereupon felt the need of showing his helplessness, he partially desires it and it is intensified in actual situations of stress. In a sense, he *wants* to be helpless to get the support of the stronger individual; the result is that he is even less able to mobilize his resources, and his panic is greater. This condition is found in patients who develop utter panic when left alone in a room.

The disturbance of the patient's self-esteem in actual situations of stress is likewise complex. Low self-esteem, as finally experienced, may consciously and unconsciously be the result of the following: The patient's self-esteem is low to start with. He reaches out for unqualified affection and dependence. To acquire this, he may even go to the point of unconsciously offering to be humiliated. In this sense, he practically offers to lower his self-esteem. Thus, his low self-esteem at first has no goal; but when he reaches out, being humiliated by the other individual and consequently lowering his self-esteem have a goal (the other's support), and the result is an even further lowering.

The patient may reach out for unqualified affection to get protection and thus be saved from the threats he perceives in his environment or to restore his feeling of worth.

Intense Drive for Superiority and Power. The patient's unconscious reasoning when there is a drive for power is as follows: "If I am superior to everyone, if I have power and can control and dominate everyone, I'll be saved from the dangers of the world, I'll be worth something in my eyes and in the eyes of the world, I'll even be loved." Such a patient may seek to achieve these goals in various fields. He may feel a tremendous drive to be superior in his work or to attain a position in which he surpasses and can command others. The drive may be directed chiefly toward accumulating money, or it may be present for the most part in the realm of subjective fantasies. The actual striving for these goals and the resultant feeling of esteem, which is itself in turn highly exaggerated, are again a complex matter. The individual first feels threatened; he reaches out toward superiority and power. He then feels a new threat, which is potentially more intense than the first. He expects counterattack in the direction either of humiliation or of thwarting his plans or of injury. To guard himself and to cope with these new threats, he makes a renewed effort toward the goals. Thus the finally resultant striving for power aims at relieving the originally low self-esteem and toward overcoming the new threats. This drive may also aim at relieving threats from the environment as well as catastrophic self-devaluation. The most extreme pathological result of this trend is a "delusion of grandeur." This type of patient considers himself a remarkable and exceptional person, he thinks that he can do amazing things, or that he has achievements to his credit which are entirely out of keeping with his real status. He may be convinced that he is one of the prophets or one of the apostles, Napoleon, or Jesus Christ, or the Virgin Mary, or Joan of Arc.

As previously mentioned, these measures evolved by the individual are typical of the devices he may use to overcome his fears, his conflicts, and his frustrations. Such devices are discussed in the following chapter.

SUGGESTED READINGS

Good source material is to be found in the writings of Adler. See also Maslow's papers on "dominance-feeling" (self-esteem) in monkeys, apes, and humans (616, 617, and 620). Chapter V of Plant's book (736) is recommended for its discussion of the relationship between self-esteem and security feelings. See also Freud's *The Problem of Anxiety* (311) and Sullivan's *Conceptions of Modern Psychiatry* (913).

VIII Coping with Dangers: Defense, Amelioration, Devious Solutions, Etc.

We have stated that in response to various threatening situations the patient reacts as if he unconsciously anticipated a catastrophic state of worthlessness and helplessness, of rejection, abandonment, injury, and complete frustration. The special emphasis in this catastrophic anticipation may be on one or another feature, such as humiliation or injury, but this anticipation is common to every serious situation with which the patient has to cope. This fear may arise in situations which to healthy people are not threatening, as when the patient has to perform a complicated social task, or when he wants to gratify a bodily urge, to relax, to get in contact with other individuals, etc. However, he does not unqualifiedly accept his fear, and he does not submit to it (unless he is completely discouraged); consciously and unconsciously he attempts to do something about it. In general, the following aims can be recognized on the part of the patient:

1. He attempts to diminish his distress by various means.
2. He takes definite positive measures to strengthen himself and thus to be able to overcome his fear.
3. He attempts to reach certain goals in spite of the fear that these goals produce.

The various mechanisms and devices to be discussed usually accomplish one or more of these aims. We shall group them, however, according to the aspect that predominates in the purpose of the device and its main goal. The various reaction patterns which will be described have been established through clinical observation (Freud [304, 310, 311, 313], Janet [455], Adler [12], Horney [431, 432], Rado [747], Kardiner [483, 484]). Many of them have been verified by experimental methods, such as hypnosis and animal experiments (Erickson [245, 246, 248], Maier [604], Lewin [560]).

MEASURES TO DIMINISH DISTRESS

AVOIDANCE OF THE SITUATION

The unconscious psychological formula here is: "If I avoid the dangerous situation, I will escape pain and catastrophe." For example, for many years the patient described in the first chapter kept away from men and from situations which might have brought her close to them. A more obvious form of avoidance is seen in certain types of phobia. Thus a patient may have to take a train to visit someone whom he dreads encountering because he expects humiliation, domination, and injury, but whom he feels obliged to visit. He develops anxiety attacks while riding in the train, and is unable to continue the trip. In this way he avoids the situation which he really dreads. Similarly, some individuals may avoid contact with people who are superior to them in any significant way. Others may avoid situations of responsibility or those in which they have to lead because these situations are fraught with fear for them. In other situations they feel safe. Physical illness may serve this same purpose of avoidance or escape. In the following illustration, avoidance is seen in cats in response to a conflict situation:

Masserman (627) subjected cats to an air blast blown across the food box at the moment of food-taking. Some animals starved themselves with the food openly displayed and readily available, whereas others accepted only small amounts of food from the hand of the experimenter provided that it differed materially from that used in the conflict situation.

REPRESSION, AMNESIA, AND INHIBITION

Here it is as if the patient unconsciously said to himself: "If I don't know about my dangerous impulses, I won't have them at all; they don't exist." The patient does not know that he wants or feels something. Thus the woman mentioned in the first chapter did not know that she was angry at her husband for his wanting to leave her. A whole series of incidents may not be consciously remembered by patients.

A patient developed attacks of palpitation together with periods of depression about six months before applying for treatment. When he was first asked what the circumstances were under which these complaints started, he said nothing unusual. He thought hard about the circumstances, discussed them repeatedly, and again he said, "Nothing distressing occurred at that time." After repeated interviews he remembered that about that time he had had a quarrel with a friend of his over money matters, following which they had not seen each other for some time. The quarrel was patched up, but they never really became good friends again. To check up on his memory, the patient asked his wife about the time of the quarrel. She confirmed the fact that the quarrel had occurred just before the onset of the patient's depression.

Forgetting may occur not only to avoid anxiety resulting from forbidden wishes, but also to avoid discomfort and hurt to self-esteem. However, as the following experiment will illustrate, there are multiple factors operating. It illustrates the influence of opposing psychological forces on memory.

Koch (510) gave students a series of ten short quizzes. When they were given their grades on the tests, they were asked to rate them on a scale from 1 to 5 to indicate their satisfaction or dissatisfaction with them. Five weeks after the last quiz, the students were asked to recall all ten grades. The "1" grades were best recalled, and whether the "2" or "5" grades were next best seemed to depend on whether the "5" grades represented threats to passing the course. Thus, although in general the more unpleasant grades were less well recalled, the students' continued attempt to cope with truly dangerous situations is reflected in their remembering the grades which represented realistic threats to them.

(See also Flanagan [276] and Rosenzweig [802].)

Usually patients not only shut impulses out of awareness, but almost completely suppress a desire or emotion. There were many years when the patient described in Chapter I was not aware of any sexual desire.

EMOTIONAL DETACHMENT

Another device which the patient may use to avoid distress is emotional detachment. In general, he says, in effect, "I do not have any emotions which would lead to danger. I maintain my distance, my isolation, from events that can cause trouble." In some individuals such emotional coolness is a constant trait; they never get enthusiastic about anything, never get really close to anyone emotionally. Others show this detachment only in certain situations; they may be intensely emotional about their work or about certain hobbies, but remain emotionally aloof from people.

FAILURE OF AN ORGAN TO FUNCTION IN THE ACTIVE SITUATION

The unconscious psychological formula is: "I cannot avoid the dangerous situation, but I can protect myself against catastrophe if I fail." The most important organ which will be used by the patient in an active situation fails. Examples are impotence in man, frigidity in woman, headache, loss of appetite, spasm or paralysis of certain muscles—e.g., the arm muscles of a musician who dreads exposure and humiliating failure before an audience. In Erickson's experiment, cited in an earlier chapter, the subject suffered hysterical blindness; he could not read the handwriting in the letter addressed to his friend, although it was clearly legible.

RENOUNCING CONTROL

This is present in connection with violent, obscene, obsessional thoughts. Thus a patient has thoughts of injuring others; but the thoughts appear in a form which enables him to say, "These are not my thoughts, they come to me from without, I am not responsible for them." It should be mentioned that these violent impulses are themselves a reaction to catastrophic anticipation. However, the patient's "lack of control" over this or other symptoms is further "willed" (unconsciously) by him; he is motivated by fear of catastrophic consequences if he acknowledges them as his own.

BLAMING OTHERS

The formula is: "I am not to be blamed for failure. Others around me are." The patient makes a mistake in his work because of serious emotional problems but blames the condition under which he has to work; a man is impotent and blames the woman.

WIT, HUMOR, CLOWNING

The psychological formula is: "I am not distressed in this situation; I am not afraid of it; I can laugh at it." This type of behavior is used as a protection by individuals who feel extremely awkward in a situation, who find it difficult to be with other people, who are afraid of being rejected. Witty behavior may cover up their distress. They may use cynicism and wit to guard against intrusion into their private worlds, which are full of trouble and worry. Clowning may be resorted to by boys who are much distressed by their feeling of being ridiculed, rejected, and humiliated because of stoutness or deformity, for example. The clowning covers up their distress, but it accomplishes more: they retain contact with and obtain the affection of their friends. Thus, in this device, a distinct compensating, ameliorating trend is also noticeable.

ATTEMPTED JUSTIFICATION (RATIONALIZATION, SELF-VINDICATION)

The psychological motif in rationalization is: "I am not afraid; I am not guilty; I have no conflict because what I have done has a sensible, rational purpose." Two kinds of devices are involved here; the second is more serious than the first. The first merely attempts to make the patient's behavior appear rational so that he can escape humiliation and ridicule and self-contempt. Thus a patient may have complicated conflicts and fears about asserting himself, about having initiative, about getting close to people. He will not recognize and admit this fact, but will instead give such reasons as, "It doesn't pay to strive too hard. One is safest alone. In this way I can't be taken advantage of," etc. The second type of device is seen when a patient rationalizes engaging in an activity which disturbs someone else. For example, a superior who hounds his subordinates may give the need for efficiency as the reason for his behavior; the mother who dominates and tortures her child may give her interest in and love for him as the reason for her behavior.

AMELIORATIVE, REINFORCING, OR DEFENSIVE DEVICES

It is characteristic of ameliorative and defensive devices that the patient who uses them tries to accomplish more than the mere avoidance of discomfort. He wants either to be helped and protected or to strengthen himself, and he usually uses a variety of devices to attain these two goals.

The general pattern of these reactions is about as follows: The patient is confronted with a variety of tasks in various fields of activity, and he has to face dangers which revive or sustain his catastrophic fear. Unconsciously, in his behavior and in the multiplicity of his reactions, he says, "If I take certain measures, I'll be safe even though the situation is dangerous; I'll be able thus to obtain my objectives and the pleasures that I want."

DEPENDENCE; DESIRE FOR COMPLETE CARE

The formula here is: "If I have the complete help of another, stronger individual, I shall be safe and I can attain my goal." This attitude may be expressed in fantasies in which the patient finds a superior person who showers favors on him and thus makes him well and happy. It may show itself in the patient's daily behavior, as when he asks someone else's advice and follows blindly on every occasion. It may show itself in such dramatic symptoms as "astasia-abasia," in which, in spite of having no serious organic ailment, the patient is unable to stand or walk and must therefore remain in bed and be taken care of. It is manifested in some patients who feel completely lost when alone. They suffer severe states of anxiety accompanied by violent bodily symptoms, such as gasping and pain around the heart; and their symptoms lessen or disappear only if someone who is devoted to them is present. Similar conditions may be present in emotional depression, or when a patient is terror-stricken at crossing the street unless a certain individual goes with him. Investigation shows that such patients desire unqualified affection, interest, and care from another individual (Horney). These dependency devices may also be used as mechanisms for domination (Adler).

SUBMISSION, OBEDIENCE, INGRATIATION

"If I obey a stronger individual, I'll have his protection and will enable myself to reach necessary goals." Such a formula in its simplest form leads to obliging behavior; the patient complies with everyone's request and is extremely humble. He may express this attitude in fantasies in which he is used, sexually or otherwise, by other people. In a woman this attitude may express itself in her need or feeling of obligation to submit sexually to any man who pays some attention to her, even though she herself does not desire him. It may express itself in homosexual submission. It may be one factor in the symptoms of waxy flexibility (see Glossary).

SELF-DEBASEMENT

"I want to submit, I want to show that I am insignificant and worthless, in order to obtain what I am asking for." Such an unconscious formula may result in a strong tendency to self-debasement, a tendency which has another aspect, namely: "I want to show him that I am worthless, that I am insignificant, that I am contemptible, so that he will forgive me for being hostile toward him, and will help me." The manifestations of this attitude can be seen in severe depressions, in which the patient accuses himself of all sorts of crimes which he has not committed; he is a sinner who does not deserve to live, and he is being punished (delusion of sin and guilt). Such symptoms may, in some cases, represent not so much a purposeful coping with the problem as discouragement.

TURNING AGAINST ONESELF

In this reaction the patient directs toward himself an impulse that was first directed toward someone else. The unconscious formula is: "I will hurt myself instead of hurting him. If I do this, I will be forgiven and helped; I will escape worse punishment." The impulse most frequently involved is a hostile one. In emotional depression the patient usually accuses himself of acts and impulses for which he really blames someone else. The very fact of suffering and incapacity has the implication of the patient's harming himself instead of someone who disappointed him or treated him unfairly, but on whom he feels absolutely dependent. In its extreme form this attitude is manifested as suicide. In other cases, it may represent extreme discouragement and low self-esteem.

ATTACK, VIOLENCE, HOSTILITY, AND PROJECTION (DEFENSIVE HOSTILITY)

The formula here is: "I am in danger in various situations, but I shall be safe and able to reach my goals if I successfully attack and incapacitate my adversary." This device may show itself in constantly overbearing and dominating behavior, or in elaborate fantasies of destruction.

During a series of delayed-reaction experiments by Harlow and Maslow, one very savage baboon was used as an experimental animal. When presented with the experimental situation, the animal was apt to go into a fury and dash itself against the bars, trying to scratch or bite the experimenter. It often snatched the cups on the table, ripped them loose from their strings, and bit them to pieces in a wild rage. It attacked the keeper of the zoo, to whom it had hitherto been friendly. Later, the mere sight of the experimenter was enough to throw the animal into a wild, screaming, disorganized rage.

Projection takes two basic forms. (1) Blaming the environment: "It is not my fault I failed. The difficulties were too great." (2) Attributing one's own unacceptable impulses to the environment: "I am not the bad one; it is the environment that is bad."

Sears (842) secured self-ratings and ratings of each other from nearly a hundred college men on the traits of stinginess, obstinacy, disorderliness, and bashfulness. A measure of the "true" amount of the trait possessed by the subject was obtained by averaging the ratings given him by his associates. A measure of the amount he attributed to others could be obtained by averaging his ratings of others. By taking *insight* into account, it was shown that a projection mechanism was operating in the judgment process. Insight was assumed to exist when the subject put himself in the same half of the distribution on a given trait in which his associates placed him. A comparison was made of the amount of each trait attributed to others by subjects who possessed and by those who lacked insight. The results indicated that those who lacked insight had a greater tendency to project than did those who recognized the presence or absence of the trait in themselves.

(See also Posner [738].)

NEED TO CONTROL, TO BE SUPERIOR, TO DOMINATE

The formula is: "If I dominate the situation, I am safe from attack and from helplessness; I am strong and I can attain my desire." A patient who uses this device may have fantasies in which he is the head of a jail and all the prisoners have to obey him. It may show itself subtly through sexual seduction, at times homosexual, the idea being, "If I can seduce him (or her), I shall have mastered him (or her)." In still other cases a patient will enter only those situations and relationships, either work or social, in which he can be superior and dominate.

SELF-AGGRANDIZEMENT

The formula is: "I am unique, I am remarkable, I possess exceptional qualities, I do not have to feel worthless and helpless. Being remarkable gives me satisfaction, and I can also achieve other goals." This attitude is sometimes evident only if considerable psychological study of the patient is made. It may show itself in thoughts of greatness, which are at times entirely fantastic, such as flying in an airplane over the nation's capital and controlling by means of death rays everything that goes on in the country. The attitude may express itself rather dramatically in the delusion of grandeur. A less obvious expression is seen in people who consider themselves superior in some respect to everyone they know.

REACTION FORMATION

The formula is: "I do not desire something which is objectionable; on the contrary, I intensely desire the opposite." The impulses involved here are chiefly hostile and sexual in nature. This attitude is seen most frequently in character traits and in the broad reaction patterns of those people who, when they break down in a difficult situation, have obsessional thoughts of violence and thoughts of a sexual and excretory nature. Such people are *excessively* kind, fair, moral, and idealistic. With these reaction patterns they not only protect themselves against the dangers apparent if they follow their own impulses of anger or sex or rage, but also considerably enhance their evaluation of themselves.

ELATION WITH DENIAL

The formula underlying this device is: "I will not acknowledge my fears, my conflict, my self-contempt, my feelings of being disapproved; I will not be helpless and hopeless. On the contrary, I will evaluate myself highly, I will be very active, I will be happy." The patient is emotionally elated and very active; his thoughts flit from one subject to another. The same phenomenon is observable, in a less intense form, in the slighter, more fleeting elation of people who constantly swing from emotional depression and pessimism to emotional elation and glowing optimism and high self-evaluation (206, 555, 661, 298).

GRATIFICATION OF BODILY URGES AS A SOURCE OF SOLACE AND STRENGTH

The formula here is: "I will eat, I will have sexual relations (or urinate or move my bowels or take a bath), and then I won't feel alone, I won't feel helpless and weak; on the contrary, I will derive pleasure, I will feel stronger and be safe." The most frequent function used for this purpose is eating, particularly eating sweets. Thus, whenever a patient experiences a disappointment or feels depressed and lonely, he may indulge in food.

MEASURES TO REACH THE GOAL IN SPITE OF OBSTACLES

Most of the devices described in the preceding section imply attempts to reach a goal directly or to relieve anxiety and increase the feeling of strength. The measures that will be discussed in this section are motivated predominantly by the desire to reach the goal in spite of obstacles. It is necessary to repeat here that many of these measures or aims may be recognizable in a single symptom.

COMPROMISE FORMATION

The unconscious formula is: "If I strive for the goal in a straightforward manner, I shall not be strong enough to reach it, or dangers will prevent me from reaching it; but if I do not try to reach the goal fully or if I use qualifications which partly deny it, I may attain approximately what I would like to get." It is also a technique of attaining two goals when there is conflict between them.

Compromise formation is seen in the patient described in the first chapter. She wanted closeness and emotional dependence, and she also wanted to satisfy her sexual desires. She could not strive for this goal directly for several reasons. Her desire for dependence was so strong and her feeling of worthlessness so intense that she was afraid of rejection. Because of her hostility, which arose from this and from her feeling of inferiority, especially with men, she was afraid of being injured, particularly in the sexual act, and therefore kept away from men. Under the special circumstances and in response to the character and behavior of her husband, she managed to establish the desired relationship, but with limitations: "I am close to him but I am not bound. I can relinquish him if I wish."

Another form of compromise is manifest when some act is done in such a manner that it falls short of its assumed purpose. For instance, a patient gave her antagonistic in-laws a present which suited her own house but not theirs. Thus she did what was expected of her, but they secured no pleasure from it.

The term "compromise formation" is often used in another sense. For example, the patient's symptoms may satisfy both the tabooed desire and his sense of guilt. Obsessive thoughts, in a sense, are of this nature. Through them the patient expresses hostility or sexual impulses, but at the same time he suffers. It is as if it were permissible to express a "bad" impulse, if only one "paid" for it. Many bodily symptoms have aspects which satisfy the patient's opposite urges and needs. Thus an uncontrollable contraction of the muscles of the arm may express an urge to attack, but with simultaneous incapacity and suffering.

Some patients unconsciously do not dare to take the initiative and to commit themselves fully to any action for fear of failure and catastrophic humiliation. They therefore maneuver so that another individual will persuade them to take a certain course of action, whereupon emotional responsibility falls on the other person.

Maier (604, 606) trained rats on the so-called jumping apparatus, in which the animal is forced by an air blast from a platform to one of two windows, which are marked differently. If the rat jumps to the correct window, it obtains food. If it jumps at the wrong one, the window does not open, and the rat falls to the floor. When various modifications in procedure forced the rat to respond to a stimulus card which it had previously been trained to avoid, some of the rats exhibited the following behavior: They executed an abortive jump—i.e., a jump so weak that they hit the stimulus card with their sides rather than head-on. This was a compromise response, which also made the resulting fall easier.

LIMITATION OF THE SITUATION

The formula is: "If I put certain restrictions on the situation or on the act, I eliminate the dangerous aspects." For example, a woman patient who keeps some of her clothes on while having sexual relations says that in this way she does not give herself fully to the man. Her guilt feelings and also his domination are thus lessened. A girl who is strongly attracted to men may see them only infrequently.

COUNTERACTING (DOING AND UNDOING)

The formula is: "I will carry out this act which means dangers for me; but I will engage in another act which eliminates these dangers."

A patient was very tender toward his wife. But after each occasion of emotional tenderness he would walk through the park for the purpose of looking at other women. His idea was: "If I get close to my wife, she will throw increased responsibility on me and won't permit me to lean on her. If I go out and look at other women, I assert and establish my independence of her." When the patient attempted to force himself not to look at other women, he could not be tender to his wife.

The term "doing and undoing" more frequently refers to patients with obsessional thoughts. In them, the thought of killing or an obscene thought is followed by a pious act which serves the purpose of undoing the effect of the thought.

RIGID REGULATIONS

The formula is: "I can guard against unexpected danger, I can carry out my desires, cope with the situation, and still feel safe only if I follow rigid rules in my behavior."

The simplest examples of this behavior device are furnished by patients who extol and insist on, or anxiously follow, a very rigid routine in work. The patient who feels insecure in social contact follows a system in meeting people. He may be able to meet them only professionally; hence he invites people to his house only with the idea of professional contact. This motivation may be strikingly present in every contact he makes. Similar reactions are seen in patients who must have their desks arranged in a certain inflexible order or whose eating habits are rigidly set or who consider social behavior customs of the utmost importance. Some obsessional attitudes belong in this category. For example, one patient had an obsessional fear of infection. He could have sexual relations with his wife only if she took a shower, scrubbed herself with a brush, dressed completely in white, covered her hands, feet and head, and did not brush against anything—even a chair—on the way to their room.

SUBSTITUTION AND DISPLACEMENT, SYMBOLIZATION

The formula here is: "Instead of doing something that is dangerous, I will do something which is similar to but not identical with it. In this way

I can safely reach my goal." Although substitution and displacement have been discussed in the chapter on frustration and examples have been given, they will be further considered at this point.

Substitution and displacement are very similar. "Substitution" usually refers to using another bodily organ instead of the one which affords feared or condemned (usually genital) gratification. "Displacement" more frequently refers to emotional reactions or general activities in which the individual responds emotionally to a situation which is in reality different from the one to which he is genuinely reacting.

It has already been mentioned (see page 66) that the aggression of four out of five members of an autocratically led group was twice focused on the remaining youngster (displacement from the leader) to such a degree that the scapegoat left the group. At times displacement occurs when the original object is not available.

Miller put a pair of white rats into a box with an electrified floor and turned off the current only when they had assumed a belligerent posture. In this manner he trained them to fight with each other. On subsequent occasions a small white celluloid doll was introduced into the box with the pair of rats, but they ignored it in order to adopt their fighting postures. If only one rat was placed in the box with the doll, however, the rat would start to fight with the doll.

A severe form of substitution was shown by a married woman who, instead of retiring with her husband, derived genuine erotic pleasure from picking and grooming the skin of her back and face for hours at a time.

Any part of the body or any article of clothing may be substituted for the genital organs in this type of substitute activity. Instances of fetishism belong here, as when a person gets all his pleasure from being aroused and gratified by shoes which belong to the person he desires.

More complicated forms of substitution are seen in the following: The individual is afraid of genuine emotional attachment, of self-assertion, of final commitment to what he wants to undertake. Whenever situations arise in which he would like to do a certain thing or in which he is requested to do it, he withdraws and masturbates or engages in elaborate fantasies of self-aggrandizement. His formula is: "This way I am safe and I get some enjoyment out of life." It is obvious that such measures are highly complex and involve the individual's image of himself, of other people, and of his activity. This device serves the further purpose of solace as well as substitute activity.

VIOLENCE AND SELF-INJURY

The formula is: "I can carry out the activity if I violently attack the other individual, of whom I am afraid." In other instances it is: "Only if I let him hurt me or if I hurt myself can I derive pleasure from the activity." Here belong sadism and masochism in genital activity. The individual can obtain pleasure only, in the case of sadism, if he hurts his partner, or, in the case of masochism, if he is hurt. In the extreme form such attitudes may lead to "lust murders."

REVIVAL OF EARLIER FORMS OF BEHAVIOR (REGRESSION)

The formula here is: "I am not able to cope with the situation in the form of action that is required. I am not able to obtain safety and satisfaction by pursuing my present goals, or pursuing them with my present means. I will therefore pursue goals which I had once before, and with which I was more successful, or I'll pursue my present goals in a manner that at one time was successful."

A good illustration of this type of phenomenon is the recurrence of enuresis (bed-wetting) in children. A child who is well trained in cleanliness may start wetting his bed again when a difficult situation arises. Such a situation is frequently the birth of another child. The older child, who previously felt secure, now feels seriously threatened in regard to the affection and love of his parents. The bed-wetting is partly a direct expression of anxiety, partly an attempt to show his need of parental attention and help, and partly an attempt to be a helpless infant and thus get all of the parents' affection. In such a situation a child may also want the bottle or the breast again.

The revival of earlier goals or of earlier modes of solution is at times equally obvious in the adult. It is manifest in some aspects of his outlook on life, in his fantasies and dreams, as one part of his reaction to situations of stress. Instead of enuresis, the adult may have bladder discomfort and have to get up repeatedly at night. He may have dreams of being fed, or of being a child who is given candy and ice cream by an adult.

Several animal experiments illustrate the phenomenon of regression. These manifestations are known as "instrumental regression" because the goal remains the same but the technique by which the animal attempts to gain it represents revival of a technique which had formerly been discarded.

Sanders (817), using a T-maze, trained five rats to turn in the direction of their original position habits to obtain food. "Original position habit" means initial tendency to turn in one direction rather than another. After learning was completed, he started to train them to go in the opposite direction. When this new learning was well started, the animals were given an electric shock at the choice point. Four of the animals regressed at once and again turned in the direction of their original position habit. The fifth one regressed later. This represents disorganization in that the electric shock did not alter the fact that the better course would have been to go in the second direction. The animals were then given enough training on the second habit so that practice on the two directions of turning was equivalent. Then Sanders started to train them again to go in the direction of their original position habit, and then again introduced shock at the choice point. This time the rats did not revert to the learned (second) habit. Thus, in *this* experimental situation, regression took place only in the direction of the genetically primary response.

Mowrer (692) trained a group of five rats to turn off the electric shock in a grill on which they stood by pressing a foot pedal. Another group was also given shocks but had no pedal to press. These latter rats learned to sit up on their hind legs to escape the shock. When this had been well learned, they were permitted to learn how to use the foot pedal. Then both groups were frustrated by having shock introduced to this foot pedal, so that they received a shock from it when they tried to turn off the floor shock. The rats that had originally learned to escape by standing on their hind legs almost immediately regressed to that habit, while the other rats continued to press the pedal. This suggests that regression can occur to a response that is not primary in the rat's choice.

The following experiment illustrates regression to an earlier level of development:

In the experiment by Masserman (627) described above (page 88) the cats began to indulge in kittenish vocalization and behavior, licked and cleaned themselves excessively, became sullen, or courted an unusual amount of fondling by the experimenter.

SUGGESTED READINGS

The best clinical readings on this subject, which is ordinarily labeled "defense mechanisms," are Anna Freud's *The Ego and the Mechanisms of Defense* (298) and Horney's *The Neurotic Personality of Our Time* (431). Symonds' *Dynamics of Human Adjustment* (919) covers the field excellently. Another very important book recommended for general reading in psychopathology is Kurt Goldstein's *The Organism* (357). D. M. Levy's monograph (544) on his experiments with sibling rivalry gives the most empirical picture we have of these reactions to conflict and frustration. Erickson's article "Experimental demonstrations of the psychopathology of everyday life" (248) is a good experimental study of human beings; and Maier's *Frustration: The Study of Behavior Without a Goal* (606), a study of animals. See also Mowrer's "An experimental analogue of 'regression' " (692). A long-standing classic relating to this subject is Veblen's *The Theory of the Leisure Class* (943). This may demonstrate how much of one's own behavior subserves unconscious aims.

IX The Precipitation and Maintenance of Psychic Illness

There may be found in the psychopathological individual: (1) suffering and unhappiness; (2) certain manifestations called symptoms; (3) impaired efficiency; (4) impairment of the ability to enjoy; (5) lack of adequate insight. Furthermore, the periods of intense and acute reaction can be differentiated from the periods during which some complaints are present but the individual somehow "gets by."

As has been repeatedly stated, the nuclear constellation in psychopathological disturbances of any severity is the expectation of a catastrophic state of helplessness, involving feelings of rejection, worthlessness, condemnation, annihilation, and complete frustration. The patient may manifest this catastrophic expectation in a variety of situations, such as complicated social tasks, contact with other people, bodily gratification, relaxation, and sleep.

Some of the patient's symptoms and character traits are the direct result of emotional stress, anxiety, tension, anger, or discouragement and, as such, serve no purpose. Many others are the result of the various defensive, ameliorative, and goal-reaching devices mentioned in Chapter VIII, often combined with the direct results of emotional stress.

AREAS OF DISTURBED FUNCTION

Patients suffer profound disturbances in regard to their image of themselves and of others, in regard to their feelings of strength, and in regard to particular situations which may possibly involve catastrophic fear. They feel safer in some fields of activity than in others, and therefore they seek such fields. This latter fact contributes considerably to the differences in symptomatology in various patients. It is important to differentiate here, however, between the situation in which the disturbance is genuinely aroused, and the forms in which the disturbance expresses itself.

The disturbance may manifest itself in the sphere in which it really arises. Thus the patient may do poor work, make serious errors, be tense, and become exhausted because his fear of displaying initiative, self-assertion, and rivalry makes it dangerous to succeed. In such instances, the patient's image and concept of himself (self-esteem) and of others—e.g., his superior, his rivals (insecurity feelings)—are involved.

Even though the disturbance manifests itself where the trouble really lies, its expression may be greatly distorted. This is particularly true of obsessional manifestations. Thus a woman may feel completely dominated and threatened by her husband and unconsciously be very angry at him. Whereas in her behavior she is tender toward him, admires him, and caters to all his wishes, she has such intense thoughts of hurting him—cutting his throat, for example—that she does not dare have sharp knives about the house.

The manifestations may be completely displaced. Thus the patient may be afraid of crossing the street or of high places, although he knows perfectly well that no "real" dangers are connected with these situations. Such displaced manifestation occurs in response to genuine difficulties in other situations in one of two ways: (1) The situation of which the individual is afraid is indispensable to the performance of some part of the function that is causing the difficulty. For example, a man whose office is on the twentieth floor of a building was thrown into a sudden panic. Investigation showed that he was afraid to be close to his wife and to assume responsibilities, and that she wanted him to earn more money. He was suddenly struck by the thought that he might suddenly become ill, the elevator might not stop, and he might not be able to get out of the building. (2) The situation or the object represents to the patient unconsciously what he is afraid of in an entirely different situation. This same man at times became panicky when he entered the subway station because he felt the walls close in on him. The narrow, confined space unconsciously meant to him his wife's crushing condemnation, which would be disastrous and from which he could not escape if she decided to avenge herself for his anger toward her.

PARTIAL GOALS

The various means—the partial substitute devices—which the patient uses to attain his goals come in themselves to represent important goals for him, and he is emotionally disturbed if these partial goals are threatened or unattainable. For example, the patient may seek complete dependence as a means of attaining safety, protection, and help in satisfying his main needs. If the individual on whom the patient depends does something which he interprets as rejection, he reacts with anger, fear, or a feeling of worthlessness and humiliation. Similarly, a patient may want perfection in all his activities and superiority in every situation as a means of protecting himself against helplessness, defeat, and fear, and strengthening himself in attaining his primary goal—success and pleasure. If anything threatens his perfection, he does not fear only helplessness, he genuinely resents this threat. In a sense, the state of perfection has become a goal in itself. From this it is clear that every significant act in which the patient engages is not directed toward one single aim, but implies a complexity of partial goals and devices.

VICIOUS CIRCLES

The patient often uses contradictory devices for amelioration or for reaching goals and therefore has conflicting needs. Thus he may want both to be completely dependent and to attack violently. He wants to escape the consequences of both these attitudes, but needs emotional warmth and closeness. Similarly, a patient may want to debase himself, but at the same time use the self-aggrandizement device.

Even the initial psychological constellation of a patient's strivings may have elements of conflict and danger in it. For example, a child wants to reach for a toy in the presence of his severe and humiliating mother. Because of the whole relationship with the mother, this impulse contains the unconscious constellation: "I can do this only with her permission because I am weak and dependent on her; but she will not give me permission." This necessitates either carrying through the wish defiantly and chancing her disapproval, or asking her for permission and risking her refusal and the accompanying humiliation. Either case means further conflict for the child. If he takes the toy, he faces possible catastrophe. If he asks for it, he faces possible refusal and humiliation which are catastrophic in character. Even if he gets it, though he will feel somewhat relieved and gratified, the tension will remain because he will feel humiliated at having cowered before his mother, will still feel worthless and unloved, and may expect future disapproval. If he renounces his desire, he still will not feel that he is someone, that he is loved by his mother, that he has security, that he can depend on her; hence renunciation adds to the resentment toward her already created by humiliation and lack of love. The response to such a situation, with its immediate implications and its ensuing conflicts, thus creates in him an emotional constellation which cannot be relieved by any adequate action. The tension occasioned by his earlier experiences and by this new experience continues to increase, thus preparing him for conflicting reactions to new situations. The conflict as such also intensifies and maintains the feeling of helplessness and of inability to master the situation, and thus contributes to and renews the expectation of catastrophe.

In such a chronic situation as the above, practically every one of the child's attempts to reach a goal will either fail completely or be only partially successful. With the tensions and conflicts which remain, there remain also the problems with which the individual is unable to cope. He has both a feeling of helplessness and an actual impairment of function, a psychological state which implies renewal and maintenance of catastrophic expectations. This sequence, which is a "vicious circle" (Horney [431]), is one of the most important factors in the persistence and recurrence of abnormal psychological manifestations. The concept implies that the patient takes certain measures to enable himself to function or to escape catastrophe, but that these measures renew his difficulties if he fails, and even, to some extent, if he succeeds. This concept can be applied both to internal psychological experiences and to the patient's actual relationships with other people.

Both types of vicious circle are present in childhood. The child who reacts with the basic psychopathological constellation to parental handling does not react merely to distressing situations. The child's evaluation of the parent and of his acts becomes distorted and magnified. Furthermore, his own behavior changes and becomes the stimulus for parental mishandling. Thus there develops a constant interplay and interlocking in the psychological problems of the child and the parent.

INTERNAL VICIOUS CIRCLES

Complete dependence leads to expectations which are continually thwarted because of their extreme and irrational nature; this leads to anger. Complete dependence also goes with loss of self-esteem, the assumption of being looked down upon; this likewise leads to anger. Anger, however, means attacking the individual through whose help the patient had hoped to avoid catastrophe. This in turn renews the fear of catastrophe; therefore the patient has to continue his dependence on this individual, but to an even greater extent.

If the chief ameliorative device is violent counterattack and attempt to vanquish the enemy, the vicious circle is again at work. The patient expects a similar attack from the foe; but, since he is defenseless, this would mean catastrophe; therefore he has to continue his attack.

Since the renunciation of a desire is based on the expectation of catastrophe, it is usually felt as unfair. The reaction to this is anger, through whose anticipated consequences the fear of catastrophe is renewed. For this reason renunciation has to be continued.

Self-aggrandizement leads to the fear of being resented, attacked, and humiliated by others, which in turn renews the feeling of failure, of catastrophe. Therefore self-aggrandizement has to be continued to an even greater degree.

The individual may not dare to use the genitals in heterosexual relations because of fear of failure or injury; and in his attempt to obtain and give love in a special way, he may become homosexual. This lowers his self-esteem, not only because of cultural ideals which he himself espouses, but also because the very act of retreat is humiliating to him. Thus, even though he may obtain considerable satisfaction from the relationship, his feeling of humiliation, of helplessness, and weakness is renewed, and with it his conflicts, and increased feeling of helplessness, and the fear of catastrophic situations. Hence he has to continue this relationship in spite of feeling increasingly worse.

ENVIRONMENTAL VICIOUS CIRCLES

The patient's behavior follows certain lines and patterns implied in the relatively subjective attitudes mentioned above. He enters into relationships to satisfy the needs implied in those attitudes, but the reactions of other individuals to his behavior are such that in the long run he must maintain the very attitude that causes the difficulty. For example, a patient attempts to maintain his security and freedom from anxiety and to attain his goals by adopting an overbearing and superior attitude. This attitude may be created by internal conflicts and catastrophic anticipations; but the hostile reactions of other people will provide his expectations of catastrophic counterattack with a real basis. Those whom he humiliated and conquered want to humiliate and conquer him. Inasmuch as their success would mean catastrophic defeat for him, he has to continue the same overbearing, attacking, and superior behavior.

Another type of vicious circle develops when the measures used by the patient to allay his anxiety contain false and irrational assumptions. A patient wants to relieve his feelings of worthlessness by achievement, let us say; and he expects this to make him loved as he feels he should be loved. The error here is that these measures, even if successful, do not really bring him the love he expected. To secure that, his own emotional structure and his approach to people would have to change; he would have to be able to accept affection when it was offered to him. The result is that, at least partly, he feels disappointment and rejection. But since he again evaluates this in his own terms, the measures he uses are the same as before.

Potentially or actually, consciously or unconsciously, memory patterns are constantly revived. By "revival of memory patterns" is meant not memories and thoughts alone, but also memory patterns in organic function, in behavior, in needs and desires, in emotional conditioning. The adult who has an unconscious feeling of rejection and is afraid of further rejection may have dreams and vague memories that seem to reinstate early experiences of actual physical punishment and withdrawal of gratification. To this extent, the sick adult is afraid not only of losing prestige and his neighbor's affection, but also (in a sense) of being beaten and whipped, of having his mother's breast withdrawn, and of having his father scold him (as if he were still a little boy rather than a grown man).

THE INABILITY TO LEARN FROM EXPERIENCE

The inability to learn by experience is often mentioned as the most characteristic quality of the patient with serious psychopathology. This does not refer mainly to his occupational activities, in which, as a matter of fact, he may be quite superior, but to the repetitiveness of his crucial reactions. On the obvious side, the patient may keep getting into the same kind of difficulties over and over again; e.g., his love relations end badly because of poor choice of love-object, his occupational relations get ruined because of his rebelliousness or submissiveness. On the less obvious side, it refers to the persistence of his dominant psychopathological trends, his anxieties, hostilities, dependencies, excessive self-evaluation or disparagement, the pursuit of conflicting pleasure goals, all of which make him seek certain disadvantageous situations and avoid others which would be to his advantage. Quite obviously, this inability to learn has three different aspects. On the one hand, certain reactions are overaccented; on the other, certain other reactions are choked off; and, lastly, certain spontaneous qualities are never given a chance even to develop. The three factors reinforce each other. On the overaccented side, for example, the dangerous quality, e.g., of interpersonal relations, because of the fear of rejection, attack, sexual exploitation, are accented and clung to, and reinforced by the desire to avoid the anticipated risk. The compensatory and substitutive measures of emotional detachment and self-sufficiency get accented in addition. This can be seen in the course of the treatment when a patient evaluates a new contact with good potentialities for friendship or love-relation as threatening and is ready to flee from it until the therapist points out that the factual information does not seem to warrant such an evaluation. The reactions that are choked off are the enjoyment of the free interpersonal contacts that the patient has had or has in so far as he is momentarily capable of having them in his day-to-day existence. This may manifest itself in the treatment in several ways. The patient may not mention spontaneously the positive qualities of the other individual or his own fleeting positive reaction. He may not mention, until far along in the treatment, past experiences which represented close relations with other people. The richness of free experience of mutual support and free sexual give-and-take is nipped in the bud. As a result, certain emotional qualities and skills are not acquired by the individual, and this prevents the occurrence of such experiences as would require them. These experiences do not have a chance to occur at all. This becomes evident in the course of the treatment by the complete novelty of some of the patient's experiences as he gradually becomes capable of establishing close emotional relationships.

THE ROLE OF THE EXTERNAL SITUATION

The intensity and quality of symptoms depend in large measure on the external situation. There may be long periods of time when the situation is such that the patient who has a relatively low intensity of fear and uses adequate ameliorative measures will function well. For instance, he may feel that the complete dependence and help forthcoming from one individual guard him against danger. Under these circumstances, the feelings of disappointment, humiliation, jealousy, anger, etc., are relatively slight, but nevertheless strong enough to force him to remain dependent; by and large he can function well, at least well enough.

To what extent a patient can function well all the time depends on various internal factors. There are people who go from one crisis to another, regardless of their opportunities and circumstances, almost as if they were, literally, searching for situations which would make them suffer and be unhappy. This will be clearer if we first discuss what happens to an individual who functions relatively well under certain conditions but reacts severely when a new acute situation arises. The factors that are of importance here are threats to vital needs of the personality because of chronic deprivation, frustration, or conflict.

DEPRIVATION, DISAPPOINTMENT, FRUSTRATION

What the individual is deprived of may vary considerably. As a rule, it is something which a great many people consider important and significant—a position, a mate, a fortune. Sometimes, however, it lacks this universal significance; it may be merely a small gift which he treasured and admired. Frustrations of this latter type usually cause only distress; there is no serious, generalized breakdown. The significant situation which represents frustration sometimes does not seem frustrating because the individual represses his reactions to it. For example, a man became depressed for some unknown reason over the approaching marriage of his son. Although consciously he did not object to his son's marriage, further investigation made it clear that unconsciously he considered as a catastrophic frustration the "loss" of this son, to whom he was deeply attached. The death of one's mate or one's child, termination of an engagement, divorce, being deprived of opportunity to satisfy one's bodily wants, are all situations which may represent severe frustration and precipitate more acute breakdowns.

The question now arises why frustration of this type is such a disturbing and near-catastrophic event in the patient's life. There are several reasons for this.

What the patient lost satisfied not merely the healthy desire of someone who says, "I want this; I can have it"; rather, it represented the fulfillment of an absolutely vital but "sick" need which enabled him to avoid a catastrophic state.

The individual may have an essential lack of confidence in himself and a feeling of helplessness, and be convinced that he cannot by his own efforts replace what he lost. For example, a woman who is so dependent on her husband that she can make no decision without his help and support will feel that the bottom has fallen out of her whole life if he dies or leaves her.

Frustration frequently results not from a sudden and acute change in the situation but from a gradual change in a continuing situation. Thus the woman who wants unlimited strength and superiority in her husband may constantly look for more and more evidence that he has all the qualities and stamina that she wants him to have. When she begins to realize that he is not the man she thought he was, she feels frustrated, cheated, disappointed. Here a severe conflict situation arises because her hostility toward him is intense, but at the same time she feels dependent on him. As a rule, conflict situations accompany frustration because of the hostility toward the person who is held responsible for the frustration.

SITUATIONS OF THREAT; ACUTE CONFLICT

Other situations which may precipitate an acute breakdown are those in which the patient is exposed to an actual threat, to actual distress. This type of situation is likely to arise when one's superior in work or one's mate is unfair, domineering, and humiliating, or when someone in authority finds himself challenged either by a rival or by his inferiors. In the case of the domineering and humiliating superior or mate, the reaction and its development are as follows: The individual who has a basic fear of feelings of worthlessness and helplessness feels tremendously threatened and expects utter humiliation and enslavement. He reacts to this threat not only with fear but with anger which is proportionate to the tremendously unfair, heartless, and catastrophically threatening manner in which he feels he is being treated. But his anger creates a new difficulty because he feels completely powerless to do anything about the situation; he cannot stand up for his rights or speak up or extricate himself in any way. And thus there arises a state of acute conflict between his feeling of utter helplessness in the face of tremendous threat and his intense resentment and hostility.

A man was a successful salesman as long as he worked in his father's place or for another firm where he was treated fairly. He then became a salesman for still another firm. The manager was a blustering sort of man who always disapproved, never praised, and never gave any credit for performance. The salesman developed dizziness, a moderately high blood pressure, attacks of trembling and of anxiety, particularly when he sat in the barber's chair. His symptoms became so marked that he had to take a vacation. During this period he felt somewhat better, but when he returned to work the symptoms reappeared. Then he went to a psychiatrist, who discovered that he felt humiliated and downtrodden all the time; although he resented this intensely, he never protested because he was afraid of counterattack in the form of being discharged. This situation was one of intense conflict. After considerable treatment, the patient became able to demand different treatment, to complain to the owners, and in fact either to put the manager in his place or to look for a better job—steps hitherto impossible because of his feelings of helplessness and worthlessness and the acute conflict situation. Sometimes such a good outcome is impossible if, for instance, there is no possibility of another job. Then psychology can help little or not at all.

CONDITIONS OF CONTINUOUS CRISIS

As we said earlier, the majority of patients manage to function under favorable circumstances, but get into difficulties when a situation of acute stress arises. This statement must be amplified somewhat. While it may be correct to say that the quality of the patient's needs and conflicts is essentially the same during both the smooth and the acute period, their intensity changes tremendously. Even after the actual external situation of stress is remedied, the patient frequently continues to suffer and have symptoms. In other words, once the breakdown occurs, he may not feel comfortable in situations which he stood very well previously. There are two reasons for this: (1) All of life involves a continuous solving of problems; getting up in the morning, going to sleep at night, attending to bodily wants, seeing other individuals, etc., are all problems in a certain sense. After a severe breakdown all or most of these functions may present *acute* problems or situations of stress for the patient. (2) Because of his acute fear and need, the patient clutters up all his relationships with desires, expectations, and requests which continuously lead to frustration or acute conflict. Or he seeks new relationships for the purpose of fulfilling his needs; constant frustration and acute conflict are the result because of his inflated, unreal expectations from these new relationships or the sick manner in which he handles them. This is essentially the case with individuals who for years go from one self-made crisis to another.

SUMMARY: THE NATURE OF NEUROTIC ILLNESS

Psychopathology implies that following situations of stress, the individual manifests suffering, symptoms, impaired efficiency, lessened ability for enjoyment, lack of adequate insight.

The most distressing manifestations appear in response to new and difficult situations; but less obvious ones are present before and after the acute periods.

Psychopathological manifestations in general cover a wide variety of phenomena belonging to the sphere of affects, thinking, and volition in an interrelated manner. They may appear in any situation and in connection with any function of the individual: in his behavior and organic function, in the performance of complicated tasks, in relaxation, sleep, etc.

In all neurotic manifestations, the patient's vital needs are involved as well as his evaluation of himself (self-esteem), of other individuals (security feelings), and of the situation with which he has to cope. Thus one can say that in neurotic manifestations the patient's whole personality and whole body are involved.

The central motif of psychopathological manifestations is the anticipation of a catastrophic situation, with the various colorings of loss of help, approval, and affection; helplessness; bodily injury or pain; humiliation; and the impossibility of satisfying vital bodily needs.

The patient then attempts to diminish his distress, increase his strength, override his fear, and reach certain goals in spite of the fears aroused. He attempts this by means of various devices, or "mechanisms."

The patient's needs, goals, and devices have contradictory aspects; that is, they are incompatible with each other.

This leads to a psychological conflict, which is present in every psychopathological reaction. Any measure that the patient takes is inadequate to relieve his tension fully; furthermore, it often arouses contradictory needs in him.

For these reasons, whether the goal is reached or not, a vicious circle of reactions is ordinarily set up. This renews the patient's feeling of helplessness and increases his use of ameliorative devices. These vicious circles are further strengthened by the binding effect of the external situations and the interhuman relations which the patient seeks. The vicious circles are largely responsible for the persistence and recurrence of psychopathological reactions.

The intensity of suffering or the relative well-being of the patient depends to a considerable extent on external situations. If the situation is favorable, the ameliorative devices are relatively effective, and the disturbance and distress are kept at a minimum. Furthermore, most patients retain some healthy and well-preserved functions and some shreds of security and self-esteem.

The anticipation of catastrophic situations, together with the use of ameliorative devices, begins in childhood and is maintained throughout life with the aid of vicious circles of reaction. The most important determinant of the catastrophic anticipation is stress and strain in the relationship with the parents. This is intensified by the inevitable vicissitudes of life and by biological and cultural dependence on the parents. (This will be discussed in succeeding chapters.)

Cultural factors in psychopathological reactions exert their effect through interhuman relations in actual situations. The most significant effects of our cultural milieu are determined by the smallness of the family, resulting in an intensification of the dependence on the parents; contradictory emotional and ideal demands—a demand for obedience on the one hand, and for self-assertion and rivalry on the other; forbidding any emphasis on certain bodily activities.

SUGGESTED READINGS

For general reading on the nature of psychopathology and its self-maintenance, the works of Freud and Adler are of paramount importance. More recent works are by Horney (431, 432), Kardiner (483, 484), and Goldstein (357). Pavlov's neurological theories (725) are also recommended. A. Meyer's writings are of a fundamental nature (646).

PART III

The Etiology of Psychopathology

It has been accented in the section on psychosomatics that psychopathology must be approached from the point of view of the total organism in its environmental setting. This applies equally to disorders which start predominantly on the basis of reactions to stress and strain and to those that start primarily with anatomical damage to various organs, particularly the brain. It is convenient to group the various factors entering into the making of the ultimate picture as genogenic (hereditary factors), histo- and chemogenic (anatomical damage or toxic influences), and psychogenic (emotional stress and strain).

The nature of these factors can be dramatically illustrated on the following case:

> An adult woman developed an abscess (accumulation of pus) of the brain. She was operated upon for this and recovered from the abscess. However, not long after, she began to have convulsions (epilepsy). Considering her very difficult home situation, her physician decided on psychological treatment, although the symptom was clearly organic in nature. As a result of psychotherapy, she stopped having convulsions.[1]

In this case, the histogenic factor was very obvious: the damage done to the brain by the abscess. As we will see in subsequent discussion, the genogenic factor was also present, because the readiness to react with generalized convulsions is often inherited. Yet the most important factor in this case, from the point of view of practical cure, was the psychogenic element.

[1] Based on a case presentation in S. Cobb, *Borderlands of Psychiatry,* Harvard Univ. Press, Cambridge, Mass., 1948.

X Genogenic Factors: Histogenic and Chemogenic Factors

HEREDITY AND CONSTITUTION: GENOGENIC FACTORS

We first have to classify the relationship between "constitution" and "heredity." The term "constitutional tendencies" implies that the organism, under given circumstances and in response to given stimuli, is more likely to react in a certain way. Differences in reaction tendencies—to feeding, to training, and to discipline—can be observed in infants soon after birth. Noticeable variations exist among infants from the time of birth in their reflex behavior. In the same infant, certain reflexes may be stronger than others, or he may respond more readily to one type of stimulation than to another—he may react violently to loss of support and not at all to an auditory stimulus (884).

Observation of infants' general motor activity—nursing, sleeping—and of their responses to certain tests was carried out. The test procedure utilized was an extended form of the Moro Test: a padded weight was dropped near the child, and, beginning when the infant was three months old, the weight was not padded. The intensity of the child's "startle" response was observed. These observations were done daily for the first ten days and later periodically. They led to the classification of three congenital types: "active," "moderately active," and "quiet." The quiet child, who tends to withdraw under stress, needs more than an average amount of stimulation, patience, and reassurance. He has to be introduced gradually to changes and to new situations. The active child fares particularly badly under restraint, which stimulates aggressiveness, stubbornness, and rebelliousness. Another test used, the Oral Test, consisted of presentation, removal, and restoration of the nipple. The active child responds by becoming very active and may even have a startle response and may take a short time to quiet down before sucking on the restored nipple. The quiet child tends to withdraw in the face of thwarting and needs help to suck again on the restored nipple. The moderately active child is more responsive to the removal of the nipple, is more resourceful in his attempt to regain it; and the acceptance of the nipple on the restoration is more active. The congenital activity type is environmentally modifiable. Destructive environmental influences tended to shift it further in the direction of the extreme; the quiet response became quieter and the active response more active. The effect of an emotionally stable mother, satisfactorily related to her child, influenced the response by keeping the pattern the same or shifting it toward the midline (319).[1]

The most important determining factors in constitutional tendencies are hereditary factors, and some authors use the two terms synonymously; others group with constitutional influences all early factors that have a long-range influence on the bodily and psychological reaction tendencies of the organism.

In 1934, quintuplets were born to the Dionne family. On the basis of the weight of evidence, including mild "webbing" between their second and third toes, they are to be considered monozygotic (developed from one egg). For this reason the hereditary influence must be considered identical in all of them. There were, however, definite differences observable in the children at the age of four. One of them, Marie, was always the last to acquire new techniques and was the smallest in size. Both Marie and Emilie had a peculiar manner of grasping objects. It can be concluded on the basis of evidence otherwise known that all the children came from one egg which divided twice, after which one of the embryos divided for a third time, and that Marie and Emilie came from the last division. For this reason they were behind the others in their development, and as a result they have to take second place in competitive situations (828).

Thus the intrauterine influences, the time of the division of the egg, and the relative amount of room the children had in the uterus would be

[1] On the basis of extensive measurement, Kretschmer differentiated among "pyknic," "asthenic" ("leptosome"), and "athletic" types. The pyknic type is characterized by a tendency to overweight, a large round chest, and a short neck. The asthenic type is characterized by a tendency to underweight and a flat chest. The muscular, or athletic, type is long-limbed. Many patients with manic-depressive psychoses belong to the pyknic type. Patients suffering from dementia praecox (schizophrenia) are more often asthenic and athletic. Many workers in the field consider this differentiation over-simplified. Sheldon (857-859) described the following three basic constitutional components: (1) endomorphy, characterized by massive and highly developed digestive viscera and, usually, obesity; (2) mesomorphy, characterized by the predominance of bone, muscle, and connective tissue, large blood vessels, and strength and toughness; and (3) ectomorphy, characterized by flatness of the chest, slender, poorly muscled extremities, long, delicate bones, and relatively poorly protected nervous system and sensory tissue. His three personality components include (1) viscerotonia, characterized by love of comfort, sociability, and gluttony (jolly, fat man); (2) somatotonia, characterized by vigor and push, with action and power as life's primary purpose (burly athlete); and (3) cerebrotonia, characterized by avoidance of sociality, lack of somatic and visceral expression, "hyperattention" and alertness (nervous bookworm). Instead of being categorized as belonging to one or another of the "types" in these two variables, each individual is measured for the relative presence of each of the characteristics. Thus, an individual who may be primarily a mesomorph may also have some of the characteristics of endomorphy and ectomorphy. The same is true of the three personality trends. In a study of 200 cases, a correlation of +.79 was found between endomorphy and viscerotonia, of +.82 between mesomorphy and somatotonia, and of +.83 between ectomorphy and cerebrotonia.

considered by some writers as resulting in "constitutional tendencies." In fact, the small size of these children at birth was the result of the intrauterine environment—namely, there being five in a space designed for one—and influenced for a long time the reaction tendencies of these organisms.

Other long-range influences on reaction tendencies may be mentioned, such as birth injury and iodine deficiency in the mother during pregnancy, which latter would prevent the adequate development of the child's thyroid gland.

A nineteen-year-old boy was the youngest of four siblings. His father was in business; his mother was a housewife. The mother was inclined to be worrisome and fretted much about the children when they had relatively minor ailments. She favored the patient. The patient's father was somewhat excitable, particularly when he had business worries, inclined to be dictatorial, and had temper outbursts if he did not have his way. He wanted his youngest son, the patient, to go into business with him. The patient, however, was not inclined to do so, and after some wrangling suggested that he go to college and then go into business. The father agreed to this after some storming and some tears on the part of the mother. The patient, who had always been shut in, unsocial, and shy with girls, made out well the first six months of college. After that he became more withdrawn, began to neglect his appearance, and locked the doors because "they are sending gases after me." He heard voices which called him bad names, and finally he refused to eat because there was "poison in the food." The patient was sent to a psychopathic hospital. He was able to make a social and occupational recovery in a year's time without adequate insight.

The patient here described suffered from a schizophrenic reaction which will be discussed later in the book. Obviously, it is a very severe illness. The patient undoubtedly was exposed to a variety of stresses and strains in his life which played a role in his illness. The illness might possibly have been prevented if psychological help had been available at an early period. However, the severity of the illness, as average human lives go, is completely out of proportion to the degree of stress to which he was exposed. It is a reasonable assumption that the patient had a strong tendency to react in this manner to stress.

The subject was the oldest of eleven children, six of whom were taken care of by the state charities aid. The father was a habitual drunkard, the mother irresponsible. The first four children they simply deserted. Up to the age of fifteen, this boy's life was a very disorganized one. He was placed in an orphan asylum at six, and then at the age of nine was put into a farm home where he was severely beaten and made to work hard without opportunity for recreation. The agency placed him in another home, where the father was a drunkard and often beat him. Three years later he ran away and found another home on his own initiative. These people were kind and warm, and he was happy there, eventually marrying one of the daughters.

He is now a steady worker, manages his business adequately, has an essentially satisfactory marriage, and takes great pleasure in his daughter.

He does have minor disturbances. He loses his temper easily, worries about his business. He is resentful toward his mother for not having preserved the home at all costs. He sometimes has slight pains in the region of the heart.

In spite of his extremely deprived childhood, he is an essentially adequate person, with certain characterological difficulties and a minor psychosomatic disorder. It seems reasonable to conclude that he had very sound emotional reaction tendencies.

In the following we will discuss the studies on the problem of hereditary—i.e., genogenic—factors in reaction tendencies of the individual.

Studies in Heredity: Law of Dominance. For the sake of clarity, we will briefly describe the fundamentals of plant and animal studies. The law of dominance can be illustrated by one of Gregor Mendel's experiments with garden peas. When he crossed green peas with yellow peas, the first (F_1) generation resulting were all yellow, from which he concluded that yellow was the dominant trait. When he crossed several of the F_1 yellow plants with each other, the offspring resulting from this second cross contained 6022 yellow and 2001 green plants (a ratio of approximately 3:1). The green factor he called a recessive trait.

Gene and Chromosome Theories. Hereditary traits are carried from generation to generation by genes. These genes are contained in chromosomes, which appear in the nucleoplasm of all cells of the organism during division. The cells of each organism contain a fixed number of pairs of chromosomes, the number being constant for each species. Each chromosome contains several genes governing various traits, and the other member of the chromosome pair contains the same number of genes governing the same traits. Thus each individual carries at least two genes governing each hereditary trait. Mature germ cells contain only half the number of chromosomes found in the body cells, having only one member of each pair. The fertilized ovum, however, contains the full number of chromosomes, receiving one member of each pair from each of the parents. This makes it understandable why large samples are needed to overcome the chance factor in studies on heredity. When the germ cells of Mendel's hybrid yellow plants divided, half of them contained the dominant (yellow) gene and half of them contained the recessive (green) gene. It was a matter of chance which male cell fertilized which female cell. Only those new plants were green where the two recessive (green) genes came together. Mendel's crossings resulted in approximately 8000 offspring.

Unit Character. The color of the peas in the experiment described was a unit character. In other words, the color was determined by one pair of genes. Most traits in human beings, however, are governed by more than one pair of genes. This makes the problem more complicated, partly because the ratios become more intricate, and a larger number of offspring is necessary to obtain valid results. For example, eye color in the fruit fly is determined by seven pairs of genes. About 100,000 offspring are necessary in experimenting with this trait.

Influence of Environment in Development. A fish *(Fundulus)* having two eyes under normal conditions has been produced with only one eye by placing the egg in water containing magnesium salts. When eggs produced by a one-eyed fish were allowed to develop under normal conditions, they reverted to "normal."

We can now realize the difficulties of heredity studies in human beings. It is impossible to control human mating, inbreeding is taboo, propagation is slow, the number of offspring is small, and environment cannot be experimentally altered.

The problem "Is mental disease inherited?" is the wrong question. The correct questions are: (1) "Are there mental disturbances in which there is a genetic factor?" (2) "If so, what is the meaning of 'genetic factor'?" (3) "Are there mental disorders in which the genetic aspect is so great as to outweigh all other factors—in other words, that could be called inherited?" It is obvious from the formulation of these questions that various disorders have to be considered separately.

MENTAL ILLNESSES WITH MENDELIAN RATIOS

Two rare forms of mental illness, with serious change in the nervous system, which are entirely determined by genogenic factors regardless of environment, are amaurotic family idiocy and Huntington's chorea. Sjogren concluded, from a study of the adolescent type of amaurotic idiocy, that it follows a *recessive* and monofactorial (unit character) mode of inheritance. He studied 59 families with 413 offspring, of whom 115 were afflicted (approximately 3:1 ratio). This disorder is described in the section on psychopathology in childhood (Chapter XXI). Huntington's chorea is characterized by irregular, jerky, involuntary movements, affecting the voluntary muscles of the body, and by mental deterioration. It runs a chronic and progressive course. This disease is determined by a *dominant* gene and follows Mendelian ratios.

It should be noted that in these two disorders the overwhelming genetic factor could be clearly established because of the clear-cut presence of the Mendelian ratios. An important point to emphasize is that Huntington's chorea may not manifest itself until the patient is in his thirties. Thus the age period is an important aspect to consider; if the siblings die at an earlier age, they have to be disregarded in the study.

MENTAL ILLNESSES WHERE MENDELIAN RATIOS HAVE NOT BEEN DEMONSTRATED

The Family-Line Hypothesis. In the mental disturbances to be discussed, no Mendelian ratio has been found. The genetic factor has been assumed in them because of their more frequent occurrence in the families of individuals having the disease than in the general population. We will now examine studies based on this approach.

During the Revolutionary War, Martin Kallikak had an illegitimate child by a feeble-minded girl. Later on he married a Puritan girl and raised a family. In 1898, Dr. H. H. Goddard traced the descendants of Martin Kallikak and found that those descended from the feeble-minded girl were feeble-minded, alcoholic, "insane," and morally defective in general, whereas the descendants of his wife were all good citizens. Goddard concluded from this that these traits were inherited from Kallikak's respective mates.

There are many shortcomings to be found in this study. Most of the evidence was gained by hearsay, and it deals with ancestors, about whom information is hazy and inconclusive, especially for diagnosis. Syphilis is treated as hereditary. Goddard did not take into account the influence of bad environment among the offspring of the feeble-minded girl.

In general, even if the determination of the presence of psychopathology is done at first hand, the familial incidence in itself proves nothing about the genetic predisposition, no more than does the common observation that children speak their parents' language. In other words, the effect may be entirely due to the pathological influence of their contact with the environment. Practically all the studies and statements about psychoneuroses, about alcoholism, and about criminal behavior up to this point belong in this category. (Mendelian ratios have been demonstrated in some forms of feeble-mindedness.)

Foster-Children Studies. In general, foster-child studies indicate that hereditary tendencies are not strong enough to lead to serious disturbances under improved environmental conditions.

In a study of the intelligence of foster children, Freeman, Holzinger, and Mitchell (287) compared these children with their real and foster parents, with their siblings, and with other children in the foster homes. They found that the intelligence ratings of the children approached that of the foster parents after adoption and that the degree of change depended on the age of the children at the time of placement and the length of time they were in the foster home. One of the most significant findings was that related to those children whose own parents were feeble-minded. The mean IQ of these children was the same as the standard for children in general, and the ones in this group who were feeble-minded were all adopted at a late age. Of twenty-six children who had two feeble-minded parents, only four had an IQ below 70.

Table 1 contains the results obtained by Roe and Burks (781) in a study comparing foster children of alcoholic and psychotic parentage with those of normal parentage. Study of this table reveals that there is no significant difference in level of adjustment between those foster children whose own parents were normal and those whose own parents were abnormal.

Schizophrenia. The following study combined three procedures.

The procedures used were (1) the family-history method, (2) the contingency method of statistical prediction, and (3) the twin-study method. The family-history

TABLE 1[2]

Parentage Group	Overall Personality Adjustment of Children: Very Well Adjusted	Well Adjusted	Fairly Satis-factory	Malad-justed	Seriously Malad-justed	Totals
Alcoholic	2	12	8	11	2	35
Normal	2	9	4	4	2	21
Psychotic	2	4	1	3	0	10
Alcoholic-Psychotic	0	3	1	2	0	6
Totals	6	28	14	20	4	72

method has already been explained. The contingency method compares the morbidity rates for representative samples of consanguineous and nonconsanguineous groups. The twin-study method determines the concordance rate (both twins affected) in identical (monozygotic) twins and compares this with the concordance in fraternal (dizygotic) twins. It further compares the concordance rate in identical twins living in the same environment with that in identical twins living in different environments. In this study, 691 pairs of twins, one or both of whom were schizophrenic, were studied. Of these, 517 were dizygotic and 174 were monozygotic. The combined number of family members for both groups of twins studied was 4394. Table 2 shows the incidence of schizophrenia among the relatives of the twin patients.

TABLE 2[3]

Relationship	Incidence in Percentage
Marital partners	2.1
Step-siblings	1.8
Half-siblings	7.0
Parents	9.2
Full siblings	14.3
Dizygotic twin	14.7
Monozygotic twin	85.8

These figures convincingly establish the presence of a genetic factor in the group of patients who manifest the symptom complex of schizophrenia. The problems connected with this disorder will be discussed in the section on special syndromes. (See Chapter XXXIV.) The figures presented show an

[2] A. Roe and B. Burks, Adult adjustment of foster children of alcoholic and psychotic parentage and the influence of the foster home, *Memoirs of the Section on Alcohol Studies, Yale Univ.*, No. 3, 1945, p. 64.

[3] Based on statistics in F. J. Kallmann, The genetic theory of schizophrenia, in C. Kluckhohn and H. A. Murray, *Personality in Nature, Society, and Culture*, Alfred A. Knopf, New York, 1948, pp. 60-79.

increasing rate of incidence of schizophrenia correlated with increased degree of consanguinity with the twins. Also, the schizophrenic process has a greater tendency to show a similar course in pairs of monozygotic twins than in pairs of dizygotic twins where both twins are affected.

Two of the figures show the effect of the environment also: The concordance rates for opposite-sexed and same-sexed two-egg (dizygotic) twins varied from 10.3 to 17.6 percent. (The combined figure given in Table 2 is 14.7 percent.) This clearly implies the different effect of the same environment treating boys and girls differently from each other. Even more clear-cut (see Table 3) is the implication of the difference in the concordance rate between separated and nonseparated one-egg twin partners (475, 476).

To this may be added the consideration that the effects of the environment could not be entirely eliminated. If one-egg twins lived for a period

TABLE 3.[4] Concordance of Schizophrenia in Separated and Nonseparated Monozygotic Twins

	Incidence in Percentage
Separated[a]	77.6
Nonseparated	91.5

[a] Separated for five or more years before the onset of illness in one twin.

of time in their formative years in the same environment, they both might be irreversibly affected by it. Further, one-egg twins identify with each other very intensely, so that even the knowledge of the co-twin's illness provokes intense anxiety. This is the case to some extent even if they have never lived together. This anxious identification is a regular observation even in siblings after one of them breaks down with a psychosis. We may thus assume that the figures presented represent not only the relative strength of the genetic factor but also the environmental reinforcement. Nevertheless, the environmental factors alone cannot account for the consistent progression of the concordance paralleling the degree of consanguinity with the twins. For example, full siblings and dizygotic twins have the same concordance rates. If environmental factors alone were responsible for the development of the disease, the dizygotic twins would be expected to have a higher rate than ordinary siblings because of the greater similarity in their environment.

"Genetic factor" in this formulation has one of two meanings. (1) Some individuals exposed, by and large, to the same stresses as other individuals develop schizophrenic reactions instead of, e.g., anxiety hysteria or compulsion neurosis. In other words, the genetic factor would play a significant role in determining the fact that they develop schizophrenia rather than

[4] Based on statistics in F. J. Kallmann, *op. cit.*

some other disorder. Some modification of this interpretation would be that the individuals with the schizophrenic genetic factor break down with that disorder when emotional stress passes a certain intensity. Some clinical experience is in accordance with this evaluation of the genetic factor. (See Chapter XXXIV.) (2) The genetic factor implies special vulnerability, particularly to certain types of stresses which are unavoidable in the process of growing up and becoming socialized. The individuals finally develop a schizophrenic reaction. The genetic factor then would determine both the quantitative element (vulnerability) and the qualitative aspect of the reaction. The fact that even the unseparated monozygotic co-twins do not have a concordance rate of 100 percent, further that monozygotic co-twins who have been separated for more than five years have a lower concordance rate than those who have not been separated, as well as the clinical experience referred to in the above consideration show that schizophrenia is a disorder which is both preventable and potentially curable. As will be seen in the childhood and adult sections and in the section on therapy, the method of treatment may be somatic and/or psychological. The latter essentially consists of uncovering and remedying the effects of the stresses and strains under which the patient broke.

Manic-Depressive Psychosis. Similar conclusions are warranted about manic-depressive psychosis, although the studies about that disorder have been neither as extensive nor as carefully done as the study presented about schizophrenia. Rosanoff found that both monozygotic twins were affected in 69.6 percent of the pairs studied, dizygotic twins in 16.4 percent of the pairs. The total number studied was fifty-eight pairs of twins.

Epilepsy. Epilepsy in its "major" form is characterized by convulsions, with loss of consciousness, and in its "minor" form most frequently by staring or engaging in a repetitive movement or activity, with loss of consciousness and loss of memory. (For a more complete description of this disorder, see Chapter XXXV.) In 85 percent of epileptic patients, an abnormal electroencephalograph (EEG) (see psychosomatic section, page 457) is found between seizures. Ten percent of normal people show abnormalities in the EEG that are similar to those found in epileptic patients. A pertinent finding for our problem is the following:

> Lennox, Gibbs, and Gibbs (538) have made electric records of 70 pairs of twins and of 262 close relatives of epileptic patients. Although the pattern of cortical brain waves is a fluid and not a fixed characteristic, it is a hereditary trait. Of the 262 relatives, 53 percent had dysrhythmia. In 78 families records were obtained of both parents. In 27 percent both parents had abnormal records, in 53 percent only one was definitely abnormal, in 10 percent one parent's record was on the border line, and in only 10 percent were the records of both parents entirely normal.

(See also Lennox [537].)

As has been illustrated with the case presented at the beginning of this section about the woman who developed convulsions following a brain abscess, the psychogenic factor in epilepsy may be very significant as regards the frequency of attacks. Thus we have another illustration here of a genetic factor which determines the form of the illness as well as, possibly, the degree of sensitiveness to environmental stress.

Psychosomatic Disorders. In two groups of psychosomatic disorders familial incidence is rather common. One group is the allergic disorders (vasomotor rhinitis, asthma, infantile eczema, urticaria); the other is the cardiovascular disorders, particularly arterial hypertension. The psychogenic factor, as a rule, plays a major role in these disorders. The genetic factor may be considered somewhat controversial, as some workers in the field consider the whole disorder psychogenic. This view is probably incorrect, first because many patients retain their allergic sensitivity on skin tests (a weal forms at the site where the offending agent is introduced) even after they become free from their symptoms, and second because infantile eczema with familial allergic incidence often shows a clearly selective sensitivity to milk protein. Very likely, therefore, we have here another illustration of a genetic factor determining the form of illness and probably in response to special types of emotional constellations.

HISTOGENIC AND CHEMOGENIC FACTORS

The importance of the histo- and chemogenic factors varies with the type of disorder and the individual patient. The relative significance of one factor may overshadow all others—e.g., in meningitis, brain abscess, the acute effects of head injury, or acute carbon monoxide poisoning. In other conditions—e.g., cerebral arteriosclerosis, general paresis, alcoholism, vitamin deficiencies—the reaction of the total personality to the direct effect of the damage may also be very important.

Quite a different relationship exists in some of the psychosomatic disorders—e.g., in allergy. Here there may be a very definite chemogenic element, but the significance of the emotional stress may be equally important or predominate over the other. In these disorders, the individual may get a symptom—e.g., an asthmatic attack—if enough of a certain chemical not toxic to other individuals is introduced into the body through respiration or ingestion. Such a substance may be the proteins in egg white. The disturbance may continue even when the offending chemical is eliminated or may return even after the chemical susceptibility has greatly decreased if the patient is subjected to relevant emotional stress. Similar susceptibility has not been demonstrated for any of the other psychosomatic disorders but is strongly suspected.

HISTOGENIC AND CHEMOGENIC FACTORS DIRECTLY AFFECTING THE BRAIN

These disturbances may be grouped as inadequate development of the brain (aplasia and hypoplasia), degeneration of the brain after adequate development, physical injury to the brain (trauma), infectious disorders brought about by direct invasion of the brain by germs. The last can be either acute—e.g., meningitis and brain abscess—or chronic—e.g., usually, syphilitic infection.

Chemical influences, either from outside or from within, may exert their effect through the presence of harmful substances or through the absence of substances indispensable for health. Poisons introduced from the outside may be lead and mercury (relatively rare), alcohol, and other drugs. Indispensable chemicals from the outside may be absent in certain forms of avitaminosis—e.g., pellagra (vitamins B and G). In carbon monoxide poisoning, the carbon monoxide combines with the blood hemoglobin, and, as a result, the brain is deprived of adequate oxygen. Toxic substances produced by the rest of the body may be present in severe infection—e.g., pneumonia. In such a situation there are no germs attacking the brain itself; the toxins are produced in the lungs but reach the brain through the blood stream. Toxic substances may accumulate in the blood stream in disturbances of the kidney function when the kidneys cannot eliminate them. Absence or insufficient amount of chemicals indispensable for the growth and functioning of the brain is present in underfunctioning of the thyroid gland (cretinism, myxedema). Disturbance may be the reverse if too much of the thyroid hormone (thyroxine) is produced and has a toxic effect on the brain. The intensity and reversibility of these processes vary and will be discussed in connection with the relevant problems in the section on syndromes.

HISTOGENIC AND CHEMOGENIC FACTORS INFLUENCING OTHER PARTS OF THE BODY

In psychoneurotic disturbances—e.g., hysteria, compulsion neurosis, anxiety states—the chemogenic factors play a much smaller role. This role may be of several kinds. It may determine the organ that will be disturbed in the main as a result of the emotional conflict. Thus a patient may have a primary physical disturbance, let us say gastrointestinal upset. Not long after, however, the predominant symptom occurring at each time of emotional stress is a gastrointestinal complaint. This phenomenon has been called "somatic compliance" (Freud). The basis of this acquired susceptibility to the organ disturbance has not been determined.

Another type of chemogenic disturbance refers to the consequences of disturbances of organ function. The organism cannot get adequate rest because of psychogenic sleeplessness or by always being "on the go" or by frequent rage reactions and continuous anxiety. The resultant physical fatigue and tension then lead to further psychological reactions.

Psychogenic disturbances of more localized organ functions–e.g., loss of appetite, vomiting, and diarrhea–may influence the patient's eating habits. Other local psychogenic disturbances may be vasoconstriction–e.g., cold extremities–which then makes the patient more sensitive to cold and disturbs his ability to use his extremities under such circumstances. Similarly, in patients with potency difficulties, the physiological events that accompany adequate sexual performance and orgasm do not take place. The result may be a vague discomfort and then avoidance of situations leading to repeated sexual function or a driven attempt to keep repeating the function in the hope that it will become adequate. Either way, there is further psychological reaction to the physiological phenomenon.

SUGGESTED READINGS

A good popular work on heredity is Scheinfeld's *You and Heredity*. The studies on the influence of various factors are well presented by Pollock, Malzburg, and Fuller (737). We strongly recommend the respective section in Kluckhohn and Murray (505). A very stimulating and many-sided book is Cobb's *Borderlands of Psychiatry* (166). Plant's book (736) and any of Adler's are recommended as attempts to express the personality's functional use of the hereditary, constitutional, and environmental influences. A. Meyer's articles on neurotic constitution and mental reaction types are further recommended (643-645).

XI Individual Psychogenic Factors

DEVELOPMENT OF THE ORGANISM

The discussion of the development of various functions is important because the effect of various etiological factors leading to psychopathology depends much on the developmental level of the organism. This applies as much to the physiological (histo- and chemogenic) as to the psychological factors. The effect of all of them can be more devastating when the organism is helpless and immature. On the other hand, the infant or the child can recover more completely than the adult if no permanent damage has been done and adequate remedial measures are taken. One of the characteristic effects of any of the etiological factors is retarding further development of the respective functions. This includes feelings of adequacy as well as sexual strivings, motility, and intelligence. Another effect is the establishment of a tendency to revive, in case of later stress, the modes of adaptation which prevailed at the time of the initial traumatic influences.

A great deal can be learned about the infant by observation, but of course no verbal information can be obtained directly from him. Certain "psychological" functions are not yet present, and great caution is needed in all theoretical constructions about the infant.

The infant's needs and desires and emotional reactions are at first probably extremely vague and undifferentiated. Almost certainly he at first has only bodily needs which are not clearly directed toward definite objects. It is only through gradual development, repeated experiences, and conditionings—most of which are, of course, nonverbal and nonconscious—that these needs become directed toward definite objects and situations leading to gratification, satisfaction, and elimination of distress.

The infant has drives of various sorts, and he behaves in a manner which can be reasonably interpreted as distress if these drives are not stilled. He shows similar distress reactions to some stimuli, such as injury, which can be assumed to be painful. He is affected in a positive way by gratifications of various sorts, such as the satisfaction of needs and drives, rocking, warmth, and sensory stimulation (stroking, tickling, sexual stimulation).

EMOTIONAL GROWTH

During the first week, outside of screaming (distress) and quiescence following relief, the infant is apt to sleep twenty-four hours a day. After about a week, there are more positive signs of pleasure—the infant will turn toward the mother when taken up to be given the breast. Soon after this, the baby will stare at a face offered him and follow it with his eyes, although he is still unable to fixate on any other object. Perhaps the human face is the first object of fixation because the infant sees it whenever he experiences relief from distress and experiences pleasure. Beginning with the third month, babies follow the movements of grown-ups even at a distance of from ten to twenty feet and smile and babble at the sight of the full face in movement. The baby smiles before this period, but not in response to a specific external stimulus. The negative emotions show the following development: By the end of the fourth month, the baby shows displeasure if the adult stops playing with him, but he will not scream if only an object (e.g., his rattle) is taken away. In the sixth month, he will also cry at his playthings being removed. This apparently implies a recognition that he is losing something he wants. A very important patterning takes place between the "positive" and "negative" emotions, apparently initiated by the development of "intelligence" to the point of recognition of individuals. The child now smiles at the appearance of his mother and familiar friends, but looks either coy or anxious when a stranger appears. Some children look bewildered, others hide their faces, and some scream. This "eight-months anxiety," so called because it reaches its distinct development at about that month, is easily overcome by continued smiling and a friendly attitude on the part of the adult. In the course of the next two months, the child becomes more possessive and will select one particular object—e.g., a teddy bear—as his favorite sleeping companion. If, in a room with several babies, the adult singles out one to play with, a small hand is likely to reach through behind the bars of a crib and tug at his coat. The baby so behaving feels neglected because of another ten-months-old baby and is taking steps to remedy matters. Thus, by the tenth or the twelfth month, the child is capable of showing anxiety, disappointment, anger, and jealousy; on the positive side, love for one specific person, sympathy and friendliness for other persons, enjoyment of his toys, and a positive sense of property toward one special object are shown.[1] The emotional attachment to certain individuals whom the child recognizes and who take care of him represents a crucial emotional step. From this point on the affection of a particular person

[1] Freely paraphrased from R. A. Spitz, Emotional growth in the first year, *Child Study*, 1947, **24**, 68-70.

becomes as important for the child as the satisfaction of his bodily (particularly oral) wants.

ORGAN FUNCTIONS

The Mouth. The organ that is most significant for a long period after birth from the point of view of both utility (nourishment) and satisfaction (akin to pleasure) is the mouth, and with it the whole digestive tract. For this reason, disturbances in the infant are most likely to be manifest in connection with the functioning of this organ. This may be either because of inadequate nourishment or because the pleasure needs of the mouth are not adequately satisfied. (See the quoted observations of D. M. Levy [541] and M. Ribble [769], page 68.)

Another common observation which is of interest is the fact that in many social groups one of the most customary ways to still a crying infant is to give him something to suck. From this we can postulate that somehow the use of the mouth, together with the satisfaction derived from it, can serve as a measure for the amelioration of distress (and helplessness) arising from other sources. This behavior—eating or drinking as consolation—is often seen in adults.

Because of the intimate connection between the period of greatest dependency and the predominant function of the mouth during this period, eating and food in general remain throughout life the symbols of dependence and being cared for. (See also Chapters V and XX.)

Excretory Functions. Excretory functions gradually acquire considerable psychological importance, partly in connection with intellectual maturation, increase in motility, and training in cleanliness. Most infants do not mind being wet and soiled as long as the excreta are warm. Further, they become interested in both the function and its product. There is a state of tension preceding the expulsion of the excreta, followed by relief and some amount of pleasure upon expulsion. In their all-inclusive curiosity and handling, at a certain level of development children will play as innocently with feces as with any other object and with greater interest because it is a product of their own body, of which they are vaguely aware. This may be a definite emotional problem for the mother, and her attitude may make it a problem for the child as well. Depending on the age at which toilet training starts, the excretory functions acquire a dominant emotional significance for a period of time. This is most commonly the case in countries of Western civilization at about the age of two and three. The emotional attitude that is considered most commonly associated with the anal function is hostility. The reason for this may be that the child, having a measure of control over this function, can use it for the purpose of defying the adult's demands for regulation. Also, the strongest aversion by the adult is expressed toward feces, which fact makes them a harmful substance.

The Genital Function. Some genital activity—occurrence of erections, touching of the genitals, indication of pleasure from external stimulation, etc.—is present in most infants at a very early age.

Halverson (380) observed nine male infants varying in age from three to twenty weeks for 8.5 consecutive hours per day for ten days. Tumescence occurred at least once on every day with seven of the children and on nine and eight days respectively for the other two. There were great individual differences in frequency, the actual number of tumescences varying from a median of four to a median of thirty-five per day. Frequently they appeared to occur in series. Micturition, defecation, and hampered feeding (induced by a small-holed nipple) were frequently accompanied by tumescence.

The 636 series of tumescences observed were accompanied by restlessness, fretting, or crying on 371 occasions, and by stretching or flexing the legs stiffly on 169 occasions. Ninety-one times they were accompanied by only slight stirring, or else the child was quiet. On five occasions thumb-sucking occurred. Detumescence was accompanied by crying on thirty-three occasions. In general, the behavior following detumescence seemed to represent playful activity or relaxation.

Strong heterosexual attachments between children occur at as early an age as two years.

Bell (56) observed 800 "affairs" and obtained reports from about 1700 adults on their own juvenile love affairs. He found that these love affairs were at times highly sexualized and produced the physiological signs of sex excitation, although this was not usual.

Orgasm has been observed in infants as young as four months of age. Thirty-two percent of a group of twenty-eight infants under one year of age have been observed to have orgasm. In the age range from two to five years, 57 percent, from six to ten years 63 percent, and from eleven to thirteen years 80 percent of the children observed have reached orgasm. Seventy percent of preadolescent boys studied admitted some sex play. Fifty-seven percent of postadolescent boys and adults recalled such preadolescent experiences (494).

Genital activity usually increases at about the age of four or five. Masturbation or other genital play is common at that age in both sexes.

Frequently there is a repression and cessation of sexual activities and attitudes in children from the age of about six up to puberty. This is commonly referred to as the "latency period." This is not found in societies that do not disapprove of sexual manifestations in the young. The glandular development connected with puberty brings about a considerable increase in sexual needs and desires, and with them a strong revival of emotional problems and conflicts. It is at this time that the individual masters these problems for better or worse.

Most forms of genital activity occur in childhood and preadolescence, although their universality and openness depend on the child's environment. These activities may include curiosity, exposure, and looking with children of both sexes, with a heavier accent in the heterosexual direction if the opportunities are equal. They also include play with the organ (masturbation) and handling the organ of the other child. Accidental factors of being discovered and being disapproved of play an important role in the emotional consequences of these activities.[2]

By the age of four or five the relationship with the parents has become a dominant aspect of the interest in genital activity (sexual differences, conception, and childbearing). In the monogamous patriarchal society the resulting classic form of the constellation is the so-called Oedipus complex, in which the child has erotic desires for the parent of the opposite sex and is in rivalry with the parent of the same sex. The rivalry leads to hostility and to fear of retribution, including genital injury, as well as to "ambivalence conflict"—namely, a painful awareness of love and hostility toward the same person. (See Chapter XII.) There is awareness of two different kinds of human being and of some relation between them, while the wearing of clothes prevents the discovery of the differences in the genitals. This awareness becomes even more definite after the discovery is made. Further, the regulation of this activity takes place in relationship with other individuals. These two factors and perhaps the intense pleasurable aspect of the activity and certain cultural attitudes—e.g., accent on love—finally make this function one of the strongest carriers of interpersonal needs and problems.

Children very often, in fantasy and play, fuse the functions of the mouth, the excretory organs, and the genitals. The following observations were made of a group of thirty-one children, over a period of approximately three years, whose ages ranged from two years, three months, to six years, five months.

Oral:

"George and Frank, having climbed up to the window overlooking the lane, to see a motor, began to spit on to the window; Dan joined in; they all spat vigorously, and said, 'Look at it running down.' . . ."

Excretory:

"The children were getting water to drink in cups, and Harold told the others that he had given Frank some 'wee-wee water' to drink. He often says 'there's wee-wee water in the bowl' in which he washes his hands. Later he said he had drunk 'wee-wee water,' and that the water in the cups was that."

Sexual curiosity:

"When the children were playing a family game with the puppy as baby, Duncan said: 'Undress him.' Priscilla: 'Yes.' Duncan: 'and then we can see his bim-bom'; there was great laughter and excitement among the children and all repeated, 'see his bim-bom.' Priscilla undid the rug in which he was wrapped and

[2] For contrast with other societies, see Mead's *From the South Seas* (635), Malinowski's *Sex and Repression in Savage Society* (610) and *The Sexual Life of Savages* (611), Kardiner's *The Individual and His Society* (483), and Murdock's *Social Structure* (701).

called to the others to look: 'Come on, come on, look underneath.' The puppy stood on its hind legs near Priscilla. Duncan: 'Oh, he tried to get to your what-d'ye-call-it.' "[3]

Organ Functions and Psychopathology. Psychopathology in connection with the functions of the mouth and the eliminative and genital organs can arise in two general ways. (1) The function of these organs is seriously disturbed either by a histogenic or a chemogenic process—e.g., infection—or through severe interference by persons in the environment. These disturbances then involve more or less the total personality because of the significance the functions of these organs have at various periods of development. (2) Disturbances in interpersonal relations influence the function of the organs concomitantly with anxiety, hostility, or substitutive pleasure-seeking. The functions of these organs then become the carriers of these interpersonal problems; e.g., the child may vomit to express his rejection of the parent. All these processes will be elaborated upon in the respective sections on special syndromes.

INTELLECT, MASTERY, MOTILITY, SPEECH

Motility, intellect, speech, and mastery are closely related as regards the individual's handling of the world and his image and estimation of himself and of his environment.

With the development of motility, the child can actively approach objects that he is drawn to and can retreat from them if they arouse his discomfort. He now evaluates himself as an active being with increasing resources. These are some of the highlights in the development of motility: The infant is usually able to turn toward the nursing mother during the second or third week, to hold up his head when lying on his belly at the age of three months, to reach for objects at about four months, to sit up at six months, to stand supported at about nine or ten months, to stand unsupported and to begin to walk at a year and a half. By the third year, practically all movement patterns have appeared, but the development continues until the age of twelve.

Light is thrown on the process of motor, perceptual, and intellectual development from the third year on by the Bender Visual-Motor Gestalt Test. This test consists of the presentation to the child, with the request to copy, of nine drawings, "Gestalts," originally developed by Wertheimer. The first card, for example, contains a circle and a diamond-oriented square touching each other on the horizontal plane. From two and one half to four years the children's drawings are scribblings, representing motor play, without any special meaning. They are performed by large arm movements

[3] S. Isaacs, *Social Development in Young Children*, George Routledge & Sons, London, 1933, pp. 113, 122, and 141.

in a rightward clockwise whirl or in large pendulum waves if the child uses his right hand, and leftward counterclockwise whirls if the left hand is used. The total body motility shows similar developments. Up to the age of six, the child has a tendency to continue whirling movement around the longitudinal axis of the body. If an examiner turns the child's head, the child will move in the direction toward which the head is turned and will continue to do so even after the examiner stops turning the head (Bender).

The child's Gestalt drawings tend to take on a differentiated form, single loops or parts of loops, through the stopping of the movement by inhibition. Up to the age of four the small child usually produces scribbles in response to Gestalt figures as a stimulus. Patterns toward "Gestalten" are formed by such combinations of loops as are adapted to resemble the perceived stimulus.[4] Thus the optic field is organized on the basis of movement. Differentiation of form, maturing of motor apparatus, and the capacity for object representation take place rapidly between the fourth and the seventh years and progress clearly to the eleventh year, which is the period when the language function, including reading and writing, is developing.

Movement and action represent strivings that press the individual toward relief and pleasure, although tension and enjoyment are not as clearly marked as, e.g., in eating. Activity further has a reference to the self in the sense of resourcefulness, and to interpersonal relations because the action concerns other persons and the individual becomes the target of their actions in turn. Bodily contact is very important for children. They engage in it, desire it, and accept it very easily up to about puberty. They allow the examiner to pick them up and, under normal circumstances, show a considerable amount of trust in being held by the examiner even with their heads down. An increase in this tendency to contact, either in the form of passivity or in the form of anxious clinging, will be discussed with the special syndromes. Motility and action further have a coloring of nearly all possible experiences of the individual—enjoyment, anxiety, guilt, aggression—because these experiences either require movement or may lead to its inhibition.

With the development of speech, new means of reaching the environment and of being reached by the environment appear. The infant's resources increase along with the power of motility and intellect. A new form of activity is enjoyed. A richness in emotional and intellectual experience appears, made possible only by the simultaneous development of language, including reading and writing as well as speech. The phenomenon of symbols becomes elaborated; i.e., a word comes to represent an object, an action,

[4] This presentation closely follows L. Bender, Psychological principles of the visual motor Gestalt test, *Trans. N.Y. Acad. Sci.,* Series II, 1949, **2**, 164-170. See also Bender's "A visual motor Gestalt test and its clinical use" (69) and *Instructions for the Use of Visual Motor Gestalt Test (and Test Forms)* (64).

or a relationship. Various children acquire language ability in different ways. Some learn words, at the same time learning how to put them together. With other children, the single word seems to have very little function for a long time, and it is more the general inflection and sequence of sounds that matter and have meaning for them. When they finally begin to speak, they speak in paragraphs instead of single words.

Communication with the environment gives speech all the aspects of positive and negative emotional constellations with the parents, siblings, and mates. Further, language becomes intricately interwoven with every type of experience of the individual: organ functions, attack and escape, reactions of pleasure, guilt, and even "namelessness." It is probable that memory before the third or fourth year of age is so scanty, even in psychoanalytic reconstruction, because language had not yet adequately developed. The intimate connection between speech and total personality is indicated by the following studies:

A remarkable correspondence could be established between the personality sketches based on speech records which were made by investigators who did not know the actual subjects and the personality sketches made of the same individuals on the basis of close knowledge of their behavior (687). Similarly, interpretations based on the voice record of a high-school boy corresponded closely with the interpretations by another clinician based on the boy's Rorschach record (467). These evaluations of the voice record were based on the formal aspects of speech, such as vocal range, basic pitch (last syllable in a declarative sentence), major or minor key, stress and emphasis, pathos, speed, pauses, monotony, quality or timbre, and nasal resonance.

Intelligence—i.e., the ability to recognize and to grasp meanings and interrelations—is very close in the child to curiosity. The child behaves under its influence as under the influence of other drives, but, as with motility and speech, the tension-relief and pleasure sequence is not sharply accentuated. The reference to the self and the interpersonal aspects are also clear-cut. Curiosity and exploration are directed toward the self as well as toward the world; successful and unsuccessful problem-solving and attainment of goals lead to a feeling of mastery or of failure. Exploration, problem-solving, and mastery invariably increase interpersonal pleasure or invoke attack, arousing fear and guilt, and thus lead to new sources of strength or helplessness. It has been mentioned that the crucial step of emotional attachment to single individuals is obviously dependent on the "intellectual" ability to recognize them. Intellect, as motility and speech, also becomes intricately bound up with all aspects of the individual's experiences.

The "developmental quotient" (DQ), commonly used as a measure up to the age of three, includes the infant's motility patterns and his social orientation, thus covering a wider range of functions than the intelligence quotient (IQ). Both developmental and intelligence tests, as investigations have shown, are dependent upon and correlated to a very large degree with the individual's life experience.

The Gesell developmental scale tests four aspects of infant behavior: *motor* (muscular coördination, muscular control, and locomotion), *language* (vocalization, use of words, and comprehension of meanings), *adaptive* (handling and use of objects), and *personal-social* (responsiveness to others, development of socialized behavior such as habits of cleanliness, play activities, and communication). Standards for various age levels, ranging from four weeks to three and a half years, have been developed. Some sample items from this scale are given below:[5]

Motor	Adaptive	Language	Personal-Social
		28 Weeks	
in supine position, lifts head sits erect momentarily held in standing position, bounces actively pellet: rakes with hand, contacts	bell: in hand approach and grasp cube: holds 2 more than momentarily shakes rattle transfers bell	polysyllabic vowel sounds	takes solids well play: with feet to mouth mirror: reaches, pats image
		12 Months	
walks: needs only one hand held	cube: tries tower, fails pellet and bottle: tries insert, releases, fails dangles ring by string formboard: looks selectively at round hole	2 "words" besides *mamma, dada* comprehension: gives a toy	coöperates in dressing
		18 Months	
walks fast, runs stiffly walks up stairs, one hand held small chair: seats self turns pages, 2-3 at once	cubes: tower of 3-4 pellet and bottle: dumps draws stroke imitatively formboard: piles 3 blocks	looks selectively at pictures 10 words, including names picture card: names or points 1 ball: follows 2 directions	hands empty dish when finished feeds self in part, spills toilet: regulated daytime pulls toy carries doll

[5] Based on A. Gesell and C. S. Amatruda, *Developmental Diagnosis,* Paul B. Hoeber, New York, 2nd ed., 1947.

Motor	Adaptive	Language	Personal-Social
		24 Months	
runs well, no falling	cubes: tower of 6-7	3-word sentence	verbalizes toilet needs
walks up and down stairs alone	imitates circular stroke	uses *I, me, you*	pulls on simple garment
kicks ball	formboard: places blocks	pict. c'd: names 3 or more	verbalizes immediate experiences
turns pages singly		pict. c'd: identifies 5 or more	refers to self by name
		carries out 4 directions	parallel play
		36 Months	
alternates feet going up stairs	cubes: imitates bridge	book: gives action in picture	feeds self, spills little
jumps from bottom stair	names own drawing	uses plurals	puts on shoes
rides tricycle	copies circle	tells own sex	unbuttons accessible buttons
stands on 1 foot, momentary balance	formboard: adapts, no error	comprehension quest.: answers 1	understands taking turns
	repeats 3 digits	obeys 2 directions using prepositions	knows a few rhymes

AGGRESSION AND HOSTILITY

The problem of aggression and hostility is as important in psychopathology as the problem of fear, and is closely connected with the problem of motility and mastery. We have mentioned the considerable increase in the child's activities during the development of motility and intellect. An important aspect of this activity is the fact that it possibly destroys, inflicts pain, or injures. This type of activity has been called aggression and even "sadism," although many deny that its primary aim in the child is to destroy or to inflict pain; i.e., it may be *merely* activity. In a more specific sense, hostility has been defined as an activity which has exactly the aim of destroying or inflicting pain. Of course, not only the skeletal musculature and the hands can be used for this purpose, but also the mouth and, in fantasy at least, any other organic function. An individual may act aggressively if he is in danger or has been hurt, or if he can thereby derive some other benefit, such as obtaining a desired object or satisfying a desire. The situations in which aggression and hostility arise are serious frustration, serious humiliation, and, in general, situations in which the individual for some reason feels entirely or almost helpless and catastrophically threatened. Hostile impulses and acts are of great importance in psychopathology because they lead either to serious consequences or to their expectation. Moreover, these impulses are one of the most frequent targets of adult disapproval; they lead to actual punishment, and thus in time to fear of counterattack and of injury, to the fear of further humiliation, abandonment, rejection, and deprivation in regard to bodily wants. The feeling of hostility is also one of the most potent sources of feelings of guilt.

DREAMS

Dreams probably occur in infancy, as indicated by the transient appearance during sleep of sucking movements or of crying and restlessness and, in older infants, of movements similar to those occurring during play, fright, or anger. Children's attitudes toward their dreams also reveal the indefinite separation between the world and the self and the incompletely developed sense of reality. Young infants probably take their dreams for actuality, and children of three or four have trouble separating dream from reality and also consider that dreams really exist "out in the room" (Piaget).

The records of forty-two consecutive children of from two to five years of age, admitted at the Payne Whitney Nursery School, were studied, and 190 dreams were collected and analyzed. There were considerable variations among the children in their wish and ability to report their dreams. Human beings and animals figured predominantly. The parents appeared in benevolent roles but, on the other hand, were readily identified with powerful destructive animals which threatened the child with total destruction. The dreams reported were predominantly anxiety dreams. The very young child (two years old) expressed the fear of being bitten, devoured, and chased without naming the agent. Later (three, four, and five years old), devouring animals were identified (195). The following dream was given by a boy of four years, seven months, who related it spontaneously in the midst of his playing with the boy and girl dolls: "One time when I was sleeping, I saw . . . (lowers his voice) . . . a sly old fox. It was real." ("A sly old fox?") ". . . He bi . . . he bi . . . he didn't bite me. He said 'I'm going to eat you up.' " ("He did?") "I said 'I'll . . . I'll shoot you with my gun.' " ("Was it in the night, or during the day? . . .") "It was in the night. . . ." ("Were you sleeping or were you awake?") "I was sleeping." ("Was it a dream, or was it just thinking?") ". . . It was real." (The child obviously means that it was real *in the dream.*) ". . . And . . . the boards on the ceiling . . . the BOARDS. . . . Just real. . . . Just make-believe ones." (As later ascertained, he was referring to beams at the ceiling of his room, which were "real" in his dream.) ("Make-believe ones?") "Yes, but when morning came . . . when morning came, there wasn't any boards." (The child gave the above account with an expression of intense anxiety.) ("And was that something you dreamed, or something that happened?") "It was a real one." (I.e., a real fox.) ("How did you know that?") " 'Cause I saw it." ("Oh, you saw it?") (With an excited voice:) "I saw it come down, and it . . . and it . . . and it talked." ("It talked? How did it talk?") (Excited voice:) "It said . . . it said . . . 'gr . . .' for the talk. . . ."[6]

Children's dreams in general are easily understandable if one knows the child's life situation. It is only in late adolescence that children's dreams

[6] J. L. Despert, Dreams in children of preschool age, in *The Psychoanalytic Study of the Child,* Vol. III/IV, International Universities Press, New York, 1949, pp. 162-163.

acquire the full complexity and sophistication of adult dreams (Mittelmann), thus illustrating the development of full intricacies of emotional life. Children show in connection with the dream three predominant aspects of their psychic life: (1) fulfillment of wishes for oral pleasure, possession, superior power, and hostile victory—e.g., in rivalry (S. Freud); (2) their relative helplessness in stress situations; (3) in the face of this, they are uttering cries for help.

CHILDREN'S PLAY

The play of children has a fivefold aspect: (1) enjoyment of the activity for the sake of the activity; (2) gratification of special strivings, such as the oral, excretory, and genital; (3) attempts at mastering situations and achieving and accomplishing tasks (this may be illustrated by climbing up a pole or walking a narrow curbing); (4) attempts at mastering anxiety experienced in a situation in which the child was passive (e.g., he may have been taken to the doctor for an examination, and, in the game, he carries out a similar activity on the playmate); (5) establishment of interpersonal contact.

Fantasy plays a considerable role in play, and it is one manifestation of the child's loose separation between fantasy and reality. The nature of the interest and the activity, of course, varies with the child's age, but certain general characteristics of the play apply beginning with the age of two. The child should be able to play most of the time constructively—in other words, use toys and media for the purpose for which they were designed or be able to put them to some other use, naturally commensurate with his level of development. He should be able to play jointly with one or several individuals. There should be relatively little sheer destructiveness, aimless throwing around of objects, and constant discarding of one toy after another. There may be considerable fantasy accompanying the play, particularly in lonely children, in whom it may reach the point of regular imaginary companions. This, however, is on the border of the pathological. An illustration will be given here to emphasize certain points.

1. Pie (talking about the tram he is drawing): "*They don't have any carriages hooked on. . . .* (He was addressing no one in particular. No one answers him.)"
2. "(To Béa), *'T'sa tram that hasn't got no carriages.* (No answer.)"
3. "(To Hei), *This tram hasn't got no carriages, Hei, look, it isn't red, d'you see. . . .* (No answer.)"
4. "(Lev says out loud, 'A funny gentleman' from a certain distance, and without addressing himself to Pie or to anyone else.) Pie: *A funny gentleman!* (Goes on drawing his tram.)"
5. "*I'm leaving the tram white.*"
6. "*I'm doing the stair-case, look.* (Béa answers, 'I can't come this afternoon, I've got a Eurhythmic class.')"
7. "*What did you say?* (Béa repeats the same sentence.)"

8. "*What did you say?* (Béa does not answer. She has forgotten what she said, and gives Ro a push.)"
9. "(To Béa), *Leave him alone.*"
10. "(Mlle B. asks Ez if he would like to come with her), *Come here Ez, it isn't finished.* [10] bis. *Please teacher, Ez hasn't finished.*"
11. "(Without addressing himself to anyone,) *I'm doing some black stones. . . .*"[7]

This excerpt is first of all an illustration of the play activity of children under certain circumstances. Secondly, it illustrates certain characteristics of this activity, particularly in its vocal expression. Speech, like many of the other activities, is engaged in at times for the sake of speaking. Remarks 1, 5, and 11 are addressed to no one. Remark 4 is also addressed to no one and is simply the repetition of a phrase which struck the child's fancy (echolalia). Piaget called this kind of speech a monologue. Remarks 2 and 3 are addressed to others, but he obviously expects no reply. He believes that someone listened to him, and that is all he wanted. Nos. 6, 7, and 8 are exchanges of remarks and questions in which, outside a momentary attempt at contact, everybody follows his own line and everybody is satisfied. Piaget called this collective monologue. Nos. 9 and 10 are definitely addressed to somebody and either give information or expect to accomplish a change. Piaget called this socialized speech as against the previous varieties described, which he called egocentric inasmuch as they primarily represent the activities of the speaker's own self. These varieties of focus can be distinguished in any type of play activity, not only in speech. Socialized speech would be paralleled by play activity for a joint goal—e.g., building a sand-castle together.

ATTITUDES OF THE CHILD TOWARD THE ENVIRONMENT

The pattern of attachment and of positive reaction to the parent has a special coloring, depending on the child's stage of development and on his dominant organic needs and functions; and it acquires a gradually increasing richness of emotional and intellectual content.

Although the normal and psychopathological aspects of this relationship have been discussed in various parts of this book, we wish to emphasize the following points:

1. The infant or the child has a definite need for parental affection, help, appreciation, support, and praise.

2. He engages in certain activities and refrains from others for the sake of approval and affection.

3. The child tolerates easily a fair amount of disapproval and punish-

[7] J. Piaget, *The Language and Thought of the Child,* Kegan Paul, Trench, Trubner & Co., London, 1926, p. 7.

ment if he feels that he is essentially loved and if the parental demands are not over-severe.

4. The behavioral aims set by the parent acquire a definite emotional coloring and are given a high evaluation. They are accepted by the child on the basis of either "My parents want this, and I want it too; I am like them" (identification), or "If I behave this way, they value me; if I don't, they will reject me and hurt me," and, later, "If I behave this way, I value myself; if I don't, I am worthless" (ideals, conscience). In these ways the child makes the attitudes in his environment his own (internalization).

5. The older infant and child evaluate the strength and power of the parents very highly; they want not only to love them, but also to consider them supreme and all-powerful. In a word, they *need* to respect them.

6. A measure of conflict is apparently unavoidable in the process of growth and training. Because of the relationship with the mother, any serious threat issuing from her is constantly renewed, constantly reacted to, and again renewed. The child feels this threat as a total organism. Under circumstances of intense frustration, parental rejection, and impossible demands, the basic psychopathological constellation arises. Thus the child's relationship with the parent is the most potent source of catastrophic expectation.

7. During the process of growth, the infant and child are, of course, exposed to and influenced by other environmental factors, such as illness, injuries, siblings, playmates, schoolmates, teachers, relatives, and strangers. All of these may play a somewhat similar role in the child's life as do the parents. Both in the parental relationship and in all other relationships, cultural factors are significant. Thus, in our culture, the individual is supposed gradually to acquire increasing self-determination and freedom of action and to be treated and regarded more and more as an adult; this is particularly true after puberty, and entirely so after he becomes self-supporting. Close emotional attachment is limited, as a rule, to a few individuals.

A considerable shift in the accent occurs with the child's attendance at school, both as regards relations toward equals and toward authority, as regards modes of restitution and compensation, and as regards substituting intellectual activity for gratification of emotional and bodily needs (sublimation). The new environment may represent new stresses with which the child is even less able to cope than with the home and play environment, or it may represent consolation for the stresses of the other settings.

The great new problems of puberty are threefold: (1) Sexual strivings increase. (2) There is a new accent on self-assertion, independence, and "growing up," which accents the sexual striving also. (3) The individual, with his resources considerably developed, engages in much more effective and therefore more dangerous and fateful activities than before. A fire-setter at the age of five may cause property damage amounting to $5; an adolescent fire-setter can cause damage of $150,000. These problems will be discussed further with the syndromes of adolescence.

IMAGE AND EVALUATION OF ONESELF

The human individual learns to differentiate between himself and the outside world very gradually, and by a complicated process which can only be constructed. It probably involves the child's intellectual development, certain sensory experiences (as having two sensations simultaneously when he touches his own body), and the fact that parts of his body are always near him, that they are visible and touchable and are sources of comfort and discomfort, that they are movable, with the simultaneous experience of motion and vision. By constrast, external objects may be near or far or completely absent at times, or may be at hand or are removed if they are sources of pleasure or pain. The experience of tension and relief in connection with bodily needs, particularly hunger, very likely plays a major role in this process. The regular experience of the infant is that his hunger does not get stilled through his own activities alone, and relief and pleasure involve something which finally turns out to be something outside of himself—another object, another person. Some investigators believe that the distinction between the outside world and the self starts with these latter experiences. An instructive light is thrown on the development of the image of the self through the child's drawing of the human figure. About the age of three children begin to draw recognizable heads, perhaps because the first thing they notice about a person is the face in movement, which is the first object of their smile at the age of three months. It may also have to do with the fact that they tend to draw with circular movements, and the circle is one of the earliest forms they can intentionally produce. Shortly after, they add the legs and feet. At about the age of four, the arms and trunk are added, and at about eight the neck. However, many additional details and recognition of proportions—e.g., whether the arms are wider at the shoulders than at the wrists and whether they are equal to the trunk in length, whether ears are present—are not adequately developed until about the age of twelve.

The separation of the self and the world and the realization of the nature of the outside world is a process that is not quite complete, even under the conditions of Western civilization, until about the age of fourteen or fifteen; and, of course, in unconscious mental processes (dreams) it is never accomplished. This incompleteness of separation in the conscious processes is shown in the child's notions about thought, names, dreams, and objects. The child assumes that the name of an object is integrally connected with the object; when the child begins to distinguish the name from the thing named, he places the name everywhere in the surrounding air where it is spoken. At about ten, the child begins to understand the origin of names.

"Ar (6½) remarked during a building game: *'And when there weren't any names. . . .'*

"Bo (6½) replied: *'If there weren't any words it would be very awkward (on serait très ennuyé). You couldn't make anything. How could things have been made'* (if there hadn't been names for them)? The name thus seems to be a part of the essence of the thing and is even a necessary condition of its being made."[8]

"Roc (6½, a girl) is a typical case of this second stage: 'Now tell me, where is the name of the sun?—*In the sky.*—The sun is in the sky. But where is the name?—*In the sky.*—Where?—*Everywhere.*—Where?—*In all the houses.*—Is the name of the sun here? —*Yes.*—Where?—*In schools and in the class-rooms.*—Whereabouts in the class-rooms? —*Everywhere.*—Is it in this room?—*Yes.*—Where else?—*In the corners.*' "[9]

He assumes that dreams actually exist as real things in the outside world. In the first stage of his development, the dream comes from the outside and remains external; in the second stage, the dream arises in us but is external to us; in the third stage, about the age of twelve or fourteen, the dream is internal and of internal origin.

"Kun (7; 4) says that dreams come *'from the night.*—Where do they go?—*Everywhere.*—What do you dream with?—*With the mouth.*—Where is the dream?—*In the night.*—Where does it happen?—*Everywhere. In rooms, in houses.*—Whereabouts?— *In the bed.*—Can you see it?—*No, because it is only at night.*—Would anyone know you were dreaming?—*No, because it's near us.*—Could you touch it?—*No, because you're asleep when you dream.*—Is the dream made of thought?—*No.*—Where is it? —*In the night.*—Where?—*Near.*—Is it the thoughts we think with?—*No.*' And later: 'Could anyone see it?—*No, because if you looked at it, it would go.*' "[10]

Consciousness is attributed by the child to all things in the beginning. Later, things that can move are considered conscious, then things that can move of their own accord are conscious, and finally consciousness is restricted to animals.

Vel (8½) is asked, " 'Can they [clouds] feel the wind or not?—*Yes, it drives them.* —Can they feel heat?—*Yes.*' But as far as mere consciousness is concerned, any object may be conscious at times: 'Can the bench feel anything?—*No.*—If someone burnt it, would it feel that?—*Yes.*—Why?—*Because it would get smaller.*' . . . 'Does a bicycle know it goes?—*Yes.*—Why?—*Because it goes.*—Does it know when it is made to stop?—*Yes.*' . . ."[11]

[8] J. Piaget, *The Child's Conception of the World,* Harcourt, Brace & Co., New York, 1929, p. 62.

[9] *Ibid.,* p. 75.

[10] *Ibid.,* p. 93.

[11] *Ibid.,* pp. 174-175.

The child also believes that he or any other person makes the sun and the clouds move when he walks, thus assuming—obviously on the basis of illusory experience—that his actions directly influence the behavior of a certain object.

"Giamb (7): 'Does the moon move or not?—*It follows us.*—Why?—*When we go, it goes.*—What makes it move?—*We do.*—How?—*When we walk. It goes by itself.*' Giamb then invents the explanation that it is the wind that blows the sun and the moon, but he maintains all the while that it is we who control this movement: 'If we didn't move, would the moon go on or not?—*The moon would stop.*—And the sun?—*It goes with us too.*' "[12]

The phenomena discussed above are present in all, but the age at which they disappear varies from child to child and depends upon the cultural setting.

The development of the concept and image of the "self" is concerned with needs, urges, and drives, and has throughout a strong emotional coloring. It is obvious that the individual's image and evaluation of himself will depend greatly on whether, in this process, he is relatively secure or constantly frustrated and catastrophically threatened. The following facts are important in this connection:

1. There is a strong need and desire for a positive evaluation of the self on the basis of achievement (self-esteem) and moral standards, and this evaluation is greatly desired from others as well (prestige and approval).

2. In the evaluation of the body and of various reactions there is partial approval and partial disapproval. Some organs and their functions and some psychological reactions are strongly condemned and shut out of consciousness. If this is done on a large scale, it is definitely pathological. Similarly, there may be an over-valuation and aggrandizement of the whole body or of parts of it, or of the entire image of the self, or of some psychological function. This, too, is definitely pathological.

3. One of the most important factors in both the formation and the final pattern of the evaluation of the self is the relationship with parents, siblings, and playmates. The fact that the parent interferes with some of the child's actions and encourages others is significant in its formation. The parent's positive evaluation of the child as an individual is reflected in the child's evaluation of himself. If the situation is such that it leads to the basic psychopathological constellation, then the evaluation of the self is characterized by feelings of helplessness, worthlessness, and insignificance. The integrated set of attitudes toward the self has been called the "self-system" (Sullivan).

4. These remarks about the evaluation of the self should not be taken as purely introspective statements. Self-evaluation manifests itself in the phenomena that we call thoughts, emotions, motives, and actions. It is a func-

[12] *Ibid.*, p. 147.

tional, dynamic concept, and as close as we can come to expressing what we mean by reactions of the organism as a whole.

ORIGINS OF PSYCHOPATHOLOGY IN FAMILY RELATIONSHIPS

There are two types of factors that contribute to psychopathology in the parent-child relationship: (1) attitude of the parents toward their child and their method of handling him; and (2) disturbances in the family constellation—e.g., one of the parents is dead. The first type of factor can be subdivided into four varieties: (a) parental rejection, (b) parental domination, (c) parental anxiety and over-concern, and (d) excessive manifestations of love. Usually, in actual situations, these four factors are mixed, although one of them may predominate over the other three. The manifestations of these attitudes in the parents' behavior may be obvious, as in brutal treatment, or subtle, as in constant "polite" criticism. The parents' anxiety also may be expressed through constant frenzy over the child's health or, on the other hand, through a gentle over-concern about the adequacy of his clothing. Another, subtler form may be the mother's bargaining for the child's affection, offering love as a reward for obedience and threatening to withdraw it as a punishment.

ATTITUDES OF THE PARENTS TOWARD THE CHILD AND THEIR HANDLING OF HIM

Parental Rejection. The two obvious forms of rejecting behavior by the parents are neglect of the child and complete lack of demonstrativeness. These may manifest themselves while the child is still an infant in that the mother does not pick him up or fondle him, does not feed him in time, and neglects his cleanliness. Whether all or only some of these elements are present depends also on the mother's conscience and social status. The effects of the latter will be discussed in another section. (See Chapter XII.) Beginning with the second and third year, the child may be able to get some substitute care from siblings or other children, but the effects are often rather severe: a deep feeling that the world is hostile, along with feelings of isolation, humiliation, and of being unwanted and unworthy of love. The main trend observed in the rejected child may be toward aggressiveness, affect hunger, or lack of affection and withdrawal. Aggressive manifestations may be rebellious, hostile, jealous, attention-getting, annoying, and hyperactive behavior at home and in school (918). Other manifestations may be truancy, lying, and stealing. Affect hunger may utilize pathetic appeal for love and states of helplessness or whining and nagging for attention. One of the most characteristic products is the "kissing bug." Frequently one finds these trends in combination. The following case illustrates a combination of affect hunger and aggressiveness.

"A patient was referred to the Institute for Child Guidance at the age of nine years, with a complaint of enuresis and temper tantrums. . . . The history of the case is featured by the child's affectionate response to grown-ups, his making up to any stranger, the explosive and dangerous temper tantrums, and marked jealousy of the other children in the foster home. . . . When his mother is about he is always sitting on her lap, he holds his face up to be kissed and puts his arms around her neck. . . . On one occasion he tried to break up a game in which the other boys were playing. The foster mother sent him to his room, whereupon he tore up the bedding, and pulled all the pictures off the walls. On another occasion he attempted to hit a boy with an axe. . . .

"The patient lived with his father and mother in the first year of life. After the death of the father he was placed in an institution for a year, then for two years in a boarding home, from which he was removed by his mother. He was placed again in a foster home in which he had been living for a year and four months at the time of referral. There are certain elements in the history that indicate a certain modicum of affection from the mother and in the homes in which he was placed. . . .

"In this case, treatment consisted in getting placement with a foster mother who could give him a great deal of affection. There were only four interviews with the psychiatrist. . . . Marked improvement in behavior occurred and continued for two years. A follow-up made when the patient was twelve years, six months old, showed complete cessation of the temper tantrums, good school adjustment, growth in responsibility, though no improvement in the enuresis."[13]

The absence of emotional warmth in the patient is often a much more serious manifestation and more difficult to correct than the two just described.

"An eight-year-old girl . . . was adopted a year and a half before referral. After an illegitimate birth, the child was shifted about from one relative to another [and] finally . . . came to the referring foster parents. The complaints were lying and stealing. . . . When they [had] brought her home and showed her the room she was to have all for herself, . . . she showed apparently no emotional response. Yet she appeared very vivacious and 'affectionate on the surface.' After a few weeks of experience with her, the mother complained to the husband that the child did not seem able to show any affection. . . . The child was deceitful and evasive. All methods of correction were of no avail. A psychoanalyst . . . recommended that the parents stop all correction and give the child a great deal of affection. This method was tried . . . with no result. . . . However, she did well in her school subjects, in keeping with her good intelligence. She also made friends with children, though none of these were close friendships. After . . . a year and a half . . . the mother remarked, 'I have no more idea today what's going on in that child's mind than I knew the day she came. . . .' "[14]

Parental Domination. Domination by the parent may take the form of (1) a very strict, rigid regime, (2) over-ambitiousness on the part of the

[13] D. M. Levy, Primary affect hunger, *Amer. J. Psychiat.*, 1937, **94,** 644-645.
[14] *Ibid.*

parent for the child, (3) an unqualified demand for continual obedience, and (4) denying and punishing behavior on the part of the parent. The last represents a serious combination of domination and rejection.

Parents who institute a rigid regime frequently have a tendency toward compulsiveness. The over-ambitious parent is frequently disappointed in his own life and career and wants to achieve through the child what he has missed. The request for unqualified obedience stems from a need to be the dominant person in a relationship where the victim has no strength to fight back adequately. All of these attitudes may have very strong subcultural sanction. The effects on the child of parental domination depend on whether it is conveyed through cruel and harsh or relatively moderate methods. If it is relatively considerate, the effect may be a "good child." Such children "are better socialized and have more acceptable behavior than the children of submissive parents. . . . They are more interested in and have a better attitude toward work at school. On the other hand, they tend to be . . . sensitive, self-conscious. . . ."[15] The general effect of domination of the child is a destruction of his self-esteem, courage, and confidence. The following incidents in a child's life illustrate denying and punishing behavior on the part of the parent.

1. "Children in Eleanor's grade were to ask their father some question or other and report to the class next day. Eleanor remained after class to ask if she could have a question to ask her mother instead, as she couldn't talk to her father since he didn't like her to."

2. "Eleanor had been referred to an oculist. Nothing done for month of September. Eleanor told teacher her father wouldn't get her glasses because it was just an idea to make money. . . ."

3. "In the Stanford-Binet test Eleanor was very confused. She could not control her attention but talked incoherently about anything that came into her mind. She had a pronounced stutter which disappeared during the course of the examination. She said that her father used dirty words to her and slapped her all the time. . . . He didn't hit John and Betty. . . . When she was two years old, [she] was a pretty girl . . . but now she isn't pretty anymore, she says, so he doesn't like her."

4. "A few days later Eleanor told teacher father had brought presents home for them but she couldn't have hers. Mother explained later that when Eleanor hears father's car drive in she goes upstairs to bed to avoid seeing him. This particular time he called her downstairs to give her her present but not knowing what she was wanted for Eleanor called down that she was too tired. This sent the father off into a rage and he said she couldn't have hers next morning when the other two children told her there was a present for her. The mother persuaded him to give it to her three days later. . . ."

5. "Eleanor cannot speak to her father without stuttering badly. This enrages the father. She does not stutter when talking to the mother or children."[16]

[15] P. M. Symonds, *The Psychology of Parent-Child Relationships,* D. Appleton-Century Co., New York, 1939, p. 118.

[16] *Ibid.,* p. 67.

Parental Anxiety and Over-Concern. This shows itself through continuous worry and alarm over most of the child's functions when he is still an infant, particularly feeding, elimination, and the possibility of illness of any kind. The parents' fear of handling the child may lead to inadequate contact or tense, jerky movements on the part of the mother. This tenseness then gets conveyed to the infant. As the child gets older, the parental attitude manifests itself mainly through "overprotection." Maternal overprotection manifests itself mainly through excessive contact between mother and child, prolongation of infantile care, prevention of the development of independent behavior, and alternation between lack and excess of maternal control (549). The overprotection may be of the dominating or of the indulgent type. As a rule, parental overprotection makes the child dependent and infantile and fails to teach him how to meet the ordinary hazards of life. Indulgent overprotection heightens self-esteem, but the security of the individual is maintained only as long as the original situation prevails. Primarily dominating overprotection leads to loss of strength and of self-esteem. The overt result in people who were overprotected as children in this manner is submissiveness and dependency. The following case, a boy eight years old, illustrates maternal overprotection:

"*Excessive Contact:* When he was an infant, mother could never leave him for an instant. When he was two years old, she had moods of despondency because she could not get away from him. She feels worried and unhappy when patient is out of her sight. Has been sleeping with him the past six months because he has called her. . . . Mother says they are attached like Siamese twins.

"*Prolongation of Infantile Care:* Mother dresses him every day (age 8), takes him to school . . . and calls for him. . . . Breast fed 13 months. Mother fed him the first five years, . . . still goes to the bathroom with him and . . . insists on holding his hand when they walk together. . . .

"*Prevention of Independent Behavior:* He has one friend whom mother takes him to see every two weeks. Mother does not allow him to help in housework for fear he'll fall and break a dish, etc.

"*Maternal Control:* Mother must have a light burning for him until he falls asleep. He goes to bed at 10 P.M. Mother always gives in to him; does everything for him; is dominated by him. He spits at her and strikes her."[17]

Excessive Manifestations of Love. Excessive manifestations of love include constant verbal expressions of great affection and devotion, extensive hugging and kissing, and frequent giving of presents.

The consequences of "too much love" always include excessive sensual stimulation, which may be largely unconscious but leads to guilt, with its derivative manifestations, because of its incestuous aspect. It further includes over-valuation of the self, having been chosen as the parent's favorite. Other aspects depend on the manner of handling with which "too

[17] D. M. Levy, Maternal overprotection, *Psychiatry,* 1938, 1, 578-579.

much love" is combined. If the child is held too close, as in overprotection, there is conscious or unconscious rebellion against restricted freedom and the parent's unfairness. If the parent is unqualifiedly approving of everything the child does and finds excuses for all his flaws, there may be lack of restraint and of self-criticism. This leads to disciplinary problems and clashes within and without the family, in part because the child feels that the over-indulgent parent is backing him in all his clashes. If the parent idealizes the child and expects great achievements of him, there may be a strong conflict between love and gratitude toward the parent, on the one hand, and resentment of the implied demands and anticipated disapproval in case of failure to come up to expectations. Naturally, combinations of these attitudes are possible.

Sound Parent-Child Relationships. By contrast, the following case illustrates sound relationship between a child and his parents.

"His parents seem to be in agreement in all things for the boy. He is . . . encouraged to go in for athletics in which field he excels. . . . Parents attend games and thus show interest.

"In summer . . . at the seashore . . . he has his own sailboat. . . . The father is keenly interested in sailing, so he and the boy are together a great deal during the father's vacation.

"When the parents have taken trips in the past, Wilson always accompanied them. Now that he is older he does not go many places with his parents. . . . Being a football hero [he] is much sought after by girls. They all tell how quiet he is but that he seems to enjoy the fun although he can't make it. He is very fond of dancing and goes to all school and community dances and takes a girl.

"His parents show a keen interest in and sympathetic understanding of his school work. . . . They appreciate that he is not a brilliant boy. . . . However, they know . . . that he really tries very hard so they encourage him in every way possible.

"His mother told me recently that Wilson had told her he would like very much to get into more school activities such as the monthly paper, but that it was only the bright ones that could do that and still keep up their work. He also said he knew he wasn't very smart in school. His mother told him that after all he was fortunate that he could do so well in athletics and they were satisfied that he was doing his best."[18]

It should be noted that this child is not "perfect" either and that he has his problems, just as did the adult whom we characterized as "normal" (Chapter II). He has some feelings of inadequacy over his intellectual ability, and perhaps he is on the "too quiet" side in the company of his contemporaries. He may have problems when it comes to the choice of occupation. Because of his interest in intellectual achievement, he might fall in love with a girl much his superior in intelligence. The parents' harmonious, accepting, and encouraging attitudes help him in handling his difficulties. Of

[18] P. M. Symonds, *op. cit.*, pp. 63-64.

course, his relationship with them may also be put to a strain under the impact of the difficulties that may arise.

DISTURBANCES OF THE FAMILY CONSTELLATION

The Only Child. The only child is likely to be overprotected, and he is never dethroned by any later children. His parents may spoil him, make him dominating, egotistical, and, at the same time, essentially weak in his character structure. In that case he tends to be deeply hurt when he is not the center of interest and attention. Of course, all of these consequences can be prevented by intelligent handling and by having him come in contact with other children of his age early, under the guidance of adults other than his parents—e.g., in kindergarten.

Quarreling, Separation of Parents, Divorce. All such events make the child feel threatened because one of his most important sources of security—namely, reliable, loving parents—is lacking. He has further conflicts because he sides with one of the parents, is hostile toward the other, and fears retribution. In case of divorce or separation, he may blame the parent with whom he is staying for having lost the other parent. This again leads to resentment and fear of loss of love and of retribution. Further, he is apt to compare his family unfavorably with others and feel ashamed. Parents who are separated or divorced often treat their children with excessive love combined with the jealous attempt to keep them to themselves. The effect of this kind of handling is the same as has been discussed. There is further the danger of cross-identification, the boy identifying too much, even in the sexual role, with his mother. This will be discussed in further detail in the following section.

One Parent Absent; the Orphan. If one of the parents is too frequently absent over long periods of time, the child may get too much attached to the other and consider the frequently absent parent as a rival. This may lead to hostility and guilt. If the parent with whom the child stays is severe and rejecting and the frequently absent parent permissive, the child may idealize the latter, blame the other parent for the absence, and feel sorry for himself for being deprived so much of the absent parent. Less frequently, the child may feel that he lacks something that other children have—namely, the constant presence and help of both parents.

If one of the parents dies when the child is young, the child may feel deprived of a supporter, particularly in comparison with other children. This feeling may be particularly strong if the living parent is severe or is harassed by financial difficulties. The child then may feel that he has lost a protector against the world in general and against the surviving parent in particular. This leads to a strong ambivalence toward the surviving parent, who may be blamed for the death of the other parent. This may further lead to a feeling that fate is potentially against him in everything that he undertakes. If the surviving parent is over-affectionate, the attachment may become too strong, with resultant guilt feeling over more or less unconscious incestuous implications and with an undercurrent of rebellion and desire for freedom.

A nine-year-old child was brought for treatment because of unruly behavior in school and occasional stealing. He was an only child, and his father died when he was four years old. The mother was demonstratively affectionate, calling him her "boy friend" in the last two years, with a strong tendency towards overprotectiveness because of her anxieties. She often called for him at the end of the school day and persuaded him to wear rubbers if the sky was at all cloudy. The other boys started to call him a "sissy." As he soon admitted in the treatment, he also had sexual fantasies about his mother about which he felt guilty. His symptom represented a roundabout rebellion against his mother, whom he unconsciously considered the seducer and who, he also felt, was making him appear feminine and a "sissy," inferior in comparison with the other boys.

In similar situations there may be cross-identification, making for a tendency toward homosexuality. This may further be intensified by a desire to avoid similar entangling restriction of freedom by other women and by a longing for the father.

The feeling that fate is against the child may be particularly strong if both parents die when the child is relatively young or if the step-parent is harsh. The attitude toward the step-parent or foster parents is frequently characterized by a combination of two feelings: on the one hand, that the parent is not as devoted as a real parent; on the other, that there is less guilt about feelings of hostility. It should be mentioned again that none of these constellations necessarily makes for psychopathology if the parents are aware of the risks and give more affection when the child is in doubt but refrain from over-indulgence, overprotection, and domination.

THE PARENTS' MOTIVATIONS; COMPLEMENTARY REACTIONS BETWEEN PARENTS AND CHILDREN

The parents are moved by deep-seated motives when they handle their children consistently in harmful ways. The motivation for maternal overprotection is an illustration of this. Factors that influence this have been found to be the following: (1) increased maternal longing for a child—e.g., because of long periods of sterility, death of offspring, or spontaneous miscarriages; (2) sexual incompatibility—in Levy's group of twenty overprotecting mothers, 80 percent were sexually maladjusted, about double the usual figures for unselected wives, whose sexual maladjustment ranges between 30 and 50 percent (Davis, 30 percent; Hamilton, 46 percent; Terman, 33 percent; Lewenberg, 46 percent [549]); (3) limited social life in common with the mate—75 percent in Levy's, 88 percent in Lewenberg's group, contrasted with 38 percent of the unselected group; (4) privation of affection in the mother's early childhood—68 percent of forty-eight mothers in Foley's group and 80 percent of twenty mothers in Levy's group were deprived of either maternal or paternal affection, contrasted with 15 percent of forty mothers in the unselected group; (5) a good deal of responsibility—work, helping support the family—early in life; (6) thwarted ambition, 60 percent in Levy's group. The fathers of overprotected children can be generally characterized as submissive, stable husbands and providers who have little or no authoritative role in the child's life. The phrase "discipline of the child was left entirely to the mother" is used in thirteen of the twenty records.

In intricate and difficult relationships there is a complementary effect between the attitudes of the parents and those of the children. The parents' handling leads to certain reactions on the part of the child, and then the parents react to the child's behavior. Further, there are complementary disturbing reactions between the parents. This self-perpetuating state of affairs will be illustrated in the following example.

The Wife

The thirty-year-old mother came for psychoanalytic treatment because of obsessional thoughts of cutting her child's throat and the equally disturbing complaint that she was sexually frigid. It soon turned out that her husband had periods of psychoneurotic depression and suffered from premature ejaculation, and that her child had nightmares. The mother since the age of five has had strong trends toward perfectionism, first arising out of sibling rivalry (sister and brother), rivalry with her mother, and feelings of rejection. The trend became greatly intensified after her marriage as she felt that she had failed in all major functions of life: as a child because of her rivalry with her mother, as a wife because of her sexual frigidity, as a mother because of her child's symptoms, and as a person because of her symptoms and because she did not utilize her artistic talents. She had hoped that her marriage ten years earlier would remedy all her problems through the all-powerful and all-loving figure of her husband. In this expectation she was soon disappointed but repressed her resentment toward her husband, and then tried to repress her resentment toward the child, but developed, instead, her obsessional thought.

The Husband

When the patient was five years old, his father died. There was a temporary stay in an orphan asylum, and then a protracted exposure to a domineering mother. He developed the unconscious feeling that fate was against him, that no matter what he did he would not get appreciation. His wife's disappointment in him was the assumed realistic proof of this outlook. His disturbed potency was in part the consequence of his fear of intimate relations with women and in part a reaction to his wife's disappointment in him. It turned out in the course of his treatment that the most frequent cause of his depression was his wife's criticism of him and her lack of sexual gratification. To these he reacted with recurrent impairment of potency.

The Child

The child developed infantile eczema at nine months. This disappointed the mother. After he recovered, she became both over-solicitous and perfectionistic toward him. The child took over the mother's perfectionistic demands in part but also rebelled against them. Inasmuch as the parents were relatively permissive, he could express his resentment toward them, but he could not express resentment in school because of the discipline and the punishment that ensued. Hence he developed the nightmares. His aggression was shown in the course of the treatment in his drawings, which were always crowded and fairly disorganized, at first glance hardly anything except a confusion of lines. The content was telling: the school was on fire; there was a murderous battle between Japanese and American planes in which they all went up in flames.

The Interrelation Among the Three Persons

Apart from the points already mentioned, there were the following interrelations among these three persons: The mother was disappointed in the father, wanted to fulfill her life through a perfect child, and was resentful toward him because he presented problems. She further displaced the aggression she felt toward her husband, on whom she still depended, onto the relatively helpless child. The husband felt rejected and unfairly treated by his wife; this intensified and perpetuated his difficulties. This, in turn, enabled the wife to blame him for her own difficulties. He not infrequently pointed out to her that she was too demanding with the child and at times too impulsive in her punishment of him. This the wife took as a profoundly threatening criticism, a statement of failure, which reinforced her resentment toward the husband and also her perfectionistic strivings toward the child. The mother's perfectionism and disciplinary measures increased the child's resentment, leading via the school to increased anxiety. His poor work in school then increased his resentment toward and fear of the teacher. His poor work in school further alarmed the mother and made her feel that she was a failure.

In the course of several years' treatment, all of these individual and interpersonal problems and symptoms were remedied.

RELATIONSHIPS BETWEEN SIBLINGS

The relationship may be intimate, and the older sibling may support the younger one. Some element of rivalry in sibling relationships is always present and often is of an intense and protracted nature, and the older sibling may bully the younger one. There may also be sexual play.

Sibling Rivalry. The situation in which sibling rivalry is manifested most commonly and strongly is the coming of a second child who dethrones the first one. The latter, having reigned supreme in the hearts of his parents, feels neglected, and further tends to feel that he is unloved and unwanted because the new baby is in some way superior to him. Urgent demands for reassurance by the parents are often made in such instances; and it is at this time that parental thoughtfulness and affection are extremely important. The older child may turn upon the new baby. If he is young and uninhibited enough, he may actually attempt to hurt the baby. The parents' disapproval creates feelings of guilt and fear of retribution and of abandonment. He may then inhibit these attempts and instead develop anxieties, enuresis, and moodiness. These symptoms may be present even with the continuation of expressions of hostility.

Sibling rivalry with all its effects may become more harmful because the parents prefer one child (favoritism). Damage to self-esteem is greater in such cases, self-confidence and self-esteem are deeply undermined, and a feeling of rejection is created.

Order of Birth. The relationship between siblings as well as its effects on character formation is influenced by the order of the births. Thus the oldest child who is dethroned by the birth of a second child is likely to fight to regain his former favored position and to look back nostalgically upon the period when he reigned supreme. He is likely to become the leader of the younger siblings, to have fear of authority and at the same time to fear encroachments upon his own authority from below. The bullying sibling is usually the oldest child. This behavior in part compensates him for his loss, and it is also a fusion of resentment toward the younger siblings with the displacement to weaker victims of his resentment toward the parents.

The second child may be expected to follow the older child and to duplicate his achievements and be constantly compared with him. He may come to feel that he is not so good as others and become either discouraged or rebelliously striving. At the same time, his status in turn may be encroached upon by still younger siblings. In handling the second child, the parents may be more relaxed than with the first child and may no longer expect to produce the "perfect" child. This child may be less concerned with authority, responsibility, and absolute power and be more competitive with his peers.

The youngest child is, in some respects, in a similar position to that of the only child. He is frequently the pet of the whole family, and he is never replaced. Thus he may develop too high a self-evaluation. On the other hand, the youngest child may come into a family which is no longer oriented toward infants and their needs and be considered a nuisance. He is constantly confronted by people who have more rights and privileges because of greater maturity and is apt to feel envious and have a strong desire to grow up himself in order to obtain the same privileges; or he may become too anxious and submissive.

Sexual seduction, as a rule, is initiated by the older sibling. It may be hetero- or homosexual, and, in the middle class, it usually takes place before puberty and is more or less of the exploratory type. It is usually the younger sibling who feels more guilty about it and who therefore stops the activity. At other times he may find this the only affectionate aspect of the relationship with the otherwise bullying sibling. It creates guilt then, too, but in addition creates a tendency for sexual submissiveness, hetero- or homosexual as the case may be.

The effects of position in the family are not, of course, identical for all people having the same position. These are general tendencies, but it is necessary to understand each person individually along with the particular set of circumstances he had to deal with and his own particular ways of dealing with them. This is true not only as regards order of birth but as regards all the other factors discussed.

Relationship with school, playmates, and subcultural groups may be equally important for the development of pathology. They are discussed at other places in the book. (See Chapters XII and XXI.)

SUGGESTED READINGS

The original impulse which led to investigation of the subjects discussed in this chapter came from Freud (304, 308); Adler (11) later supplied additions. The experimental work by D. M. Levy, especially on sibling rivalry (544) and maternal overprotection (549), is particularly recommended, as is that by Bender, Keiser, and Schilder on aggression (71). A good summing up is given in one of Symonds' books (920). Halverson's article (379) should also be consulted. The most interesting reading on this subject is *The Happy Family,* by Levy and Munroe (552). The summary of Fries's work by Malcove (319) is also recommended. An amusing and instructive article is Shipman's "How to make your son a misfit" in the *American Mercury,* 1938, 43, 283-288. Pearson (726) is an excellent clinical book on the subject. Piaget's works (733-735) are experimental classics. An excellent but complex book is Schilder's *The Image and Appearance of the Human Body* (830).

XII Group Psychogenic Factors: Cultural Factors in Psychopathology

All of the individual's strivings, the manner of their fulfillment, his conflicts, are intricately intertwined with culture. By "culture" we mean relationships with other individuals, with prevailing attitudes in the group, with the actual realities of natural and man-made arrangements. In speaking of culture, we make an abstraction such as we made in discussing genogenic, chemogenic, and psychogenic aspects. There is only one *experience* for the individual; out of this, for purposes of investigation, we can separate various aspects. It is more correct to speak of variables than of separate forces.

HOW THE CULTURAL FACTORS MAY AFFECT PERSONALITY

RELATIONSHIP TO GENOGENIC, HISTOGENIC, AND CHEMOGENIC FACTORS

So far, no definite differences in psychological potentialities have been established between various ethnic groups. Various cultures favor the development of individuals in different directions. Apparently the majority of the individuals in all groups are malleable enough to adapt to these requirements, but others, possibly in part on the basis of genetic constitution, are not. This may then result in deviant behavior or in psychopathology. Among the Zuñis, ambition is frowned upon and, if persisted in, used to be very severely punished. The man exhibiting this trait and having success was apt to be sentenced to be hung by his thumbs. He became crippled, and often, if left suspended long enough, he died.

The operation of histo- and chemogenic factors as affected by culture is illustrated by the increase in injuries because of automobile accidents. The head injuries lead to immediate psychiatric manifestations, some of which are permanent or are followed by symptoms of traumatic neurosis.

The prevalence of certain infectious diseases—e.g., syphilis—leads to specific organic psychoses. The extent to which such infections spread naturally depends on the prevalent rules of conduct, the institutions—e.g., prostitution, promiscuity—and the general level of education. The effects of the infection further depend on the development of science in the group; with the availability of effective chemicals and methods of treatment, the organic disability can be prevented. Some further points will be added to this in the section on the effects of social disorganization.

PATTERNS OF CULTURE AND THE INDIVIDUAL

The culture largely determines the type of situation in which the individual runs into conflicts and frustration and what ameliorative devices he can use. He will be able to function with comfort and will not break down psychologically if he lives under circumstances compatible with physiological well-being, and if he can measure up, essentially, to the ideals held by him and by others on whom his self-approval depends.

Stresses which are incompatible with such comfort come from two sources: (1) The individual may be exposed to hardships in childhood or adulthood which are faced in common by most others in his group but which are particularly intense for him. Every adult employee has to accept the leadership of his superior; but if the superior is extremely harsh and unappreciative, the employee may buckle under the strain. The stress is particularly hard to bear if other members of the group are entirely free from it. (2) Widespread social conditions—economic depression, unemployment, war—may hit the individual very hard, but many others may be hit just as hard. The effects of such universally felt pressure may be different from those resulting from pressure on some individuals but not on others. Thus one's self-esteem will not be hurt as much by a financial failure if all one's friends have also failed.

Before discussing our own culture, the nature of the interrelation between the individual's strivings and his environment will best be illustrated by an example from Bali. This cultural group has been studied by observation, by interview, and by documentary movies (52).

The relationship between adults, particularly the mother, and the child is characterized by stimulating the child's emotional activity without permitting a climax. The child, flirted with or aggressively teased to a high pitch of affection or rage, is suddenly ignored. The adult goes into an absent-minded state of "awayness" and is completely heedless of the child, even though he is in a howling tantrum. Sibling rivalry is intense and overt. After the "breast baby" becomes the "knee baby," he tries violently to distract his mother and to act out his hatred and resentment of the new baby. The mother usually chooses to pay special attention to the new baby after she has aroused the older child by affectionate flirtation. The latter finally turns for consolation to the father, who plays with him, cuddles him, and sometimes even suckles him a little. At about four or five the child becomes seclusive, brooding, and sullen; he withdraws into a detached state of "awayness."

The adult Balinese give the impression of being emotionally distant, never quite letting go in a positive or negative direction except on institutionalized occasions, as at a funeral, and are highly formalized in their behavior. "Courtship either for marriage or for a love affair, is a matter of glances and a few stolen words, and the romantic excitement steadily dies down after the first encounter. Once married, a Balinese husband finds that the girl he has married does indeed act like his mother—for she knows no other pattern of personal relationship. His brief unreal ardor cools and he counts himself lucky if he begets children."[1]

We will now quote a description of the witch play, one of the common Balinese dramatic presentations, which "not only expresses the residue in the adults of what they experienced as children, but is also watched by children and shapes their reading of the experiences to which they are subjected daily." The witch is angry at a kind, and trains her disciples to harass the land. The kind sends a dragon to fight the witch. "Followers of the Dragon, armed with krisses, enter and approach the Witch ready to attack her. But she waves her magic cloth—the cloth baby sling—and after each attack they crouch down before her, magically cowed. Finally they rush upon her in pairs, stabbing ineffectively at the Witch who has become a limp bundle in their tense arms. She is uninvolved and offers no resistance, but one by one they fall on the ground in deep trance, some limp, some rigid. From this trance they are aroused by the Dragon. . . . Now, able to move again but not returned to normal consciousness, they move about in a somnambulistic state, turning their daggers which were powerless against the Witch, against their own breasts, fixing them against a spot which is said to itch unbearably."[2] The trance is a mixture of agony and ecstasy. Some men actually fall backward onto the ground with an extreme backward bending of the trunk, and lie on the ground writhing in some sort of orgastic climax.

Balinese of all ages readily enter a trance, especially by means of a device which consists of two rods with a connecting string, to which the person holds. One rod is then pounded up and down rhythmically and the vibration transmitted through the string.

This illustration, to which we will add some other information later, shows the following points: (1) There are certain characteristic general features and patterns of reaction recognizable in nearly all individuals of a society—e.g., the emotional distance, the not letting go, as a rule, in either a positive or a negative direction. (2) Certain relationships can be seen between experiences in childhood and behavior in adulthood, particularly if one also utilizes folklore and artistic productions: in Bali the constant teasing of the child, followed by constant frustration, finally leads to the sullen, seclusive, and brooding withdrawal into a detached state of "awayness," which latter has always characterized the adult's, most frequently the

[1] G. Bateson and M. Mead, *Balinese Character: A Photographic Analysis*, Special Publications of the N.Y. Acad. Sci., Vol. II, New York, 1942, p. 37.

[2] *Ibid.*, pp. 34-35.

mother's, behavior at the crucial time of frustration. This is the point of development of the persistent emotional distance of the individual. The trance, which apparently occurs regularly in the festive drama, is readily entered into by the Balinese on other, "private occasions." The drama gives some clues about the various roles trance may play in their emotional lives. The witch apparently represents the mother (her "magic cloth" is the cloth baby sling); she is attacked by the followers (the children) of the dragon (i.e., the father, to whom the child turned after his final disappointment in the mother). Apparently, then, the trance represents aggression turned toward oneself (they turn their daggers against their own breasts), finding emotional solace in withdrawal from the world and preoccupation with oneself, and also attaining in a thinly disguised form gratification of sexual and aggressive impulses (writhing in some sort of orgastic climax). We may assume from this that the "private trance" plays some similar role in the daily life of the Balinese. (3) There is a double relationship between the experience in childhood on the one hand and the adult personality on the other. The childhood experience fosters a certain type of personality development, and then the adult, with this crystallized personality and attitudes, continues to treat the child in such a manner as to perpetuate the same personality. A similar relationship may be assumed between the individual's attitudes and those of persons around him. His own detachment fosters a similar behavior in those around him, and vice versa. If he breaks out of his shell, he returns into it again through early rebuff or frustration. (4) States of trance in our culture would unquestionably have to be considered pathological. Can we view the Balinese trance as such? It is impossible to answer this question unequivocally. Apparently in the Balinese culture the trance is an accepted form of emotional experience and, let us add, a conflict solution including such mechanisms as withdrawal, substitution, compromise formation, and partial gratification. Perhaps, as with the consumption of alcoholic beverages in our society, the question whether one would call the trance pathological may be one of quantity. As a rule, it obviously does not have the same intensity of conflict and frustration and does not represent the same (individual) desperate solution that such deviant behavior would in our society. It is in the direction of escape, of abandoning mastery and integration, and therefore is *in the direction* of pathology. (5) Various cultures disapprove and endow with danger certain physiological and emotional strivings, allow others without much regulation, and definitely stimulate still others. Some strivings it both stimulates and inhibits. Among the Balinese, urination is entirely unregulated, and the act may be performed in the presence of anyone. On the other hand, the bowel training of children starts very early, and the act must be performed in private. Eating, particularly of solids, under certain circumstances is considered dangerous. While genital activity in childhood is not completely free, the Balinese adults often tug playfully at the boys' genitals. On the other hand, the genital interest, as well as the affectionate interest and the resentment aroused in the child by the mother, gets frustrated. Sibling rivalry, hostility, and desire for affection are constantly stimulated by the mother, only to be met by distance and by being ignored ("awayness") after it occurs. Thus, as regards these strivings, a conflict is set up very early which through further reinforcement and through internal and external circles persists throughout life. The interest in manners, rituals, art, and, as mentioned, trancelike states is, on the other hand, stimulated and, as it were, offered by the culture as a substitute way of problem solution. We may add here that in the main the Balinese evaluates the environment as potentially frustrating, particularly as regards affection and sexual satisfaction, and anticipates rejection in the face of mounting tension as a retribution for open aggression. He evaluates himself as helpless in the face of this threat, with subsequent withdrawal, self-centeredness, and self-sufficiency.

THE EFFECT OF FOOD SUPPLY AND TECHNOLOGY ON PERSONALITY

Different cultures solve the same problems differently; therefore there is no one-to-one correlation between problem and culture patterns. Some cultures—e.g., the Marquesans—faced with the problem of food shortage, store food, use magic, overvalue eating, and practice cannibalism. Others do not. One notable example is India. Another result of food anxiety is resentment toward the child who eats the food the adult would otherwise have for himself.

The following study illustrates the effect of technological changes, with their economic consequences and laws, on the aggression and anxiety of the individual, as expressed in myths, institutions, and beliefs (483).

Two societies, Tanala and Betsileo, originally had practiced dry rice cultivation, which gradually exhausted the land and necessitated periodic moving from one area to another. Then Betsileo changed to wet rice cultivation, which did not exhaust the land. This made individual land ownership possible. Following this change, power was consolidated in the person of the king, who allotted land for use to certain individuals (nobles), who could then rent it out to tenant farmers. The king could reclaim the land at will. Thus a true feudal system, involving oppression and poverty, was set up in contrast to the democratic societal structure in Tanala. This resulted in economic insecurity in the members of the society, which, in turn, caused increased anxiety and aggression. The increased aggression led to fears of retaliation. These changes in Betsileo are expressed in several ways. One is the increased amount of malevolent sorcery practiced and the suspicion that everyone practices it. Any act of aggression is expected to be retaliated for in kind. Thus it is believed that, if a man strikes a snake and the snake becomes ill, the man will become ill; if it dies, he will die. The levirate (the practice of the brother of the deceased marrying his widow), which is practiced in Tanala, is not practiced in Betsileo because, if a man were to marry his brother's widow, he would be suspected of having murdured him.

PROBLEMS PRESENTED BY OUR CULTURE

Before proceeding to present the problems for the individual inherent in our culture, the following additional points have to be made:

1. Even relatively simple cultures, as the Balinese, are not entirely homogeneous. For example, in some of the villages everybody has had trances, but in other villages no inhabitant has had trances, although they have all seen them. Geographic differences are much greater in such a complex culture as ours.

2. Closely allied to the previous point are (a) the problems of minority groups, which have in part their own "subculture," with its characteristic conflicts, but in addition may be exposed to the prejudices of the larger part of the population; (b) differences in the problems connected with economic and social status.

3. The insecurities and the compensatory aspects of the culture are partly institutionalized and represent various degrees of reality situations to the individual. Economically exploiting institutions, such as excessive rent, low wages, uncertainty of employment, obviously make for anxiety for the individuals when there are no restitutive measures. Some institutionalized remedial measures may relieve the individual but arouse anxiety in others and ultimately in himself. Thus, a Kwakiutl chief attributes death in his family, according to group belief, to somebody's evil magic and takes it as an "insult"; he then reëstablishes his prestige and self-esteem by committing a murder in revenge. This very likely leads to an unconscious fear in him, with which he then further has to cope by reinforcing his status.

STRESSES OF OUR CULTURE

The American family is "small"; it consists only of parents and children. As a result, the child must of necessity seek to satisfy his most important emotional and bodily needs—the need for affection, protection, dependence, food, ideals, etc.—within the confines of this narrow family (483). Along with this emphasis on the narrow family, there is the attitude that others are potentially unreliable. This further tends to turn the individual toward his own family in seeking gratifications. To mention one contrast, among the Zuñis every adult treats any child as if it were his own; the resultant attitudes toward family members and others are, of course, widely different from those in our culture. With us, because the parents are a child's exclusive protectors, their stature becomes greatly magnified; hence any resentment toward them is particularly dangerous and contemptible, and the rivalry with other siblings for parental favors intense. The bodily urges which seek gratification are stimulated in the close confines of the family, and are forced further in that direction by the injunction against gratifying them anywhere. The child's sexual desires, for example, thus become directed toward the parents or siblings; but, since gratification at that source is taboo, this affords another source of fear, guilt, and conflict (483).

Contradictory demands are made of the child and the adult as far as emotions and ideals are concerned. The two most significant demands—for obedience and self-assertion—are raised to the level of ideals. Adequate adaptation to them is possible if the process of obedience does not destroy the child's self-esteem, self-confidence, and feeling of being loved. If these are seriously damaged, his need for dependence becomes intensified. The two impulses are contradictory, and they form the basis of one of the conflicts most characteristic of psychopathological reactions in our society. Rivalry, ambition, and the striving to surpass others in achievement or in wealth are strongly accented throughout life. This may lead to a double conflict: on the one hand, to the constant fear of being surpassed, which in turn may lead to further intensification of the competitive strivings or to a submissive orientation because of the giving up of opposition against stronger individuals in the hope of gaining support from them; on the other hand, to conflict with the ideals of coöperation and fairness. These conflicts are closely fused with those of obedience and self-assertion. A large part of these strivings may be unconscious.

Another demand calls for the suppression of certain bodily urges aiming at gratification, by threatening injury, disapproval, and condemnation if they are not suppressed. As with the hostile impulses, this may result in self-condemnation and guilt. The restriction is not only direct; it manifests itself also in indirect ways—e.g., in not naming the organ or discussing such pleasures (483). The arousal of guilt, while probably a spontaneous tendency in the human being under certain circumstances, is undoubtedly very much intensified and fostered in parent-child and adult-to-adult relationships in our civilization. If a child behaved in the manner exhibited by the jealous and aggressive Balinese child, the main method of handling in our civilization would be, not studied indifference, but punishment, humiliation, and particularly moral condemnation, with consequent arousal of guilt. The anthropologists often speak of our culture as a particularly guilt-ridden civilization. The two strivings which in the main lead to feelings of guilt are the sexual and the hostile. These strivings, as well as the guilt, may be in large part unconscious.

The child thus has constant bodily urges which he is forbidden to gratify. Later in life, however, the individual is expected to exercise the very function which has always been forbidden. He can do so only if the circumstances are not too adverse and if his security, self-esteem, and confidence have not been seriously damaged. Otherwise he may feel a serious reaction of guilt, a fear of disapproval, and a feeling of helplessness. It is for this reason that genital activity and the emotional relationships surrounding sex are the field in which psychopathological disturbances frequently occur or through which they manifest themselves. The relatively superior evaluation of the male and of masculinity adds further to the stresses connected with sex. The woman may feel inferior both anatomically and emotionally, and this leads to envy of the male, to hostility toward him, and to fear of the superior being. This is apt to be intensified by the relatively greater educational restriction of girls as regards self-assertion and sexual freedom, and by the realistic difficulties some women experience in obtaining a job or getting advancement in certain professions. Her feelings may lead the man to fear her because of her hostility toward him.

Another set of contradictory influences leading to frustration is in the economic field. Everyone is urged to get rich, both through accent on economic ambition and more indirectly through advertisements, stories, and movies; but, obviously, this is possible for only a few people. Self-esteem, prestige, and security become involved in these desires. As the individual grows up, he finds that the people who have the desired things are more respected and admired. Such conflicts prepare the soil for psychopathology or create situations involving frustration to a degree beyond the individual's power to cope with it.

The case discussed in Chapter I illustrates the role of cultural factors in psychopathological reactions. The father's death and the mother's emotional distance from the patient were particularly important because the only two individuals from whom she could expect full affection, protection, and satisfaction of her bodily needs were her parents. The patient's attitude toward her work also shows the influence of cultural factors. Ambition, achievement, and competition are highly valued in our society. Consequently, success in her work could have considerable compensating and consoling value, and could be substituted for what she missed in relationships with people. Because of this aspect of her work and her fear of competition and rivalry, she felt secure only if the perfection of her work could not possibly be challenged.

By and large, our society is characterized by a great deal of social, economic, and geographic mobility. It is perhaps the most mobile society developed so far, although economic mobility has considerably lessened since the passing of the frontier days. This mobility has a double aspect: on the one hand, it helps to foster unattainable goals in individuals, leading to later disappointment; also, with the great accent on individuality and geographic mobility, the person's feelings of loneliness and isolation are more easily aroused. But this is far outweighed in the positive direction by both the actual possibility and the hope of getting out of a situation in which the individual may at first have felt trapped and helpless. It further enables the individual to find his own niche away from the repressive, rejecting, frustrating, and condemning group. Further, the general setup allows a considerable degree of emotional closeness and affection and physiological satisfaction. It also allows a great deal of self-assertion, self-expression, and achievement. These can give the individual direct reinforcement and also allow for a great deal of consolation and substitute gratification.

EXPERIMENTAL STUDIES

The complex psychodynamics of the individual's relationship with the cultural mores as he encounters them in most of his contacts as well as in his family cannot be experimentally duplicated. However, certain aspects of them can be singled out for such investigation (562).

In a series of experiments, boys' clubs were formed to do handicraft work under the leadership of older men. The leader of the "autocratic" group told the boys what to do; he dictated activities step by step so that the boys never knew what the next step was. He arbitrarily assigned a work task and companion to each boy. He alone praised or criticized each boy's work, and in this he was personal; otherwise he remained aloof from the group—not actively hostile, but rather impersonal.

In the "democratic" group, all the policies were a matter of group discussion and decision, and the general steps to the group goal were outlined in advance. The division of tasks was left to the group, and each boy could choose his work companion. The group leader was objective or "fact-minded" in his praise and criticism; he tried to be a regular group member without, however, doing too much of the boys' work for them.

In the "laissez-faire" group, there was complete freedom for group or individual decision without leader participation. The leader was available to supply materials or information when asked, but he took no part in discussions. He commented infrequently on activities unless questioned, and made no efforts to participate in or interfere with activities.

The factor of personality differences in the boys was controlled by having each group work under various social conditions—democracy and then autocracy, etc. The results were the following:

In one experiment, expressions of hostility were thirty times as frequent in the autocratic as in the democratic group, and acts of aggression were eight times as frequent. Many of the latter were directed toward two successive "scapegoats" in the group; none were directed toward the autocratic leader.

In another experiment, one of five autocratic groups showed the same aggressive reaction as was found in the first experiment. The boys in the other four autocracies showed an extremely nonaggressive, "apathetic" pattern of behavior.

Other results were as follows: (1) A change from democracy to autocracy caused an increase in dominating behavior; a change from autocracy to democracy caused a decrease. (2) When "I"-involved types of language—e.g., hostility, resistance, demands for attention, hostile criticism, expressions of competition—were counted, 73 percent of the language in the authoritarian group was of this type, as compared with 31 percent for the democratic group. (3) There was more ascendant, dominating behavior and less objectivity toward one another in the autocratic group. (4) The democratic group was more constructive. This was revealed in its superior work as compared with the careless and unfinished work of the autocratic group. (5) There was a greater feeling of "we-ness" in the democratic group. The "I" feeling predominated in the autocratic group.

Four types of evidence showed that the lack of aggression in the apathetic group was caused not by absence of frustration but by the repressive influence of the autocrat: (1) The outburst of aggression when transferred to a freer atmosphere which showed the bottled-up tension that the boys felt. (2) A sharp rise in aggression when the leader left the room. In the apathetic autocratic atmosphere it rose to ten times its former level; the boys' work also deteriorated. (3) Other indications of generalized apathy, such as absence of smiling and joking. (4) The fact that nineteen out of twenty boys liked their democratic leader better than their autocratic leader, and seven out of ten liked their laissez-faire leader better than their autocratic leader.

The relative determining value of the deliberately created social atmosphere, as compared with that of either the personality make-up of the group or the personality of the adult leader, is apparent in the fact that there was a moderate amount of aggression in the democracy and an abnormally small amount in the apathetic autocracy, regardless of the leader's personality or of the group's personnel. When the boys were transferred to a new atmosphere and a new leader, they changed markedly. For example, in the laissez-faire atmosphere aggression was very high, although different groups and different leaders were involved. One form of overt aggression was manifested in out-group hostility. In the democracy this took the form of wars fought in a spirit of fun between clubs which met in the same room, whereas in the autocracy it took a different form—strikes, rebellious acts, reciprocal aggression between members of the group, and scapegoat attacks, which usually occurred as release behavior after a decrease in leader pressure. In the transfer from the autocratic to the democratic group there was a decrease in the dominating behavior of autocratic members, and vice versa.

Such experiments show clearly the influence of the social milieu, even when the role of individual personalities is experimentally controlled. They should help toward an understanding of the role of social determinants in the etiology of psychopathology.

THE RELATIONSHIP BETWEEN PSYCHOPATHOLOGY AND SOCIAL DISORGANIZATION

PATHOGENIC EFFECT OF UNEMPLOYMENT

In discussing the effect of unemployment, Lazarsfeld (530) and Eisenberg (234) speak of three basic attitudes, the *unbroken*, the *distressed*, and the *broken*. The unbroken are the unresigned individuals who maintain their morale though not content with their situation. The distressed are those who fluctuate markedly between acts of aggression or rage and despair, resignation, or escapism. The broken individuals are the resigned, apathetic people who have lost hope and interest in life and adapt themselves to an extremely restricted way of living, with a very low level of aspiration.

These attitudes are related both to the individual's present situation and to his personality make-up. Obviously, the most important among the first group of determinants is the length of unemployment. As unemployment continues, the individual tends to proceed from an unbroken attitude to a distressed and finally to a broken attitude. But his personality, including his particular system of values—both, of course, products of his life history—will be important in determining pathogenic effects. For instance, the unemployed neurotic person may deteriorate almost immediately, whereas the healthier individual may be able to feel unthreatened and retain his strength and his feeling of being accepted over a long period, so that, if a job is offered, he is fit to take it. Differential values for various groups in our society also play a part in this. For example, it is still generally considered to be the man's role to earn a living and support his family, whereas the woman's place is in the home. Consequently, it is not surprising to find that men deteriorate more rapidly with unemployment than do women.

The loss of morale in the unemployed cannot be said to be due to sheer deprivation—restriction in food, clothing, and shelter—because, when these needs are satisfied, as when the individual receives relief or is supported by his relatives, he may still become demoralized. Rather this is a question of frustration in the sense of threat to his self-evaluation and his sense of security. The unemployed person usually expresses this in terms of the loss of social standing in his own eyes and in those of others. In our society an individual's worth is judged largely by the position he holds; when he loses this, he loses practically every claim to social status. These values are so strong that, even if an entire community becomes unemployed, every member of it may lose morale and feel ashamed of his condition. This was adequately demonstrated in an investigation of Marianthal, an Austrian town which depended for its livelihood on a textile mill. When the mill shut down, everyone was unemployed. All the people suffered consequent deterioration even though they were *all* unemployed and it was clear that their condition was not due to their own inadequacies.

The desire to maintain respectability and social status is apparent in various ways (except in those who have been "broken"). It can be seen in the efforts of the unemployed to dress as well as possible in order to hide their actual status. Casual observation of their homes frequently reveals signs of former glory—perhaps a carefully preserved party gown, a vase, or possibly an old car constantly taken care of to keep it going.

If the unemployed did not retain the values put on prestige and status, the likelihood is, of course, that they would not become demoralized. For instance, Dollard (214) has shown that lower-class Negroes in the South, who have never had any hope of advancement, consequently give up trying, and therefore seem to suffer little from a low social status that is ruinous to other people. By maintaining values that cannot be achieved, the individual puts himself into a conflict situation for which he can find no solution. Breakdown ensues sooner or later unless he achieves his values by securing a job or by changing his values. For example, the person's self-esteem may be saved if he realizes clearly that his unemployment is not his fault, but the result of a defect in the total institutional system. He may sustain his feeling of security by working with others in an organized effort to obtain jobs, to have remedial laws passed, or even to reconstruct society to eliminate unemployment altogether. (See also 346.)

AUTHORITARIAN EDUCATION

It is unquestionably true that one of the primary aims in education is to make the child a willing, moral, law-respecting member of his society, and that discipline and social training are therefore necessary. But more than this is necessary. His education must enable him to feel secure and independent as an adult. This is obviously impossible if the discipline is so rigorous that it endangers the child's self-esteem and independence.

"The headmaster [was] a tight-lipped sallow-complexioned old fundamentalist. . . . Gaunt, his face a mask of deep wrinkles, . . . he inspired me with so much more terror than respect that I still see his ghost at times. . . . Not once in all those years did I see his face soften into a smile. . . . His conception of his task was not to guide and shepherd, but to correct a crowd of hopelessly bad children who were inclined from birth—as that lovely Catechism specified—'to do evil and hate God.' . . .

". . . The instilling was frequently done . . . with the aid of a brass-edged ruler of ebony wood. . . . Upon the slightest provocation: a mere whisper in the classroom or a giggle, he advanced upon you without a word, seized hold of your wrist, and brought down his stick on your knuckles, not in anger, but with calm deliberation. If you wept in pain and humiliation, . . . he locked you up for the rest of the day in a small dark room where the coal was kept and which swarmed with rats and mice."[3]

EFFECTS OF SOCIO-ECONOMIC CONDITIONS

THE WORK OF THE CHICAGO SCHOOL OF SOCIOLOGISTS

A long series of intensive sociological studies of the city of Chicago have indicated many correlations between various indices of social pathology and urban areas.

[3] Pierre van Paassen, *Days of Our Years,* Hillman-Curl, New York, 1939, pp. 5-6.

Generally, the city was found to be organized in a concentric zone pattern. Zone 1 was the amusement and bright-light area, and here were found the hoboes, the prostitutes, the drug addicts, and other people without financial or home stability; Zone 2 was the slum area; Zone 3 contained inexpensive private residences, and Zone 4 the more expensive private residences; Zone 5 was the zone of the commuters and wealthier people in general. Extremely high correlations were found between these zones and the incidence of juvenile delinquency, tuberculosis, venereal disease, drug addiction, crimes, vices, and other indices of social disorganization or pathology. In every case the highest percentage occurred in Zone 1, the next highest in Zone 2, and so on, with the lowest percentage in Zone 5.

This kind of data indicates that a section of a city has a character of its own which, at least from a statistical point of view, is independent of the individual characterists of the people who move into and out of it. This is substantiated by such findings as the following:

The social-pathological statistics for a city area remain roughly the same over a long period of years, in spite of the fact that different waves of immigration pass through it. In one case, for instance, five different national groups successively occupied one section; yet the statistics for that area remained the same. As each national group moved out of the area and into another, it took on the characteristics of the new area. Thus an immigrant group in which crime was absent became criminal when it moved into an area with a high crime rate, but ceased being criminal when it moved into a noncriminal area. Another equally important fact is that a differential study of the Negro group in Chicago shows that the Negroes living in Zone 1 show the characteristics of this zone, whereas those living in Zone 2 and Zone 3 show respectively the characteristics of those zones.

THE FARIS AND DUNHAM STUDY

Faris and Dunham (259) have recently reported the results of their sociological study of mental disease in Chicago. This brilliant study shows clearly the relation between mental disease and urban areas.

The figures on the occurrence of mental disease in general indicate the same pattern of distribution shown in earlier studies for poverty, unemployment, juvenile delinquency, adult criminality, suicide, family desertion, infant mortality, communicable diseases, and general mortality. That is, there is a regular decrease from the center to the periphery of the city. Further analyses of the same sort were then made for specific categories of mental disease. Schizophrenia in general showed the "typical" distribution pattern of mental disease as a whole; but analysis of the main forms of schizophrenia brought out some differences. For example, the rate of incidence of paranoid schizophrenia was highest in the rooming-house district; that of catatonic schizophrenia, in first-generation immigrant neighborhoods. In general, catatonic schizophrenia is correlated as perfectly with the zone pattern of the city as is the paranoid form. The same typical correlations with the zones of the city (with minor variations) were also found for alcoholic psychoses, senile psychoses, and drug addiction. The distribution of manic-depressive psychosis was completely different. This showed practically no correlation with city zones, indicating that, while schizophrenia is a poor man's disease, manic depression strikes rich and poor impartially.

Such data as these, of course, do not *prove* any causal relations between mental disease and socio-economic factors, but indicate only that they are correlated. Nor do they necessarily prove that heredity has nothing to do with schizophrenia; they indicate only that the same underlying factors that give rise to poverty, crime, and disease also give rise to all the mental diseases studied by Faris and Dunham, with the notable exception of manic-depressive reactions. The only hypothesis that Faris and Dunham allow themselves to formulate is suggested by the extremely high relationship between paranoid schizophrenia and social isolation.

It is generally conceded by psychiatrists that schizophrenia is usually a withdrawing from the environment or a loss of contact with it. Faris and Dunham point out that this withdrawing may be forced upon the individual by social conditions. They postulate three steps: (1) the normal sociability characteristic of the child; (2) the rejection of this sociability or the lack of opportunity to express it, as when one lives in an area where one has no friends; (3) the giving up and withdrawal. Paranoid schizophrenia was found in tremendously high percentages in the hobo sections and in those rooming-house areas where friendless bachelors lived alone in tiny hall bedrooms. Opportunities for social communication are undoubtedly necessary for normal psychological and social development, and it is obvious that an unfavorable social environment might mean the withdrawal of such opportunities. Without doubt, mental diseases appear to be more prevalent where the population is mobile and heterogeneous than where it is stable and homogeneous, and where life conditions are complex and precarious rather than simple and secure. In this connection Plant's finding (736) that high mobility—i.e., much moving from place to place—is correlated with insecurity in children is of interest. The higher incidence of schizophrenia in the respective urban areas may also be facilitated by the tendency of individual schizophrenics, as well as of families with several schizophrenic members, to move down in the social scale.

SUBCULTURAL CONFLICT

We have described the general conflicts to which most members of a culture are apt to be exposed. We have also mentioned that the culture is not something homogeneous but represents groups with predominant orientations that clash with those of other groups. The individual who is exposed to such clashing trends may then have stresses of a characteristic kind. These subcultural groups in the United States may be immigrant groups or native ones.

CONFLICTS IN IMMIGRANT GROUPS

One subcultural group is represented by the second-generation immigrant child who has the problem of adjusting to two cultures simultaneously. He may be partially identifying himself with both of them, or he may want to identify himself with the new one but be under pressure from the old one. The second type of problem arises when, for example, according to the mores of the immigrant group, the parent is strict and restrictive. The son may then feel very resentful toward the father, whom he considers tyrannical, and may strongly sympathize with and be emotionally attached to the mother whom he considers victimized by the father. With girls, the conflict may arise over excessive parental restriction—e.g., having to be home early and not being allowed to go out with boys at an age when most girls in the environment have freedom of choice in these matters. The resentment toward and fear of either or both of the parents is intense and is at times solved in one of two ways: through "delinquent" behavior, representing open rebellion, or through neurosis with anxiety features, representing fear of retribution from the parents. If the individual is inclined to identify with the new environment and has no fear of the old, he may feel both insecure and inferior because of his peculiar status. He frequently becomes greatly ashamed of his family background and the folkways associated with it and may feel that everyone is laughing or sneering at him. He is generally ambitious, strives hard to achieve the superior status of the American who is completely at home in his own country.

CONFLICTS CONNECTED WITH EXPOSURE TO CLASHING MORAL STANDARDS

The study concerns fifteen men who lived in a suburb of northeast Washington. With one exception the economic status was low, with constant friction at home and alcoholism in one or both parents. When the boys were about ten years of age, some of them, playing around a slaughterhouse and barns, were initiated into bestiality, and some were also seduced into homosexual practices. Some of these boys were part of a ring which was not dissolved until they were nearing the age of twenty.

Near the same community was a Pentecostal Church where emotional revivals were frequently conducted. Some of the boys attended regularly, entering violently into the experience of conversion. After such experiences, the boys present promised each other to give up their perversions. Only a little later, however, as their sexual appetites mounted, and following the merciless taunts of two neighborhood bullies who were the offspring of antireligious parents and thus outside the influence of the revivals, these resolves were shattered. Every broken resolve led to feelings of guilt, which increased with time, so that in later adolescence the boys were almost continually miserable. They quit school, did odd jobs, or "mooned about" in their misery.

Five of the seven boys who participated in both the perversions and the revivals were later committed to a psychopathic hospital. One of the remaining two died on the streets of the city either in a depression complicated by alcoholism or in a psychotic stupor. The other one participated in bestiality only during the earlier years, went to church only socially, and so attended very few of the revivals. Five boys of the group of fifteen entered into the sexual perversions without suffering subsequent commitment to a mental hospital. Two of these were the ringleaders. One of the five attended the revivals frequently, but only at his mother's behest. The other boys were exposed only to the perverted practices (four) or only to the revivals (one) or to neither (three) and met the other boys through other activities.[4]

CONFLICTS CONNECTED WITH SOCIO-ECONOMIC AND OCCUPATIONAL POSITION

The prevalent tendency is to divide American society into six classes: upper-upper, lower-upper, upper-middle, lower-middle, upper-lower, and lower-lower. These may be determined in one of two ways. The first is by rating the type of house and the neighborhood a person lives in, the source of his income, and his occupation. The second is by having several persons give information about community members as regards their class membership, their reputations for engaging in activities, possessing certain traits, and belonging to institutions which are considered superior or inferior, and their social position relative to other members of the community (952). Interests, goals, morals, methods of child training, by and large, differ with class position. Conflicts for the individual may arise in several ways. He may be moving from one class to another, with change in the type of work and source of income resulting also in an increase in income. He himself may be sensitive about his previous position, and he may actually meet with a certain amount of distance because of having "arrived" recently. Another type of conflict may arise from the fact that the individual occupies a "mixed" position. By occupation and source of income he may belong to a higher class than by the amount of his income and, as a result of that, the neighborhood that he lives in. The ideology that he wants to impart to his children may be closer to the "higher" group. This creates, in the children, a conflict somewhat similar to those discussed in connection with exposure to clashing moral standards. For the parents it causes anxiety about the children, accompanied either by feelings of inadequacy on their own part or by excessive severity toward the child, leading to intrafamily clashes. The individual's mixed position may lead to another kind of difficulty, as illustrated by the following example:

[4] This presentation is based on J. McV. Hunt, An instance of the social origin of conflict resulting in psychoses, in C. Kluckhohn and H. A. Murray, *Personality in Nature, Society and Culture,* Alfred A. Knopf, New York, 1948, pp. 367-374.

"If an individual, a gold-miner, for example, is upper-middle class in terms of economic status, lower-middle class in terms of social status, and upper-lower class in terms of ideologies, he will find only few people with a similar personality structure. If he wants to associate with an upper-middle class person he has not enough education; if he wants to associate with an upper-lower class he is resented because of his wealth. The only solution to this dilemma is to find another person with a similar distribution of prestige factors in the personality. A second solution consists of equilibrating social and ideological status to the economic status. . . . However, this striving may be thwarted because it presupposes a change of social techniques which usually are not very modifiable during the mature years of a person's life. Striving without success constitutes of course a source of stress and strain."[5]

Another source of conflict may be the individual's unattained or unattainable desire to change his class status. Today, the most effective means for moving up to a higher social class is through education. The educational system, however, tends to hinder social mobility as well as to aid it. Teachers' judgments of students are frequently influenced by the students' social status, and they tend to favor students from upper social levels as against those from lower social levels (953). Thus the student from an upper social level is more likely to feel encouraged to continue his education than is the student from one of the lower classes.

Further, the individual may find himself in disagreement with the dominant procedure followed by his class in its dealings with another class. If he belongs to the owner or managerial group, he may believe in unionization when his own group as a whole is opposed to it, and he may not be in a position to keep out of the struggle even in his own plant. The individual belonging to the employee group may not believe in the possibly dominant high-handed leadership or in submitting to their "racketeering" conditions, but he may not be able to get a job unless he submits without rebellion. The union organizer or leader may be in a conflict because of the threat to his life from individuals hired by the owner and managerial group. Conditions in all of these respects, of course, keep changing.

In addition to the points previously mentioned, certain forms of avitaminosis (see Chapter XXXV)—e.g., pellagra—are also "poor men's diseases." Rheumatic arthritis, which has a psychogenic factor, at least as far as relapses are concerned, is more frequent in slum areas. Conversion hysteria—i.e., bodily complaints without demonstrable local pathology (e.g., numbness or paralysis of the arms)—is more common in the lower socio-economic and cultural groups. In the lower class the expression of anger is permitted,

[5] J. Ruesch, Social technique, social status, and social change in illness, in C. Kluckhohn and H. A. Murray, *Personality in Nature, Society, and Culture,* Alfred A. Knopf, New York, 1948, p. 124.

without subsequent anxiety, and there is a predominance of fractures, accidents, and traumatic diseases. In the lower-middle class, psychosomatic conditions show a preponderance, possibly because of the group's tendency to conform and to repress; the unsolved conflict may therefore have a tendency to express itself in physical symptoms (812). There are figures available on the incidence of certain disorders in miners in Scotland in comparison with the rest of the population. The increased incidence of respiratory and joint diseases and of accidents is easily understandable on the basis of the physical aspects of the occupation. However, the increase of "gastritis" (2330 per 100,000 in comparison with 1141 per 100,000 in the nonmining general male population) is convincing evidence of greater tendency to certain forms of psychopathology. Gastritis is commonly called gastric neurosis as it usually represents a disturbed function of the stomach in response to stress (376).

CONFLICTS CONNECTED WITH MINORITY GROUP STATUS

The double aspect of this problem was found to be present in eighty individuals of the Negro population ranging in age from seventeen to twenty-five who were studied through autobiographies supplemented by one or more interviews, including free association and dream analysis. The problems that they share with the whites are the usual intrafamily problems of attachment to parents, sibling rivalry, and reactions to discipline, the effect of the last depending in part on its severity. The special problems have two different aspects. One is simply that because of their more limited opportunities, a larger percentage of the Negro population belongs to the lower class socio-economically and has its general characteristics—namely, more frequent breaking up of the family, exposure to delinquency, more frequent incidence of exposure to alcoholism and lack of sexual restraint—and there is a more frequent dominance of maternal authority. A special ethnic problem is the preoccupation with skin color and other racial features. In this respect, there may be blind acceptance of white racial prejudices and measuring one's personal worth by degrees of proximity to white complexion or other Caucasian features. These are frequently mediated by the child's parents and other significant people in his primary group. This then leads to a serious problem of injured self-esteem and feeling of inadequacy. A further development from this may be indifference to and detachment from the problem, life with a low level of aspiration, an attempt to live up to the white standard, compensatory measures of trying to read and know everything and to excel intellectually, or, finally, direct or indirect defiance and resentment. A not uncommon feature of this group was extraordinary stress on social status, manifesting itself in insistence by some Negro parents that their boy must get all A's in school and that their daughter must join such-and-such a sorority. Such parents constantly engage in a struggle for a higher class status. Obviously, the two sets of problems—namely, the sibling rivalry and relationship with the parents, on the one hand, and the problems peculiar to the ethnic quality, on the other—are intricately interlocked. Thus submissiveness toward the parent and self-effacement in that situation may lead to a similar handling of the interracial problem; or, on the contrary, the resentment toward the parent and toward the sibling may reinforce the resentment over the racial discrimination. Some of the problems mentioned are dramatically illustrated by the following excerpt from one of the autobiographies.

" 'The bottom fell out of everything for me, and I was more disturbed than I had been before or since. My main prop was gone. I had not realized how much I had depended on her for support. I didn't cry at the funeral because my father and uncle cried. I was mad, not just angry, mad with hatred. My grandmother had died of acute alcoholism. They taught her to crave bootleg whiskey. We had to bury her on money borrowed from friends. We were too poor to carry insurance. My sister died in infancy, and she was buried on borrowed money, too. A feeling of hopelessness came over me. Nothing mattered—high school, nothing. It was then that the whole rotten business of being poor and a Negro at the same time caught in my throat. I became an articulate rebel. I became argumentative and critical. Why? Why? Why? that word became an obsession!' "[6]

The reactions described up to this point are most apt to be present in individuals who have risen or are rising to the middle class. (See also 739.) Four studies have been made which show the effect of rural versus city environment and Southern versus Northern environment on the intelligence level of Negro children. They indicate that intelligence level increases with prolonged exposure to better educational environment.

In two studies, all twelve-year-old Negro boys attending several New York City schools were given an intelligence test. The scores of those boys who had been born in the North were compared with the scores of those who had lived in the North for one year, for two years, for three years, etc. The average score increased as the length of residence in the North increased. A third study yielded the same findings on a group of twelve-year-old Negro girls. A fourth study on twelve-year-old Negro boys in the public schools of three Southern cities compared the scores of the city-born children with the scores of those who were born in the country in the same manner. Similar findings were obtained—the longer the child had lived in the city, the higher his score (503).

INCIDENCE OF ILLNESS IN RELATION TO CULTURE

Several careful studies indicate that certain disorders may change, as regards sex incidence, with cultural changes, and that their frequency in some ethnic groups may increase.

A review of the incidence of perforated ulcer at the New York Hospital from 1880 to 1900 revealed that perforated ulcers were about as common among women as among men—i.e., in the ratio 6:7. Beginning in the period of 1901–1906, the ratio of males to females changed. Table 4 shows the figures for the years 1901–1939.

[6] B. Dai, Some problems of personality development among Negro children, in C. Kluckhohn and H. A. Murray, *Personality in Nature, Society, and Culture*, Alfred A. Knopf, New York, 1948, p. 447.

Similar changes have taken place in Germany, France, Scandinavia, and the English-speaking countries (461). The possible explanation of this shift in incidence is the conflict revolving around self-esteem and desire for independence, on the one hand, and dependency needs, on the other. In the periods when the incidence was as great among women, the only acceptable career for them was marriage. They were usually completely dependent financially and therefore had to accept and suffer a marital situation in which the male was possibly tyrannical and inconsiderate. In the present situation, they have the opportunity for independence and professional activities when they so wish, but it is also culturally approved for them to give up their occupation and become financially dependent upon the man. The man, on the other hand, had to carry a greater burden under nineteenth-century circumstances inasmuch as his wife did not earn a living even if the financial stress was great. On the other hand, he was a more or less unchallenged master in the house. At present, his burden can be eased in situations of economic stress through his wife's also working, but the strain on self-esteem is too great; nor is he "lord in his own castle." Also, it is culturally unacceptable that the wife should work and support a dependent husband.

TABLE 4[7]

	Males	Females	Ratio
1901–1906 (5 years)	10	4	2½:1
1907–1914 (7 years)	55	9	6:1
1915–1930 (15 years)	260	16	16:1
1931–1939 (8 years)	36	3	12:1

TWO WORLD WARS AND CHANGES IN PSYCHIATRIC DISORDERS

There was a much greater incidence of conversion-hysterical symptoms in the First World War, whereas there was a much greater incidence of anxiety states and organ-neurotic or psychosomatic disorders in the Second. Gastric complaints were particularly frequent. The difference between the incidence of conversion hysteria and anxiety state may be explainable partly on the basis of relatively greater emotional sophistication at the time of the Second World War and may also have had to do, in the First World War, with the conditions of trench warfare, in which the soldiers were immobilized for long periods of time. In support of the influence of sophistication as a factor is the fact that, during the First World War, anxiety state was known as an "officer's neurosis," because it occurred more frequently among officers than among enlisted men and because the relative incidence of conversion hysteria among officers was low.

[7] B. Mittelmann and H. G. Wolff, Emotions and gastroduodenal function; experimental studies on patients with gastritis, duodenitis and peptic ulcer, *Psychosom. Med.*, 1942, **4**, **17**.

The gradual increase in psychosomatic disorders in the general male population and particularly among Negroes during the Second World War, as shown in Table 5, can be accounted for by the increased stress and strain, hostility, and anxiety of the war period. The increase among the Negroes is a more complex problem. The relative absence of the disorder in peacetime was probably correlated with the relative separation of the trends in the life of the Negro from the stress and strain aspect of national life. As

TABLE 5[8]

	Incidence Rate per 1000 Registrants Examined		
	Whites	Negroes	W/N Ratio
Peptic Ulcer			
Peacetime[a]	3.6	.6	6
Wartime[b]	5.2	1.4	4
Percentage increase	44	133	–33
Effort Syndrome			
Peacetime	3.7	.8	4.6
Wartime	10.0	4.5	2.2
Percentage increase	170	464	–50
Asthma			
Peacetime	4.8	3.9	1.3
Wartime	8.5	7.8	1.1
Percentage increase	73	100	–16

[a] Based on Selective Service figures prior to September 30, 1941.
[b] Based on Selective Service figures for November and December, 1943.

previously mentioned, the lower-class Negroes in the South who have never had any hope of advancement gave up trying and looked for gratifications in more primitive forms of pleasure-seeking (Dollard). With the war, they too became involved in the stressful activities.

RELATIONSHIP BETWEEN THE INDIVIDUAL AND CULTURAL, SOCIAL, AND HISTORICAL EVENTS

The following points can be made briefly about this interrelationship:

1. Historical, cultural, and social changes of major proportions never occur without stresses and strong resistance. The reason for this is twofold. The attitudes of the individuals forming the group are more or less crystallized in institutions—form of government, systems of ownership, marriage and divorce laws, etc.—which have consequences of their own nature. Even

[8] Based on a table in L. G. Rowntree, Psychosomatic disorders as revealed by thirteen million examinations of selective service registrants, *Psychosom. Med.*, 1945, 7, 29.

when changes are desired, they cannot be effected without major reorganizations and displacements, which are resisted by many individuals.

2. War, apparently, is not an unpreventable phenomenon in human history, in spite of the proneness of human beings to aggression, anxiety, and defensive attack, and in spite of the fact that, parallel with the development of organization and technology, organized war has reached increasingly larger proportions in human history. There have been periods in which large ethnic groups, including Japan, existed without war for about three hundred years. Warfare appears to have been unknown during the earlier part of the New Stone Age in Europe and the Orient. Settlements lacked defensive structures. Organized offensive warfare was unknown in aboriginal Australia (504).

3. The individual's personality and his individual experiences play a significant role in his acceptance of or opposition to certain trends. Opposition to National Socialism in Germany was found to be correlated with the following factors (550): a father who was neither domineering nor a strict disciplinarian; absence of a father or father-substitute; a demonstrative, affectionate mother; being an only or a favored child; marriage to a person of a different religious or national background; political or religious anti-Nazi influence; and foreign travel.

Prejudice against minority groups is related in part to the individual's need for self-magnification by disparaging another group.

Frenkel-Brunswik, Levinson, and Sanford (296) compared the attitudes expressed in clinical interviews by a group of women scoring high on a scale of anti-Semitism with a group of women with low scores. The "high" group tended to idealize and were submissive toward their parents; the "low" group more frequently appraised them objectively and expressed attitudes of independence. The "high" group tended toward self-glorification mixed with unacknowledged feelings of inferiority, conventional, rigid morality, an emphasis on sex as a means for achieving status, and "pseudoadmiration" for the opposite sex, with an underlying resentment.

In a study based upon attitudes expressed toward Jews, Campbell (148) found that "10 per cent of those economically satisfied expressed hostility, but 38 per cent of those economically dissatisfied expressed hostility. Correspondingly, 75 per cent of those economically satisfied either expressed liking for Jews or gave no evidence of dislike, while only 39 percent of those economically dissatisfied either expressed liking for Jews or gave no evidence of dislike." Persons dissatisfied with the political scene were also inclined to express dislike toward Jews. When the two ratings of satisfaction-dissatisfaction were combined, the correlation with attitudes toward Jews was most clearly seen.

Hovland and Sears (435) found that in fourteen Southern states the annual frequency of Negro lynchings correlated −.70 with the annual farm value of cotton from 1882 to 1930. The lower the farm value of cotton, the greater was the interference with the normal activities of people living at a marginal economic level.

(See also 390.)

4. The reaction of the individual victims to extreme hardships—e.g., as represented by the German concentration camps—depended in part on their cultural and political background and the individual personality. The politically educated prisoners sought support for their self-esteem in the fact that the Gestapo had singled them out as important enough to take revenge on them. The nonpolitical middle-class prisoners were first unable to comprehend what happened to them and assumed that their being victims must be a mistake. After they realized their actual situation, their morale broke down, and they were apt to cheat their fellow prisoners and to disintegrate. Suicides were practically confined to this group. The upper-class prisoners segregated themselves. They expressed their conviction that they would be released within a short time because of their importance (89).

SUGGESTED READINGS

Malinowski's books on the Trobriand Islanders (610, 611), Benedict's *Patterns of Culture* (78), Mead's *From the South Seas* (635), and Waller's *The Family: A Dynamic Interpretation* (951) are usually recommended. A good introduction to the general field, textbook style, is Linton's *The Cultural Background of Personality* (577). For discussion of detailed problems, see Newcomb, Hartley, et al. (710) and Kluckhohn and Murray (505).

Outstanding books on culture-personality relations are those by Dollard (214), Plant (736), Kardiner (483, 484), and DuBois (222). A shorter summing-up of the anthropological influence on psychology is given in Maslow's chapter in Stagner's *Psychology of Personality* (892). A good discussion of the relation between society and the child's personality is found in L. B. Murphy's *Social Behavior and Child Personality* (704). Adler's approach may be understood from one of his books (14). Freud's *Civilization and Its Discontents* (307), Fromm's books (321, 322), and Adorno, Frenkel-Brunswik, Levinson, and Sanford's *The Authoritarian Personality* (16) are further recommended. Havighurst and Taba's *Adolescent Character and Personality* (395) is an excellent study. On the relationship between sociological factors and illness, we recommend Halliday, *Psychosocial Medicine* (376), and the work of Hyde and his collaborators (446-448).

PART IV

Therapy

XIII Aims and Nature of Psychotherapy

The most important and adequate form of help available for psychologically distressed individuals is psychotherapy. This is a method of treatment which aims to help the impaired individual by influencing his emotional processes, his evaluation of himself and of others, his evaluation of and his manner of coping with the problems of life. It may also include, if need be, influencing and changing his environment and thus altering the problems he has to deal with and simultaneously increasing his potentialities of mastery and integration. What types of disturbance require psychotherapy? Any type of disturbance which is emotional in origin or which contains a large emotional factor may be benefited by it—for example, anxiety attacks or palpitation of the heart occurring in situations of psychological stress. Even a patient who has an organic heart disease may be incapacitated, not only by the effects of this disease, but also by the stresses originating from life problems which throw an additional burden on the damaged heart. Thus even a primary "organic" disturbance may contain an important emotional factor.

Any discussion of the aims of psychotherapy must represent a fusion of the immediate needs of the patient, the demands of society, and accumulated psychiatric knowledge. It is convenient to differentiate between clinical and dynamic aims in psychotherapy. The former term refers to obvious phenomena in the improved functioning of the patient; the latter to less obvious changes, which, however, have a wide influence on various aspects of his functioning. The first, obviously, cannot be accomplished without the second.

CLINICAL AIMS OF PSYCHOTHERAPY

RELIEVING SYMPTOMS

To the patient who comes for treatment because of intensely distressing symptoms, the main aim of therapy is to relieve his suffering in the quickest and most direct manner. He may have suffered from less annoying symptoms for years—he may have been a problem as a neighbor, as a husband—but that does not concern him now. What he wants is direct aid for incapacitating symptoms. The relief of severe symptoms is one of the unquestionable aims of psychotherapy, but the therapist recognizes that the symptoms are the end product of the patient's conflicts, frustrations, and disturbed relationships with his surroundings. Instead of treating the symptoms directly, the therapist may focus his attention on the patient's life problems, helping him, if necessary, to reorganize his character, in the expectation that, as the patient grows stronger, his symptoms will disappear without primary attention.

INCREASING THE ABILITY TO BE HAPPY

In every maladjusted individual, the ability to enjoy life in one or another of its aspects is at least partially impaired. The patient may not recognize this fully, except in retrospect after he has improved. In other patients there may be the further complication that they crave forms of pleasure which cause suffering or lead to unhappiness—for instance, masochism. Such forms of activity must ultimately be replaced by forms of enjoyment compatible with health. A particularly important factor in the attainment of happiness is the ability to form genuinely affectionate relationships.

INCREASING EFFICIENCY

The achievements of disturbed individuals characteristically do not come up to the level of their capacities. To improve the individual's functioning, the therapist will try to release his inhibited capacities indirectly—that is, by correcting the underlying stress and conflict. In this way he is enabled to accept responsibilities, to concentrate on a task, and to persevere.

AIDING IN SOCIAL ADAPTATIONS

This implies the patient's desire and ability to contact other individuals and to adapt himself more or less to their way of life. A closely allied trait is flexibility. Some maladjusted individuals suspect everyone, rather than the specific few whom they might have reason to mistrust; they do not want partial affection from certain others, but complete worship from everyone. The therapist's aim here is to enable the individual to discriminate or to compromise, if need be.

INCREASED SPONTANEITY

Some people always do what they "should" do and rarely what they want to do (618). The purpose here is to enable them to find out and to follow their inclinations and their dislikes and to realize what type of *sound* person they want to be. Fromm emphasizes that all psychotherapy may be summed up as an attempt to achieve a proper balance between spontaneity and adaptation. The therapist's aim should be to help the patient realize the discrepancy between his deeper inclinations and his obvious patterns of behavior, and to encourage him to pursue his legitimate goals, with adequate regard, of course, for social limitations.

ADJUSTING BODILY FUNCTIONS

The general aim is to help the patient attain the best physiological functioning, with due regard to social patterns. The need for help is obvious in patients who suffer from a serious disturbance in the functions of various organs, but it is important in patients who feel anxious or guilty about such activities, also. Diminished, excessive, or distorted functioning, such as lack of appetite, overeating, and fetishism, may have to be adjusted. Sometimes the patient becomes aware of the disturbance, its emotional background, and the need for correction, only during the treatment.

DYNAMIC AIMS OF PSYCHOTHERAPY

INCREASE IN THE PATIENT'S FEELINGS OF SELF-ESTEEM AND SECURITY

The patient's feelings of helplessness, worthlessness, and guilt, and his fear of catastrophic breakdown, must be replaced by a positive evaluation of his strength. His feelings of rejection must give way to feelings of acceptance. His fear of punishment and pain, his view of the world perpetuated since childhood as a place inhabited exclusively by stronger, threatening individuals, must be corrected and made more adult. He is, thus, enabled to give and receive affection. The resultant increase in the patient's strength has, as a further consequence, the ability to be self-assertive, enterprising, and better able to tolerate failure, disappointment, and pain. This development has been phrased by Rosenzweig (801) as increase in frustration tolerance.

RELEASE

Besides the patient's inclinations already discussed, there is further a release of certain hitherto forbidden and repressed impulses, such as aggression and some types of sexual craving. The release may occur in the form of overt action—e.g., outbursts of temper or weeping—or in the form of consciously experienced craving. Such reactions largely disappear in the course of later developments, but a certain amount of release may be indispensable for ultimate psychic health. Impulses of this type play an important role in the individual's difficulties, and he can be relieved only if they are uncovered.

INCREASE IN INSIGHT

The patient's attention shifts from his symptoms and his obvious behavior to their *meaning*. He acquires knowledge of his hidden motivations, repressed wishes, conflicts, and defenses, both past and present. He recognizes how these reactions determine his behavior. The patient gains insight only when his anxiety and guilt, which were responsible for the repression of his impulses, are allayed. With the development of insight there is a reorganization of his values and needs, and consequently some of the most pernicious and harmful reactions disappear.

INCREASE IN SELF-ACCEPTANCE

The patient learns to accept himself as an individual. This development has several aspects. With the disappearance of the pernicious impulses, with his increase in courage and self-assertion, he actually becomes a changed person; his desires and behavior no longer clash with his ideals. He has learned to accept his healthy cravings, and he realizes that the impulses he has and did have are common to all human beings. With this, his feelings of being unique in his sinfulness, of being unworthy of the company of others—that is, his feelings of isolation—disappear, and he can relate himself adequately to the group.

If a patient has a permanent defect, such as being crippled or blind, he may learn to accept his disability. If he is in a distressing situation which cannot be corrected at the time, such as having a cruel parent, he may learn to accept, without self-contempt and fear, the fact that he is resentful.

INCREASED INTEGRATION AND REACHING TOWARD POSITIVE GOALS

With the gradual disappearance of fears, inhibitions, and conflicts, with the increase in spontaneity and the release of fundamental inclinations, the patient is enabled to develop new patterns of goal-seeking. The joy of success renews his desire for new activities. In a sense, the whole psychotherapeutic process is an educational one. Man being the highest organism in the scale of intellectual development, one aim of all psychotherapy is to release the intellectual functions to their fullest potentialities—that is to say, to enable the individual to integrate his emotional and intellectual activities into a harmonious unity.

THE RELATIONSHIP BETWEEN THE PATIENT AND THE THERAPIST

PERSONALITY AND TRAINING OF THE PSYCHOTHERAPIST

The personality of the therapist and the manner in which he relates himself to the patient and reacts to his problems are of the utmost importance.

The therapist should have a true appreciation of individual differences and a respect for various personalities. He should recognize that the world is not made up of one kind of person. This characteristic is often called a tolerance for differences in other people—respect for another's individuality; it used to be described by such terms as "sacredness of the human individual." The therapist's task is to find out in what direction the patient naturally tends to go, and then to help him proceed in that direction more efficiently.

The therapist should have an adequate knowledge and evaluation of himself. He should neither overestimate himself as an individual nor have distressing feelings of inadequacy or insecurity. In other words, he should be a fairly strong individual. His knowledge of his own stress situations should enable him to understand the patient's sufferings and struggles.

The therapist must have a very extensive training. The first step in training is for the psychotherapist to undergo psychological analysis himself. An adequate realization of his own moderate tensions, conflicts, and difficulties will enable him to put them aside so that they will play no part in his treatment of other people. He should have no serious emotional difficulties, for he might thus be entangled in his patient's difficulties, disapprove of him, force him into wrong directions, or be blind to his shortcomings.

The good therapist should be interested in people in general and desirous of helping them. He needs a generous allotment of kindness and sympathy so that he may identify himself, to some extent, with every one of his patients.

RAPPORT

Good rapport means a frank, trusting attitude on the part of the patient, which enables him to pour out his difficulties to the therapist. It implies hope of being helped, and eagerness to coöperate to that end. Through it, the therapist can use his knowledge and influence to help the patient, and the patient can take advantage of this help.

This essentially good relationship between patient and therapist is important for another reason. The patient has many conflicting attitudes and reactions toward the therapist, most of which are unconscious. In some treatments, as in psychoanalysis, these attitudes must be discussed. Unless a feeling of trust has been established, the patient will be incapable of discussing them or withstanding the effect of their discussion.

PERMISSIVE ATTITUDES

The attitude of the therapist who listens to everything without condemning, censoring, or being shocked has been described as a permissive attitude. Such an attitude assures the patient that he can say what he wishes without being reprimanded or losing the therapist's respect and affection. Thus the therapist's role is one that is played by *almost no one else in our whole society.* He is almost the *only* person to whom all secrets may be told and who will be sympathetic and understanding even when he has to descend to what are called "the lowest depths of human nature." Indeed, the therapist not only permits, he actually encourages, the patient to talk freely. This is universally reported to bring relaxation and relief in itself. Furthermore, it contains an aspect of confession, inasmuch as the patient relates many things for which he condemns himself and about which he feels guilty. This makes him feel that he has faced his problems, has revealed himself honestly, has been forgiven, does not have to fear punishment and attack, and has been accepted by a person whom he considers important.

RECEIVING THE HELP AND INTEREST OF A STRONGER INDIVIDUAL

The patient regards the therapist as stronger and superior in comparison with himself. There are several reasons for this: The patient asks the therapist for help, and he regards him as superior because it is he himself, not the therapist, who is sick. He is influenced by the therapist's professional and individual prestige. The therapist's behavior, however, should not be dominating or disinterested; it should make the patient feel that he is interested in helping him. With this, the patient feels that he is not alone, but has a stronger person helping him to face the world and master his problems.

ADJUSTMENT OF IRRATIONAL ATTITUDES TOWARD THE PSYCHOTHERAPIST

All the irrational attitudes, suspicions, hostilities, and excessive demands which the patient has toward the world will unconsciously be focused upon the therapist also. Thus the relationship reflects the patient's whole attitude toward life and toward people in general. If the therapeutic process goes well, he learns to form a healthy, affectionate, and self-respecting relation with at least one individual; usually this carries over to his daily life, so that he is able to relate himself well to other individuals.

Depending on the form of psychotherapy, the attitudes mentioned are brought, to a greater or lesser extent, into consciousness. Part of the process described occurs unconsciously in every form of effective psychotherapy.

SUGGESTED READINGS

See Chapter XIV.

XIV Techniques of Psychotherapy in Adults

How do patients react to the suggestion of psychological treatment? Some welcome it because it relieves their perplexity about their condition, and because they recognize their emotional plight. Others become frightened or resentful, either because emotional disturbance implies insanity to them, or because they feel humiliated by the idea. After proper explanation and reassurance, such patients may accept the suggestion—sometimes after a further period of suffering. Some, however, refuse permanently, and continue to suffer, there being no reliable way of inducing such patients to accept treatment. Dangerous patients, of course, must be committed to mental hospitals.

Patients who come for help as a result of their own decision assume initiative and responsibility for their treatment. Patients who at first come reluctantly or "out of considerateness" for the mate or the parent assume initiative after the therapist indicates the need for therapy. This development is indispensable for adequate effectiveness of the treatment.

The problem of the relationship between theories and results in psychotherapy is a vexing one. The saying of a nineteenth-century psychiatrist, "psychiatry is the art of applying a science which does not exist," is no longer true today. Early therapies, as treatment by magic in primitive societies, were based on obviously false theories, yet they were often effective. We realize now that their effectiveness was based on suggestion, release of pent-up emotions, expiation, relief of guilt feelings, unwitting reassurance and support. Unconsciously the patient came to feel safer, and his system of defenses was bolstered. Even today practices based on theories which run completely counter to scientific thinking manage to achieve partial or sometimes even complete symptomatic cures. In the evaluation of psychological practices, theories, and findings, no moral discussions can take the place of sober scientific search for facts and methods.

A variety of techniques has been developed in treating patients psychologically. We can differentiate various integrated forms of psychotherapy, such as hypnosis, psychoanalysis, and institutionalization. In the following we will discuss both the various integrated forms and the special devices in use, including those which are largely in the research stage.

THERAPEUTIC INTERVIEWS

An interview is any type of prolonged contact between the therapist and the patient in which conversation plays a prominent role, and which centers around the patient's problems. The setup is such that it encourages the patient to unburden himself and talk about his complaints and the stresses and strains of his existence. Some patients do this almost spontaneously, whereas others require a measure of guidance from the therapist. The aim of the therapist is to have the patient touch, sooner or later, on all significant aspects of his life. He may guide the patient's conversation to further topics by repeating, in the form of a question, something which the patient has already touched on, or by raising new queries. In this procedure it is very important to observe the patient because he shows, by facial expression, changes in color, halting, and evasion, where the points of stress lie. Such signs, if they are mild, guide the therapist in recognizing what points should be taken up, and, if they become severe, what points should be left alone for the time being.

The patient should not be forced in the conversation, for this can do damage or may cause him to break off the treatment. To know in what direction to guide or not guide the conversation, the therapist must have a thorough knowledge of psychopathology. It is obvious that in the interview the patient does most of the talking, and that the interview is a diagnostic as well as a therapeutic procedure. The close interrelation between diagnosis and therapy is a characteristic and unique aspect of psychotherapy.

Interviews of this type usually last about an hour and occur once or twice a week. If there is a great need for help, they may be given daily for a period of time. If they are effective in patients who do not require institutional treatment, beneficial results may be apparent after one interview, but they should definitely be evident after about five or ten sessions; otherwise, it is futile to continue. The total number of interviews needed depends on the patient. Some gain full benefit from about five interviews; others continue for several months, improving all the while; and still others make use of the treatment, with some interruptions, for years—it being the only measure which enables them to stand the recurrent strains of their existence. Other methods which can be used in conjunction with sympathetic guidance in the patient's story of his difficulties will be discussed later.

Some therapists have stressed the desirability of minimal activity by the therapist, even in stimulating or helping the patient to reveal relevant information. F. Deutsch considers this desirable because the patient's associations, the sequence of his productions, reveal unconscious connections. Even casual questions may direct the patient's thoughts away from the next association that would arise after a pause. The therapist may repeat a particularly telling phrase used by the patient, which then leads the latter to reveal the implications of that phrase. The therapist may repeat the patient's statement, also, to stimulate him to resume after the pause becomes prolonged. Deutsch called this method "associative anamnesis" ("anamnesis" means past history).

Rogers based the desirability for minimal intervention on the idea that the patient has drives for growth and adjustment; in an accepting and free therapeutic atmosphere the patient works out his destiny better on his own momentum. This has been called "nondirective counseling." The therapist says at times simply "Um-hm" to express his interest and acceptance; he repeats the patient's statement, or he reformulates what the patient has said, choosing for this purpose aspects that are in the direction of the feeling rather than the intellectual content of the patient's utterances. In this manner, it is assumed, he helps clarify insight that the patient has already achieved; e.g., a college student was confronted with the difficult situation of informing his parents that his grades were poor:

"*Subject* [talking of his father]. No, I don't think he is—is capable of that [of understanding] because I don't get along with him, don't at all!

"*Counselor*. You dislike him a good deal?

"*S*. Yes, I—I did feel bitter toward him for a while . . . now . . . I am sort of ashamed. I think that that's it more than anything else, an experience of shame that he's my father. *(Pause)*

"*C*. You feel he isn't much good. . . .

"*S*. I—I don't know, I feel sort of strangled, that's how I feel.

"*C*. Strangled?

"*S*. By the world, I feel licked."[1]

The following comments should be made at this point about interview techniques with minimal intervention. (1) In patients who speak relatively easily, the technique brings out the essential material, with adequate feeling tone. This process is the fundamental and indispensable part of any sound psychotherapeutic procedure. (2) A careful examination of some of the comments given by the counselor in "nondirective counseling" shows them to be rather potent comments carrying the situation radically beyond the point at which the patient has spontaneously arrived; e.g., in the above example the two comments referring to the father, "You dislike him a good deal?" and "You feel he isn't much good," express greater hostility and condemnation of the father than the patient ever expressed. Not only that, the comments attempt to dissipate one side of the conflict—namely, the patient's guilt over the way he feels toward his father. The patient is obvi-

[1] C. R. Rogers, *Counseling and Psychotherapy*, Houghton Mifflin Co., Boston, 1942, p. 136.

ously not capable of doing this yet and keeps reverting to a more attenuated statement which reëxpresses the feeling of guilt ("I am sort of ashamed"). The term "nondirective" for such comments does not seem applicable. (3) Some patients need direct questioning for a long period in the course of the treatment. Without this they are not capable of presenting relevant material; instead of forming restorative contact with the therapist, they experience the interview as a failure, increasing their feeling of inadequacy and rejection. (4) As will be shown below, interview therapy in its various forms may be a very effective curative procedure; in other patients, however, deeper penetration into the intricacies of the problem is necessary, and extensive use must be made of interpretations.

Why and how is the patient benefited by therapeutic interviews? The answer lies in what we have discussed in the preceding chapter. The fact that the patient talks to an individual whom he considers strong and capable of giving help, who listens to everything and who encourages him to speak without condemning or punishing him, in itself allays his fears and guilt, and makes him feel more worth-while and accepted. Together with this, there is an implicit development in spontaneity and frankness through the very fact of talking about forbidden and avoided subjects. He gradually feels that he has faced himself and his problems. The burst of emotions frequently occurring in interviews leads to release. The comparatively healthy and self-respecting relation established with this one individual, the therapist, carries over to the patient's daily life. With the shift of the patient's attention from his symptoms to the circumstances and relationships out of which they arise, there is a considerable development of insight.

It is obvious that some of these developments in the interviews are similar to the effects obtained by confiding in a trusted and sympathetic friend. Besides this, however, the therapist, because of his special knowledge, guides the patient's conversation to all significant points of stress; furthermore, such emotional entanglements as insistence on complete dependence or submissiveness, or subsequent feelings of humiliation, are prevented.

The improvement in the patient can be objectively and quantitatively demonstrated. In fourteen cases the self-references of the patients were classified as positive (seeing himself as good, strong, happy), negative (seeing himself as unattractive, frustrated, worried), and ambivalent (seeing himself in a mixed light). In successful therapeutic cases the number and proportion of negative self-references tended to decline, and the number and proportion of positive self-references tended to rise in the course of therapy. The final interview showed an almost complete lack of negative and ambivalent self-references. After an agreement on common criteria, three judges independently evaluated and counted these self-references from verbatim records of the interviews. The reliability of the method was above 80 percent (251).

Interview therapy may be particularly effective in relieving the acute symptoms of any psychoneurotic disturbance of relatively recent origin. It can be very effective in patients who have mild disturbances of a psychotic type, but can still function in society. In addition to organic treatment, it can be of further benefit to patients with psychological disturbances complicating an organic ailment.

Although other measures besides the interview may be used in treating the patient, a survey of his difficulties should never be omitted. This is needed so that the therapist may know what measures are imperative—for example, proper supervision if the patient is suicidal, and what measures should not be used lest they cause an aggravation of the patient's condition. Likewise, the therapist must not overlook an organic disturbance; if necessary, he must advise physical examination and laboratory tests.

INTERPRETATION

Interpretation consists of the therapist's pointing out the nature of the patient's reactions to situations, his unconscious conflicts, cravings, and anxieties; it is based on the therapist's observation of the patient and on the information he has received from the patient.[2] It is one of the most effective and, if improperly used, one of the most dangerous weapons of psychotherapy. One type of interpretation occurs implicitly in most interview therapy. The very fact that the therapist guides the conversation from the patient's symptoms to the situation in which they arose implies a connection, particularly if he directly asks the patient what occurred on a given day before this complaint started. After hearing of the incident, he may ask, cautiously at first, "Do you think you were disappointed, afraid, or angry?" The patient may come to this conclusion himself, and the therapist may agree. If the patient comes regularly for a prolonged period of time, the therapist may begin, with due caution, to point out to him feelings of humiliation, attitudes of dependence, etc., and, with limitations, may interpret his dreams. Recklessly used, interpretation can cause intense emotional storm. There are very serious reasons for the patient's lack of awareness of his motivations, and the interpretation may threaten his whole security system. Interpretation is one of the main tools of psychoanalysis and will be discussed in detail under that heading.

REASSURANCE

We will discuss under this heading how the patient is made to feel (1) that he can be hopeful, (2) that he is accepted and loved (security), and 3) that he

[2] The term "deep therapy" is sometimes used for any procedure that changes an individual's character structure for the better. Coördinate with this usage is the definition of "symptom therapy" as any technique that removes the symptoms without changing the character in any profound manner. However, it now seems probable that changes in character structure may be effected by therapies in which insight is unnecessary, as in work with children, particularly if the child's environment is changed at a relatively early age.

is worth-while and can respect himself (self-esteem). Properly conducted interviews work implicitly in this direction by the very fact that the patient reveals his innermost secrets, experiences of rejection, humiliation, failures, and aspirations to an individual who is important to him and who listens to him with respect and sympathy.

While some patients prefer an aloof, impersonal attitude in the therapist, the majority thrive best if he is warm and sympathetic in demeanor, facial expression, and voice. The patient derives reassurance from the fact that he is accepted for treatment, the implication being that he is not really hopeless. It is useful, in addition, if the therapist actually tells the patient that he can be helped. If, during the interview, the patient asks direct questions about his condition—whether he can be helped, by what methods, and why, the therapist must use his judgment as to whether he ought to answer them and to what extent. If the patient is very anxious but is emotionally able to trust the therapist, the answers should be firmly encouraging. Other patients, eagerly asking for reassurance, become alarmed by the therapist's statement that they are not in mortal danger because it implies to them that he does not realize the gravity of their condition. If the urgency in such patients is great, the therapist has to preface his encouragement by assuring the patient that he is fully aware of his suffering and difficulty. It is apparent from this that the form of reassurance has to vary considerably from patient to patient.

Voicing the conviction that the patient is worth-while, that he has good capacities, and that he can be loved and accepted by others can have a powerful effect on him and may prove to be life-saving. At other times, praise given to a person who does not feel worthy of it defeats itself by creating suspicion of the therapist's motives. This mistrust breaks the rapport and by disturbing the relationship may make all the other efforts of the therapist worthless.

ADVICE

Many people conceive advice to be the most important task of the therapist, but this is not so. It is best, as a rule, for the therapist to refrain from giving direct advice in a situation, but merely to help the patient to discover the answers for himself. The reason for this is that some patients resent advice even though they have asked for it; as soon as they get it, they proceed to prove it wrong. Others, not being able to carry out the suggestion because of their conflicts and anxieties, begin to feel worse or worthless over the failure, or blame the therapist for it. In some emergency situations, however, direct advice must be given to prevent disastrous action on the part of the patient. Some exceptional patients accept directions from the therapist approvingly and do not become disturbed, whether they carry them out, modify them, or fail to fulfill them successfully. In such instances, after cautious attempts, the therapist should not refrain from giving advice, but should emphasize that he is giving his own evaluation of the situation, and that he counsels the course which, in his opinion, seems best. The patient should feel free to accept or reject it.

The following is an illustration of how contact with the therapist helps the individual to arrive at a decision by himself:

A student, who seemed very distressed, came begging for help. She had a serious problem which she could not possibly solve by herself; she needed someone else's opinion and advice. Her story, as she told it, was that she had to choose between two men who wanted to marry her. One was poor and without any prospects; the other was somewhat older and could offer her a great deal more security. It was soon evident that she wanted to talk herself out completely, for she interrupted whenever the therapist started to ask a question. So he just sat back, nodding, smiling, frowning, or grunting at the proper moments, but saying nothing. As she talked, she seemed to become more and more definite about being in love with the first man and not with the second. After about an hour, she made her final decision. She seemed greatly relieved, thanked the therapist profusely for his help, said that she could never have reached a decision without the aid of a psychologist, and left. The therapist had said hardly a word throughout.

INFORMATION

Information given to the patient by the therapist is often essential and useful, and, of course, has emotional implications for the patient. It should be given with proper regard for his emotional needs and with the full realization of the fact that his lack of knowledge in certain subjects has emotional reasons. Knowledge of sexuality is most often needed by the individual, particularly if he is a child or adolescent, and often even if he is an adult. Enlightenment regarding conception, intercourse, masturbation, etc., may be necessary. Proper knowledge allays insistent curiosity and, with it, the fear of rejection and guilt engendered by this curiosity. The fear is further allayed when the patient realizes that his impulses are common to all human beings. Adequate enlightenment imparted early, before erroneous conclusions with their emotional repercussions have become an integral part of the personality, may do wonders in relatively mild disturbances. The limitations to the value of imparting corrective information which runs counter to the patient's emotional needs are exemplified by women who believe that "all men are brutes seeking only sensual gratification." It is futile to tell them that they are wrong and to try to back up this statement because their conviction is motivated by complex fears.

Objective means can sometimes be helpful in correcting an erroneous self-evaluation of the patient. Intelligence tests may convince the patient that he is not as stupid as he thought he was, and personality inventories may show him that his case is not as extreme as he thought. By various other means it may be possible to have the patient make an inventory of his assets and liabilities on the basis of objective evidence. Measurements, norms, and indices of variations from the norm, whether anatomical, psychological, or physiological, may all be helpful in allaying persistent doubts. Even if the objective information thus obtained is not flattering, it may still serve a psychologically good purpose. It may help the patient accept his limitations in one field, and look for success and satisfaction in another.

PERSUASION AND EXHORTATION

There is an implicit appeal to the patient's judgment and his desire for well-being when it is explained to him that he has a psychological illness and that he would derive benefit from having it treated. This, however, cannot be called persuasion since it is not done insistently. The patient may be refusing treatment for emotional reasons which cannot be reached by the short cut of logic. More persistent reasoning with the patient may be necessary during the treatment to prevent him from taking a harmful course of action.

These measures are quite different from an appeal to the patient's reason for the purpose of ridding him of his symptoms. Holding them up to him as being contrary to logic does little good since they are brought about by emotional factors, and the patient is only made to feel more inadequate and deprived of sympathy.

Appeal to the patient's moral and social values and to his sense of duty, as a therapeutic measure, is harmful because it makes the patient feel more worthless. It can be used in some emergency situations, however—e.g., to tide the patient over a period of suicidal danger. No therapist should disregard individual differences or dogmatically impose his own standards and ideas on the patient in the attempt to provide him with a positive way of life. He must be wary of trying to make a religious patient an agnostic, or vice versa. The patient's ideals and aspirations must be decided on the basis of self-development.

INFLUENCING THE PATIENT'S ENVIRONMENT, GUIDANCE

The following types of relationship exist between the patient's psychopathology and the necessity for environmental change: (1) The patient is in a position to handle all his problems if he works out his psychological difficulties. It is true under these circumstances that a great deal of his conflict reflects that of his culture and of his own past. However, as a result of those experiences, he developed anxieties as well as compensatory and substitutive methods to which he is now clinging. These change gradually if he is willing to take responsibility for them and is willing to risk altering them. (2) The patient has realistic problems—e.g., somewhat intolerant parents or an unfair employer. However, the behavior of these persons can be forced to change if he himself behaves self-assertively. (3) The difficulties of the family members are so great that they cannot change without psychotherapeutic handling. In that case the therapist himself or another therapist must be instrumental in altering the orientation of the key persons. (4) Neither the patient himself nor the therapist can influence the environment psychologically, but some other agency—e.g., a social service organization—can offer the patient a different environment, as in the placement of children. (5) There is no way to alter the realistic situation—unemployment, parental behavior, delinquent environment. Under these circumstances therapy may be impossible or limited in its effect.

The severity of the patient's problem determines the urgency and even the possibility of change in environment. Living alone is not a great strain on some patients, or they can soon take steps to find a living partner; other patients are shattered by living alone yet may antagonize people to such an extent after arrangement is made for joint living that the relationship is broken off. Some patients can change to a new occupation while still earning at their present jobs; others cannot do this.

As regards technical procedures, the therapist may contact the patient's family or his friends, either to gather needed information, or to provide for adequate supervision and help, or to correct conditions unfavorable to the patient. If the patient is in serious danger of harming himself, this is imperative. In other instances, an understanding and helpful friend or member of the patient's family can help a great deal by giving him emotional support and guiding him in practical situations. Contact by the therapist with the patient's family is an emotional problem for the patient which he may welcome, or of which he may be afraid for fear that the therapist will side with the family against him. With adequate handling, however, it can be done with benefit both to the patient and to his family.

Companionship and participation in the activities of the group relieve the patient's feeling of isolation and raise his self-esteem. The therapist may encourage him to make friends and to join clubs or other social organizations. Such suggestions should be given when the patient has become emotionally able to reach out toward other people and to coöperate in ventures with them. Here, too, the help of a social worker or of a friend may be needed. Newly found friendships and love may completely alter the patient's emotional life. If they are the right kind, they may bring him relief and happiness, which ultimately must always be found outside the therapeutic situation. If they are the wrong kind, they will bring more suffering.

The therapist should always be alert to the problem of his patients' ambitions and aspirations. Most patients have them when they enter treatment, and become better equipped to follow them when their conflicts are resolved; others develop them during the treatment. To patients who feel perplexed and at a loss the therapist should give all assistance in their attempt to orient themselves. Here the aid of applied psychology may be invaluable.

READING IN PSYCHOLOGY

Reading in psychology may be helpful to disturbed individuals, particularly to college students, if it is accompanied by interviews and discussions, and if the right kind of books are chosen. Unless such a book conveys reassurance, support, and permissiveness, and unless it is clear in its presentation, it will frighten the patient more. There are very few books of this type available, but an outstanding work like *The Happy Family,* by Levy and Munroe, shows that it is not impossible to popularize a thoroughly scientific point of view and apply it to the stresses and strains of everyday life.

TRAINING IN BEHAVIOR

Individuals who have changed their social environment—for instance, some college students who come from rural districts, poor families, or immigrant homes—may be ill at ease and shy and generally lack poise because they are unprepared for conventional social intercourse. They can frequently be made happier, more effective, and better liked by adequate social training—wearing the conventionally right clothes, learning the ordinary social clichés and etiquette, learning to dance and to handle introductions properly. The therapist himself may give him some advice, or he may suggest that he learn all this from a friend.

Other patients are benefited, at the proper point in the progress of psychotherapy, if they are given some suggestions on how to behave in certain situations and with certain people. Thus they may be urged to admit ignorance and naïveté when they feel them, rather than to act sophisticated; in other words, to be frank and honest whenever possible. Such suggestions are effective if the patient already has proper understanding of his past behavior.

Mildly maladjusted college students who lacked self-confidence were told in detail how to act on certain occasions so that they would appear self-confident to other people. Some of them reported later that, after they had convinced themselves of the success of their deception, they actually began to feel more self-confident. An extension of this method is that of imitation. The individual who is shy or who feels that he behaves incorrectly is instructed to select a person who behaves as he would like to and to imitate this person's behavior (not his total personality). After a while his behavior becomes less and less artificial and external, and more and more natural and habitual.

ACTING OUT AS A THERAPEUTIC TECHNIQUE

As will be discussed later, action and play are regular aspects of psychotherapy in children. A limited amount of "behaving" occurs, naturally, in every psychotherapy: expressive gestures and tense movements. The technique here referred to encourages the adult patient to act out impulses which occur in the course of the verbal contact with the therapist, such as shouting, walking around in the room, curling up on the couch, even passing wind and masturbating, and limited physical contact with the therapist—e.g., weeping on the therapist's shoulder. This is a controversial procedure. Many therapists maintain that such behavior results in "acting out" instead of insight, analysis, and resolution of conflicts and strivings. Others maintain that the experiences make the therapeutic process more immediate and vivid, and lead to associations and emotions, and thus to clarifications, otherwise unobtainable. Undoubtedly the problems presented by the procedure depend on how well the therapist and the patient are able to control, synthesize, and integrate the forces that are mobilized in the course of the actions.

MANIPULATION OF MUSCLES

As part of the total therapeutic procedure, which includes verbal contact with the patient covering his daily life and his past history, the patient's muscles are pressed rhythmically and quite firmly between the therapist's fingers, starting with the muscle covering the scapula (latissimus dorsi) and later progressing to the muscles of the jaw, the chest, and the abdomen. The patient's reaction to this varies among startled expressions of pain, withdrawal, anxiety, and anger directed against the therapist. Associations and emergence of memories frequently follow in the wake of these manipulations (Reich). The therapist then interprets the patient's reactions.

This procedure is frequently combined with a measure of acting on the therapist's part, such as imitating the patient's habitual braggadocio, overrefined, or monotonous manner of speaking, or sour or haughty facial expression, or actually holding up a mirror in front of the patient. The procedure is also commonly combined with the acting-out techniques.

The theory underlying these muscle manipulations is that the muscles of the patient are in a state of tension, forming a defensive armor, as it were, against outer dangers and inner impulses, the latter being tensions in the vegetative system. The manipulation of the muscles would "attack" this armor and would thus force the individual to reveal and abandon his defenses and thus finally liberate his vegetative (mainly sexual) impulses. Hence this procedure has been called "vegetotherapy." The theory is probably over-simplified and one-sided, but the utilization of this special technique may force or enable patients with considerable inner restraint to mobilize, express, and later integrate their impulses—e.g., of a hostile nature—which they cannot experience and express in purely verbal contact. This may first occur in the therapeutic situation and later in their daily life. The technique, at present, is controversial.

TRAINING IN RELAXATION

The method of teaching relaxation is complex, but it may be briefly described as an attempt to secure voluntary control over the tension and relaxation of various muscle systems by increased awareness of kinesthetic impulses in these muscles (453, 1004). The underlying idea is that tension accompanies most psychological disturbances and that this tension should be directly attacked without regard to the factors that create and maintain it. Too much has been claimed for the technique, which is based on too simple an assumption. It is, however, of experimental interest and can be used as an adjunct to other therapeutic measures.

CONDITIONING

The use of various conditioning methods for therapeutic purposes is in an experimental stage, and in the case of favorable effects the underlying processes are probably complex. They should be used only after adequate study of the patient's conflicts has been made.

The student will recall the famous laboratory experiment by John B. Watson (954) in which he created a fear of rabbits in a young child and then removed it by a process of reconditioning—that is, by changing the stimulus "sight of rabbit" from a producer of fear to a producer of pleasure.

The conditioning principle has been used in the treatment of adults, the so-called "association-set method" being a verbal form of it. For example, Yates[3] instructed one of her patients—a girl who burst into tears in the presence of men, particularly her father—to relax and repeat the word "calm." She was to connect with this word definite ideas of peace, security, and well-being, and to be convinced that this word would always bring her physical and mental composure. In this way she succeeded in maintaining her composure when faced with the actual distressing situation.

Recently Mowrer (695) and Morgan experimented with negative conditioning for the cure of enuresis. Their apparatus consists of a very absorbent blotter separating two copper wire screens. Any moisture makes a short circuit between the two screens; closing the delicate circuit causes a bell to ring, which disturbs and awakens the child. Thus, simultaneously with the undesirable urination, there is a disturbing and frightening sound. After this has happened three or four times, the impulse to urinate will awaken the child in time. The results reported by these two investigators are uniformly favorable. In spite of the fact that this is obviously only symptom treatment, no undesirable aftereffects have been noted in follow-up studies. The student should remember, however, that the problem of enuresis is a complex one and is closely connected with the problems of frustration and rejection in the child.

[3] D. H. Yates, An association-set method in psychotherapy, *Psychol. Bull.*, 1939, **36**, 506.

The observations of Max[4] may be mentioned as another example of negative-conditioning experiments in an adult. His subject associated homosexual impulses with a particular object. The conditioning process consisted of presenting this object to the patient, at the same time giving him an electric shock. Although he still retained thoughts of a homosexual nature, this special object finally lost its power to induce them in him. The student should again remember that the problem of homosexual impulses is very intricate and is connected with the problems of the organism as a whole.

In conditioned-reflex therapy for alcoholism, the patient is given an injection of emetine and then is urged to drink alcoholic beverages for three-quarters of an hour. The resultant vomiting produces a conditioned reflex to the taste and smell of alcohol. The procedure is repeated from four to eight times in the course of a week or ten days. This course is then repeated once or twice at intervals of from one to three months for a year. Of 644 patients followed up within two years after completing treatment, 74.8 percent were still abstaining; 52.5 percent of 291 patients treated from two to four years prior to follow-up were abstinent; and 51.5 percent of 259 treated over four years previously remained abstinent (535). The treatment is most likely to be effective with patients who do not have a deep psychological need for alcohol but have begun excessive drinking as a result of social and occupational contacts. In general, the procedure might best be used along with individual psychotherapy or inspirational group treatment.

SEMANTICS

The term "semantics" refers to the study of the meaning of words. As pointed out in various places in this book, language, and with it words and their meanings, has many connections with psychopathology. This is easily illustrated in patients with feelings of inadequacy and worthlessness who say that they are convinced that they are "unattractive" or that they are "unintelligent." These words mean to them a blurred fusion of self-depreciation, of conviction of rejection by others on the basis of their impulses, on the basis of blurred and displaced generalization of actual experiences, exclusion from their self-image of positive experiences—all of it equated with the pseudo-realistic concept of physical attractiveness and intelligence. In the course of treatment, as the various emotional forces emerge and are being elucidated, these meanings have to be dismantled, at times by implication, at other times by direct discussion. This can be done effectively only through the total therapeutic process of dealing with the patient's reactions, strivings, emotions, and life history.

Semantics as a one-sided therapeutic procedure assumes that human maladjustment arises out of unintelligent responses to symbols of former experiences and thus that therapy should take the form of rational evaluation

[4] L. M. Max, Conditioned reaction technique: a case study, *Psychol. Bull.*, 1935, 32, 734.

of such symbols. Some of the rules governing the interpretation of symbols are: The symbol (e.g., the word "boy") is not the object. The symbol is not all-inclusive; e.g., it does not take into account all differences among all boys. The symbol is dated; e.g., a patient's concept "boy" may refer to the experience of having been rejected by a special boy on a certain occasion (511).

GROUP THERAPY

Group therapy means psychotherapeutic procedures in which several individuals are simultaneously undergoing therapy. There is as much variation as regards procedure as in individual therapy. The size of the group may vary from three up to about fifty, and the method from giving information and reassurance (often referred to as inspirational-repressive), used mainly with large groups, to revelation and discussion of personal problems, including the method of dream analysis and something close to free association, used mainly with small groups.

Large-group therapy is exemplified by meetings of patients with similar problems—e.g., psychosomatic disorders or schizophrenia—at which special seating arrangements are provided and attendance is taken by roll call. Members report their progress in overcoming symptoms; inspirational material is read by the leader; charts of the nervous system may be presented, with explanation of the interrelation between emotional problems and the functioning of the nervous system leading to disturbances in the organs of the body—e.g., palpitation of the heart or gastrointestinal upset. Other therapists first conduct a series of lectures or readings from psychological textbooks, after which the patients are encouraged to discuss the material covered. After the meeting members are encouraged to fraternize with each other and the leader. As an example of the possible effectiveness of this type of therapy, the case may be cited of a paranoid schizophrenic who at first simply lay on his bed when the group met near by, occasionally shouting abusive remarks, then later began to ask questions truculently, still lying on his bed, and finally joined the group and became an active and interested member, with beneficial therapeutic results (495). In some psychosomatic disorders in which the problem is predominantly a somatic one—e.g., diabetic or tubercular patients—the purpose of the group discussion is not so much to influence the emotional background of the disorder as to better enable the patient to carry out the details of the treatment procedure—e.g., dieting, rest, and the use of insulin. With some patients the group procedure is more effective for this purpose than the individual one (927).

In small groups any personal problem, impulse, attitude, conflict, guilt, hostility, or anxiety is discussed on the basis of personal experiences to the limit of the ability of each group member to do so. The following illustration will show how a problem is taken up and carried forward by the members of the group.

"F/3	As a little girl I used to wet the bed. I used to hate to go to bed, fearing maybe I'd have an accident.
"Therapist	Those were horrible feelings.
"F/3	What happens when even big people dream they're going to the lavatory and have an accident in bed?
"Therapist	That's miserable, too.
"F/13	My mother told me I was housebroken at a year.
"F/17	I remember when I was about two years old a girl friend took down her pants in back of the garage and did her business. I thought it was awful.
"M/5	When I was about ten some of the boys would pull down their pants and the other boys would do acts with them. I think there's something in that that makes me shy with other men. I never connected it until this minute: a kind of fear of other men because of that.

"At this point M/ 4 volunteered:

" 'I remember when I was a kid, one day my dad came in and I wanted him to draw me a picture and he drew me one of me sitting on the toilet and after that I never cared to have anyone draw pictures any more.' "[5]

The most common tendency is to group patients suffering from similar disorders; however, some therapists favor mixing disorders. A hallucinating schizophrenic cannot be put into a group with psychoneurotics, but varieties of psychoneurotic and psychosomatic disorders may be mixed with advantage because the patients show a variety of manifestations of a similar problem—e.g., of hostility or of fear. Most therapists prefer closed groups; that is, those who start in the group stay with it until the whole group is finished. The advantage of this is an approximately even spacing of the progress of various members and a strong community of feeling and of interest. Other therapists keep the group in the main closed but add a new patient from time to time. The advantage of this is that the new patient is carried along rather quickly by the established ties of the rest of the group.

Certain types of patients can be very disturbing for the progress of the group. The rebellious psychopath with constant antagonism is apt to have a disrupting influence; the aggressive homosexual who exhibitionistically talks about his experiences arouses so much anxiety that the other participants may leave the group. The seriously depressed patient may have a retarding influence on all the proceedings. In large groups, the leader is very active and regulates the discussion. In smaller groups his function is similar to that in individual therapy, but more activity is indispensable.

[5] D. W. Baruch and H. Miller, Interview group psychotherapy with allergy patients, in S. R. Slavson, *The Practice of Group Therapy,* International Universities Press, New York, 1947, pp. 166-167.

He has to judge the immediate dynamic importance of problems that arise, their usefulness and disturbing quality, and may give them the proper turn. He has to keep back with gentle firmness participants who tend to dominate and has to encourage participants who are too shy to speak up.

It is indispensable to have a well-rounded interview with each participant before he joins the group, but, even apart from that, group sessions may be regularly interspersed with individual sessions.

DYNAMICS OF GROUP THERAPY

Group therapy has common elements with the dynamics of individual therapy and certain other aspects that are unique. The small groups have in common with individual therapy the atmosphere of permissiveness, release, insight, relief of anxiety and guilt. The special aspects are a removal of feelings of uniqueness and isolation. This develops through the experience that other individuals have problems similar to those of the patient. Further, there is identification with other members of the group and with the leader. There is a continuous shuttling back and forth between subjective and objective experience as the problems of interpersonal relations are not only revealed but actually experienced. The feeling of the community of problems and the identification with the group works in the direction of increasing self-esteem and strength and loosening guilt and anxiety. It is further probable that, because of the difference in the actual setting, other material than is revealed in individual therapy may come to the surface. Fear of the leader is sometimes decreased in the group situation, since patients may feel that they have allies in other patients and hence may relate more easily and be more forthright about opposing him. Genetically there is a tendency to identify the leader with the parental figure and the other patients with siblings. There is frequently intense interpersonal development between members of the group in the session; e.g., rivalry, disparagement (one member objecting to everything another one says), gratitude, and the cohesive forces must be estimated as very strong at times because the group does not "fly apart." In individual therapy also the patient has hostile feelings toward the therapist, but this does not lead to a termination of the treatment. The skillful leader of the group can utilize these phenomena of patient-to-patient transference for therapeutic purposes.

The description of group procedure given holds from adolescence up. With children, verbalization is at a minimum, and interpretation is practically absent. The children are mainly organized into small "activity" groups, where they work with arts and crafts materials. Sometimes the groups organize trips to museums, parks, theaters, and the like. The attitude of the leader is very permissive, and the rules and regulations necessary to permit smooth functioning within the group are allowed to develop gradually out of the experience of the members, with as little interference from the leader as possible. In this social setting relations between the members develop which may have therapeutic results; for example, the shy child may gradually, following the example of other members, become more self-assertive; the aggressive child, on the other hand, learns that he must curb his hostile behavior in order to remain a member of the group and be accepted by the others.

Special mention should be made of the group psychotherapy of the parents of schizophrenic children. The parents meet regularly under the guidance of the leader. In the course of the discussions it becomes evident to them that the problems their child represents are not unique, and therefore they learn to accept them emotionally. Their high, ambitious expectations for the child diminish; they do not consider his failings a reflection on themselves, and their self-blame diminishes. They learn techniques of handling the child from each other, replacing hostility toward the child and/or the neighbors' hostility with permissive understanding and with marshaling the neighbors' coöperation. As a result of the diminished pressure and punitive hostility, the child's behavior improves, further improving the parents' state of mind. The parents, of course, derive support from identification with the group and with the leader.

PSYCHODRAMA

Psychodrama is a therapeutic method in which the subject is asked and instructed to act out an emotional constellation as if he were an actor on a stage. It has been used for therapeutic purposes; it has also been used to prepare individuals for future situations; e.g., concerned soldiers enacted anticipated scenes of return to civilian status. It has been used in industry for training in handling interpersonal problems. (See Chapter XVIII.) In the following, therapeutic psychodrama will be discussed. A considerable degree of freedom and initiative ("spontaneity," in the language of Moreno) on the part of the patient is indispensable for effective psychodrama. However, the patient is not simply told to go ahead and enact something. The therapist (the "director") obtains information through an interview about the patient's symptoms, problems, and life situation. He then decides which aspect is likely to produce adequate reaction and clarification. An important device is the "auxiliary ego," enacted by a trained worker. When the patient is portraying himself in a scene, his auxiliary ego behaves like him, but in addition expresses thoughts which the patient himself does not utter but very likely had or was partly or entirely unconscious of in the stress situations. The patient may portray himself or another significant person—e.g., parent or spouse. It is possible then to get a clear picture—e.g., of how the mother behaves or how the patient sees the mother's behavior. Throughout the enactment of the scene, the director may simply observe, or he may enter with stimulating and provocative questions. Without a skilled director no adequate psychodrama is possible. After a psychodramatic session the therapist has to handle violent emotions—e.g., anger or anxiety—that have been stirred up and has to integrate the revealed material into the course of the progressing therapy.

A relatively simple case will be used here for illustration.

A woman twenty-five years old, coming in the company of her husband, complained of mild anxiety states and "nervousness." They had been married three years, and she was now five months pregnant. The therapist instructed them to enact in successive scenes how their courtship had proceeded. During this period of the psychodrama they were still in the process of "warming up," but it already became clear that they had both been shy and that each had been in doubt of the other one's affections. Then, in successive scenes, the marriage took place, and their apartment was furnished. Enacting their current life, it became evident that the husband worked during the day and went to night school or studied; she had become irritable with him because (revealed while "soliloquizing") she felt lonely at night. Following the irritability, she would feel remorseful because, instead of being a helper, she was a burden on her husband. The climax of the psychodrama came in the next scene. As the patient portrayed being alone at home —with the auxiliary ego participating—it became evident that, although largely repressing the fear, she was afraid that she would die in childbirth. The therapist then formulated to her what had been revealed in the psychodramatic session: her self-doubt, the conflict about her husband, and how these intensified the not uncommon fear of childbirth. He further said that the problems the two of them had were common human problems and encouraged them to discuss the situation with each other and to make arrangements for relieving her loneliness through friends. He pointed out that the husband was perfectionistic in his demands upon himself and suggested that he relax somewhat in his work and spend more time in the company of his wife.

It is obvious from the example given that the dramatic technique is one link in the chain of total therapeutic procedures in a given case. The procedure is often carried out with a fixed group of participants, and then those factors which are of especial significance in group therapy—i.e., the vicarious living out of emotional problems and identification (see page 200) —also play a role. A unique aspect of this therapeutic technique is that it involves action, the patient shifting back and forth, acting out real life situations, emotions, and fantasies. Interpersonal aspects of the patient's problems are experienced. The technique probably offers special contributions in those cases of shyness and of repression which have trouble expressing and carrying out self-assertiveness even after relevant conflicts are recognized.

SOCIOMETRY AND GROUP CONSTRUCTION

Up to about the age of twenty weeks, infants live a self-centered existence and make no contact with other infants in nurseries. Beginning with twenty weeks, they start establishing "acquaintance" with their neighbors; in other words, spatial proximity determines the relationship. Beginning with about forty weeks, perhaps based on greater intelligence and initiative, more complex organization develops. Certain children are sought after more and become leaders. These complex organizational patterns persist and are evolved still further in the course of later development. Sociometry is the investigation and formulation of patterns of attraction and repulsion in groups.

Attractions and repulsions can be investigated by observation, participation in the group, and "sociometric" tests. The last consist of asking the respective persons whom they would like to sit next to in class or live with in the same cottage. Other criteria can also be chosen, and first, second, third, or any number of preferences can be asked for. It is then found that there are (1) unchosen, or "isolated," individuals; (2) "stars"—i.e., individuals who are chosen by a great number of the subjects; (3) "pairs"—i.e., individuals who express preference for each other; (4) "triangles"—A prefers B, B prefers C, C prefers A—and "quadrangles," etc.; (5) "chains," in which A expresses preference for B, B for C, C for D, etc. If the test is repeated at a later period, the well-adjusted persons show a tendency to be chosen by a greater number of people, whereas the maladjusted are chosen by fewer or by the same number of people. These relationships (pairs, stars, etc.) are present not only in attractions but also in repulsions—i.e., dislikes.

Sociometric therapeutic or preventive procedure to diminish tensions that make for psychopathology is illustrated by the following example:

In a home for delinquent girls the new arrivals were given an opportunity to meet the house mothers (heads of the cottages). They then could express first, second, and so on, choices for house mothers. Similarly, the house mothers were given the opportunity to express preferences among the newly arrived girls. This was called the parent test. The girls then were given the opportunity to meet representative girls from the respective cottages. Again preferences were asked. The best situations, of course, turned out to be those where there were mutual likes. Similar procedures can be followed in situations where individuals work in pairs.

INSTITUTIONALIZATION

The most dramatic form of environmental change effected in the treatment of patients is institutionalization, recommended chiefly for the cure of psychotics, but also for drug addicts and some very sick psychoneurotics.

Commitment to mental hospitals or sanatoriums not only protects the community from dangerous patients, but helps the patient also. It guards him against self-injury, against social, moral, or financial harm—for example, from sexual misdemeanors or reckless financial ventures. It further removes him from the influence of people who may have precipitated his illness.

Institutional care imposes a regular routine upon the patient. He gets up, eats, and carries out his tasks according to a definite schedule. The fact that he does not decide these things for himself has a stabilizing, calming effect if the routinization is not too rigid. Furthermore, confinement frees the patient from many of the problems which have pressed upon him heavily, and it safeguards him from humiliation, sneers, and ridicule; it places him, instead, in a more sympathetic and understanding environment, in which people regard him as sick and not as an object of horror, awe, or laughter.

In some institutions the hospital program is varied to meet each patient's individual needs. Thus some patients may be allowed special consideration; for example, the patient may ask to have his psychotherapist visit him in his room instead of going himself to the therapist's office; in the case of others firmness is used in keeping them in line with the institution's routines and regulations. Activities are provided for them in a similar manner. One patient may be encouraged to participate in competitive sports, either because he was good at them before and they therefore have a restitutive effect, or to prepare him for competition in other fields; another may be encouraged to take part in noncompetitive activities, either because it is easier for him or to encourage an over-competitive individual to derive satisfaction from otherwise desired activities not involving rivalry. A patient may be assigned activities which involve coöperation with a group, or he may be assigned solitary tasks.

Occupational therapy plays an important role in any institutional program. First of all, it offers the patient an interesting, constructive task with which to occupy himself. He receives attention in the form of instruction and earned praise from someone trained in dealing with emotionally ill persons. A well-completed piece of work gives the patient a sense of achievement. It allows him to develop any specialized talents he may have, as in painting, designing, or carpentering. It also is a medium for sublimation of impulses, as when a patient with strong hostility does metal work requiring hammering.

Finally, of course, institutionalization makes various forms of psychotherapy and medical therapy available, such as hydrotherapy, electric or insulin shock therapy, malaria treatment, and other forms of fever therapy. These will be discussed in connection with the various psychoses.

SUGGESTED READINGS

A good introduction is Maurice Levine's *Psychotherapy in Medical Practice* (540). We can recommend Schilder's *Psychotherapy* (831), Diethelm's *Treatment in Psychiatry* (211), and Stekel's *Techniques of Analytical Psychotherapy* (895). Rogers' *Counseling and Psychotherapy* (783) is recommended for interview therapy, Slavson (869) for group techniques, and Hamilton (381) for social work. The title of Watson's "Areas of agreement in psychotherapy" (955) speaks for itself. Hoch's *Failures in Psychiatric Treatment* is very instructive. Fromm-Reichmann's *Principles of Intensive Psychotherapy* is a very important contribution to the field.

XV Suggestion and Hypnosis

THE NATURE OF SUGGESTION

There are two types of suggestions: ideomotor and prestige (703, 437). It is difficult to separate them perfectly, for the two intermingle in many actual instances of suggestibility; but it is possible to find extreme and therefore relatively pure instances of each. Prestige suggestion is, by definition, a response to social stimuli, whereas ideomotor suggestion may or may not be.

IDEOMOTOR SUGGESTION

William James long ago postulated the theory that, unless it were positively inhibited, an idea tended to express itself quite automatically and reflexly in corresponding behavior. This theory was attacked by Thorndike and others, mainly on the ground that "idea" is an unscientific concept which no one can define. If, however, stimuli and stimulating situations are used instead of ideas, there is a great deal of evidence to indicate that James's theory can be taken seriously. So long as there is no inhibiting force, a stimulus, whether externally or internally administered, tends definitely to elicit the response which is suitable to it or has been connected with it. The reason this ideomotor tendency is not more apparent in everyday life is that when we are conscious and wide awake we tend to inhibit it.

Consciousness is, from this point of view, a state in which inhibitory tendencies are alert and ready for action. There are various states in which these tendencies are themselves inhibited or dulled—sleep, drunkenness, fever, great emotion, abstraction and absent-mindedness, and, as we shall see, hypnosis. In reality, many of the phenomena that are called imitation, sympathy, and empathy are frequently simple examples of this fundamental ideomotor tendency.

Hull (437) describes several experiments that will serve as illustrations of ideomotor suggestion. For instance, a subject who is brought into a room where a person is straining vainly to touch a point that is just beyond his reach will himself unconsciously strain. There are innumerable examples in everyday life. For example, as the characters on the motion-picture screen smile, so also will the audience smile; as they frown, so will the audience frown. The spectators at a football game will lean over to the right as the player attempts to make a wide sweep round the right end.

PRESTIGE SUGGESTION

Prestige suggestion may be made clear by the following examples: The observers at an art gallery are apt to consider that the painting which has received first prize is the most beautiful. The opinions of the rich, the powerful, the people in authority, receive more attention and are taken more seriously than those of the poor and the weak. He who is confident and sure of himself is much more likely to have people do his bidding than the person whose self-esteem is low. The experiments of Cantril, Lorge, and others have shown that the prestige of the name of the creator of a work of art is important in determining its evaluation. Thus a group of people listening to music, supposedly by Beethoven, will rate it high; they will rate it much lower if they are told that its composer is relatively unknown.

The concept of dominance status is essential to an understanding of prestige suggestion. This is defined as the relationship whereby other people defer to one's impulses, wishes, opinions, etc. The person whose status is subordinate is likely, where there is a choice between his own opinions and those of someone else, to consider the other's opinion better than his own. Thus he usually does what he is told; he takes suggestions, both direct and indirect.

THE NATURE OF HYPNOSIS

CONDITIONING FACTORS IN HYPNOSIS

Some authors advance the following conditioning theory and experiment to explain at least one factor in the process of hypnosis.

The hypnotist asks the subject to stare at a bright light. The subject does so, and his eyes become tired. Consequently, when the hypnotist says, "Your eyes are tired," the subject's eyes are tired from staring at the bright light. As a result of a series of such incidents, the subject generalizes to the effect that, since everything the hypnotist has said so far has been proved true, whatever else he says must also be true. From then on, the hypnotist's instructions will cause the subject to act as though those instructions were true. In support of this hypothesis, this experiment was made (170):

Words flashed on a screen were followed by phenomena for which the words were symbols, while the skin resistance (PGR) was being continuously recorded. Thus the word "music" was followed by the playing of music. After a certain number of such trials, the words "electric shock" were flashed on the screen and were not reinforced by actual electric stimulation. In a group of fifteen subjects, eleven, or 73 percent, gave a PGR response greater than to any of the other stimuli. In another group of fifteen subjects, where none of the stimuli were reinforced, 13 percent, or two, gave the greatest PGR response to the words "electric shock." (This type of conditioning, based on generalization, the authors have called "abstract conditioning.")

THE "WAKING TRANCE"

Suggestion and hypnosis are normal and universal manifestations. Many of the phenomena observed in a hypnotic trance may be seen in the waking state, and most if not all of them may be elicited in everyday life, but with more trouble.

Let us now consider some phenomena that are common in everyday life and which will help us to understand the hypnotic trance—for example, the state in which attention is concentrated on a certain problem. Attention is a total response of the whole psyche in which every tool of adaptation is brought to bear upon a problem. The more the attention is focused in one direction, the less will be paid to peripheral objects or happenings, or to stimuli that are irrelevant to the problem. A person who is solving a geometry problem or reading a fascinating book will show great sensitivity to anything connected with what he is doing, but a decrease in sensitivity to everything else. He will become to some extent anesthetic—blind to what is happening around him, deaf to irrelevant noises, anosmic to irrelevant odors, etc. Certain motor phenomena may also appear; that is, he may show waxy flexibility (see Glossary), or he may become rigid or tense. There will also be some amnesia for everything that happened during this period of concentration and that was unrelated to the problem. In other words, such a person may be said to be in a trance. And if we now test the very plausible hypothesis that at once comes to mind—that in the waking trance, as in the hypnotic trance, suggestibility (or ideomotor tendency) is enhanced—we shall find it to be corroborated. The student can easily try the experiment himself. If, when he is at the movies with a friend, he waits until the friend becomes totally engrossed with the film and then whispers quietly, and without disturbing his absorption, "Raise your arm" or "Open your mouth," the command will often be obeyed. However, it must be administered with just the right intensity; furthermore, the waking trance will ordinarily be broken immediately after the suggestion is complied with.

METHODS

Usually the technique of hypnosis employs some combination of relaxation, visual concentration, and verbal suggestions. Neither relaxation nor sensory fatigue produced by concentration is absolutely necessary. For that matter, it is possible to induce trance without suggestion if the other two elements are present and the individual is particularly susceptible to trance.

Some give suggestions in a friendly way; others give authoritative commands; still others are coldly scientific and impersonal. Some use suggestions of sleep; others never do this. Some prefer phonograph records for presenting the various suggestions. All of these methods are successful. The technique finally chosen is a matter of the operator's personal predilection and of the needs of the particular patient.

Thus, in assaying the relative efficacy of various hypnotic operators and the validity of their results, we must take into account the fact that there are many kinds of hypnotic trance and many techniques for inducing them. It is not surprising, then, that different experimenters sometimes come to different conclusions. For instance, some are convinced that women are easier to hypnotize than men; others believe that the opposite is true. Some operators report great feats of endurance and remarkable memory efficiency which others do not observe in their cases.

Hypnotic regression consists of the following: A particular event in the subject's past may be chosen ("It is your first day at school") or a particular age ("You are five years old"). If the procedure is successful, the subject relives the event and displays the attitudes and feelings characteristic of the age level suggested.

In "automatic writing" the subject's hand writes while he remains unaware of this activity (see the case on page 436). In "crystal gazing" the subject is asked to stare into a crystal ball while the hypnotist describes a particular scene or merely suggests that the patient will experience vivid visual images related to the problems under investigation. Further, the patient may be told to have a dream, either while under hypnosis or during normal sleep, which will clarify certain problems. Conflict situations may be suggested to the patient. (See Chapter IV.)

THE CLASSICAL PHENOMENA OF HYPNOSIS

Amnesia. The subject who is in a deep trance will spontaneously develop an amnesia for everything that happened during the trance even if it lasted an hour and he carried on conversations and obeyed various commands. If the trance is not so deep, he may have hazy memories or even a clear recollection of what happened.

Anesthesia. In the deep trance, the subject will develop spontaneously a deafness to any other sound but the operator's voice. The operator can suggest almost any other anesthesia—anosmia, insensitivity to pain, etc.

During the course of an experimental hypnotic trance, the subject began to moan with pain and doubled up with a stomach cramp. She was asked what had happened, and she reported that she had eaten too much of some bad food. It was suggested to her immediately that the pain had disappeared, but she kept on doubling up, rubbing her stomach, and groaning. When she was asked if it hurt, she said no, in spite of her groaning. She was also told that it would not hurt when she woke up. Just after this, she broke through the trance spontaneously and awoke, but continued groaning and rubbing her stomach. She looked surprised; and when asked what was wrong, she said she didn't know. She was asked if she was in pain and said no. She was then asked, "If it doesn't hurt you, why are you behaving like that?" She replied, "I don't know. It just seems that I can't stop doing this."

Motor Phenomena. Such motor phenomena as complete limpness, complete rigidity, waxy flexibility, and localized paralysis can be induced. These will ordinarily not develop spontaneously, but must be suggested.

Hypermnesia. Experimenters have found that forgotten events at times can be recalled on command more easily in the hypnotic trance than in the waking state (see page 213).

Partial Release of Inhibitions. There is a slight weakening of the subject's inhibitions. This means simply that a subject who wants very much to do something which he cannot do in the waking state will find it somewhat easier in the trance. The most important inhibitions remain active, and people will do almost nothing in the ordinary hypnotic trance that they will not do in the waking state. The popular belief concerning the increased possibility of criminality and immorality is almost entirely false; a recent paper by Erickson (247) practically proves this, although Wells (966) presents contradictions of Erickson's results.

Loss of Capacity to Initiate Action. The patient in a trance will sit quietly and do nothing until he is given some suggestion. If he is commanded to walk about the room or perform some task or behave naturally, he will do so. Afterward, he will sit stolidly without moving. An onlooker will notice that he is slow in his movements and appears dreamy.

Heightened Suggestibility. Suggestibility is, of course, the most startling characteristic of hypnosis. As long as the suggestions are acceptable, the patient will carry them out without question. This statement holds not only for behaving and talking, but also for anesthesias, paralyses, and amnesias. Hallucinatory, visual, auditory, and painful experiences can also be suggested; as we shall see, various bodily states—headaches, nausea, sleepiness, and insomnia—can be induced by suggestion in the hypnotic trance.

"I had induced hypnosis in a boy of twelve who was extremely fond of chocolate éclairs. Giving him a plate to hold, I suggested that he should see on it a chocolate éclair. Now, on this plate was a reproduction of Millet's celebrated picture The Gleaners, in which there are three female figures, two bending forwards and one upright. After a second or two, the boy said in high glee: 'But there are three chocolate éclairs, and two of them have an odd shape, for they are bent in the middle.' This was a well-marked instance of hallucination or illusion by compromise."[1]

[1] C. Baudouin, *Suggestion and Auto-Suggestion,* Dodd, Mead & Co., New York, 1921.

HYPNOSIS AND PHYSIOLOGICAL DEPRESSION

There is some evidence that the hypnotic trance may be considered to resemble a physiological depression, akin, in some ways, to the state produced by alcohol, anesthesia, sleep, fatigue, etc. It is easy to agree with this when a hypnotized patient is observed. He breathes more slowly, he is lethargic and relaxed, his arms hang limply, his head slumps on his chest, his eyes are closed, his responses are much slower, and in general he looks as if he were asleep.

In this connection, several experimental findings are of interest. Using a plethysmograph, Walden noted a sudden short constriction of the peripheral blood vessels at the beginning of hypnosis, which was followed by a gradual dilation until the end of the trance. At the moment the subject awakened, there was again a brief constriction. Pulse rate and respiration became slower, and there was a steady but slight drop in the rectal temperature, with a concomitant rise in surface temperature. Dorcus and Shaffer found that blood pressure decreased during a trance, along with a drop in the pulse rate. Even though there is no definite evidence to this effect, Beaunis believes that muscular tension is lessened in a trance, although not uniformly; he also reports a considerable spontaneous decrease in auditory acuity. Hoff and Schilder found that some subjects who could not be hypnotized easily could go into a trance if they took a hypnotic (paraldehyde).

These and similar findings all seem to support the hypothesis that the suggestion tendency is stronger when the highest nerve centers are inhibited. However, the electroencephalogram during hypnosis does *not* show the changes that are regularly observable during sleep.

SOME FALLACIOUS NOTIONS ABOUT HYPNOSIS

Certain erroneous ideas regarding hypnosis have persisted down to the present time. Among the more common are the following: "Not everyone can hypnotize; a person must have some electrical or supernatural power or animal magnetism." This is incorrect. Hypnosis consists of creating conditions that encourage the appearance of a tendency which inheres not in the hypnotist, but in the person being hypnotized.

"Hypnosis is abnormal, weird, and supernatural; hypnosis is dangerous." Actually, in the hands of the skilled technician who uses it for scientific or therapeutic purposes, it is a powerful instrument for good. No harmful effects have ever been confirmed in the literature.

"Only people with weak wills can be hypnotized; hypnosis breaks down will power." Actually hypnosis has nothing to do directly with will power. If anything, it is the people with somewhat stronger wills who are most hypnotizable (618, 963). Even long-continued trances need have no effect on this quality. Some subjects have been hypnotized more than a thousand times without any perceptible effect on their will power (Erickson).

"Only stupid people can be hypnotized." Just the opposite is true. The ability to be hypnotized is positively correlated with intelligence.

"Immoral and criminal acts are possible under hypnosis." It has been stated earlier that this is not true.

"People are able, when hypnotized, to do things hitherto impossible—play the piano, speak an unfamiliar foreign language, etc." Actually people can do nothing in the trance that they cannot do in the waking state. A person who plays the piano well but has stage fright while playing may be able to play better when hypnotized because the fears that inhibit the display of ability may be controlled by hypnosis.

HYPNOTIC THERAPY

HYPNOTIC SUGGESTIONS

Before a patient is treated by the hypnotic technique, he should be closely studied during interviews. First of all, everything significant about him must be found out. Second, this procedure enables the more intelligent use of hypnotic suggestions. Hypnotic suggestions should not be simple, direct commands about a symptom; they should refer to situations that the patient is about to face. For example, the operator suggests that the patient will react more desirably if he puts himself in a certain frame of mind: "You will have a good time at the party; everyone will like you. You will feel gay."

The reaction to the hypnotic technique varies with the patient, and usually only a small percentage of people can go into a deep trance easily; yet adequately given suggestions are of therapeutic value, even with patients who do not go into a deep trance (Hoff and Schilder).

Suggestions given during a trance will sometimes help considerably in breaking various undesirable habits—insomnia, nail-biting, cigarette-smoking, etc. However, this is not altogether simple, for the suggestions must be very detailed and must be given repeatedly over a long period of time. It is not enough to say to the hypnotized person, "Stop smoking." He may have to be hypnotized again and again, and the suggestions be made gradually, rather than being given as a direct command. Thus the operator may suggest that the cigarettes he will smoke the following day will taste like straw or cause disgust. In relieving insomnia, the patient is not told merely to sleep well; the operator tells him that when he goes to bed he will feel relaxed, thoughts of sleep will come into his mind, and that as he thinks these thoughts he will fall sound asleep. Similarly, anxiety symptoms, various bodily symptoms characteristic of emotional stress (a lump in the throat, palpitation, etc.) respond well to hypnotic suggestions. Sometimes more serious symptoms (tics, enuresis, etc.) can also be relieved (see 871).

BREAKING THROUGH AMNESIAS

If the therapist has the patient's coöperation and can induce a fairly deep trance, it is comparatively easy for the patient to recover forgotten material from alcoholic amnesias and hysterical fugues. The patient who has "lost his personal identity" may remember his name, address, etc. Also, because of the hypermnesia in hypnosis, the trance may be a useful adjunct to ordinary psychotherapeutic work, particularly in exploring and recovering early memories, even memories of traumatic experiences that have been partially repressed.

A practiced hypnotic subject came back from a drunken week-end party with a complete amnesia for all the events of both days. A few days later she received a letter from her hostess asking for a ten-dollar bill that had been entrusted to her. In deep trance, she remembered that she had worn a borrowed dressing gown and had put the bill in the pocket of this gown. She wrote to her hostess, and the bill was found in the gown.

INTERVIEW UNDER HYPNOSIS

Any of the general processes of psychotherapy may be carried on under hypnosis as well as in the waking state. Thus the therapist may impart interpretations or therapeutic insights to the hypnotized patient if for some reason he does not wish the patient to have any memory of the process. Frank discussion is sometimes easier for patients in a trance than it is in the waking state; embarrassing or shocking subjects can be discussed more easily. It is often possible to break through a severe block or resistance that threatens to slow up treatment by putting the patient into a trance and encouraging free association.

REMOVING HYSTERICAL SYMPTOMS

In cases of hysteria, when it is desired to remove a symptom quickly, the hypnotic trance is a fairly easy means of doing this. Suggestion can be used when the patient is awake; for example, the therapist may apply an electrical current to a paralyzed limb and tell the patient that this will cure the paralysis. In one case, pernicious vomiting was stopped with aspirin tablets, simply by convincing the patient that these tablets were a wonderfully potent new medicine. However, such measures are usually purely symptomatic treatments; they do not go to the root of the disturbance. The symptom may be expected to reappear later or to be replaced by another hysterical symptom.

HYPNOSIS AS AN ANALGESIC

When a deep trance can be induced, pain may be easily dispelled. Esdaile has reported a long series of surgical operations, including amputations, abdominal, and other equally severe operations, where hypnosis was the only anesthetic. It has often been used as an analgesic during childbirth; there can be no possible harm to either mother or child.

THE INDUCTION OF RELAXATION BY HYPNOSIS

The widespread effects of the release of bodily and psychic tensions have been amply demonstrated by Jacobson (although the psychodynamics of relaxation are often much more complex than he indicates). There are scattered reports of similar effects achieved by hypnotic relaxation—fatigue and insomnia being relieved, a calm and peaceful state of mind being induced, constipation being removed.

ABREACTION OF TRAUMATIC EXPERIENCES

Under hypnotic suggestion the patient relives an emotional experience he has had in the past, either one associated with the onset of symptoms or one which, on the basis of his clinical knowledge of the patient, the therapist believes to be of importance in the genesis of the illness. The emotions accompanying the experience may recur in their original intensity or may be toned down. There is usually an attempt to reintegrate the material with the patient's present life so that he may understand its relationship with his current attitudes. The abreaction usually involves the use of hypnotic regression.

A patient suffered from a "fear of falling which disappeared soon after the beginning of the treatment, . . . after her . . . re-living in hypnosis with intense affect two childhood . . . experiences. In one she fell from a high chair and in the second she fell from a hammock at the age of seven. It is difficult to describe the vividness with which she cried in terror: 'Save me, Dr. B., save me—I'm falling!' "[2]

HYPNOANALYSIS

Hypnoanalysis represents various combinations of the techniques of psychoanalysis with hypnotic procedures. The major part of the therapy may be carried out with the patient conscious, with use of hypnosis at special points in the treatment—e.g., in order to break through strong resistance more quickly or to uncover repressed material. On the other hand, the major part of the therapy may be carried out using the hypnotic state, free association, and interpretation along with such special procedures as abreaction, suggested dreams, directed associations (the patient is asked to tell

[2] M. M. Gill and M. Brenman, Treatment of a case of anxiety hysteria by an hypnotic technique employing psychoanalytic principles, *Bull. Menninger Clin.*, 1943, 7, p. 166.

everything that comes to his mind in relation to a stated problem), automatic writing, and regression.

During the course of hypnoanalysis, the patient reacts in much the same way as do patients in psychoanalysis. Thus resistances occur, and transference reactions develop.

Almost all of the patient's therapy sessions were carried out under hypnosis. During the course of the treatment the following transference reactions occurred: Early in the treatment she developed an exaggerated deference to and regard for the therapist. She often called him "sir" and once inadvertently substituted his name for God in her prayers. She occasionally had outbursts of resentment toward him, once when he refused to give her advice about some practical matters. When her wish to have sexual contact with the therapist or to obtain a penis from him appeared most clearly, she would feel that the therapist was laughing at her for presuming to think of herself as on intimate terms with him.[3]

The following case describes the course of hypnoanalysis.

The patient was a woman seventy-one years old whose husband died one year before she entered the sanitarium. Six months following his death, she began to complain of acute stomach distress and resulting insomnia. Although she had complained for forty years of "gas on the stomach," which had begun during her sole pregnancy, it had never before disturbed her so intensely. She became depressed, withdrawn, and had spells of violent contortions and hopping and a ritual in which she would let a handkerchief drop and then watch to see whether "it stood up straight in a point" or "just fell flat."

At twenty-eight she had married a quiet, withdrawn man who strongly disliked the city. Because the patient could not tolerate country life, they lived separately during much of their married life, although they saw each other frequently. After her husband became impotent in his fifties, he began to help attractive middle-aged widows who were in financial distress. When the patient first discovered this, she impulsively went to see a lawyer for advice on a divorce action. Although she abandoned the idea of divorce almost immediately, her husband never forgave her for this impulse.

When asked in hypnosis to "go back" to the time when her insomnia first began, the patient said: "I hear Ed (her husband) . . . going down the front steps and oh . . . it's awful, awful . . . wicked, selfish . . . I am thinking . . . of, could I have ever really thought that . . . yes, I know I did . . . I'm thinking I wish he were dead!" She sobbed bitterly over the hostility which she had felt toward her husband since she had suspected him of infidelity. During the following sessions she discussed the almost irreconcilable opposites of her feeling toward her husband. She had admired and respected him, but she had wanted him to love her in a warm and demonstrative manner and had hated him for his coldness. She could not tolerate the "grudge" she carried against him for rejecting her and thought that when he died it "would be all over." She had felt "trapped" into becoming preg-

[3] Based on a case presentation in M. M. Gill and K. Menninger, Techniques of hypnoanalysis, a case report, *Bull. Menninger Clin.*, 1946, **10**, 110-126.

nant. She had acceded to her husband's demand for a child in order to "win his favor." Following the discussion of this problem, she gradually gave up her complaints of stomach distress.

She was asked to reëxperience her feelings and thoughts in relation to the handkerchief ritual, and later she was told that she would visualize the object which the handkerchief represented. After various developments, she finally said, "You know—I have been telling you that when my husband lost his desire I lost mine too . . . but yesterday it suddenly flashed into my mind that for years and years I kept dreaming about having that sacred relationship with Ed. . . . In my dream I would think to myself, 'At last I've done it—at last it's happened. Now we will be friends again!' Not that the sacred relationship is all there is to marriage but it seemed like if I could get him to become interested in me again that way that perhaps we could start all over again." Then she realized that the handkerchief symbolized her husband's penis. It then became clear that much of the patient's strange behavior symbolized her desire to undo the estrangement from her husband by renewing their sexual relationships. Thus, following his death, she felt an uncontrollable desire to lie on her back in bed. She interpreted her "hopping spells" to mean that they represented "hopping up and down with joy" in response to the unconscious thought that she and her husband were again friends. Thus her symptoms had an erotic meaning, at the same time had a "restitution value"—to undo her death wishes against her husband, bring him back to life, reinstate a good relationship between them, and satisfy her dependency longings.[4]

SUGGESTED READINGS

The book by Brenman and Gill (118) gives a survey of the field with case presentations. Wolberg's book *Medical Hypnosis* (986) is the most recent publication on the therapeutic aspects. The earlier books by Bernheim (87), McDougall (596), etc., are still readable and useful. Hull's *Hypnosis and Suggestibility* (437) sums up his work and that of many of his students. For other approaches, see the papers by Erickson and his collaborators (245-252) and by Wells (964-966). For other experiments, see Murphy, Murphy, and Newcomb, *Experimental Social Psychology* (703). A psychoanalytic approach to hypnosis is presented by Schilder and Kauders, *Hypnosis* (835).

[4] Based on a case presentation in M. Brenman and R. P. Knight, Hypnotherapy for mental illness in the aged: Hysterical psychosis in a 71-year-old woman, *Bull. Menninger Clin.*, 1943, 7, 188-198.

XVI Psychoanalytic Therapy

As in all disciplines, it is important to differentiate in psychoanalysis among (1) the method of procedure, (2) the data obtained, (3) working concepts and hypotheses, and (4) practical applications, the most important of which here is therapy.

Many short illustrations will be used to make the relationship between data and working concepts clear; in addition to these, we shall carry one case throughout the entire chapter, always giving as many facts about this patient as are needed for the subsequent discussion.

A Typical Case. A thirty-year-old woman, whom we shall call A. V., applied for psychoanalytic treatment because of an emotional depression which followed a disagreement with her husband. (This was her second marriage.) The disagreement had arisen over the departure of her husband, who was a prominent bacteriologist, from the city for a period of two months, for occupational reasons. She knew the reason for his leaving the city and approved of it intellectually, yet she asked him not to go. When he left in spite of her request, she became resentful and depressed; her depression continued even after he returned.[1] She suffered from insomnia, fatigue, loss of appetite, frequency of urination, and partial frigidity.

She was a very gifted laboratory worker and had published several articles and books on scientific problems. When not obviously depressed, she was calm, serene, and poised. Her relationship with her husband was fundamentally good. They respected and were emotionally attached to each other, and had many scientific and artistic interests in common.

The following series of events occurred during the third month of analytic treatment: One Friday, the patient stated that she felt very cheerful, that her depression had disappeared, and that she was grateful to the analyst for this. In fact, she thought that she was quite well. The analyst reminded her that some of her complaints, such as insomnia, frequency of urination, and sexual frigidity, were still present, and that she was still having dreams in which her husband was killed (hostility) and others in which she was a little girl and the analyst was feeding her

[1] The condition from which she suffered is commonly termed "hysterical depression."

(dependence). He pointed out to her that the attitudes and motivations which had been responsible for her complaints had not been clarified, that the disappearance of her complaints did not mean the elimination of the needs and reactions responsible for the original appearance of her depression, and that her feeling of well-being was based chiefly on the fact that she felt that she had the complete and exclusive care of the analyst. From now on we are concerned not so much with the analyst's remarks as with the patient's reactions and behavior in response to them.

The patient was ten minutes late for her interview the following Monday; this was unusual, because hitherto she had always been prompt. She gave no explanation for her lateness, but talked in a lively and pleasant manner during the hour, and then, contrary to her usual habit, left without saying good-by. On Tuesday she was late again, talked freely, and again left without saying good-by. On Wednesday she came on time and related a dream that she had had Sunday night. This was unusual because she regularly told of her dreams in the next interview. Her dream was as follows: She was back in the college dormitory in a room that was shaped like the analyst's office. There were five beds in the room, one of them being placed as the analyst's couch was. She was dissatisfied in the dream because she had to sleep in a room with four others, but consoled herself with the thought that eventually she would have a room to herself.

The patient thought of the following facts in connection with the dream: She recognized that the dream represented the analyst's room because of the similarity of the rooms and the location of the analyst's couch. In connection with not having a room to herself, she remembered that a former classmate of hers had once remarked: "An intelligent and scientifically trained individual can know as much about himself as an analyst can. Real friendships can do more for one than analysis. Analysts are really pretentious." In connection with the five beds in the room, she thought of the fact that she was the oldest of five siblings.

On reviewing some of the events of the last few days, the patient said that she had been late on Monday because she bought a dress before coming for the analytic hour. She was surprised to hear from the analyst that she had been late on Tuesday also. She did not remember it. Likewise, she could not remember at first that she had left twice without saying good-by, and then she said: "I don't know why I did it, I just did not feel like saying good-by." She then added, "I do not know why I waited three days before telling you about the dream. I did not think of it on Monday, and I felt reluctant to relate it on Tuesday." The analyst asked her: "How would you explain the events of the last few days?" She replied, "I don't know."

The various aspects of the patient's behavior—namely, being late twice, leaving twice without saying good-by, not relating her dream at the proper time, the content of her dream, her thoughts in connection with the dream, forgetting part of her behavior, and her inability to account for her behavior—are all data which appear to be similar in nature and are interrelated. Such data are of value only if they can be used to construct a psychological reaction and if the meaning of this reaction can be conveyed to the patient.

The analyst told A. V. that the details of her behavior during the last few days seemed to indicate that she was resentful toward him; she was conveying to him that he was incapable, that he was not doing anything for her, that there was not much sense in her coming for treatment, and that she was better off buying a dress. A. V. replied that she was not aware of any such attitudes, but acknowledged that the incidents admitted of no other explanation. The analyst then went on to say that she really did not want to disparage him, but that she wanted exclusive and complete affection and care. This was evidenced by her dream with the disappointed wish and the later hope to have the analyst (represented by the analyst's room) all to herself. This construction becomes even more convincing if we realize that A. V.'s behavior followed the analyst's comments on Friday. She evidently evaluated his remarks as meaning that he was not willing to give her this exclusive affection and care.

We can ask why the patient forgot part of her behavior, why she was unable to give an explanation, and why she spoke cheerfully and politely during all this period if she was resentful. There were several reasons for this. The chief reason becomes evident when we consider how the patient took the analyst's comments about her resentment and her desire for exclusive affection and care. She was distressed about them; they represented a blow to her self-esteem and her ideals. She felt, first of all, that she ought not to be resentful toward someone whom she respected and whom she liked, and, further, that she ought to rely on herself and under no circumstances should she crave dependence.

This case gives the student an idea of what takes place in the analytic hour, what types of problems arise, and how they are handled. We can now proceed to a detailed discussion of the methods of procedure, the data obtained, and some working concepts.[2]

METHOD OF PROCEDURE

The most common practice is that the patient comes five times a week on consecutive days, that he lies on the couch, and that the analyst sits at the head of the couch outside the patient's range of vision. However, the procedure has become more elastic in the last fifteen years, and the patient may come three or four times a week and may have the choice of sitting across the desk from the analyst or lying down. Some investigators maintain that with some patients equally significant material and equal therapeutic results can be obtained by spacing the interviews once a week or even less frequently (Alexander, Hahn-Kende).

The patient is instructed to tell the analyst everything that enters his mind, regardless of whether it is embarrassing or foolish, or whether it refers to his attitudes toward the analyst. These thoughts usually include events of the previous day, his complaints, his reactions, and his dreams. The analyst then interprets to the patient the meanings of and the reasons for

[2] The originator of the psychoanalytic method, which led to fundamental discoveries, and the most influential systematizer of the data, was Sigmund Freud. He has a relationship to psychoanalysis such as Pavlov has to reflexology. Important contributions of many other analysts are used throughout the book; for these, see Suggested Readings and the Bibliography.

his reaction patterns. The patient, as a rule, does most of the talking, in a spontaneous manner, during the hour. Continuity and general uniformity of procedure are important. At the same time, the setup is elastic; the analyst may, for various reasons, bring certain topics to the fore and vary different aspects of the procedure.

SIGNIFICANCE OF FREQUENT INTERVIEWS AND OF THE PROCEDURE

There are important reasons for the above procedure. Only if the patient is seen frequently can the analyst obtain all the data necessary for interpretations and convey them to the patient safely and effectively. The connection between the events of the preceding day and his responses to them are still fresh in the patient's mind, and he can tell them to the analyst without difficulty. Furthermore, events can be disturbing to the patient, and he is likely to suffer if the analyst does not see him within a day or two to interpret his reactions. The problem of the frequency of visits mentioned previously is an individual one. With the majority of patients, during most of the treatment, there may be no significant difference in the information obtained and the therapeutic effect accomplished between five, four, and three visits a week. With some patients, or at some periods of any treatment, raising the number of visits from three to four may make the difference between the treatment being stalled and moving ahead constructively. Frequent visits are indispensable with (1) patients showing intense emotional reactions, particularly anxiety, with which they cannot cope without seeing the analyst daily, and (2) patients who are inclined to be detached and also have involved ways of displacement and substitution. On the other hand, daily visits become somewhat burdensome for patients who move at a somewhat slow pace, adequate for three or four hours per week but not quite for five. Any of these situations may arise at periods in the course of the analysis.

The patient lies on a couch because he can relax more completely and "let his mind go" with greater ease. Moreover, this posture may assume changing emotional implications for him at various periods of the analysis—e.g., helplessness, submission, dependence, humiliation. On the other hand, sitting up is of distinct advantage with very anxious patients who need the closeness of supportive contact represented by seeing the analyst or for whom the submissive-dependent implication of lying on the couch, together with the defenselessness, is too great a threat. Still other patients are so much inclined to go off into fantasy without the reality-testing implied by seeing the analyst as a real person that their anxiety mounts or they maintain their aloof detachment and use the analysis without ever carrying the insights of the analysis into practice. Still other patients present a combination of anxiety, depression, detachment, and inhibition; these patients give inadequate verbal material, and the revelations from changes in their facial expressions become indispensable for the analyst. Again, all the situations mentioned may arise at certain periods in the course of the analysis (Fenichel, Mittelmann). The fact that the analyst is out of sight enables the patient to talk more easily about embarrassing and humiliating thoughts and feelings.

The frequency of interpretation varies considerably in practice. Some analysts prefer not to make any comment for weeks or even months; if the patient is silent, the analyst waits until the patient takes the initiative of talking, even if this means silence during most of the hour. Other analysts make interpretative comments during most, even the first few, hours—as soon as something is clear to the analyst and, in his judgment, can be gotten across to the patient; in case of prolonged silences, they ask the patient questions to enable him to go on with the work. For many patients, these differences in the relative activity of the analysts do not matter greatly. Other patients apparently can hardly progress with their problems without active stimulus, of the type mentioned, on the part of the analyst.

ROLE OF FREE ASSOCIATION

"Letting one's mind go" is usually referred to as "free association." This is a different "set" from that which the patient has when he applies himself to a given task deliberately. The feelings and thoughts that arise during free association are determined, just as thoughts and activities are determined when the individual is bent on accomplishing a task with conscious effort. The mood of free association is similar to that of daydreaming. It is mostly the patient's wishes, needs, hopes, fears, and angers that guide the flow of thoughts and feelings.

In analysis there are certain determining factors: the patient comes to the analyst for help, but he has definite expectations as to how the help is to be extended. He has definite reactions both to everything the analyst says and to events in his daily life while he is relating them to the analyst. Because many of these thoughts and impulses are such that the patient is ashamed of them or afraid of their consequences, he would exclude them, shut them out of awareness, if he chose topics for conversation as deliberately as he would set about solving a mathematical problem. This point is illustrated in the thoughts that A. V. had in connection with her dream. These thoughts were the recollection of some remarks which were derogatory to both the analysis and the analyst. Without free association such thoughts would not have emerged because the patient had conflicts about them.

The analytic procedure has unique features which are offered in no other situation. The patient learns to behave and speak and think in a way which is possible at no other time—he is encouraged to describe to the analyst, another human being, all his attitudes toward him; he is encouraged to reveal feelings which, under ordinary circumstances, are completely hidden; finally, in talking, he has to discard shame, embarrassment, and his desire to maintain a good impression. It is due to the uniqueness of the procedure, which, incidentally, the patient learns only gradually, that remarkable data are revealed and that the treatment can be successful.

ROLE OF DREAMS

Dreams are psychological products which represent a person's reactions to his daily experiences. They express psychological forces, the nature of which can be clearly determined with adequate methods of investigation. As we shall see, the dream is a source of significant information in the analysis; Freud called it "the royal road to the unconscious."

Dreams can be interpreted; that is, an analyst can state both the response they represent and the underlying event that caused them. In analyzing dreams, the analyst follows the patient's associations or asks him to tell what comes to his mind in connection with the dream. He follows this same procedure with each element of the dream. Adequate interpretation is possible only if the analyst knows the patient well, the circumstances under which the dream occurred, the events preceding it, and the patient's immediate reactions to them.

The psychological forces expressed in dreams are mostly emotional and often irrational. Frequently they are of a forbidden character; that is, in them are embodied the impulses—hostile and sexual impulses, attitudes of dependence, feelings of humiliation, fear, and guilt—for which a person fears punishment and about which he feels guilty. Even when an individual succeeds in maintaining a smooth front and convincing himself that his behavior is serene and sensible, his dreams may furnish information which reveals difficulties. Thus a man who feels perfectly calm during the day may tell the analyst that he feels well and is adequately adjusted, but he may have nightmares which indicate disturbances. In A. V.'s case, a dream and its associations gave a good clue to her attitudes; it revealed not only her resentment and disparaging attitude, but also her need for complete care. This case also illustrates the frequent wish-fulfilling character of dreams, which enables the individual to experience fulfillment of hopes and wishes which he would otherwise miss. Thus A. V. consoled herself with the hope that eventually the analyst would give her the exclusive care and affection that she craved.

Dreams frequently represent an attitude or idea graphically and often embody the phenomenon of so-called condensation. For example, one patient who was afraid to discuss a certain topic dreamed that he was standing panic-stricken at the edge of a precipice. Near him was a person in whom were combined the features of the analyst, of a former employer who had been extremely harsh, and of a very severe teacher who by failing him in high school had caused him one of the unhappiest incidents in his life. Thus in this patient's reaction to the current analytic situation was condensed the memory of two previous experiences.

Some interesting experiments have been done on symbolization in dreams. Schrotter (840) hypnotized a woman and discussed a homosexual incident with her. After she was awakened, she remembered dreaming that she had seen a woman carrying a traveling bag which was labeled "For women only." Betlheim and Hartmann (88) told stories with a sexual content to patients suffering from Korsakoff syndrome (memory disturbance with confabulation). When asked to repeat the stories, the patients gave a distorted version; for example, instead of the sexual event, people jumped up and down a stairway. Similar symbolizations occur in dreams. Displacement is also frequent. A. V. had pairs of dreams at times. In the first dream she saw a man in a coffin; in the second, someone was reading a simple news item. She felt calm during the first dream, but the second one disturbed her a great deal because the emotion she felt really belonged to the first dream. Condensation, symbolization, and displacement are some of the means by which "forbidden" thoughts are distorted in dreams.

Not all dreams are analyzable; that is, the analyst is sometimes unable to construct a sound interpretation when the situation is so involved that the patient finds it difficult or is unconsciously reluctant to reveal some of his attitudes. Whether everyone dreams every night is, of course, impossible to answer because of the lack of adequate proof, although recent work with electroencephalograms gives some indication that at least some periods of sleep are dreamless. Unquestionably, however, a person may dream and not remember it. This is shown in the instances in which a sleeping individual says something which someone else hears. Often these remarks are analyzable and can be interpreted like the dream. An analyst's patient was once heard by his wife to say in his sleep, "That's nonsense. I know as much as you do." This man's attitude toward the analyst was at the time characterized by rivalry and an attempt to show that his knowledge was as great as the analyst's.

The duration of the average dream cannot be stated with certainty. Both accidental and experimental observations show, however, that, on the basis of the dreamer's recollections after he wakes, an amazing amount can happen and an exceedingly long period of time can be covered in an extremely short time from the observer's point of view. Maury's experience is a famous example. Once, while he was ill in bed, a piece of board fell and hit him on the back of his neck as he slept. His mother, who was sitting beside him, noticed that he woke immediately. As he waked up, he remembered a long dream in which he was captured in the French Revolution, brought before the tribunal, sentenced to be guillotined, and then guillotined.

DATA OBTAINED BY THE PSYCHOANALYTIC METHOD

Certain data can be obtained through psychoanalysis that as yet cannot be obtained in full by any other method of investigation.

CONSCIOUS AND UNCONSCIOUS TYPES OF DATA

Obviously, the analyst can obtain information from the patient only if the latter tells him something or behaves in a certain way. Under other circumstances he may surmise, on the basis of his general knowledge and previous experience, that certain types of information will be forthcoming from the patient even when it is not yet available and the evidence for it is not yet obvious. Such information, however, becomes definite data only after the patient can talk about it or show it in his behavior. It is clear from this that the patient has various degrees of consciousness concerning the information that he eventually imparts in the course of the analytic treatment. Sometimes, because of shame or guilt, the patient withholds information from the analyst, although he knows it is important and that he should speak about it. Several weeks or months may pass before he imparts the information.

A successful architect of twenty-five, who had enjoyed his work, the company of others, sports, and shows, developed attacks of anxiety in reaction to a trying life situation. Difficulty in breathing was the most severe complaint. From the age of five on, he had had the recurrent pleasurable fantasy that a woman was sitting on his chest, and at puberty he actually put a typewriter on his chest to "realize" his fantasy. The patient gave this information to the analyst after one month. Before starting analysis he had been receiving interview therapy from another therapist once a week for six months. During this entire period he had not revealed this fact to his therapist because he felt too much ashamed of it. Only under the circumstances of psychoanalytic therapy was he finally able to talk about it.

At times the patient knows that it is important to tell of the events of the previous day, his reactions to them, and his dreams, but does not because he feels that he ought to have a full understanding of and insight into all of his reactions before he speaks about them to the analyst. In such instances the patient's feeling of worthlessness and his extreme need to establish his worth in his own eyes and in those of the analyst bar the way to his imparting significant information.

At other times the patient reveals something in his behavior but cannot account for it; even when the analyst interprets it, the patient is not at first aware of his motivations. The series of incidents related about A. V. is an example of this. Only after repeated occurrences and repeated comments by the analyst does the patient's motivation become clear to him.

In still other instances the patient knows about an event that occurred the previous day, but does not speak about it at first, although he does talk about symptoms that are closely connected with it. Later in the hour, or often on direct questioning by the analyst, he relates it, and the significance of the event then becomes manifest. In such instances the patient does not impart the information because, for emotional reasons, he does not recognize the connection between his complaints and the event.

A floor manager who was under analytic treatment because of attacks of anxiety was given a rush job to do by his superior. He felt resentful at first, but then he did his work. Not long after, he had a severe attack of anxiety in which he was afraid that he was dying. In the analytic interview on the next day he described his anxiety attack in detail. He did not mention his resentment toward his superior until the analyst asked him point-blank what had happened.

The connection between the two events—his resentment and the consequent anxiety attack—was significant. The attack meant to the patient that he, a helpless individual, would be crushed by a stronger one (his superior) because he had dared to feel resentment toward him. This type of reaction was one of this patient's major problems.

The last two situations—namely, when the patient imparts some information but cannot account for it, and when he does not mention pertinent happenings or mentions them but does not see the interrelation between them and his reactions—are common in analysis. There is still another situation which is usual and very significant: the patient agrees to "tell everything" to the analyst, but he cannot, simply because he is entirely unaware of some impulses which have a very important role in his difficulties.

In spite of having decided always to tell the analyst everything, A. V. could not have told him that she felt resentful toward him or that she wanted his exclusive and unlimited care and affection because she did not know of these feelings. At the beginning of the analysis she gave no direct evidence of resentment. Only after some time was it manifest in her actions and dreams, as was shown in the incidents already related. It was still later that she was able to recognize and state her feelings of resentment openly.

The conscious and unconscious data obtainable by psychoanalysis can be classified as follows:

Need for Dependence and Complete Care. A. V.'s behavior and dream illustrate the extent of the need for dependence and care. There are extreme cases in which patients will want the analyst to be with them twenty-four hours a day, instruct them on how to behave, and handle by direct action every situation in business or at home.

Hostile Impulses Directed Toward Others. These include reactions of anger, rivalry, and the desire to injure, humiliate, destroy, or triumph over others to the point of deriving pleasure from cruelty.

This type of impulse is clear in A. V.'s case. As a rule, she did not recognize her anger reactions toward either the analyst or her husband. Instead, she became depressed. After considerable analytic work, she saw that her depressions occurred after incidents with her husband in which she might have had reason to be angry. It was still later that she experienced anger toward him.

Destructive Impulses Directed Toward Oneself. These include the impulse to injure and humiliate oneself, the attitude of self-contempt, the desire to submit, to be exploited, and to be physically injured by another.

A schoolteacher undertook analytic treatment because of dissatisfaction with his love life. He was always calm; his philosophy was one of "serenity and nonparticipation" in all significant life situations. He had dreams in which he humbly scrubbed the bathroom floor of a famous educator, but he was unaware in his daily life of the self-humiliating attitude represented by this type of dream.

Ambition, Desire for Accomplishment, Pride.

This same teacher never admitted any ambition to advance himself in his work. He changed positions several times, but only, as he put it, "to be able to work less for more pay." Considerable analytic work was necessary to make him realize that his apparent lack of ambition was due to his feeling of helplessness and his unconscious fear of dismal failure if he ever strove for success. To escape the conflict between ambition and fear of failure, he adopted an exaggerated attitude of "serenity and nonparticipation."

Desire for Closeness, Affection, Love, and Warmth.

This same man never allowed himself to become fully attached to anyone. He was married, but he said that he had chosen a woman who was self-supporting and would therefore not be dependent upon him. He opposed her desire to have a child because this would tie him to her. After the tenth month of analysis his emotional condition was characterized by a vague fear and general discomfort. This occurred after situations in which he felt comfortable, congenial, and emotionally close to someone. He soon realized that his feeling of fear resulted from his desire for closeness. In other words, he did not lack the desire for closeness and affection; he was really afraid of them. Of the several reasons for his fear, only one will be mentioned here. His desire was so exaggerated that if he yielded to it, he feared there would be no bounds to what he would do. He would kiss people on the street, would even submit to them sexually. He would be subject to utter humiliation and would be effaced as an individual. Rather than this, he chose (unconsciously) to be emotionally detached, serene, and nonparticipating.

Attitudes of Superiority; Self-Aggrandizing Trends. The patient who shows these trends not only wants to be respected and esteemed; he often has the need to consider himself superior to other individuals in some attribute.

A thirty-year-old man was unusually talented in music, art, and science; but he never followed through any pursuit, partly because he felt that any accomplishment, even becoming a famous concert artist, would not do justice to his potentialities. Both his self-disparaging and his self-aggrandizing trends manifested themselves strikingly in the analysis. He felt that the analyst was superior to him in every respect; but unless he could consider himself superior in some way, he would not be able to go on with the analysis. In his desperate need for help he finally hit on a solution: He was able to feel superior to the analyst because he (the patient) could trace his ancestry back six generations, whereas the analyst could not. This solution, however, was charged with serious conflict for him. Not until four months after he became conscious of this attitude did he tell the analyst about it because he was afraid that the analyst would discharge him—and this in spite of the fact that he knew very well that in analysis one talks about everything that comes to mind.

Oral, Genital, and Excretory Impulses and Fantasies. Various bodily functions constitute a natural and indispensable part of everyone's existence. Even so, many people have conflicts about the forms of bodily functions that are approved of by their society. Frequently the individual has impulses and desires that are strongly disapproved of both by his society and by himself. The conflicts over such impulses are extremely severe. They may appear as conscious desires and fantasies accompanied by strong discomfort, or they may be entirely unconscious.

Thus a woman may have unconscious impulses to behave as a prostitute or to deprive a man of his masculinity. Other such impulses are expressed in unconscious fantasies of a woman being a man, of urinating on other individuals with the intent to humiliate them, or of committing incest. Such impulses are shut out of awareness because of shame, self-condemnation, fear of disapproval, fear of consequences, or guilt feelings.

A. V. dreamed in response to certain situations that she moved her bowels on the analyst's bathroom floor, that she possessed both male and female organs. She was ashamed of such dreams.

Memories and Reactions of Childhood. Childhood memories generally fall into one of two classes: (1) Incidents which the patient has forgotten so completely that even if he thought about a particular period in his life, he still would not be able to remember them, even though they disturbed him greatly at the time and had a significant influence on his development. The memory of sexual seduction by an adult is such an incident.

A successful businessman who, although he was in love with his wife, drank periodically when he visited prostitutes and who had periods of depression, finally remembered what he had "forgotten"; he had been repeatedly seduced by a maid when he was three and one-half years old, and he had greatly feared his parents' disapproval and punishment. The feelings of fear and guilt, the resentment toward the maid, and his conflicts about his parents had a strong influence on his development.

(2) Incidents which the patient remembers, but certain aspects of which are either completely blotted out at first or, if remembered, are not told to the analyst until relatively late in the treatment.

A gifted musician was being given analysis because of recent difficulties in his work. For many months he told the analyst that he had been devoted to his mother, had loved and admired her. He had felt no grief over her death, which occurred when he was nineteen. In fact, not until a certain period in the analysis was he emotionally aware of the fact that she was dead. He first said that his mother had treated the children with devotion, understanding, and care, but later he related the following incident: When he was five and one-half years old, he whipped a horse to see him jump. His mother, finding this out, took the whip out of his hand and said, "I want you to feel what you are doing to the horse." With this, she whipped him. The patient was deeply disturbed, and the analyst remarked that he must have been angry at his mother. Only after considerable work was the analyst able to make him realize that he had ever had any feelings of resentment toward her. The patient had not "forgotten" the incident of the whipping. If he thought of that period of his childhood, he could always recall it; but he wanted to isolate it and not connect it with the picture he had of his relationship with his mother. He had a need to keep this relationship free from any flaw on the part of his mother, and free from any anger on his part.

Most frequently the childhood memories which are more fully recovered in the analysis and whose significance is fully elucidated fall into the second class. Whichever type of memory it is, it usually deals with attitudes of hostility and sexual activities which have been partly or completely repressed because of guilt and the fear of punishment and a loss of love.

Emotions and Attitudes of Fear and Guilt. The patients are partly or completely unconscious of certain attitudes because they consider them dangerous. The danger that they anticipate may be that of being deprived of help and gratification, or injured or destroyed, or utterly humiliated, exploited, disgraced, and condemned by others as well as by themselves. These fears arise particularly in connection with reactions of hostility, self-destruction, forbidden sexual attitudes, and rivalry. It is important to realize that the attitudes of fear and guilt may themselves not be known to the patient. He represses them for several reasons. He wants to protect himself against the feared consequences of these impulses; he can do this even more by shutting his feelings of fear and guilt out of awareness. Further, these latter feelings are extremely distressing, sometimes actually incapacitating. The patient tries to attain a state of comfort and to maintain his ability to function by repressing them. It is extremely important in analysis to uncover such reactions and make the patient realize their significance. They form an important part of the data obtained through psychoanalysis.

A social worker, aged twenty-nine, entered upon analysis when his marriage was threatened with dissolution. His wife wanted to leave him because of his continued emotional distance. This man was usually calm and aloof in all life situations. Although he maintained in the analysis that he was undisturbed, that his calmness showed genuine strength, and that it was the right way of living, he often had frightening dreams in which he was shot at or elevators fell while he was riding in them.

Attitudes of helplessness, fear of abandonment, self-condemnation, and guilt played an important role in A. V.'s reactions, but one of which she was not fully aware. At times, when she was depressed after some difficulty with her husband, she had a vague impulse to walk in front of passing cars and be injured. Such impulses were the expression of an unconscious guilt because of her hostility toward her husband; her desire to suffer was her means of atoning for this hostility and regaining her husband's love and help by rendering herself completely helpless.

WORKING CONCEPTS

Working concepts are assumptions based on observations, which attempt to establish interrelations between isolated observations and which furnish the practitioner with tools that enable him to deal with the phenomena he encounters. It is convenient to group psychoanalytic working concepts in the following classes: (1) concepts which influence chiefly the practice of the analysis itself, and which are closely connected with the method of procedure; (2) concepts which are constantly used in psychoanalytic practice, but which have wide application in the study of psychology and psychopathology; (3) concepts which systematize a large body of observations and in which the element of assumption is greatest. These last will be called hypotheses.

CONCEPTS INFLUENCING CHIEFLY THE PRACTICE OF ANALYSIS

The Patient's Need for Help. The need for help is the patient's strongest reason for beginning and continuing analytic treatment. This need, the hope of fulfilling it, and the actual experience of relief make him willing to persist even when some of the analyst's comments are distressing. The patient tells the analyst particularly about his weaknesses and disabilities, and he usually expects the analyst to concentrate on them and not on his achievements. However, it does not follow that he is happy to find out the reasons for his difficulties and eager to correct them as quickly as possible. On the contrary, he has his own emotional needs and ideas of the kind of help he should be given, and he clings to them persistently. If the help offered differs from what he wants, he reacts strongly; resentment, disappointment, fear, humiliation, and self-condemnation follow. He again requests the type of help which he felt was refused him before. All these reactions are the ultimate results of his feeling of helplessness.

The analyst is constantly aware of the patient's suffering and of his need for help. In some very precarious situations, as when there is danger of suicide or of incapacity, his most immediate task is to give the patient relief by some means. More generally, however, the concept of the patient's need for help has a long-range significance for the analyst. It is on the basis of this assumption that he denies many of the patient's requests, such as a set of rules for his conduct, and that he points out reaction patterns to the patient—e.g., hostility, or the need for exclusive affection and care—although he knows that the immediate effect will be disturbing. It is obvious from this that the working assumption of the patient's need for help is quite different for the analyst than for the patient. The statements made here are well illustrated in A. V.'s analysis. The aims of analytic therapy and the factors operating in achieving these aims will be discussed in the section on practical application. Here we wish to show that the working concept of the patient's need for help influences every activity which occurs in the analysis.

Reaction Patterns. During the analytic interview the patient reacts to occurrences in his daily life and to experiences. These reactions can be interpreted to him, and they can be further used as a yardstick for gauging the progress of the analysis. The analyst considers the analysis as progressing satisfactorily if the patient is furnishing adequate data for such interpretations, and if he can utilize these interpretations in his further reactions. All types of reactions are of significance in the analysis, including attitudes of disparagement toward the analyst. For example, A. V.'s resentment in response to the analyst's comments had its continual parallel in her daily life; it was a reaction which led to conflicts, self-condemnation, and a fear of disapproval, loss of love, and loss of health. Therefore, such reactions have to be uncovered, the reasons determined, and the attitude corrected. A. V. was not being "uncoöperative" when she resented instead of welcomed the analyst's comments; it was a useful and valuable reaction. Reactions of fear, attitudes of superiority toward the analyst, emotional withdrawal, are all significant and useful if they are clear and if they can be utilized for interpretation. If reactions are not clear, the analyst's first task is to determine what is responsible for the lack of clarity; in other words, this lack is itself considered and is dealt with as a reaction pattern.

Essential Identity of the Patient's Reactions to Daily Events and to the Analyst. The patient displays the same patterns of behavior toward the analyst as he does toward people and his work; many of these patterns are emotional and irrational. Examination and discussion of the patient's reactions to the analyst give important clues as to the needs and motivations which are responsible for the illness. Thus A. V. needed unlimited and complete affection and care; the need was the same whether her husband or the analyst was involved. While she realized that his occupation made it imperative for her husband to go away, she reacted to his departure as if he were abandoning her.

Examination of the patient's emotional reaction to the analyst is important for another reason. In spite of the latter's essentially kind, understanding, and helpful attitude, the patient often reacts to him with anger, fear, and a feeling of humiliation. The reasons for these reactions lie within the patient; the reactions are transferred by him to the analyst, a phenomenon commonly known as "transference." Because of the working concept of the transference, the analyst constantly considers what reactions the patient is displaying toward him and calls his attention to them. This is one of the most important aspects of analytic work.

The question is often raised as to how it is possible for the patient to have the same attitudes toward the analyst as he does toward other people in his daily life—his family, friends, co-workers—when he knows that his relationship with the analyst has definite limitations. The phenomenon becomes understandable, however, if we realize that the patient undergoes analysis because he feels helpless; this undertaking is of great significance for him. He feels in need of help; with this he immediately displays the reasons for his need, his needs and ideas of how help is to be given him, his conflicts about these needs and desires, and his fear of the individual from whom he wants them. Furthermore, when the analyst denies him his requests and desires, he reacts to this just as he reacts to denials in other situations. When the analyst makes interpretations which inevitably cut deep and concern vital needs, he reacts to them as he does to stresses and to threats to his vital needs in life situations. Further aspects of the patient's emotional, irrational attitudes toward the analyst will be discussed under therapy.

Resistance. When the analyst constructs a reaction from the data and interprets it to the patient, the latter is usually reluctant to accept it; he struggles against it and tries to prove the analyst wrong. The patient continues to react in this way during subsequent interviews, although he has allegedly accepted the fact that his old reaction had disadvantages. Resistance is also manifest when a patient maintains a stubborn silence, when he is unable to think of anything significant, or when he talks but omits significant facts and thoughts.

"Resistance" is a collective term for some of the most important reactions brought out by the analysis. It is prompted by the patient's struggles and his refusal to give up a vital need. For example, many of A. V.'s reactions dovetailed to maintain her vital need of complete care and dependence. She unconsciously felt that disaster would befall her without this dependence, and she therefore clung to it. In the course of repeated reactions and interpretations, the analyst made clear to her the nature of her need and the reason for its tenacity; and finally she became able not only to accept his interpretation but also to react differently. The reactions which constitute resistance are just as significant as the patient's final acceptance; in fact, the largest part of the analysis deals with resistance reactions.

PSYCHOANALYTIC CONCEPTS HAVING WIDE APPLICATIONS IN PSYCHOPATHOLOGY

Some concepts which have been created or adopted in psychoanalytic work are applicable to psychological phenomena in the individual's daily life and, in general, to psychopathology. They are used by analysts and other psychiatrists for the purpose of understanding and interpreting their observations. Such are the concepts of psychodynamics, conflict, unconscious processes, catastrophic expectations, defensive and coping reactions, the vicious circle of reactions, etc., which have been discussed in various parts of the book. These and other psychodynamic concepts have been applied to the fields of general psychiatry, experimental psychology, general medicine, anthropology, sociology, social work, criminology, art, and literature (17, 25, 483, 534, 1009, 22, 176, 200, 214, 216, 223, 820, 786, 222, 843).

HYPOTHESES

As previously stated, hypotheses are a group of integrated concepts which systematize a large body of data and contain a large element of assumption. Some of the hypotheses developed in psychoanalysis have aroused considerable controversy. Furthermore, differences exist as to what observations and what concepts derived therefrom should be considered more fundamental. These problems are important because the analyst's interpretations to the patient are based not only on immediate information but also on these hypotheses.

We shall illustrate the type of data the hypotheses are based on, and the differences in emphasis, by further facts in A. V.'s life history and another series of incidents which occurred during her analysis. It will be remembered, of course, that A. V. began analysis because of an emotional depression started by her husband's having to go away for occupational reasons.

Relationship with Parents and Siblings. A. V.'s parents, both of whom were alive, lived in a distant city. Whenever she saw her mother, they got along badly with each other. In fact, her mother had always been emotionally distant and undemonstrative to A. V. She had never praised her either as a child or as an adult. She had been frequently critical of her, especially in reference to expressions of hostility or to such activities as smoking or drinking, and, as a child, to exposing herself or to talking about the excretory functions in the presence of others. Thus A. V., when a child, had always felt herself to be without affection and had felt rejected and humiliated.

At first, in the analysis, A. V. had spoken chiefly of having always been distant toward her mother. It gradually became evident, however, that she had been very resentful toward her, and had had the consequent fear of being abandoned and condemned by her.

A. V. had always been on good terms with her father. He was emotionally warm, and A. V. was attached to him. He had been inclined to scientific work, but at his family's insistence he took over his father's business. This failed when A. V. was about ten. After that the mother became the family's chief supporter, acted superior to her husband, and was openly critical of him. A. V. was much pained by these developments. It became clear in the analysis that, besides her friendly feelings toward her father, she had also felt resentment toward him, although never as intensely as toward her mother. This resentment arose particularly at the time when he had failed in business; A. V. reacted to that almost as if he had disappointed her.

As has been said, A. V. was the oldest of five siblings. She had always got along fairly well with them, although she felt resentful when her mother made her take care of them without giving her any overt appreciation and praise.

Sexual Development. At the age of four A. V. discovered a book "belonging to father" which had on its cover a picture of Columbus in chains. She used to look at this picture and become erotically aroused. This started about the time that her mother gave birth to her second child. A. V. stopped this activity at the age of six or seven, and had not thought of it since. After remembering it again in the analysis, she herself was eager to verify this memory. During her summer vacation she took a trip home and found the book in the attic.

When A. V. was about five years old, she learned about the difference in the anatomy of the two sexes on the occasion of a mutual exposure with a boy. She was much disturbed by this experience. At the period of puberty she had elaborate fantasies of being tied to a tree by threatening men in Oriental garb, and being sexually assaulted by them.

Career and Marriage. A. V. excelled in school from the beginning; she was ambitious but very sensitive to criticism, felt easily rejected by friends, and then deeply hurt. After graduating from college, she became a laboratory worker, soon excelled in that field, and, as has already been mentioned, published numerous scientific articles and books.

Although she was attractive, she married at the age of twenty-three a man with whom she was not in love. She was convinced that she would never get anyone better; furthermore, she wanted security. She soon became unhappy, however, because she did not feel stimulated by the company of her husband and because he acted superior toward her. She was humiliated and angry; she started to spend long hours in daydreaming about men, and her work suffered. She was sexually frigid toward her husband and did not want to have children. After four years they separated at her initiative, and she moved to another city. Periods of efficient and intensive work alternated with periods of fatigue and lassitude.

She met her second husband not long after she had moved to her new surroundings. They fell in love with each other; after a year's acquaintance A. V. obtained a divorce from her first husband, and they were married. As previously mentioned, her relationship with her second husband was fundamentally good, but she suffered from partial and at times complete frigidity, as well as from periods of mild depression, fatigue, and insomnia. Her husband likewise had a psychological disturbance; whenever he encountered difficulties in his work, he developed bodily complaints, such as backaches, headaches, and nausea, as well as loss of confidence in himself and a hopeless outlook toward his work. On other occasions he was irritable and unreasonable.

They wanted to have children, but A. V. could not quite make up her mind about this. At times she would be very eager to have a child, but these were overshadowed by times when either she thought it would interfere too much with her career, or she would feel too much afraid to go through childbirth.

Another Series of Incidents During the Patient's Analysis. One evening A. V.'s husband was irritable and unreasonable with her; at the same time, however, he spoke about some difficulties that had arisen in his work. She realized that he was disturbed and knew the reason for it. She was in a dilemma because she wanted to be considerate to him; in fact, she made the ideal demand upon herself that she should under any and all circumstances help him in his distress. At the same time, however, she felt hurt and resentful. Following this episode she was depressed for about five days, felt tired and perplexed, was not able to work well, lost her appetite, and slept badly. The following are two of the dreams she had during this period:

Five couples were sitting at a table, and A. V. had to divide a piece of steak among them. One of the men sitting there was a dictator. Everyone got his share except A. V. She felt bitter and resentful. In connection with the dictator, A. V. thought of the high-handed behavior of her husband when he was irritable.

In the process of weeding out her garden, A. V. chopped off the heads of some tulips. She was disturbed over the damage. The shape of the tulips suggested a sexual symbol to the patient.

During the same five days A. V. was often irritable with the analyst.

Her depression finally ended in this way: The analyst noticed during the fourth interview that A. V. was becoming more and more distressed in response to his interpretations of her anger toward her husband, her self-condemnation and helplessness, and her sexual attitudes. He commented on this and told her that she was probably taking his comments as signs of disapproval and rejection. She replied: "One cannot take these comments in any other way. There is no excuse for me to behave as I am acting." The analyst pointed out to her that her reactions originated from conflicting vital needs and helplessness, but that she was demanding unqualified, flawless performance of herself, even while she was suffering and incapacitated. The next day she felt better; she related two dreams:

She is at a dinner party at which her girl friend shoots a man. A. V. is afraid of the police.

She is at another dinner party at which a man wants to have an intimate talk with her. They go into the bathroom. The man says: "You did well in shooting X. I love you; I want to marry you."

In connection with both the shooting and the marriage proposal, A. V. thought of her husband and the analyst.

The patient felt better at this point for two reasons: One was that she could accept her hostility without the intense self-condemnation and the fear of abandonmen that were present during the period of depression. With that she acquired more mastery over such impulses. Second, she felt that the analyst (and her husband) had forgiven her for her attitudes, that the analyst was willing to marry her and in that symbolic way give her exclusive affection and care. This latter aspect represented the illusory satisfaction of the same need for complete care as a means of help that has already been discussed.

We shall now give a general presentation of some hypotheses, and shall follow this by showing how these hypotheses apply to the data about A. V.

LIBIDO THEORY: STRUCTURE OF THE "PSYCHIC APPARATUS"

THE CONCEPT OF INSTINCT

Instincts, in Freud's concepts, are strivings which manifest themselves in characteristic bodily tension, fantasy formation, emotional experiences, character traits, and, in the case of "sublimation," cultural and intellectual activities. This concept is quite different from the usual meaning of the term "instincts." If the original aim of this striving is one of pleasure, it is called "libido." This seeking for pleasure Freud calls "sexual." In other words, for Freud, the concept of "sexual" is essentially identical with the drive for pleasure, and, as such, has a much wider meaning than just genital function.

LIBIDO ORGANIZATION

During each period of development, an organ is the dominant source of pleasure, and there is a characteristic, corresponding emotional attitude toward the environment. This is called "libido organization." During the nursing period, the dominant source of pleasure is the mouth (characteristic attitude: dependence). From the age of two to about four, it is the anus (characteristic attitude: destructiveness). At about five or six years, it is the genitals (characteristic attitude: feeling of tenderness combined with self-centered attitudes). At a still later period, if development has been normal, the genitals remain the main source of pleasure, and there are a genuine feeling of tenderness toward other individuals and an acceptance of and desire for propagation.[3]

PERSISTENCE OF INFANTILE IMPULSES; FIXATION, REGRESSION

Fixation implies a relatively strong development of psychological and bodily desires belonging to one of the libido levels of the child, together with a tendency to retain or revive these manifestations. Freud assumed that infantile impulses persist in a repressed yet unchanged form throughout life. As a result of frustration in later life, repressed infantile desires are revived, especially those belonging to libido levels at which the individual is fixated. This revival of the former types of libido organization is the special coloring

[3] The theory of the "life and death instinct" implies that all phenomena of life, including psychological phenomena, are the result of various fusions of a "life tendency" (drive for pleasure and self-preservation) and a tendency toward death (destructive and self-destructive impulses; tendency to reinstate inorganic equilibrium). The concept of "repetition compulsion" implies an inner necessity to repeat psychological experiences regardless of whether they are pleasurable or painful (303).

of the term "regression" as used by Freud. The assumption is that the patient is motivated at the time of the symptom by the unchanged infantile desires. The patient's transference attitude toward the analyst is the exact repetition of the attitudes he had in his childhood toward his parents.

NARCISSISM; SIBLING RIVALRY

The infant and also the child desire exclusive possession of the parents and want to be the sole object of their affection and care; therefore they consider all other children in the family as rivals. Their love is directed primarily toward themselves. With some further broadening—feeling of omnipotence, of magic power—this direction of one's love toward the self is termed "narcissism." The hostility toward the rival siblings is called "sibling rivalry."

OEDIPUS COMPLEX; MASOCHISM

The Oedipus complex means unconscious love for the parent of the opposite sex, and hostility amounting to a death wish toward the parent of the same sex. This results in fear of injury by the rival parent, and in feelings of guilt.[4] The best evidence for such constructions is to be found in the many male patients who dream, usually in a partly disguised form, of being intimate with their mothers and of being injured by a powerful male or a large, frightening animal (symbolizing the father). Freud considered the Oedipus complex as extremely significant in character development and as the nuclear complex of the neuroses. Because of the fear it arouses (particularly of "castration"), the child renounces or represses his sexual and hostile aims, "internalizes" the parental taboos, and thus develops conscience and ideals. This takes place about the age of five or six.

As a result of the fear, guilt, and internalized taboos, the hostile impulses at first directed toward others (sadism) may turn back on the individual himself. Together with this, the genital impulse, instead of being aroused by pleasurable stimuli, may be aroused and gratified through painful stimuli. These phenomena are manifestations of "masochism."

EGO, SUPEREGO, ID

Freud differentiates three parts in the "psychic apparatus": ego, superego, id. The id is the sum total of persistent, unconscious, infantile, pleasure-seeking, and hostile strivings. The superego comprises the functions of conscience, ideals, self-criticism, and self-observation. The conflict is between these two groups of forces. The function of the ego is to consider the individual's interest, to attempt to make his lot bearable, and to consider both

[4] The name "Oedipus complex" originated from the Greek legend of King Oedipus, who unknowingly killed his father and then married his mother. When he discovered his crime, his sense of guilt was so profound that he tore out his eyes and gave up his kingdom. Under exceptional circumstances the Oedipus complex may be conscious.

the outside world and the individual's inner battlefield. Repression, effected by the ego, is responsible for the patient's impulses being largely unconscious. Id impulses are mainly unconscious in order that danger may be avoided. Superego impulses are mainly unconscious so that forbidden strivings will be repressed all the more effectively and suffering will be alleviated. The ego further attempts to straighten things out by making compromises.

APPLICATIONS OF THESE HYPOTHESES TO A. V.'S REACTIONS

On the basis of the above concepts, the following interpretations can be made of A. V.'s reactions:

As a result of her disappointment in her parents, particularly because of the birth of the next sibling, and as a result of her resentment toward them as well as her fear of them, especially of her mother (her rival), she developed masochistic patterns in regard to both her sexual activities and her hostility—"Columbus in chains," "puberty fantasies"—and later, in order to protect herself against the consequences of her masochism, sexual frigidity. She had a desire for the male organ (mutual exposure incident), and resentment toward and fear of the man who possessed it (another factor in her sexual frigidity). All these attitudes, together with the oral (evidenced in the steak dream) and anal (meeting in bathroom in the last dream) cravings, had been repressed and had remained unchanged since her childhood.

In response to the frustrations inflicted on her by her husband, all of these impulses became active. She was motivated by her unchanged desire for the exclusive possession of and love of her parents, by her anger toward and fear of them, by her resentment toward the siblings (five beds in the first dream, five couples in another dream), by her desire to possess the male organ and deprive the man of it, and to suffer and obtain sexual pleasure through injury and suffering. The husband (and the analyst) became identified with the frustrating parents and siblings. All these impulses were the id impulses. They were opposed by her superego, by her self-criticism, conscience, and ideals. This resulted in severe feelings of guilt. Her depression was the result of the self-punishing activities of her superego. Her superego itself was extremely severe and implacable; it had been severe since her childhood because of the necessity to repress these forbidden impulses. Her ego played a mediating role and attempted to maintain A. V.'s adjustment. She was angry at her husband, yet she behaved kindly toward him. She wanted to hurt him, but she herself suffered instead. With this, instead of arousing his anger, she aroused his sympathy. Thus the ego enabled her to escape the catastrophic results of yielding to the id impulses and being crushed under the superego impulses, and to retain the affection of her husband.

RECENT DEVELOPMENTS IN ANALYSIS

The following shifts of focus have taken place in psychoanalytic theory and observation:

1. Greater accent on anxiety, and, as a result, emphasis on the methods

by which the patient is trying to escape danger and distress—often referred to as "ego psychology" (311, 298, 712, 466, 267, 583).

2. Greater emphasis on problems of self-esteem, self-assertion, and the need for affection and love, these forces being viewed as total personality reactions and not as derivatives of sexual strivings (21, 747, 431, 913, 754).

3. Greater accent on the unconscious intricacies of current reactions (431).

In the following an approach will be presented which integrates, with some additions, the concepts that seem most significant and effective in the treatment of a patient (669).

THE NATURE OF DOMINANT PSYCHOLOGICAL FORCES

The following psychological forces, all of them in part or entirely unconscious, have nearly equal significance in the pathological dynamics of patients.

Self-Evaluation: Self-Esteem and Moral Worth. "Self-esteem" refers mainly to a general feeling of ability to accomplish tasks according to one's own standards and in comparison with other individuals. The most obvious disturbances of this striving are feelings of inadequacy or its opposite—namely, feeling of excess ability.

Disturbances of moral worth are manifested through self-condemnation and guilt and the feeling of being condemned by others. The opposite is the feeling of excessive moral worth, always having to do the right thing, together with the feeling of moral superiority. The two opposites of self-evaluation, as well as opposites to be discussed later, often exist side by side.

Evaluation of the Environment. This has two aspects: evaluation of the strength and emotional attitude of the environment. The healthy attitude of the individual is that his strength equals that of the environment or that he can adjust, within reason, to a stronger environment and is able to handle a weaker one without exploitation. Disturbances of evaluation of the strength of the environment are: considering the environment as all-powerful and always ready to crush its victim (helplessness), or, on the contrary, considering the environment at one's mercy. These attitudes and many of those to be discussed overlap in part. The threat of the environment may be considered in terms not only of destruction but also of complete humiliation or condemnation. As regards evaluation of the environment in terms of affection, the healthy attitude is that there can be an adequate give and take of love between the individual and most members of his surroundings. The most obvious disturbances are: a feeling of being rejected or, on the contrary, of being loved unqualifiedly, corresponding in part to the constant need to give unlimited affection and love to the surroundings under all circumstances.

Interpersonal Orientation and Behavior. The healthy orientation is the desire for self-assertion and the ability to accept disappointment within reason. The most obvious disturbances are: complete dependence on and complete submission to the environment or, on the contrary, the need to dominate it and overpower it. As regards affection, there may be constant resentment, feeling of rejection or detachment, and avoidance of situations of affection or, on the contrary, excessive attachment. The attitudes and orientations mentioned represent strivings in themselves or lead to strivings in the form of goals and "policies" on the part of the individual.

Organ-Functional Strivings. These can be grouped into pleasure strivings and strivings of utility and mastery (self-preservation). The most important organ functions here referred to are the oral, excretory, genital, and motor functions, as well as looking, hearing, touching (with other functions of the skin), and smelling. The pleasure aim predominates almost entirely in the genital function, although the urinary function never gets entirely separated from it because of their close anatomical relationship. In the oral, urinary, and anal functions, both are present with almost equal accent. The self-preservative aspect of these functions is of prime importance psychologically either because of the knowledge of their survival value or because of the experience of discomfort and threat to health in case of disturbance. In motility, the utilitarian and the pleasure aspect are equally great in childhood, whereas later the utilitarian predominates by far. As regards skin, both aspects are about equal, with perhaps pleasure predominating. In connection with looking and hearing, as a rule the utilitarian aspect predominates, but there can be heavy accent on the pleasure aspect also. The disturbances in these functions can be: (1) excessive intensification or excessive suppression of the function; (2) disturbance of the relative balance in the organization of these various functions—e.g., the oral function outstripping the genital function in the dominant pleasure aims of the individual; (3) disturbance in the relative balance of the pleasure function and the utilitarian function of mastery in these functions; and (4) the distortion of the pleasure function by indispensable accent on pain (masochism) or on cruelty (sadism). These strivings and disturbances also overlap with the ones mentioned previously and to be mentioned later. The suppression of function or excessive function is related to the anticipation of injury, condemnation, humiliation, and frustration by other individuals.

Emotional Reactions. Emotional reactions here include not only subjective experience but also the impulse to ask more of the situation, in the case of positive ones, and avoidance or mastery, in the case of negative ones. Under healthy circumstances the individual reacts to a situation essentially with proportional emotions of a positive and negative kind commensurate to the situation. The emotions here considered are anxiety, hostility, depression with the feeling of loss, enjoyment, sympathy, pity, friendship, etc. The obvious disturbances are: need for suppression of emotions, excessive emotions, and inappropriate reactions. The last implies, for example, the occurrence of anxiety or hostility when enjoyment ought to appear. A key position from the point of view of pathology is occupied by anxiety and hostility. Here again there is an overlap with the previous forces, as anxiety may be the fear of being crushed, frustrated, humiliated, and condemned. Aggression may have the same active implication—of humiliating, biting, etc.

Experiential Tendency (*Erlebnistyp*). This is the main quality of the individual's sound strivings, developed in the course of his life history: his special training, his intelligence, creativeness, his tendency to utilize internal experience (introversiveness) or to deal mainly with situations (extrotensiveness), his ability to exercise relatively extensive control over impulses, or, on the contrary, his need for considerable latitude to follow up impulses and have limited responsibilities. Some individuals are remarkably versatile, but the majority show clear-cut preferences. Under healthy circumstances the individual is in an occupation and a social and economic position which enable him to follow through these interests close to his needs and abilities. Under pathological circumstances energy may be largely spent on work incompatible with his main strivings; e.g., an intellectual, introversive person is in business, spending most of his time in buying and selling and being in contact with individuals whose philosophies of life and interests differ from his own. The consequences of this kind of difficulty may be varied. Apart from unhappiness, the individual may try excessively to intensify the disliked activity, or he may be inefficient, or, in the case of individuals who have difficulty in the amount of control required over their impulses, there may be recurrent breaking loose of objectionable activity or, on the contrary, excessive self-control. This problem, too, overlaps with the previous points because the disturbance may manifest itself in any of the previously discussed fields.

THE RELATIONSHIP BETWEEN THE VARIOUS FORCES; CONFLICT, PROTECTIVE AND COPING MEASURES

It has been mentioned repeatedly that there is an overlap between the major psychological fields and forces. There is still another integral relationship among them. Conflicts may arise within the forces listed under the same headings—e.g., between need for moral worth and need for self-esteem because of their extremeness and the prerequisites needed to satisfy them. The individual's self-esteem may demand that he be able to carry out any kind of act, regardless of any objections by himself or by the environment; the moral position may require that he must not even assert himself, let alone injure anybody. Conflicts thus arising lead to a feeling of inner disorganization, of helplessness, and of anxiety. Now, one of several things may happen. The individual may reinforce one of the strivings and solve the situation that way—e.g., carry out the act. However, after a period the guilt resulting reëstablishes the old conflict. Or the individual may try to solve the conflict by a shift to activity in another field—e.g., to obtain the unqualified love of another individual or to engage in some pleasure-seeking activity, such as genital activity—and thus obviate both the need for self-assertion and the guilt over it. These substitute activities may also solve the problem for the time being, but the excessive, self-effacing love soon leads to a lowering of self-esteem, and the sexual activity may lead to guilt. The result then is that both the feeling of inadequacy and the feeling of guilt and moral worthlessness are reinstituted.

This example has two implications for the forces under discussion: (1) the forces themselves (striving for self-evaluation, organ strivings) are the result in part of conflict, anxiety, and defensive and coping measures; (2) the pressure in any of the fields mentioned may manifest itself in any of the other fields. Thus the individual may have developed a masochistic orientation in sexual activity. Then, on the occasion of sexual urge, he may consider this activity too injurious or humiliating. The result may then be that sexual activity gets suppressed and satisfaction is sought in purely affectionate relationships. The guilt that may be present over the original striving may then add the coloring of altruistic self-sacrifice to the relationship.

THE RELATIONSHIP BETWEEN CURRENT AND GENETIC DYNAMICS

Psychopathology, at any given age of the individual, is the sum total of all currently related forces as they were shaped during his life history. The major link to be added now to these interrelationships is a double one: (1) The individual reasons, in the main unconsciously, "Such events have occurred in my past; therefore my current orientation and striving are vitally necessary." (2) Certain attitudes and orientations have been preserved from the past, essentially unaltered, and form a part of the individual's current orientation. This double link again forms a vicious circle with the current strivings. The individual's reasoning, "Past experiences justify current orientation," reinforces either his feeling of helplessness or, let us say, his violent attempt to dominate the world. This violent hostility then again leads to fear of retribution. With the renewal of anxiety, he looks for further past proofs and protective and coping measures. This sequence of events then contributes to preserving the past orientation and striving intact.

The question of the relationship between current and past dynamics may be rounded out further. Events in the past narrow down and determine in part the individual's future development. Further, the memory of past events constantly influences the individual's reaction to new ones. There is, however, an equally important process in the opposite direction. When the individual meets with new reversals, the evaluation of past events also alters. His current helplessness results in reinforcing his feeling of helplessness in the past. The evaluation of past events constantly alters and gets more complex in connection with later experiences. In fact, the same past event may be used for contradictory proof under the pressure of contradictory strivings in current situations, this being one of the reasons for the difficulties in reconstructing past events. Thus, to prove the need for extreme caution, the patient may accent in a past conflict with his father his feeling of helplessness. In order to reinforce his belief in the miraculous benevolence of the world at other times, or even simultaneously, he may accent the fact that his relationship with his father was a close one.

As regards the main traumatic situations, the most significant nodal point may be found at any period of the individual's life. The individual is constantly confronted with new problems, which he approaches with both old and new strivings and hopes, and the resultant event may lead to a new pathological constellation of forces. Thus the striving for achievement becomes considerably intensified, beginning with school attendance; it is then used to reëstablish self-esteem and the affection of other individuals, as a substitute for genital pride; in addition, it has the character of a new force. Entering an occupation or a marriage again confronts the individual with new problems and new hopes. Disappointment may lead to the final crystallization of a feeling that the world is a potentially frustrating place, that there is no way of establishing self-esteem other than to be always right, that sexual gratification is indispensably vital and at the same time leads to ultimate danger situations, that every new attempt toward satisfaction would end in failure, that therefore all extreme strivings, conscious and unconscious, are inescapable yet have to be held in check. In the treatment of, let us say, a woman of thirty-five years who has gone through this type of development, the period of failure after the early months of marriage proves to be the nodal historical period where most of the genetic threats meet. It may then be as much underplayed or forgotten by her in its various aspects and may have to be gone back to throughout the analysis against equally great resistance as any period of her childhood.

APPLICATIONS OF THESE HYPOTHESES TO A. V.'S REACTIONS

On the basis of these concepts, A. V.'s reactions would be interpreted as follows:

Because of her fundamental feeling of helplessness and worthlessness, she had a need for unqualified affection and respect from her husband. His behavior was interpreted by her as a withdrawal of support and also as humiliation and thus as a threat to her vital needs. She pictured herself in a state of catastrophic abandonment and worthlessness. To this she reacted with anger. The anger, however, led to self-condemnation, to fear of disapproval and of abandonment and injury. This resulted in her depression. Her work suffered, and this incapacity further increased her feeling of worthlessness because of her implacable demand that she never become angry and that she cope with all situations. The implacable quality of her demands was itself a result of and a reaction to her feeling of worthlessness and helplessness. With it she attempted to reëstablish her self-esteem, save herself from incapacity, and gain the approval of others. These constellations of conflict continue (in the reported reaction to the husband's irritability) until they are uncovered in the analysis and she thus partly gains mastery over herself; at the same time (still on an illusory basis) she feels she is completely forgiven and approved of, and that she will obtain unqualified care.

These are the essential features of A. V.'s reactions to the incident, to her husband, and to the analyst. She expresses these reactions in her behavior, in her bodily functions, and in her fantasies. The abandonment and loss of love are pictured symbolically in her not being fed. She expresses her anger in the fantasy of attack on her husband (and the analyst) as a man. The attitudes are expressed in such terms partly because the functions are stimulated daily in the patient's existence. She eats daily, and she sees men daily. They are further expressed in terms of memories with the following formula: "You are treating me as badly as I was treated when I was a child." Furthermore, conflicts arise in connection with these bodily functions, once they acquire these emotional connotations.

Her intense need for dependence, complete care, and affection arose in her childhood because she was dependent on her mother for her existence, for relief, for comfort, for satisfaction of bodily needs, and for affection—"when I was a child, when my mother was distant, rejecting, and overcritical, when she made me take care of the younger siblings, when she had other children instead of loving me alone, when she was intimate with my father." Even at that period the mother's distant and censorious attitude intensified the patient's reaction to the birth of the other children and to the mother's request to take care of them. Her feeling of inadequacy in recurring situations with her husband was reinforced in a similar manner by her experience of mutual exposure (discovering at the age of five that she did not possess a penis), by all the later restrictions put on her because she was not a boy, and by her first husband's disparaging attitude toward her abilities. In turn, the significance of these events was intensified, together with the hostility and envy resulting from them by her husband's current behavior.

There were three nodal points in the patient's past history. (1) The first was at about the age of four, the period when she developed the habit of "looking at Columbus in chains" and getting sexually excited. In addition to the conflicts about her mother already discussed, she was also in rivalry with her, in part because of the feeling of disparagement implied in the mother's critical attitude and emotional distance. This intensified her desire to be able, like her mother, to have children. The solution of this rivalry and hostility, along with the feeling of dependence and attachment, contributed to pushing her sexual strivings in the direction of masochism. (2) The second nodal point was in late adolescence, when she was confronted with the problem of success in her occupation and in her relationships with people, particularly men. In spite of her brilliance, she considered herself not particularly talented, as being easily outstripped by others. She felt a desperate need for attachment to men and respect from them, in part as a result of her feeling that a relationship with men was going to make up for all frustration and deprivation suffered in the past. These needs were intensified by her father's having failed in business and her mother's taking over the dominant role in the household, by her sexual maturity, with the increased sexual urge, by the desire for independence, and, lastly, by the greater freedom and the superior attitude of boys, as well as some of the handicaps that she had as a woman in her occupation. She attempted to solve these problems by her first marriage. (3) The next nodal point in her life history was in the period of difficulties and separation from her first husband, who proved to be emotionally distant, sexually inadequate, and intellectually disparaging. This, essentially, meant to the patient that she could not hope for help, affection, and restitution from the environment. It also left her with an intensified feeling of sexual inadequacy because of her frigidity, and she attempted now to gain all of these goals through self-sufficiency. This measure, however, was ineffective, and she now felt that she could not expect the satisfaction of her strivings from the world, and it was highly doubtful whether she could attain them through herself. (4) The fourth nodal point would have proved to be the current difficulty with her husband, which would have led to the final feeling of helplessness and moral inadequacy and the conviction that the world was an inhospitable place in which she could not satisfy her desires for self-esteem, moral worth, affection, and bodily pleasure. This was the point where the analysis stepped in.

She felt worthless if her mother became angry with her. Her fear of the consequences of her resentment likewise began in that period. Her serenity and emotional calm not only were a charming character trait, but contained a factor determined as follows: She felt she was worthless and contemptible whenever she had any feelings of anger toward those to whom she was attached and from whom she needed love and care. The general patterns mentioned here were recognizable, or at least traces of them appeared, in all of A. V.'s relationships and activities.

She developed the attitude of pain and submission as being inevitably connected with sexual activity as a result of these attitudes in her childhood. It was a forbidden activity, with the threat of complete rejection, disapproval, and punishment; yet she continued it—defiantly, in fact. The painful and submissive aspect partly served the purpose of saying: "I don't want to do this; I am chained as Columbus was"; and: "Don't punish me for this, I am suffering pain already"; and finally, "I am not angry at you; I don't want to hurt you. Don't be angry at me; I am hurting myself."

Another prominent conflict of A. V. as an adult was this: She wanted complete submission and dependence on the one hand, and, on the other, wanted to preserve an untouched, isolated, and superior individuality. She longed for sexual relations but considered them as complete submission and the entire loss of her individuality. This attitude was based on her desire to submit completely and thus obtain help from the male whom she considered stronger. To protect herself she had to deny the activity and was therefore frigid. This meant: "I haven't given myself fully and therefore will not be catastrophically destroyed." It also expressed her resentment toward the man on whom she wanted to be dependent, and whom she therefore considered superior (reinforced by cultural over-valuation of man, and a memory pattern of envy of masculinity). It meant: "You're not competent to give me pleasure." It further meant protection from the expected counterattack. "I don't abandon myself to you; therefore you cannot hurt me."

PRACTICAL DIFFERENCES AND SIMILARITIES BETWEEN THE APPROACHES

Various psychoanalytic hypotheses have been applied to the psychological material pertaining to A. V. We wish now to discuss the similarities and differences among the approaches.

The data and interpretations in all analyses inevitably include memory, current difficulties in the patient's daily life, and the patient's attitudes toward the analyst. They also include references to organ functions and to emotional attitudes. If the persistence of infantile impulses is taken as a guide, the analyst must show the patient where and how this unchanged infantile impulse is exerting its influence in his daily existence and in his attitudes toward the analyst. Likewise, as has been stated, if the concept of current dynamics is used as a guide, memories will be discussed and clarified. The difference lies in the relative emphasis and in the degree to which attention is focused on various types of data, and in their use to explain other manifestations. The genetic or historic approach usually places more emphasis on organ-function data, whereas the current approach places it on emotional data. The analyst makes more comments on the patient's attitude toward himself in the current approach. This topic is used by some analysts continuously as a central thread by which to elucidate the patient's emotional reactions. The impression should not be got that there are "two approaches." As in all sciences, there has been development and growth in psychoanalysis since its inception.

The broad implications of many of the concepts which constitute the systems of hypotheses are very similar. Thus one implication of the libido theory is that the patient is driven in his behavior by passionate, nonlogical needs. This broader idea also constitutes part of the approach based on current dynamics and on helplessness and insecurity. The Oedipus complex, in a broader sense, implies the psychopathological constellation which comprises emotional attachment, hostility, conflict, and fear. This broader idea of a complex psychological pattern is equally a part of the other approach. Thus, in any type of analysis, the patient as well as the analyst has to work strenuously on complex, largely unconscious, emotional strivings which the patient evaluates as dangerous, yet to which he clings desperately.

OTHER HYPOTHESES

The variety of material obtained by the psychoanalytic technique, as has been shown, is very considerable. In forming working concepts and hypotheses, various aspects of this material may be singled out as having more fundamental implications, even to the exclusion, conceptually, of other material. There are two reasons why this is feasible in practice. As previously mentioned, the analytic procedure has a great many implications unvoiced in the treatment itself, so that actually more is happening, and in a different manner from the way it is formulated. Secondly, the majority of patients are elastic enough to respond well, in part because of the unvoiced implications, to a variety of techniques and interpretations. Difficulties arise only in a fraction of the patients because special rigidities are left untouched by the special emphases or gaps in the approach. In the following, the distinctive emphases of some investigators will be sketched briefly, mainly for the general orientation of the student. Some of the authors to be discussed instituted definite technical changes in the treatment, and some separated from the International Psychoanalytic Association.

ADLER (INDIVIDUAL PSYCHOLOGY)

The accent in this system is placed on disturbances of the feelings of adequacy. These disturbances lead to the striving for power, domination, and superiority called "life goal." This striving is carried out in one of two ways ("life style"). The aggressive way is often considered "masculine" because of the higher cultural evaluation of "maleness." The other way is the submissive, suffering one (hysterical symptoms), which still aims at the domination of others—e.g., of the mate. The therapist actively inculcates in the patient "social feeling" and "courage" (10-12).

HORNEY

The accent is on self-evaluation in terms of "feeling helpless in a potentially hostile world" (basic anxiety). For the purpose of "safety," the individual develops a variety of vital trends: dependency, unqualified need for affection, submissiveness, superiority, perfection, detachment, etc. All of these strivings lead, as a result of inherent contradictions (feelings of humiliation or fear of complete enslavement), to a reëstablishment of the anxiety. The accent is almost exclusively on current unconscious reactions (431, 432).

RANK

Rank had two different phases, which exerted their influence independently of each other. The first based all psychodynamics mainly on "birth trauma"—in other words, the experience of separation from the mother, which on the one hand leads to the longing for return to the womb, and on the other to a fear of the repetition of the separation (753). In the second phase he accented disturbances of self-assertiveness and independence, together with the constructive forces inherent in the personality—"will therapy" (754). The accent in the second phase was heavily on current dynamics. The date for the termination of the treatment is set by the therapist, based on his judgment, to make the patient take his final steps toward independence.

JUNG (ANALYTICAL PSYCHOLOGY)

Jung accented two main ideas: (1) Personality types he considered innate and classified according to introversion and extroversion and, as subtypes of both of these, thinking, feeling, acting, and sensual types. Pathology arises from the individual's following his own type to an extreme by suppressing other reactions or by suppressing his innate type and living the life of a different type (473). (2) His other distinctive main idea is the "collective unconscious," which has several aspects, as a rule not clearly formulated as differing aspects: (a) Intricate unconscious images called "archetypes" (e.g., the rescuing hero or the all-benevolent or terrible woman) influence the individual's reactions. (b) These images, as unconscious dynamic forces, are present in every individual. (c) They are innate and are present regardless of experience. (d) They are present in all mythologies of most ethnic groups. (e) Therefore they are considered to be the result of ancient group experience (471). It should be noted that the last is based on the theory of the inheritance of detailed psychological experiences. In practice, of course, Jung's followers do pay attention to the individual's experiences; e.g., if the individual is completely under the sway of the archetype of the dominant mother, this is attributed to the fact that his own domineering mother has made it impossible for him to liberate himself from it. (See also 977.)

FERENCZI

Ferenczi, toward the later period of his activity, accented above all else the dynamic force of the experience of being deprived of love in early childhood and the necessity of action—e.g., weeping on the therapist's shoulder—in the therapeutic situation for the revelation of unconscious psychological forces. Hence the therapist should be as permissive as the patient's need requires; e.g., there should be no definite time limit to the session (929).

ABRAHAM

Abraham accented experiences during "pregenital phases of libido development," particularly the oral phase. The developments occurring during this phase, particularly as a result of hostile strivings, were then considered the nucleus of all psychopathology by Klein—e.g., oral-incorporative and oral-destructive (500, 501). (For further elaboration of Klein's theories, see the discussion in Chapter XVII. See also Bergler [81].)

These authors have made significant contributions, which are utilized throughout this book. Here some of their distinctive emphases have merely been stated briefly. For further details of their various approaches, the reader is referred to their publications.

THERAPEUTIC AIMS AND EFFECTS OF ANALYSIS

The general therapeutic aims of psychoanalysis are the same as those discussed in connection with psychotherapy—the disappearance of symptoms, increased efficiency and ability to enjoy life, increased ability to stand stress and to make the best of one's opportunities, and the like. The special therapeutic aim is an extremely thoroughgoing recasting of those reaction patterns which are responsible for the patient's difficulties. Not only are symptoms relieved, but there are also changes in some aspects of his relationship with others, his evaluation of himself and of others, his goals and the way in which he seeks to attain them. No other therapeutic method today seems able to accomplish this to the same extent as psychoanalysis.

The length of time that the treatment requires depends on the patient's difficulties and on how thorough a recasting is desired by himself and the analyst. Usually the patient shows an early improvement. If a satisfactory analysis is interrupted for any valid reason, the patient may nevertheless derive benefit from it. The lessening of symptoms is often rapid, particularly in patients who are suffering markedly when they start the analysis; but the symptoms return in varying intensity when new life stresses arise and when new disturbing topics are taken up in the analysis. Gradually the patient's behavior in situations of stress improves; and finally his behavior rises above its previous level even in situations in which he excelled. Completely satisfactory analyses may vary in length from about two to five years.

Not all patients are equally benefited by psychoanalytic treatment. There are four prerequisites for a patient to be analyzable: (1) He must desire to be treated. Often the explanatory statement that he needs treatment suffices to create a willingness to undertake analysis. Some patients at first are averse to analysis either because they are afraid of becoming completely dependent or because their need for self-esteem is so intense that they want to handle all their difficulties, no matter how great, themselves. Such patients may eventually change their outlook, however; and their treatment is often very successful. (2) The patient must have enough intelligence to realize that his suffering may have emotional causes, and to understand the analyst's explanations. Feeble-minded people, for example, are not analyzable. (3) The procedure should be adapted to the patient's illness and individuality. Border-line psychotic patients may come for treatment by their own decision; frank psychotics do not, yet many of them can be analyzed with a modified technique. (See Chapter XXXIV.) One might say in general that any technical modification or measure that takes care of issues that are beyond the individual patient's coping capacity at the time not only does not interfere with the analysis but helps it; and such measures are at times indispensable. Such auxiliary measures are simultaneous analysis of husband and wife or of parent and child by the same analyst (Mittelmann, Sperling);

direct contact at regular intervals with other members of the family to get their coöperation and to handle their difficulties (Mittelmann); the use of hypnotics or hypnosis in the therapeutic session when the analysis "stalls" after satisfactory progress for a long time; temporary hospitalization in severe cases, with possible auxiliary use of "shock" treatment in case of psychosis to make the patient more accessible. Analysis in a private office not only may be of no help, but may actually be dangerous because during a reaction to stress situations the patient may commit suicide or engage in some violent act. (4) The patient's life goals must be essentially good; if they need to be changed, his situation must be such that he can do so. Furthermore, he must be able to obtain from his surroundings an indispensable minimum of emotional support. For example, a patient suffers from anxiety attacks; he has spoiled his relationships with most people, and he must therefore live alone. He may be very intelligent, but he may have broken off his professional training. Because of his dissatisfaction with his station in life and because of the unbearable strain of living alone, analytic treatment may not be able to bring him even to the point where he could alter his situation.

The question whether the patient's psychological disturbance is amenable to psychoanalytic treatment, whether he can change his life goal if necessary, and whether he can obtain the minimum emotional support from his environment cannot always be easily answered at the beginning of the analysis. The analyst may begin the treatment even though he has serious doubts, and the analysis may be successful.

It must not be assumed that a patient who has been successfully analyzed is free from shortcomings. He is making the best of his opportunities and will continue to do so increasingly after the analysis is completed. Furthermore, he is able to handle his minor shortcomings successfully. Under new and very adverse life situations, he may need help again.

Table 6 (page 250) shows the effectiveness of psychoanalysis in the treatment of different emotional disorders.

If an individual undergoes analysis as part of his professional training, the analysis proceeds essentially as has been described. The reason for this is that no one is free from fears and difficulties, although he may cope with them more successfully by means of various psychological devices. His manner of functioning in life, however, can always be improved. A successful analysis will enable such a person to live his life more fully. While his psychological devices are being broken through in the analysis, he may go through considerable emotional stress, for analysis can never be a purely intellectual experience.

We shall now describe the changes that took place in A. V. during the analysis, and we shall follow this by a discussion of the factors which operate in psychoanalytic treatment.

The Progress of A. V.'s Analysis. A. V.'s analysis lasted three years. The emotional depression which she had had for four months before she started treatment disappeared within two weeks. (A. V.'s depression was of a milder type and did not belong to the group of manic-depressive reactions [see Chapter XXXIII].) Her depression recurred in a milder form whenever she had any difficulties with her husband, whenever her work was not accepted as well as she had hoped it would be, and whenever the analyst introduced a new problem. Her working ability improved gradually, almost from the beginning of the analysis, except during her periods of depression. As the third year of her analysis approached, she was working with more steadiness and enjoyment than she had done at any other time in her life. She was free of the distress which had resulted from her having set too high

TABLE 6[5]

	No. of Cases	Apparently Cured	Much Improved	Improved	No Change or Worse
Psychoneuroses	383	125	117	110	31
Sexual disorders	33	12	4	13	4
Character disorders	83	13	34	25	11
Organ neuroses and organic conditions	32	15	10	6	1
Psychoses	92	10	13	37	32
Total	623	175	178	191	79

goals for herself, as far as her work was concerned, and periodically falling short not only of her high expectations, but of the average she should have attained. Her sleep disturbances, loss of appetite, and frequency of urination began to improve at about the sixth month, but with some fluctuations; they did not disappear entirely until after two and one-half years of analysis. Her frigidity began to decrease after about eleven months, and her sexual function became steadily adequate after about two and one-half years.

Her over-sensitiveness to some of her friends began to diminish after one year of analysis. About the same time her relationship with her mother, whom she saw occasionally, showed improvement. It became evident that in response to her mother's treatment of her, which, to be sure, had an element of rejection and disapproval in it, A. V. herself had been behaving in a hostile and rejecting manner. This, in turn, had caused her mother to become even more distant emotionally from her.

Her relationship with her husband fluctuated considerably without any essential change for about one year. She had greater difficulty in recognizing and accepting her reactions of hostility, her need for unqualified dependence, and her fear of abandonment in reference to him than to the analyst. It distressed her con-

[5] Based on a table in R. P. Knight, Evaluation of the results of psychoanalytic therapy, *Amer. J. Psychiat.*, 1941, **98**, p. 445.

siderably when the analyst showed her that these disturbances led to physiological and psychological dysfunctioning. As has been said, all these reactions clashed with her intense ideals, her need for moral approval and unqualified performance. Her husband's periods of hopelessness and bodily complaints have also been mentioned. During such periods he leaned on his wife for help. At other times, however, he jealously guarded his right of self-determination and would irritably construe any request on her part as interference with his liberty. He often reacted in this way when *she* felt a desire to lean on him.

It is to be noted that some personality characteristics of these two individuals dovetailed. One of A. V.'s ideals was to be able to cope with any situation. This, of course, included helping her husband when he was not well. Her own feeling of helplessness and her profound need for affection and care, however, aroused in her a strong need to lean on him after she had helped him. She wanted his presence, and she wanted him to be attentive; but on such occasions he was apt to feel that she was trying to dominate him, and he would therefore refuse. Her reaction to this would be the feeling that he was rejecting and humiliating her. She would become resentful; but because of her helplessness, her fear of abandonment and self-condemnation, she would also become depressed and need him even more, whereas he would guard his rights all the more. In fact, exactly this situation prevailed when A. V.'s husband had to leave the city. When she asked him not to go, he told her that even if he could make the sacrifice and remain with her, he would not do it, so as not to set a precedent for being dominated.

A very important part of analytic work is to make the patient see and understand the intricacies of his relationship with the individuals who are closest to him. The difficulty here is to make him see not only his own attitudes but those of his mate as well. This latter implies criticism and consequent fear. It further implies considering someone on whom the patient wants to depend completely as imperfect.

A. V. began to see her own reactions toward her husband more clearly after one year of analysis, whereupon they lessened in severity. Still later she began to realize that many of her difficulties were reactions to his difficulties. Her resentment toward him and her dependence on him lessened. At the end of two years, however, it became clear to both her and the analyst that she could not progress beyond a certain point unless her husband underwent some treatment. A. V. was attached to her husband and had never seriously considered leaving him. Her need for unqualified performance had lessened, and her courage had increased sufficiently so that she could definitely request him to be treated and tell him that she herself could not progress any further under the circumstances. Out of consideration for her, and because of a need for self-esteem, he overcame his reluctance to seek psychotherapeutic aid. This he had previously rejected because he considered it a sign of weakness to accept anyone's help. A. V.'s husband finally received interview therapy from another therapist for a period of six months. This effected a desirable change in him which enabled A. V. to work out her remaining problems. It was during this period that she gradually understood and overcame her fear of childbirth. Two years after the completion of the analysis, A. V. had a child; and she has continued to function well in all significant situations during the three years that her case has been followed since the completion of the analysis.

CURATIVE FACTORS IN ANALYTIC TREATMENT

Now that we have presented an account of the psychoanalytic procedure and of its therapeutic effects, we shall discuss what psychological factors are operative in achieving these results. Many of the factors are the same as those discussed in connection with psychotherapy in general. These will be referred to briefly, the emphasis being placed on the features characteristic of the analytic procedure.

Support and Reassurance by the Analyst; Permissive Attitudes. Although these topics have been discussed previously, it should be mentioned here that the patient desires the analyst's *unqualified* and *unlimited* support, reassurance, and approval. He is not permitted the illusion that he is receiving this; if he is, any topic he or the analyst discusses will only serve to maintain this illusion. How much the analyst comments on this attitude depends on the immediate analytic situation and on how much deprivation the patient can stand at the moment.

Effects of Investigation of Attitudes Toward the Analyst. The fact that the patient manifests all the significant psychological attitudes in relationship to the analyst turns the analysis into a living experience for him. He must face and work out his emotional problems in this new interhuman relationship; thus he experiences his impulses under a unique set of circumstances. Comments on his reactions are made at the time they occur; he must face them. Furthermore, the impulse is not met by the analyst with moral approval or disapproval, or with counterattack or submission; nor can the problem be settled by action as in the patient's daily life. It is met with understanding and explanation, and with the implication that the patient should change his method of dealing with problems. Therefore the "fate" of the impulse and its effect on the patient's whole personality are different from what they would be under other circumstances.

The most important irrational attitudes that the patient has toward the analyst are: the expectation that the analyst will cure him by a sort of magic act, and that the analyst is all-powerful, omniscient, and perfect; an attitude of and a desire for complete submission in order to obtain the needed help; the assumption that the analyst looks down on him, especially because of the above attitudes, and that the analyst wants to dominate or overpower him and keep him in subjection (counterpart of complete submission); anger toward the analyst for this reason and for his refusal to give the desired help; a desire to rule the analyst and to do to him everything that he thinks the analyst will do to him; fear of the analyst because of the anger toward him, chiefly fear of loss of his love and approval, and fear of injury; desire for gratifications; impulse to attack the analyst at certain parts of the body, and fear that the analyst will attack him at the same places.

The patient's various attitudes toward the analyst arise and are recognized partly spontaneously, but they are brought out particularly in response to the analyst's interpretations.

Unconscious Attitudes Becoming Conscious. The exact therapeutic effect of the becoming conscious of an unconscious impulse is a complicated question. Permissive and supportive attitudes on the part of the analyst often play an important part in the resulting relief. Another significant aspect is the following: The patient, because of his fear, shuts a distressing problem out of awareness and in that way renounces control over it; he becomes helpless to handle it. As a result of analytic work, his fear of the problem lessens, and it becomes acceptable to him for consideration. This has a further effect: He now receives a key to a problem which has distressed and perplexed him, and he acquires mastery over it. In some cases this effect of analytic work is very striking.

A patient arrived for the analytic interview in a disturbed emotional state and complaining that her feet felt numb. The complaints persisted throughout the entire interview, in spite of repeated attempts at interpretation. She finally related an incident which had occurred not long before this interview and which up to this point she had not mentioned or thought of. She had expected a telephone call from her husband at noon, which had not come. She had felt that this was inconsiderate of him, and was angry and hurt, but then she had become worried lest he might be leaving her. Soon afterward her complaint had started. As she discussed this incident with the analyst, her complaint disappeared. In this instance the patient had been afraid of the consequences of her anger toward her husband and had therefore repressed her impulse and the memory of the incident. With the aid of the analyst, she acquired enough self-confidence to see the immediate problem and acquire mastery over it.

This patient was well along in her understanding of the type of problem that this incident presented, and it was for this reason that the effect was so immediate and clear. Usually a patient is at first afraid to become conscious of attitudes which have been repressed, and he struggles against the analyst's efforts to enable him to see them. The lessening of the fear and the acquisition of mastery in such instances are achieved after some period of time.

Forcing the Patient to Change His Attitudes. As has been said, all interpretations have the unvoiced implication that, although they arise from helplessness, the patient's goals—e.g., complete dependence—have pernicious consequences and should be changed by him. The patient, however, reacts to this as if it were a threat to a vital need, and he pursues the same goal in a different form. Again this is interpreted to him, and thus the struggle goes on until he feels himself forced out of the attitude; he then, almost in desperation at first, begins to make a new effort. Thus every important change in the patient's reaction patterns is a result not only of lessening anxiety, increased self-confidence, increased feelings of mastery and approval, but also of being forced to abandon goals whose realization is refused. In this process the patient's desire to proceed further with his problems and to acquire increased self-esteem also plays a role. From this and what has been said under the two previous heads, interpretation is seen to be one of the most powerful therapeutic weapons of psychoanalysis.

Resolution of Conflicts and of Vicious Circles; Relief of Bodily Distress. As a result of the analytic work, the feeling of helplessness and worthlessness and the catastrophic expectations are gradually relieved. With this, both the intense need for dependence and the hostile reactions subside, as well as the self-condemnation, the feelings of guilt, the self-aggrandizement, and the frantic struggle to reach implacable ideals. Thus the conflicts grow less intense and are finally resolved, and compromise formations and substitute bodily gratifications are abandoned. The tense struggle to reach normal functioning abates, as does the continuous tension resulting from unsatisfiable psychological and physiological needs. Consequently the whole vicious circle of reactions is halted.

Increase in Self-Confidence and Well-Being. Almost from the beginning of the analysis there is an increase in the patient's self-confidence and in his psychological strength. This is true in spite of the fact that the patient's fears become recurrently intense. The self-confidence and strength are not to be taken here as always meaning subjective comfort. They imply that the patient takes up problems which previously he could not face at all, regardless of the fact that they frighten him. These terms further imply that many of his functions improve when he is free from intense stress. Direct encouragement and reassurance are rarely given in the analytic interview. The patient often asks: "What can I do to have more self-confidence? How can I overcome my fears? In what ways is analysis going to help me?" The analyst may answer such questions once, but his answers are invariably interpreted by the patient either as containing magic help in themselves or as falling far short of the kind of help he needs. Usually the patient repeats such questions later as if he had not asked them before and as if he had not had an answer. The reason for this is that these questions are really disguised statements and requests on the part of the patient; therefore they have to be analyzed, not answered. The remarkable fact is that the patient's self-confidence increases as a result both of the implied supportive and permissive aspects of analysis and of the resolution of conflicts and dangerous attitudes, and also because of increasing mastery. As the analysis progresses, successfully completed tasks and new gratifications increase the patient's desire for new efforts and in turn increase his self-confidence and strength, thus establishing a healthy circle of psychological and physiological reactions.

SUMMARY

The following is an analytic outline of the functioning of the psychologically ill individual in his cultural environment, and of the processes of readjustment.

1. The individual constantly seeks out or is confronted with inevitable situations with which he has to cope. These situations are:
   a. Gratification of specific bodily needs (e.g., food, sex, relaxation, and sleep).
   b. Pursuit of complex intellectual goals (e.g., occupational activities).
   c. Pursuit of emotional satisfaction (e.g., friendship).

   In all these situations complex cultural influences affect both the external situations and the individual's impulses. The individual's behavior in these situations is healthy, first, to the extent to which it follows the formula "I am worth something; I can pursue this goal; other people are friendly toward me; if they are not, I can still cope with the situation, and I can reach my goal later, if not now" (good evaluation of oneself and of the environment), and, second, to the extent to which the goals are not unsolvably contradictory and are compatible with physiological satisfaction and restitution.
2. The individual may be motivated in the same situations by needs and strivings which are derivatives of catastrophic expectations, of unsolvable conflicts, and of physiological strivings not compatible with adequate homeostasis. To the extent to which these factors enter into his behavior, it is considered pathological.
3. The individual's reaction patterns are best formulated in terms of current motivations and interrelations, part of which is the memory system and the retention of earlier reaction patterns. The expectation of a catastrophic situation, as well as the reactions derived from it, always includes the following aspects:
   a. The individual's evaluation of himself and of others.
   b. Impairment of function, with further resultant feeling of helplessness.
   c. Emotional reactions of fear and anger.
4. The resultant final behavior is determined by three factors:
   a. Direct results of emotional stress.
   b. Defensive and ameliorative measures.
   c. The attempt to reach the goal or its substitute in spite of all hindrances.
5. Conflicts arise as a result of contradictory measures which the individual takes to escape the catastrophic situation and to alleviate his suffering. The contradictory needs and the extreme character of each need (e.g.,

of hostility and of craving for dependence) make impossible action which is completely satisfying. This leads to continuous tension.

6. Current pathological reactions are perpetuated, at least potentially, through circular reactions. Both the incapacitating and the ameliorative reactions revive the fear of catastrophe directly or indirectly.
7. The individual is largely unaware of his significant motivations and their interrelation. The lack of awareness is an active process and is maintained by him to escape suffering and catastrophe.
8. Disturbances in bodily functions have four determinants:
   a. Strong emotional reactions are accompanied by disturbed physiological functions.
   b. The bodily function expresses attitudes—e.g., defiance, dependence—toward other people.
   c. Fear arises in pursuit of certain bodily wants, and other goals are substituted.
   d. Tension phenomena arise from the fact that some aspects of the goal desired cannot be attained.
9. Catastrophic expectations, conflicts, and their derivative reactions first appear in the individual's childhood, at first in the pursuit of bodily gratifications, but very soon also in connection with parental relationships and with any situation in which the parent is involved. The reaction patterns become largely "internalized," but the evaluation of other individuals (interhuman relations) is always included in them. The tendency to unhealthy reactions in critical situations persists throughout the individual's life largely because of the circular aspect of these reactions.
10. In analytic treatment the individual's harmful reactions are dealt with by appropriate emphasis, varying with the individual on:
    a. His relationship with the analyst.
    b. His relations with persons and situations in daily life.
    c. Situations of his childhood.
11. Analysis attains its therapeutic effect by supportive, reassuring, and permissive implications, by giving the patient insight and increasing his mastery of his problems, by forcing him out of defended attitudes, by disentangling vicious circles of reaction, and by relieving emotional and physiological tension; further, through all these processes, by relieving his feelings of helplessness and worthlessness, his insecure evaluation of the world, his anxiety and guilt, and by increasing his self-confidence and his joy in success.

SUGGESTED READINGS

All of Freud's writings, particularly *A General Introduction to Psychoanalysis* (310) and *New Introductory Lectures* (308), are recommended. For a popular delineation of the field, see Kubie's *Practical and Theoretical Aspects of Psychoanalysis* (517). Reik's *Listening with the Third Ear* (764) makes very interesting reading. An integrated, encyclopedic survey is given in Fenichel's *Psychoanalytic Theory of Neurosis* (267).

For an understanding of some recent developments, the following are recommended: Ferenczi and Rank's *Development of Psychoanalysis* (270), S. Freud's *The Problem of Anxiety* (311), Anna Freud's *The Ego and the Mechanisms of Defense* (298), Horney's *The Neurotic Personality of Our Time* (431) and *Our Inner Conflicts* (432), Kardiner's *Psychological Frontiers of Society* (484), Rado's articles (747, 749), and Alexander and French, *Psychoanalytic Therapy* (21). For divergent approaches, see Thompson (929).

XVII Psychotherapy in Children and Adolescents

PSYCHOTHERAPY IN CHILDREN

The essential aim of psychotherapy in children, as in adults, is to make the child feel essentially worth-while and loved and to enable him to accept his age-appropriate impulses and desires within certain social limits. The age-appropriateness may not be obvious to the parents who require a degree of "understanding and intelligence" of the younger child of which he is not capable or who may be ready to allow a lack of control in the older child that is self-understood in a younger one but inappropriate for the older.

The personality make-up of younger children is still very elastic. Conditions which would be very difficult to change in the adult may yield rapidly under treatment provided the environment can be made to coöperate. A five-year-old child who had been sucking her thumb and blankets since infancy, with frequent vomiting, masturbation, and temper tantrums, gave up most of her symptoms in the course of a few weeks and remained well for years after. (See page 328 for a more detailed presentation of this case.)

PLAY THERAPY

The following points are of particular importance in the therapeutic handling of children:

1. The child is more an acting organism than a verbal one. Most of the interrelation in the actual therapeutic sessions takes the form of what has been called "play therapy." This consists essentially of presenting the child with an assortment of toys, drawing materials, and, wherever possible, a faucet and water. The toys should always include, in miniature, human figures, ranging from infants to grandparents, and household furniture, including bathroom, bedroom, and kitchen. In addition, there should be a variety of animals, soldiers, guns, and bows and arrows handy. Many children start to play spontaneously with the toys, sometimes after asking a question or two about what the toys are there for. At other times the thera-

pist says, "Would you like to play with some of these things?" The child's initial behavior reveals whether he is shy or makes contact easily, whether he plays in an organized manner, or whether he is over-active. The games that the child engages in may be mainly neutral and may reveal at times very little about the nature of his difficulties. At other times the games are very telling because of their repetitive and sustained aggressive quality; e.g., there are constant fights between the human figures or the child engages predominantly in trying to damage the various toys. Neutral or revealing, the play has certain therapeutic effects. The very fact that the child is engaging in a pleasurable activity makes him like the therapeutic situation and leads to a positive attachment to the therapist. The child feels that he is in a permissive atmosphere, particularly if he is subjected to severe restrictions at home. For children who feel essentially nonrestricted only special elements in the play have permissive implications: aggressive play in case of repressed resentment toward siblings, parents, or teachers, and gratification of impulses otherwise suppressed in daily existence. The impulse expression may be indirect; e.g., the figure representing the sibling meets with an accident, or the one representing the patient is given the bottle to nurse. In other words, the emotional implications of play are very extensive even when no verbalization takes place. At other times the therapist comments on the implication: "I guess you like the bottle just like your baby brother," or "I guess you're angry at your baby brother because he gets the bottle." The child's feeling about the verbalization may be revealed mainly by his general reaction, whereas, obviously, an adult would either accept or reject such a comment by words. The further implications of play therapy will be discussed in subsequent sections (see release therapy and psychoanalysis; see also the discussion of play, pages 136-137).

The child's drawing, a pleasurable activity, has the same positive implications as play in general. In addition, even with "neutral" content, the formal aspects of the drawing may be revealing of the child's problems. The drawing may be confused to the onlooker in that a profusion of lines cross each other and the page is overcrowded, indicating a great deal of disorganized, repressed aggression and anxiety. At a later period the same child's drawings may be highly detailed—e.g., all bricks and shingles being drawn on the houses—representing an "obsessive" attempt to control impulses through rigid attention to the minutest details. The content—e.g., monsters—may be revealing of the child's anxieties and the predominant colors indicative of the child's mood—e.g., black of depression. The same features may also represent an active expression of tensions, strivings, and needs, and, in this manner, the activity may be a therapeutic outlet for the child's emotional forces. For some very shy children the drawing may be the only avenue of expressing warm emotions toward the therapist. Thus a very shy eight-year-old child who was suffering from asthma would talk and play little in the therapeutic interviews but would recurrently draw a heart with lively crayon colors and write under it, "This is to ——— (the therapist's name), from ——— (the patient's name)." Clay-modeling and finger painting may be permissive and constructive expressions of the rebellion against rigid cleanliness and of repressed interest in excretory products.

In many instances the therapist may facilitate play centering on conflict situations by asking the child, or suggesting to him, that two dolls should represent Daddy and Mommy and other dolls have names taken from the child's environment. Further, the therapist can suggest in action that a situation from which the new episode in the play starts represents one to which the child has been reacting with conflicts; e.g., the family is at home in bed or at the dinner table, or it is sleeping time, or the child does not want to eat and the mother starts scolding, etc. Such devices, however, should not be forced. If the child does not enter into the suggestion, it is best to drop it.

2. Verbalizations, both in the gathering of information and in interpretation, naturally have to be in the child's language. This implies not only that the words used by the therapist must be in the child's vocabulary, but also that the manner in which they are asked and the devices used must be adapted to the child. The devices are characterized by a great deal of indirectness. Thus the child is usefully asked, "If a little fairy came to you and said you could have three wishes that would come true, what would you ask for?" The child's replies can be quite revealing, apart from being age-related. Children with an organic disturbance or with physical handicaps frequently ask for things like roller skates, thus expressing their preoccupation with physical performance and their inadequacy. Or the child may reply, "I would wish that Father should come home"—after the father had deserted. If the reply is, "I would wish to have a lot of money," then the question, "What would you do with the money?" may be additionally revealing, indicating struggle with poverty or attempt to help out the struggling parent whose anxiety over finances and other matters seriously impinges on the child's emotional life. The question, "If you were shipwrecked on a desert island and you could have one person, whom would you choose?" may also be quite revealing. If a boy, after the age of ten, still replies, "Mother," then his infantile dependence is quite evident. If a five-year-old child does not choose his mother (or father), the hostility toward the parent is quite evident. Another device has the following form: "If a child, not you, but another child, did this-and-this, what would it mean?" Often the child who would not enter into the discussion of the meaning of his own behavior will give the relevant reply. An eight-year-old child became unruly and aggressive, throwing the toys about in one of the play sessions. When finally the therapist said to him, "If another child did this, what do you think would be the reason?" he replied, "He would be disappointed." The

child had previously asked for a rifle, which the therapist, by agreement with the child, had promised to get within a week. However, one of the child's most characteristic problems was that he could not tolerate waiting for things he wanted; therefore, in the play session just described, two days later, he was acting in a hostile manner.

At times, while the child is engaging in relatively neutral play—e.g., tossing the ball, drawing, or building with blocks—the therapist may engage him in conversation about emotionally relevant events such as trouble at home or with playmates.

Some children, after the treatment has been in progress for some time, evade all problems by not talking about them and by shifting immediately to cheerful neutral play when the therapist brings them up. At the same time there is no change in the symptoms, and the child voices his disappointment in the treatment to his parents. The therapist then may emphatically tell the child that they both know that he is having plenty of trouble but that he has not been wanting to admit it and to see what it is due to; that kind of procedure, the child is told, will not help; his troubles will continue until they are discussed and explained, and it is high time to talk about them.

3. The child should know what his symptoms and problems are; otherwise these therapeutic implications of play may not occur. If asked after a friendly contact has been established, "Do you know why you came here?" he usually replies, "I don't know," or "Mother (or somebody else) wanted me to come." When asked, "Why did Mother bring you here?" he again usually replies, "I don't know." The therapist then should tactfully and considerately mention the various symptoms in the framework: "Does this-and-this bother you?" or "Would you like me to help you with ——— (e.g., your bad dreams)?" The verbal replies of the child to such remarks are unsatisfactory, as a rule; nevertheless, the purpose of his visits is made clear. It may be added that often the child has been merely told by the parent that he will be taken to a "nice man to play with," or, on the contrary, that he will be taken to "doctor" because he was bad—with clear implication or actual threat of punishment. The latter kind of "preparation" shows up in the initial visit as fear, which the therapist can dispel by discussing with the child the threatening remarks and by assuring him that the purpose of the visits is to help him. With young and fearful children it is best to allow the mother to stay in the room during the first few visits. However, even if the child has had adequate preparation for the treatment, he rarely gives satisfactory replies to questions about his difficulties. It is obvious from this that the child has only a limited intellectual and emotional understanding of the fact that he has problems and is sick, and he usually admits less than he understands. The important information about the child's difficulties, the daily events in his life, and his past history must be gotten from grown-

up people in his environment, most commonly the parents. To begin with, the decision to come for treatment almost never comes from the child himself, except in adolescents. The child's decision to continue with the treatment usually requires supportive decision from the grown-ups in the child's environment. These differences between children and grown-ups, of course, are those of degree. There are many sick adults who have no insight, and who therefore are not willing to come for treatment. If they are unhappy, they blame somebody in the environment. There is a half-facetious saying, "The husband has the problem, and the wife comes for treatment." In such situations the adult cannot be prevailed upon to give the therapist a chance to entice him into treatment via play therapy—a procedure which is often successful with children. The gaining of insight can also be quite impressive with some children.

Anna Freud relates the story of a six-year-old girl who was unhappy, inhibited, and dreamy to such an extent that there was a question of mental deficiency. It later turned out that she had unusually high intelligence but was suffering from a compulsion neurosis. For her first hour she came to the therapist's office in the company of a somewhat older friend, and she simply became acquainted with the environment. The second time, the therapist mentioned two children whom the patient knew and the reasons for which they had been sent to her for treatment: one because she could never tell the truth even when she wanted to, the second because she cried so much that she was bothered by it herself. The therapist then asked the patient whether she had been sent to her for some similar reason, whereupon the patient said directly, "I have a devil in me. Can that be taken out?" The therapist replied, "Yes, that will be possible, but it's no easy job," and that, if the therapist tried it with her, she might have to do a lot of things which she wouldn't find at all pleasant. After some serious meditation the little patient replied, "If you tell me that that's the only way to do it and to do it quick then it's all right." Soon she even had an understanding for the necessary length of the treatment. After a three weeks' trial period, when the parents were undecided whether to continue with the treatment, the child asked whether her devil could be taken out in three or four days more. The therapist told her, "No, it would take a long time." Thereupon the child sat down on the floor and pointed at the pattern on the rug, asking, "Does it need as many days as there are red points here? Or so many in addition as there are green points?" The therapist pointed at the great many medallions on the rug. The child understood this and did her best to convince her parents of the need for longer treatment.[1]

This example also shows how all verbalizations in the course of the treatment have to be in the child's language.

4. The child is actually and emotionally more dependent on the environment than the adult. In the treatment of every child it is therefore indispensable to be in close contact with the environment, not only for the

[1] Based on a case presentation by A. Freud, *Introduction to the Technic of Child Analysis*, Nervous and Mental Disease Publishing Co., Washington, 1928, pp. 5-6.

gathering of information but also for the correction of crucial external difficulties.

Handling the Parents. Therapeutic methods have no chance of succeeding with the child if the parents continue their rejecting, humiliating, over-strict, over-solicitous, or excessively permissive attitudes. At times the correction of these is very difficult because the parents have deep-seated emotional problems which manifest themselves in their handling of the child. Instead of changing, they rationalize, displace the blame, and depreciate or even terminate the child's treatment. The following practical devices may be useful: After orienting the parent about the child's condition, the therapist may mediate between the parent and the child concerning controversial rules of conduct as regards eating, sleeping, allowance, friends, studying, evening hours, etc. After the discussion with the parent, the therapist conducts the session with the patient. In the course of this he takes up, at times with gentle firmness after the patient denies them, such issues as, e.g., the reluctance to eat certain articles of food. After stating certain principles—e.g., that green vegetables are necessary for a healthful diet ("You want to grow up and be strong")—he says that the patient has to choose one or two green vegetables daily but may reject the rest. At the end of the interview the parent is called in, and the agreement is essentially confirmed. The effect of this procedure is not only a reasonable assurance that the child will follow these minimal arrangements, but, even more, that conflicts are eliminated that set the parent and child against each other several times daily, with their hostilities, anxieties, guilt, defiance, domination, and rejection.

The contact with the parent has to be kept up because of frequent relapses or because for a long time the parent may drop one injurious form of conduct and substitute another for it. Frequently the parent's own problems move into the focus of interviews, and the parent is advised to undergo therapy himself. In the majority of clinics it is considered preferable to have separate therapists for the child and for the parent because of potential jealousy or the feeling on the part of the parent or the child that the therapist favors the opposing side. There should be a close contact between the two therapists; otherwise too much useful and, in some cases, indispensable information is lost. Although it is a more difficult problem and requires more experience for a therapist to handle the parent as well as the child, such a procedure may have definite advantages. The therapist then has all the information at his disposal; and, further, in critical situations he can reassure both the parent and the child about the difficulties presented by the other. Much of the anxious exaggeration and distortion or omission of information about the conduct of the other party, together with the secondary focusing of personal problems on the other party's difficulties, can thus be avoided.

If a very difficult home situation is impossible to correct, an attempt should be made to place the child in a different environment. "Bad home situation" may mean that the parents are grossly neglectful, brutal, or psychotic, are bad alcoholics, or engage in gross sexual practices at home—e.g., prostitution. These problems occur usually in the lower economic or cultural groups, and the placement has to be made through a social agency. Alcoholism or psychosis may be a problem in higher economic and cultural groups also. In that case other members of the family may take suitable measures—e.g., hire a governess or take over the care of the child with the parents' consent. The more common problem in the higher economic and cultural groups is a severe neurosis, often with a psychotic tinge, on the part of the parent, combined with an unwillingness to let the child go away from home—e.g., to a boarding school—or to leave the child alone long enough for him to show a definite therapeutic gain. Soon such a parent uses the lack of steady improvement on the part of the child to discredit all psychotherapeutic procedures.

Handling the School Problems. Difficulties in school are very common in children with emotional problems. It may become indispensable to give the teacher some explanation and advice on the handling of the child's problems. Otherwise, even if the home situation is corrected, the difficulties in school may perpetuate the child's symptoms. The parent's or the therapist's discussion with the teacher often results in a more permissive attitude as well as in positive measures on the latter's part, such as open praise on the proper occasion or sending the child on errands which are considered signs of special distinction. Further, the coöperative parent may ask the child at home whether he is afraid of a coming examination or of the results of his homework, instead of taking his sudden unruliness or his complaints about headache and stomach-ache at their face value and thus becoming alarmed or irritated about them. The child then often admits that he is worried about his homework and accepts the parent's help instead of getting entangled in a new fight. The school problem will be further discussed in another chapter. (See Chapter XVIII.)

Handling the Problems of Companions and Playmates. A child of preschool age may have no playmates of his own age group and then may "tag along" and be unwelcome in the more complex activities of the older children. In such situations the parents may attempt to move into a different neighborhood, or they may bring the child together with the children of friends, take him to playgrounds, or, what is apt to be most effective, place him for at least part of the day in a nursery school or kindergarten.

Delinquent contacts occur with the older age group. In such a case the best procedure is to have the child join a settlement house or a scouting organization. Group identification and group contact, as well as filling his time up with activity, are indispensable for every child. In case of boredom he will naturally keep turning to the delinquent group if that is the most readily available. Furthermore, organized activity with the support and guidance of a benevolent adult is very helpful therapeutically to shy and withdrawn children.

RELEASE THERAPY

In release therapy the child is guided in his play and is permitted to engage in bursts of violent activity under the controlled setup of the therapeutic situation. A relatively small number of such sessions was followed by the disappearance of the child's symptoms under the following conditions: (1) The child's problem was precipitated by a specific event—a frightening experience, the birth of a sibling, or the divorce of the parents. (2) The child was under ten years of age, so that his problems were of relatively short duration; if the child's fears had persisted so long that they affected the social relationships, his handling of the sex problem, or even his intellectual functions, release therapy in itself was distinctly inadequate. (3) Regardless of the child's age when he was referred for treatment, and regardless of the specificity of his problem, the problem must have occurred in the past; release therapy could not be used successfully for longstanding problems which continued during the period of treatment—for example, the results of intense maternal rejection or overprotection.

By overcoming anxieties and inhibitions that have to do with orderliness and hostile expression, release therapy makes possible an extension of a personality which was presumably bound down by a discipline administered too early or too severely. In this process a permissive and accepting attitude on the part of the therapist is extremely important. In release therapy the therapist's interpretative function is reduced to a minimum.

A girl aged five years, the youngest of three children, was referred because she refused to be a girl, cut off her curls, insisted on being called by a boy's name, and fought against wearing girl's clothes. The difficulty started when she was about four years old. The difficulty was related to jealousy of a boy of her age, who showed off his strength to her and pooh-poohed girls, and of her brother, aged thirteen, the next older sibling, whom her governess distinctly favored.

For external reasons it was possible to have only five sessions with the patient. These consisted chiefly of release of destructive behavior on boy dolls. . . . In the fourth session she said that girls were better than boys; they could wear pretty things.

A follow-up one week after the last session revealed that the patient made no protest against wearing girl's clothes and stopped insisting on being called by a boy's name. A follow-up interview six years after the treatment indicated normal feminine development.

It is important to realize that there are cases in which the important task of treatment is to give the child insight into his own motivation—that is, to interpret to him the meaning of his symptoms. Release therapy alone cannot do this. In some severe cases it is at once clear that the child's attitude toward the therapist is too suspicious or too anxious to permit him to risk the rapidity of release therapy. Furthermore, in children with severe neuroses, the problem is primarily psychoanalytic.

PSYCHOTHERAPY IN ADOLESCENCE

Psychotherapy of adolescents takes place mainly on the verbal level, and the technical procedures are very similar to those used with adults. Psychopathological manifestations and their dynamics are apt to be revealed most openly by coöperative adolescent patients. Their readiness to communicate with the therapist through speech instead of play and action is nearly that of the adult, while at the same time their problems have not yet been subjected to the same rigidity of defenses and substitutive gratifications and compensations as in the adult. For this reason adolescents often respond faster to psychotherapy than either adults or children. This occurs only if the environment can be made to coöperate, because, in their dependencies and in their helplessness against environmental pressures, they may be almost as vulnerable as children.

In some of them the mechanism of denial and the idea of magic escape are paramount, and therefore they may withhold information on inescapable facts. For instance, a sixteen-year-old adolescent girl was taken to the doctor for examination because she had a puffed face and swollen legs. This was caused by kidney trouble. However, the kidney trouble was a complication of a six months' pregnancy. In spite of the fact that her sister, with whom she was on friendly terms, had asked her whether she was pregnant, she denied it. When the doctor was taking her history, she denied even to him that she had ever had sexual relations. An adolescent boy attempted to cash a bond of his father's, but his signature was not accepted by the bank. The father was informed of this. Although the boy knew that the therapist would be informed of the event by the parents, he did not mention it himself. The most serious problem in the treatment of adolescents is that of acting out, which becomes particularly important in conduct disorder and in sexual problems. The acting out cannot be prevented with certainty, but certain measures are useful and effective most of the time. However, if the relationship between the patient and the therapist is good, the acting out does not take a very serious or injurious form. The four measures are (1) to try to get at the problems before the patient acts, (2) to keep constant watch on current stresses, (3) to encourage and ask the patient to talk about what he plans to do, and (4) to maintain contact with the family whenever there is risk of acting out. In connection with the third point, it should be mentioned that, when he *does* say what he wants to do, one should discuss the motivation, point out the consequences, and show him the harm that it may do to the treatment.

PSYCHOANALYSIS OF CHILDREN

Child analysis will be illustrated and discussed in connection with the following case:

An eight-year-old boy was brought for analytic treatment because of the following disturbances: (1) He was suffering from eczema, which at this time was localized in the bend of his elbows, the bend of his knees, and around his lips. The eczema started when he was five months old and reached its height when he was nine months. It led to considerable scratching and bleeding of the skin. No dietary measures or local applications were effective, and, therefore, at the age of two years, he was hospitalized, and his hands and legs were tied for prolonged periods over the course of several weeks in order to prevent scratching. Up to that point he used to suck his thumb, but he discontinued this practice then. At about the age of five the eczema localized fairly persistently on his penis, and he would scratch it violently. (2) He had been cranky and restless since the age of two and a half, following an incident in which he climbed up on the window sill and got caught between the radiator and the sill. He suffered a bad burn and again had to be hospitalized. This burn on his leg left a permanent although not seriously deforming scar. (3) He had been doing poor work in school and was a disciplinary problem because of minor but continual infractions of rules, such as talking, giggling, and fighting. He had been a good pupil in 1-A and 1-B, but his work fell down within two weeks after he entered 2-A, where he had an impatient, overstrict teacher. In spite of the fact that his later teachers were understanding, his school work and his behavior had not recovered. (4) He was unpopular with the children, got into frequent scraps, threw stones at them or hit them on minor provocation. His behavior toward his brother, thirteen months his junior, had been very aggressive since his mother became more affectionate with the younger, one year before. (5) He frequently refused food served or ate little of it. His taste was capricious. (6) He would not bathe himself and would not wash or clean his face, hands, or teeth unless there were constant reminders from his mother.

There were several points of importance in his past history. When he was an infant, the mother handled him with as little intimate contact as possible and was strict about rules of feeding regulation. If he cried, the principle was to "let him cry." In the beginning, she breast-fed him but then changed to bottle feeding because she was "too nervous" to breast-feed him. Later the mother used to be excitable with the children and used to strike them—an infrequent practice in her socio-economic group. When the patient's eczema became localized on his penis and he used to scratch—e.g., while in the subway—the mother became frantic and took him to a child psychiatrist. The child psychiatrist, on getting the details of the mother's handling of the child and observing the mother's excitement, recommended that the mother should undergo analytic treatment first. This she did, with considerable improvement in her handling of the child and her general state of happiness. In the process of resolving her emotional problems following the termination of her treatment, she divorced her husband. This occurred while the child himself was in the fifth month of his analysis. The father was a less assertive person than the mother, with a tendency to self-effacing submissiveness. His relationship with the children was a fairly close one, but he had a tendency to be critical, in an unobtrusive way, of both them and the mother.

The child's behavior in the first hour was characterized by a very lively outpouring of fantasies. He said, "When I was one year old, my hands were tied to the bed and I went like this (he swung his arms forward and upward) and threw off all the bandages." He further said, "I have a white stallion in a corral. I ride him most every day. I can jump on his back while he is running and without touching him." He then related a somewhat confused fantasy about the teacher he had had in 1-A and 1-B: Her father was the owner of a gold mine, and there was an Indian village whose inhabitants were constantly attacking the surrounding countryside. She was put in charge of the gold mine, which produced one thousand dollars a day, so that she could buy the Indian village and in that way stop the attacks. Toward the end of the hour the patient remarked, "My teacher was cruel (meaning his present teacher). She did not want to let me leave. (The teacher wanted to keep some of the boys, including the patient, after school for some infraction of discipline.) I have waited for this for two years, to come to you."

These remarks indicated the following: his feeling, as a result of having his hands tied, that the world was a restricting, hostile place in which he had no means of defending himself; grandiose fantasies resulting from this as a way of overcoming anxiety, together with the tendency to vehement motility to show his "great strength" and to master situations; the desire for being a grown-up and for superior masculinity; the intense sensitiveness and hostility (the Indian tribe, the cruelty of the teacher); the desire to have this mastered (buy up the Indian village); and the intense desire for help and for attachment and love ("I have waited for this for two years").

The therapist was able to form a general picture of the child's problems on the basis of the information received from the parent and on the basis of the child's behavior. This is possible in the first session only under exceptionally favorable circumstances. Further, it takes a long time before the therapist is able to communicate his ideas, if they are further confirmed in details, to the child. In fact, it is commonly characteristic of child analysis that there are long periods when no clearly relevant information is forthcoming.

CHARACTERISTICS OF THE TECHNIQUE

Details of the Technical Procedure. The child is seen alone by the therapist several times a week for approximately one hour. Very anxious or young children are best seen in the presence of the mother in the first few hours. The frequency used to be five times a week; the more common procedure now is three times a week. The reason for the frequency is the same as in the adult: Too much information would get lost, the freshness of the reactions would fade, and distressing reactions might become too intense if the child were seen less frequently. The reason for three visits a week instead of five is in part that, with too great an infringement on the child's free time, what with schoolwork and homework and traveling time, he would feel too much deprived and as a result his resistance to the treatment might increase. Play technique—that is, the use of toys, moving about freely, drawing (in other words, "free activity")—is an indispensable part of the procedure, at least up to adolescence. The activity of the child, in part, has the same significance as the free association of the adult. In other words, the thoughts, fantasies, and impulses that the adult would be verbalizing, in the customary analytic procedure, the child usually acts out in part in the analytic interview. The child's play may also represent an attempt at problem-solving and at mastering a situation. The child may also repeat in play what he has seen happening at home or engage in a neutral kind of play which would correspond to the adult's talking about indifferent material.[2]

Relationship with the Parents. It has been mentioned in the general section on psychotherapy of children that contact with the parents or with some adult close to the child is indispensable. This holds for analysis also. Crucial information about the symptoms and about past events can rarely be gotten in an adequate form from the child. Even when one does get information, it is difficult to know how accurate it is. Initial information in the analysis is limited and unconsciously biased even in adult patients, but this holds to such a degree in children that it would make the treatment completely uncertain. The information obtained from the parents in the course of the treatment is also indispensable. In general, the child is told that the analyst is in contact with the parent for the purpose of being better able to help him. Children accept this arrangement, although, naturally, at times it does evoke resentment or jealousy in them, which can also be adequately handled. The analyst has to use his judgment as to when to utilize information gained from the parent in his comments to the child. Information from the parents about external events may make the child's behavior in the treatment understandable—e.g., when he becomes surly and destructive in the treatment hour after disappointment at home. As regards introspective experiences, children often tell their dreams, feelings of disappointment, and

[2] The interpretation of play activity was first done by Freud himself when he was guiding the treatment, by the child's father, of a five-year-old child who was afraid of horses; e.g., when, at a certain point in the course of the treatment, the child started to charge with his head against the father's abdomen in a playful way, this was interpreted as an expression of his hostility toward his father. Freud utilized play very sparingly, and he did not crystallize out this technique and did not establish it as a method of procedure. A Viennese analyst, Hug-Helmuth, stated that the child's play can be used as a regular source of analytic information. The technique was crystallized and standardized by Melanie Klein, particularly through the device of using small toys as representative of persons, objects, and situations in the child's surroundings. This made the full development of the analysis of children, beginning with the age of about two and a half years, possible.

anxieties spontaneously to the parent and not the analyst. The following is an illustration from the child with the dermatitis.

Vacation, during which he was going to go away to camp, was approaching, and therefore the treatment would be interrupted, and his mother was making preparations to go to another state to arrange for her divorce. At this point he had a flare-up and spread of the eczema over his thighs, abdomen, and chest. The child remarked to his mother, "You didn't keep your promise. You said the doctor would cure me of my sores and it got worse." In the analytic session the child mentioned nothing of the flare-up and engaged in apparently neutral games, such as playing checkers and making drawings about Indians and soldiers of the same type he had frequently made before. The therapist then told him that he had information from the mother about the flare-up of the eczema and the quoted remark. The child then willingly confirmed the facts, and the analyst remarked that this can happen in the course of treatment and suggested that they find out what brought about the flare-up. It was then for the first time that the child really accepted the idea that emotional problems contributed to his symptom; he said, "It starts to itch, and then I can't help myself and I scratch." The analyst asked him, "When does it start to itch?" The child remarked, "It always does when I hit the punch ball, and all the boys depend on me" (meaning that he might miss, cause his team to lose, and be disapproved of and rejected by them). In the course of further discussion he admitted that he was worried about the treatment stopping and about his mother going away.

If parental difficulties are too serious and are not corrected, the child's treatment either fails or is seriously limited. If the mother in the case cited had kept up her alarm over every sexual manifestation of the child and had kept hitting him frequently, the anxiety, hostility, alarm, and guilt would have been too severe for adequate elucidation; and, even if elucidation had succeeded, the child could not have helped continuing his reactions. Understanding and knowledge of the parental difficulty are also important for understanding the child's reaction; e.g., the mother's irritability and upset about her divorce and the father's tendency to be critical throw significant light on the child's behavior in the therapeutic interview.

The final decision for the child's coming for treatment naturally depends on the parents; further, when the child is disinclined to come, either because of preference for listening to the radio or playing games or because of resentment or anxiety and guilt over the topics that are being touched upon, parental support of the treatment may become well-nigh indispensable.

General Character of the Child's Reaction. The child's reactions in the course of the treatment have the following characteristics: recurrent directness and transparency; predominance of verbal denial, abundance of fantasy life, indirectness of most of the reactions, and gross rationalization. The recurrent directness results from the absence of relatively consistent control of impulses and lack of rigid psychological organization. The first interview of the child under discussion revealed a surprising amount of fundamental dynamic information about him. One sometimes has similar information in adult patients in the first dream they bring for analysis. The ease of denial, the abundant fantasy life, the indirectness of reactions, and the gross rationalization come from the as yet inadequately developed sense of reality. Denial may be patent. The child often does not mention or flatly denies crucial and significant events even after he has realized that the therapist needs information in order to be able to help him.

An illustration for this was given previously when the patient failed to mention that his eczema had flared up. On this occasion he readily admitted the facts when the therapist brought up the issue, but on frequent occasions he unequivocally denied that he had nightmares, got bad marks in school, or had had a very bad fight at home.

Less consciously and directly, denial means the shutting out of awareness of a painful fact—e.g., of the feeling of helplessness in the face of a threat. As amply illustrated by our patient, the combination of denial of this kind with remedial fantasy is one of the characteristic features of the child's emotional life as revealed in treatment (298).

The indirectness of the child's reactions means the absence of a direct verbal confirmation of facts or interpretations; the child does not contradict them, either, and goes on to produce further relevant material. Indirectness further means that the child's anxiety or resentment in the session is mostly not verbalized but shown only by a fleeting facial expression or by a change in activity. The child with the eczema frequently switched to the neutral game of playing checkers after he engaged in some aggressive games with dolls, such as trying to pull them apart or twist their heads off. The children's positive reactions to the therapist are shown, not infrequently, through their calling him an endearing nickname—e.g., "Docky" instead of "Doctor"—or accidentally calling him "Mommy" or "Poppy."

On one occasion the therapist had a sore back and for a few sessions could not fully participate in the lively activity that, at the time, the child regularly engaged in. The patient inquired about the reason for his not fully participating, and the therapist told him. The child did not come back to this topic, but a few sessions later, after a friendly and successful clarification of a point, he asked the therapist whether his back was better.

The gross rationalization consists of the child's telling his parents or the therapist a completely slanted version of the facts, using this as an explanation for his behavior. Thus a child may be eager to come for the sessions as long as he can simply play and no relevant topic is touched upon verbally; but if the therapist then brings up an issue—e.g., sex or excretory functions—the child may tell his parents that it is a waste of time to go for treatment, because the doctor does nothing to help, or he will simply say that the doctor is asking foolish questions. Similarly, he is ready to blame somebody else for his difficulty, completely omitting the fact that his own action started it—e.g., striking another boy or stealing something.

What has been said in the section on psychotherapy about the child's preparation for and attitude toward treatment and the method of handling them applies to analysis also. Even after the right preparation the child does not consistently accept the idea that his difficulties represent emotional problems.

In spite of the fact that he had been told in the past that his eczema continued because "he got excited" and he had been eagerly waiting for two years to start the treatment, he constantly made comments to the effect that he would get physical treatment after he was through with the therapist, and he did not give relevant information about the emotional aspects of his eczema until he had the flare-up mentioned.

This relative lack of insight is connected partly with the child's immaturity, but, of course, it also represents frequently a "resistance" phenomenon caused by anxiety, guilt, shame, or humiliation over the problems that have to be touched upon. The child, in the course of the treatment, shows all his significant attitudes toward the therapist to a greater or lesser degree. Adult patients also vary in the degree to which they "transfer" their irrational emotional problems onto the person of the therapist.

The child entered upon the treatment with the expectation of a miraculous cure. When he had the flare-up of his eczema, he was disappointed and resentful, not only as regards his mother, but also as regards the therapist. His anxiety about being abandoned by the therapist came out in a variety of ways. He used to count the number of months, weeks, and sessions that he would have before vacation time and recurrently thought that the therapist would send him to somebody else for further treatment. Further, during prolonged stretches of treatment, he not only wanted to equal the therapist in skill, strength, and knowledge in games, but also wanted to surpass him.

INTERPRETIVE COMMENTS

Although the larger part of the therapeutic session is spent in activity, verbalization of the child's problems is an integral part of the process. The verbalization may consist of the therapist's calling attention to a manifestation or raising a question at the proper time—e.g., "Isn't it funny that you get all excited if you miss the target even once?" The most important type of verbalization is interpretation, which requires the same kind of judgment as to timing and topic as for the adult patient, and, of course, has to be done in the child's language. The interpretation may be a simple statement—e.g., "You are angry at your brother." The following more complex example will illustrate the effects by which the efficacy of a comment can be judged:

The therapist heard from the mother that the child remarked, "The doctor wants to find out whether I am an active child and then he will send me to someone else." The therapist decided to take this up with him, because it indicated some fear of rejection and abandonment. Secondly, the phrase "active child" seemed to refer to the problem of the child's arms and legs having been tied and to his remedial fantasy, related by him in the first hour, that he had thrown off the bandages as an infant by simply raising his arm. Further, over long periods of time in the treatment he recurrently engaged in lively games, such as shooting arrows or hitting the ball with a bat, showing a tendency to excited, vehement, although not destructive, motility, with excess movements. When the therapist quoted the child's remark as told to him by the mother, the child said, with a somewhat anxious facial expression, "Aren't you going to send me away?" The therapist remarked, "No, I won't send you away. I will treat you and try to help you." He then added, "I guess you want to be very active to make up for the trouble you had because your hands were tied down, and sometimes you get excited, because you want to be very active." The child listened to this with a pleased facial expression and said, "That's right. I want to do things," and then proceeded to give to his activity a new direction which had not occurred in the sessions before. He got up on the low play table and jumped off a few times with obvious pleasure and feeling of accomplishment. He then put the chair on top of the table and very skillfully jumped off from there, obviously with a slight anxiety but with a joy in accomplishment. He then put a second chair on top of the first chair. The therapist remarked to the child that this structure was too shaky and suggested that it would be safer to put the table on top of the couch; while the therapist held the table, he could jump from there. The child accepted the suggestion and proceeded to jump with a little more anxiety but very skillfully from the greater height. He then said, "I got wings also, so I can jump very well." He took a towel, put it around his shoulders, and jumped with great enjoyment. Obviously, in this manner he proceeded now to master, through adequate activity, the anxiety which had previously resulted in vehement and excited activity. Also, he substituted playful fantasy (the wings) for the grandiose fantasy of such performances as jumping on the back of the running stallion (see p. 268). The therapist then tried to take up the questions how and why the child was afraid of being sent away when found to be "active," and he remarked, "I guess you thought I didn't want you to be very active and excited." The child met this comment with a puzzled facial expression and said, "No." The therapist dropped this point because he felt that either his assumption was incorrect or the child was not ready to go into the matter. He then asked the child, "From whom did you hear the words 'active child'?" because the phrase had an adult ring. The child said, "From nobody." The therapist asked, "Are those your own words?" whereupon the child replied, "They were the first words I ever learned." This obviously represented a fantasy, the meaning of which, however, was revealed in the child's further spontaneous remark, "When I decided to break loose, you know, to throw off the bandages, I could have waited till other children played, but I decided to do it, otherwise I would still be in the hospital, and, you know, I would never have met you," thus confirming by implication the construction that the experience of being tied down was a very traumatic, anxiety-provoking experience, with which the child was trying to cope both by his abundant self-aggrandizing fantasies and through anxious and vehement activity. The end of his remark also indicated a grateful and warm feeling for the therapist for having helped him with his interpretation.

As mentioned under psychotherapy, at times conversation about disturbing events and attitudes at home or in school may take place while the child is engaging in an essentially neutral activity such as drawing. In still other instances, after the treatment has been in progress for some time, the analyst may have to point out emphatically to the child that he has been avoiding all the problems which must be faced and understood before he can be more satisfied and happy.

Problems of interpretive handling of anxiety and guilt will be discussed in a later section (pages 278-279).

DATA OBTAINED BY THE PSYCHOANALYTIC METHOD: CONSCIOUS AND UNCONSCIOUS TYPES OF DATA

It has already been said that children either fail to mention or on direct questioning actually distort information that is unquestionably conscious—e.g., disturbing events of the previous day. Information from the environment is used without analyzing the omission or denial, in contrast to the procedure with the adult, except occasionally to a very limited extent—e.g., "You don't like to talk about that because it upsets you or makes you feel that you are bad." It is at times difficult to evaluate to what extent something is unconscious in the child's reactions, impulses, thoughts, and fantasies, for the very reason that the child does not talk about them. Undoubtedly, just as in the adult, there are degrees of awareness of the mentioned psychological elements.

It has already been told how the child was trying to cope with his perpetual anxiety through abundant fantasies and vehement excited motility. After a fight with another boy, in which he was frightened because the other boy picked up a broomstick, he related an elaborate story about having waylaid the offending boy and his gang with a gang of his own. In the ensuing fight, he said, he jumped on the rock and his gang shot arrows and conquered the other gang. Of course, the child knew that this had not happened. There was a partial awareness on his part that he always had to come out on top. There was probably no awareness that anxiety was the motor of this fantasy and of the one related in the first interview about having a white stallion on whose back he could jump without even using his hands. Nor was there awareness of the anxiety background of his vehement motility.

The conscious and unconscious data obtained in the therapeutic sessions can be classified as follows:

Hostile Impulses Directed Toward Others. As in the adult, these include reactions of anger or rivalry and the desire to injure, mutilate, destroy, or triumph over others to the point of deriving pleasure from cruelty. The hostile aggressive coloring of the activity can be more or less obvious. The game of shooting arrows is suggestive of this. The hostile coloring was much more obvious when the child took a doll representing his teacher and tried to pull it apart by the legs.

Destructive Impulses Directed Toward Oneself. These impulses come out most frequently after the child engages in an aggressive act against the therapist. Thus some children first shoot arrows at the therapist, by which he is supposed to get badly injured. At other times the children, after engaging in violent aggressive play or activity, injure themselves accidentally by bumping into things or by falling. A more serious type of reaction may occur in situations of severe anxiety with hostile features.

As mentioned, the child had a flare-up of his eczema when he was afraid that he would be abandoned both by his mother and by the therapist. He felt disappointed and bitter toward both. At this time he narrowly escaped being hit by a car. On the same day he accidentally cut himself with a jackknife, causing a minor injury.

Ambition, Desire for Accomplishment, Pride; Attitudes of Superiority, Self-Magnifying Tendencies. In children, one of the nearly universal desires is to be as big, effective, and powerful as a grown-up.

On one occasion the patient decided to shoot arrows at a target and alternately had the analyst do the same. The target hung on a high nail, and the little patient was at an obvious disadvantage. When the therapist wanted to lower the target, the patient refused, got up on a chair, and said, "Now I am bigger than you are." In the early part of the treatment this child invariably managed situations so that he either hit more targets—e.g., by standing much closer than the therapist—or counted himself as having hit more targets by disregarding the shots that went wide of the mark.

Feelings of Inadequacy, Disturbed Self-Esteem, Feeling of Rejection. These may manifest themselves in remarks by the child that he is stupid, that he cannot do anything well, and in his rejecting a remark on the part of the therapist when he exclaims, "You did this well!" A combination of the feeling of inadequacy with anticipation of failure and intolerance of being second in accomplishment may manifest itself in more indirect ways, such as refraining from activity (A. Freud). Similarly, the child may directly exclaim, "Nobody loves me!" or "Everybody hates me!" Or, in more indirect ways, he may avoid situations in which he anticipates rejection.

Desire for Closeness, Affection, Love, and Warmth. This is very strong in all children and may manifest itself with a variety of directions. The shy child may make a drawing of a heart on Valentine's Day and write on it, "From ——— (his name) to ——— (the therapist's name)." Younger children may actually climb on the therapist's lap and curl up. This need was very evident in the patient in many of his remarks already quoted as well as in his occasionally taking the analyst's arm and momentarily resting his head on his shoulder.

Need for Dependence, Support, and Complete Care. More indirect manifestations of this desire may be the child's wanting to take some toy home with him or asking the therapist to go with him to the movies. These manifestations also imply a warm, appreciative attitude toward the therapist. Taking home a bow and arrow or a pistol from the therapist's office also serves the purpose of increasing the child's stature before other children. The need for complete care frequently has a miraculous magical coloring, as was illustrated by the attitude of the patient during the first interview. It may also have the coloring of wanting affection to the exclusion of everybody else and then may manifest itself in reactions of jealousy at seeing other children in the analyst's office or finding out that other children have played with the toys.

Oral, Excretory, and Genital Impulses and Fantasies. These are always present in the analytic material for several reasons: (1) There is a constant source of impulses from these fields in the child's daily life. (2) They represent problems, sources of pleasure, and modes of mastery for the relatively immature organism. (3) They are significant carriers of conflict centers in the relationship with the persons in the child's environment. (4) They represent intellectual problems and problems of curiosity in fields where the child does not yet have complete knowledge and experience. In the last category are the infantile concepts and theories about sexual differences between male and female, theories of conception (e.g., oral impregnation) and of childbirth (e.g., through the umbilicus or through the anus). The child may engage in filling the toy bottle with milk and then nurse on it or he may touch his penis and rub it through his clothes as the patient at one point in the analysis mentioned he did. The child may try to bite or actually succeed in biting the therapist or one of the dolls or may at some point in the session suddenly want to go to the toilet. Putting the dolls on the toilet or scolding them for having soiled themselves is common. Some children may actually lose sphincter control in the therapeutic session.

The manifestations may be in the form of disguised (at times symbolic) or open fantasies or activities. Thus guns, arrows, and similar weapons may represent a penis; accidents and cutting off of an arm may represent castration; repeated collisions may represent intercourse; the underside of things may represent the excretory or the genital organs; an opening may represent the mouth, a house the human body. These activities or objects should, as a rule, be considered symbolic only if they appear in the context of relevant material. Thus the playing with guns may be an expression of the normal aggressiveness of the respective age groups of boys or the expression of hostility or an attempt to overcome anxiety by self-reinforcement, or they may represent genitals symbolically. The last interpretation is warranted if the activity occurs during the discussion of sexual problems, or if, let us say, playing with a female doll, the child puts an arrow to the genital region.

Fantasies of Incorporation and Retribution.

The child with eczema recurrently repeated his fantasy that "the doctors will want to operate on me to cure me of my sores." On being asked why he would be operated on, he would say, "To take out bad things inside." He related either fantasies or misinterpretations about the time he was in the hospital and about the doctor's cutting out the tongue of one of the children. He further added, "If you are afraid and you scream, they'll give you ether and they cut you open and you never know what they took out. If you are not afraid, they don't give you ether and you know what they did to you." After a while he continued: "If they cut out all my sores, even if on my back, if they gave me ether and I didn't know it—I would scratch till I got them back even on my back." The fear of loss of self-determination and of castration is fairly evident in these fantasies, but there is also the fantasy of there being "bad things" inside. He blamed his mother for "having given him eczema" by giving him chocolate as a "small child." On one occasion he made a drawing of an "Egyptian goddess" who had all kinds of treasures inside her; several thieves tried to get into her to get the treasure and take it away, but only the "good guy" succeeded after having shot all the others. These two fantasies (chocolate, goddess), combined with the first one (the bad insides), are suggestive of forceable taking, incorporation, inner poison, retribution, and fear of being robbed (Klein).

Occurrence of Symptoms in the Therapeutic Session. Symptoms may appear in the session because the discussion or enacting of the incidents or dreams of the preceding twenty-four hours stirs up the same conflicts and manifestations as occurred in the patient's daily life; or the patient experiences in his relationship with the therapist the same impulses and emotions as are of crucial significance in his daily existence.

The patient described asked the therapist during one of the few sessions remaining before vacation time to play checkers with him for money because, he said, he needed money for certain purposes, and he added, "I want a coin to remember you by; I will copy it on paper and put your face into the place of the President." He was afraid of refusal because the therapist several months previously declined to play for money after agreeing to it in some sessions. With the appearance of anxious anticipation the patient started to scratch his abdomen, having developed a sudden itching. Itching and scratching appeared in two other constellations in the therapeutic sessions. One was the setting of anger at the mother, the teacher, or other children if this was intense with some anxious undercurrent. The second was in connection with genital activity. Thus on one occasion he played with his penis on and off for two or three minutes through the pocket of his trousers and, following that, absent-mindedly scratched various parts of his body (extremities and chest.

Memories and Reactions of Earlier Years. It is difficult to evaluate the accuracy of the child's statements about events in his earlier years. It is further difficult to know how much of it is memory and how much fantasy. The adult sooner or later states with definiteness whether he is convinced of the reality of a memory—although this does not necessarily settle the issue of accuracy or completeness—or whether he is uncertain. The child presents memories with outward definiteness, or he denies events unqualifiedly. As a rule, the crucial information has to come from the parents. This information on early events is partially or entirely missing in the child's recollection.

The patient said in the first interview that his hands had been tied to the bed when he was one year old, and he added the story that, with a sudden forceful lift of his arms, he tore off the bandages that tied him down. There was no doubt, on the basis of information obtained from the mother, that the child remembered having been restrained. Through the years he had recurrently commented about this to his mother and brother. However, it was impossible to determine whether he actually did believe that he had freed himself once and for all. This fantasy was crucial in throwing light on his denial of threatening situations, and on his trying to cope with his anxiety through grandiose imagination and vehement motility, and he accepted the idea that the incident could not actually have happened. With the straightening out of his emotional life, he did not desperately need this illusion any more, but it could not really be decided with certainty whether he had ever fully believed in the fantasy.

There is considerable variation among therapists of adults and children as to how far they go in the attempt to "reconstruct" crucial earlier events when the patient has at no point a spontaneous memory of even part of a probable event. It is a useful procedure to utilize information about crucial events in the child's early life obtained from the parent if the child manifests trends that at least by implication refer to the consequences of the event and the discussion would throw light on significant problems. The therapist can do this by saying either, "Probably this-and-this happened to you when you were little," or "Your mother told me that this-and-this happened to you and it had this-and-this effect."

Emotions and Attitudes of Fear and Guilt. The child may have an attack of anxiety in the therapeutic session. At other times the anxiety or the guilt may be fleeting but still clearly noticeable. At still other times it can be deduced mainly by the sequence of activities—e.g., when the child suddenly stops an aggressive or sexual act or discussion and engages in a neutral game, such as playing checkers. It is particularly important to uncover the unconscious anxiety or guilt behind compensatory and coping measures.

This had to be done gradually in connection with the aggrandizing fantasies of the patient with the eczema. The problem was approached after he clearly showed the connection in a number of incidents, both in his daily life and in the therapeutic sessions. Thus, after the difficulty in school was mentioned, he told the story that, using a spyglass, he shot the teacher, discharging the arrow from his house into the school. Once, in the course of play, he bumped into a piece of furniture and for a moment looked frightened and hurt. A few seconds later he said that this did not hurt, he was even better than the Lone Ranger, he could jump over everything on his white horse.

The patient may resist the uncovering of the anxiety because the comments are a threat to him; they hurt his self-esteem and arouse his guilt over forbidden strivings.

In his first attempt to comment on the patient's fantasies, the therapist used the word "afraid." The child immediately broke in with the emphatic assertion, "I am not afraid of anything; I am never afraid." He even objected to the word "worried." He did, however, in later comments, let the words "bothered," "troubled," and "upset" pass. Pointing out the nature of the fantasy and the anxiety behind it meant to our patient that he could be tied down again or be subjected to an equivalent threat and would be deprived of any means to cope with the danger. He used to counter the early attempts in this direction by some such remark as, "Yes, I can do those things, and I have a weapon that is even stronger than you; I have a man-sized bow and arrow at home." This remark implied that through his comments the therapist became a threat to him, that he warded off the comment and immediately reinforced his previous position.

This kind of defensive reaction could be gotten around in part by making comments on relevant behavior after some improvement. Thus, in the beginning, whenever he played shooting arrows (tipped with a rubber cup) with the therapist, he always had to have the arrows hit the therapist but had to deny even the occasional instances when he was hit. After a period of treatment he did not mind being hit by the arrows. The therapist said, "You used to mind when you were hit, but now it doesn't upset you." The patient accepted this and added, "Yes, I used to do that when I was little."

DREAMS

Children tell their dreams more frequently to their parents than to the analyst, although at times the reverse is true. The topic of the dream can be brought up by stating that the parent informed the analyst or, in the course of play with dolls if the child is inclined to engage in such activity at the time, the analyst can say that the doll representing the patient had a dream, and then the child may relate the dream. In telling about it or enacting it, he may make some changes from the way he first reported it to the parent.

The large majority of dreams that children have in the course of their treatment are anxiety dreams, and a few are of a pleasant, wish-fulfillment type. They are relatively simple and transparent. One rarely gets associations to them from the child, but they are easy to interpret if one knows the child's situation and the events of the preceding days. By and large, dreams are very useful in child analysis, but do not play quite the same role as in most adult analyses. The interpretation given does not make the same revealing impression as in the adult analyses.

The child with eczema told his mother, at the time his difficulties in school were at their worst, that he dreamt there was a killer in the yard outside the house. In the subsequent hour the analyst brought up the dream. While enacting it with dolls, the child said, "Then they discovered that the killer was the teacher." He interrupted the play with the dolls at that point. The next morning he said to his mother, "Last night I killed the teacher," and he added, "And I will do it, too, but nobody will know because I will leave a note in somebody's name," and further added the fantasy that he would go to the cemetery, dig out some human flesh, and put it on a dummy, so that when the police looked for him to catch him they would think that that body was his, and in that way he would escape.

These two dreams, the events in the hour, and the child's fantasy illustrate the child's hostility, which he acknowledged before; but he had been denying the intensity of his resentment as well as his fear of retribution.

HYPOTHESES

Two general systems of working concepts and hypotheses have been crystallized out in the development of child analysis. One of them works with the idea that pleasure-seeking strivings, with subsequent hostile attitudes as a result of frustration and rivalry, are the initial and largely unconscious motivations, which then lead to fears, mainly of sexual injury, and to guilt. The fears represent retribution and punishment for the forbidden strivings. The patient then copes with his problems by a variety of means known as defense mechanisms. These organized methods are crucial in the approach to the patient's total problems (A. Freud).

The other approach puts emphasis on hostile strivings arising in early infancy during the period of maximal (oral) sadism at the time of teething, intensified even by such inevitable frustration as waiting for food. These hostile strivings are expressed also through pleasure-seeking anal, urethral, and genital activities. With the initial lack of differentiation between himself and the world, the infant, in fantasy, incorporates orally the hated objects and is in turn afraid of being incorporated by them. This leads to the feeling of being persecuted by hostile objects within and without, and later, with increasing differentiation between himself and the world, to the fear of losing the benevolent objects (Klein).

The conceptual framework presented in the section on adult analysis can be used in the approach to children also. To repeat it briefly, attitudes of self-evaluation (self-esteem and feeling of moral worth), feelings of relative strength and helplessness, interpersonal behavior (e.g., submission or domination), organ-functional strivings aiming at pleasure, at relief from discomfort, and at self-preservation, and emotional reactions of anxiety and hostility are to be considered equipotential dynamic forces with conscious and unconscious manifestations. In the process of conflicts, frustration, and dangers, defense and coping mechanisms are set into motion. One significant aspect of this is that any one of the forces enumerated may be intensified, repressed, or expressed through any of the other forces. In the functioning of the individual, in all habitual and significant functions of the individual, there is a fusion of the various strivings. The relative intensities of these forces vary with the child's age and environmental position. The individual's conflicts and coping mechanisms are self-perpetuating and a part of this is the relationship of the past to the present. A current feeling of weakness increases the interpretation of past experience in terms of anxiety, and the memory and retained pattern of past reactions give direction to the evaluation of the current situation.

The symptoms and dynamics of the child with the eczema regularly referred to in this section can be formulated as follows:

There were five nodal points in the child's psychopathological history.

1. In early infancy the mother's anxiousness affected the child in two ways: (a) She was afraid to handle him, and as a result there may have been a deprivation of stimulus and warmth. (b) The anxiety of the mother may have been communicated to the child through constrained or jerky motility. Possibly as a result of these two factors and an allergic sensitivity, he developed infantile eczema, with the recurrent itching. This development represented an additional stress through an increase in aggressiveness (turned toward the self but with incomplete cessation of tension), partial pleasure source (relief through scratching), and renewal of pain. This led to an increase in helplessness and in need for the affection and support of the mother, possibly with blame of her and resentment toward her for the lack of relief.

2. The child's hands were tied to the bed at about the age of two to prevent scratching. This was a frustrating experience in that it thwarted all motility and increased the child's hostility and fear of retribution. It made him feel completely helpless in the face of this fear. A disappearance of the eczema might have compensated for this, but its persistence, because of emotional factors, resulted in a permanent conviction of the world's being hostile and of the mother's allowing the world to frustrate and attack, and set in motion a grandiose compensatory reinforcement of illusory strength and esteem of the self (e.g., the fantasy of throwing off the bandages with a sudden swing of the hands). It may be added here that the child remarked to the mother for a year or two after this event, "You would have gotten better results with me if you hadn't allowed them to tie my hands. Anyhow, when the nurse took my bandages off to wash me and when she wasn't looking I scratched extra hard just to get back." The oral frustration and anxiety are evidenced by the facts that he stopped sucking his thumb after his hands were tied and that he blamed his mother for the onset of his eczema because she fed him chocolate.

3. He suffered a severe burn on his right thigh by climbing on the radiator at the age of 2½. He blamed his mother and his brother for this. As regards his

mother, he gave two different versions. One was that she put painful medicine on his lips and he had so much pain that he was ready to jump out of the window. That is why he got up on the radiator. The other one was that she had let the radiator get hot in the summer. He blamed his brother by saying that he cried so much that he (the patient) wanted to get away from him. Thus he took the burn as another proof that the world, with the permission and support of his mother, was hostile and punishing.

4. At about five years of age, during the Oedipal period, in connection with increased masturbation, the eczema became localized on his penis for a prolonged period, causing, in turn, increased stimulation as well as increased fear of genital injury. His guilt and his fear were increased by the mother's distress over his scratching and by the threat of one of the nurses that, if he did not stop scratching, his penis would be cut off.

Sensing threat everywhere and considering himself helpless in the face of it, on the one hand he became defensively hostile with other children; on the other, he was constantly ready to engage in violent motility and grandiose fantasies to save himself. At the same time he considered himself extremely vulnerable because he was afraid that any injury might be particularly violent because of his "sores" and would make them spread. Along with this, his readiness to feel his self-esteem hurt became very great, as did also his desire to get from the world what was denied him; to find gratification and consolation, he had to have everything he desired: he always had to win at games. His guilt over his genital strivings, his masturbation, his Oedipal longings, and his aggression further decreased his self-esteem and intensified the consequences mentioned. It also increased his fear of punishment and retribution. His difficulties in school resulted from the fact that he over-reacted to school discipline, which was threatening to him, and therefore he had to disobey it through prohibited movements. He also considered it unfair and rebelled against it, with the fear of retribution. He could not persevere in subjects which were difficult for him to begin with because they were too much of a blow to his self-esteem. He blamed the teacher for his failure and became all the more hostile to her; he had fantasies in which he killed the teacher with his "man-size" arrow and then had nightmares in which he was killed by a teacher-substitute.

5. The critical point in the patient's treatment and the fifth nodal point in his traumatic experiences was caused by the parents' separation. This has already been referred to previously. It renewed his feeling of the world being full of hostile forces, renewed his feeling of abandonment, first increased his mistrust of his mother (he blamed her for the separation), then increased his Oedipal conflict and fear of retribution by his father, and, because of the flare-up of the eczema, endangered his confidence in the analyst's help. This crisis could be dealt with because of his strong attachment to the analyst and because of the parents' cooperativeness as regards the handling of the child.

PREVENTION OF PSYCHIC ILLNESS

There are no guaranteed ways of preventing neurotic reactions in infants and children. The reason for this is threefold: first, there are constitutional differences; second, there is a difference between therapeutic and preventive principles; third, the effectiveness of preventive measures depends entirely on the sensitivity and emotional health of the person who takes care of the child. The difference between therapeutic and preventive principles is best stated in the following way: Let us say that the child has repressive parents as regards self-esteem, aggression, and sexual urges. Through contact with the permissive therapist, the child's symptoms disappear. The conclusion then is drawn that permissiveness in all the areas mentioned would have prevented the neurosis. This is not necessarily so, because, obviously, complete lack of repressive measures could lead the child into conflict with nearly everybody and could also intensify his irrational attitudes. A balance between permissiveness and repression is not easily maintained; even if it is, the child's *interpretation* of the repressive measures may lead to difficulties. Apart from such unavoidable difficulties as physical illness and a bullying playmate or sibling, he may consider even minimal repression as excessive or consider it as rejection. Similarly, if help is always given to the child when he meets difficulties, he may become too dependent or may feel he is being dominated. If requests for help are always denied, he may feel he is being let down and rejected.

By and large, it can be said that an awareness of these conflicting needs of the child is necessary for prevention. Secondly, an awareness of the child's developmental level is required. Thirdly, a patient awareness of the difficulty of controlling impulses and overcoming anxieties, and a minimum use of repressive and punitive measures, are both needed. These statements apply to all problems of feeding, sphincter training, self-assertiveness, obedience, genital urges, freedom of movement, and hostility. A recent illustration of the new trend and also of the difficulty is the development of self-demand feeding. Contrary to the rigid schedule, the principle is to feed the infant whenever he wants to be fed. In spite of this measure, some children get into difficulty. The reason for this is that the caretaker's total behavior may be anxious, rigid, demanding, or rejecting. Further, the infant or the child may use the intake of food as a compensatory measure for consolation and thus develop digestive difficulties. Thus, under certain circumstances, the self-demand system may be worse than the regular schedule. It may further be added that the total behavior of the parent is as important as any special measure about feeding regulation and bowel training. Many infants weather even a premature bowel training without trouble if it is done in a kind and warm manner and if the parent does not get alarmed over relapses; and bowel training at one year or a year and a half can cause trouble if it is done in a rigid, repressive, and punitive—or over-permissive—manner.[3]

[3] For detailed information on the handling of specific problems, see B. Spock, *The Common Sense Book of Baby and Child Care* (890), and A. Gesell and F. L. Ilg, *Infant and Child in the Culture of Today* (342).

SUGGESTED READINGS

Recommended on the general topic of psychotherapy for children are Allen, *Psychotherapy with Children* (26), Axline, *Play Therapy* (39), Hamilton, *Therapy in Child Guidance* (382), and Mittelmann's article (670). For psychoanalysis of children, a good general article is Mahler, "Child analysis" (601); A. Freud's *Introduction to the Technic of Child Analysis* (297) and Klein's *The Psycho-Analysis of Children* (500) are classics in the field. Homburger's "Configurations in play—clinical notes" (424) presents a brilliant approach. The January, 1935, issue of the *Psychoanalytic Quarterly* is a summary of articles on child analysis.

XVIII Applied and Preventive Techniques in School and Industry: Psychiatric Social Work

GUIDANCE IN INDUSTRY

PROBLEMS OF PSYCHIATRY IN INDUSTRIAL SITUATIONS

Psychological difficulties manifest themselves in industrial situations through absenteeism, inefficiency at work, alcoholism, quarrelsomeness, and physical complaints. Thus an individual may complain that his eyes cannot tolerate the light in a part of the plant in spite of the fact that he has worked there for years with no difficulties and that he is suffering from no eye disorder.

The difficulties listed may be present from the beginning, but the clearest cases are those in which someone who has worked efficiently for years suddenly gets into trouble and disciplinary measures are of no avail. Emotional problems in industry arise (1) in connection with conditions at work and (2) in connection with problems on the outside.

In connection with work, difficulties may arise as a result of accidents; as a result of promotion to a job which the individual, because of his limited capabilities (lack of skill, emotional limitations), cannot adequately perform; because the foreman or other members of the management are handling the employees poorly; because a close attachment is formed between two or more employees and one with psychopathic tendencies induces the others to be defiant and break rules.

Four systems have evolved in dealing with the various aspects of the problems described, all used with success on the limited scale on which they have been tried.

PERSONNEL TRAINING AND TEST PROCEDURE PLAN

This plan involves the following techniques:

1. Physicians, psychologists, and counselors are trained to elucidate problems with workers who have difficulties in work adjustment or who come to them seeking help for recognized emotional problems. Employees are referred to them when they seek transfers to different departments or ask for leaves of absence or when their work becomes inefficient—all for insufficient reasons.

2. Lectures are given to foremen aimed at making them aware of the emotional symptoms which herald a decrease in industrial efficiency, and methods of handling the difficulties through the appropriate balance of sympathy, support, and firmness are taught. A manual has been developed in the form of stories to illustrate the problems—e.g., of the anxious employee—and their handling. The following, based on an actual case, illustrates how the manual presents the material to the foremen:

"The story of Donald Lee is the story of a good worker who went sour because of worries about his home.

"Donald was what is known as a 'worrier.' . . . After Donald had been in Joe's [the foreman's] department for several years, he began to act even more worried than usual. . . . He made many errors. He became jumpy and got into quarrels with the other men. . . .

" 'Don [said Joe], I can't help but notice you're not getting along. Have the boys got the heat on or something? Your work's slipping.'

"At first Don seemed to resent Joe's questions. . . .

"The next day, however, Don was more friendly. . . . 'Joe, I'd like to talk to you about something. . . .

" 'You know, I've been married five years—known Katherine since she was ten years old. We got a three-year-old boy and expect another baby shortly.

" 'Katherine's been acting queer lately. She always used to be happy but now . . . she's always scolding me and the kid. It worries me so much I can't keep my mind on my work.' . . .

"Joe thought this over and then asked, 'What does the doctor say about her?'

" 'I don't know. I haven't asked him.'

" 'Why don't you get in touch with him the first thing,' Joe suggested, 'and find out what's the matter. Maybe it's just her condition.' "

Don went to see the doctor who explained that Katherine tired easily and that was why she was cranky. He suggested that someone help her with the work. Don then told this to Joe.

" 'What can I do?' asked Don. 'I can't afford to hire a girl.'

" 'Well, I'll try to have you transferred temporarily to the second shift,' Joe said, 'so you can be home during the day to help Katherine.' . . .

"Joe had Don put on the second shift and the arrangements were made.

"Things seemed to go better for Don almost immediately. . . ."[1]

[1] K. Brodman, *Men at Work: The Supervisor and His People,* Cloud, Chicago, 1947, pp. 83-86.

The foremen also refer workers to the psychologist for counseling.

3. Selection and placement procedures are instituted which include aptitude, intelligence, and personality testing and psychiatric interviewing. These procedures are carried out after the employee has been hired in order to ensure his coöperation. The Cornell Selectee Index and the Cornell Word Form are used in order to guide the psychiatric interview and to assess the strength of any psychopathological tendencies which might be present. (See Appendix I for a description of these tests.) An attempt is made to place each employee in a job which is commensurate with his capacities and which would not tend to elicit emotional problems. Questions are asked about his preference for solitary work or for work in a group, and, if possible, he is placed accordingly. A person with low average intelligence would do well sweeping the yard but would get into difficulty if placed in a skilled job above his capacity. If the various personality assessment procedures suggest that serious problems might arise, the applicant is advised to come for consultation if they do.

A statistical study of the effectiveness of this plan was carried out on a group of veterans who started to work at the Caterpillar Tractor Company after discharge from the armed services (673). Of a total of 508 veterans examined, 79 were found to have moderately severe or severe personality disturbances. Psychiatric aid was given to those veterans who had difficulty in adjusting to their work. Of this group, 22 percent left their jobs for reasons such as going into business for themselves, getting a better job, and leaving the community, as compared with 27 percent of 373 veterans without significant personality disturbance; 34 percent left their jobs because they did not like the work or the wages, because they found the work too difficult, or without giving any explanation, as compared with 26 percent of the "normal" group; 4 percent of both groups were discharged because of uncoöperativeness or very poor attendance; 40 percent of the group with personality disturbance were working adequately when the report was made, as compared with 43 percent of those without significant disturbance.

VOLUNTARY CONSULTATION PLAN

Trained counselors are placed adjoining the working rooms in the plant. The employees are aware of the counselor's presence, and any time they wish to discuss any problem or vent their grievances he is at their disposal. There is no advice given; no steps are taken to remedy the grievance directly. The counselor looks for leads to the real trouble and encourages talk in that area. His object is to lead the employee to a clear understanding of his problem so that he himself will come to realize what action to take.

This method of handling problems in work adjustment was derived from the following experiences during a study whose purpose was to improve working conditions (633):

Five experienced operators, whose job was assembling telephone relays, were transferred to an experimental room. Base output was determined by records of output for two weeks before removal into the special room. Over a five-year period the conditions in the experimental room were varied with respect to rest pauses, working hours, etc. There was a continual improvement in the output rate of the operators, *regardless* of the experimental changes made, including one period when a return to "original conditions" was instituted. The operators had no clear idea as to why they were able to produce more in the test room, but their comments uniformly indicated a preference for the happier working conditions in the test room and the absence of the feeling that they were working under any pressure there. Actually the girls in the test room were more thoroughly supervised there than they had been previously, but apparently they reacted favorably to the different character and purpose of the supervision. In the test room, conversation was tolerated; the operators knew that they were taking part in an important experiment which might lead to the improvement of working conditions; close social relationships developed among the girls in the test room; and the group developed leadership and a common purpose. The investigators concluded from this study that the mental attitude of the operators was the only thing that seemed to show a continuous relationship with improved output. Subsequently an interviewing program was conducted, in the course of which over 21,000 employees were personally interviewed about the attitudes of the workers toward conditions in the plant. The psychological benefits accruing to the persons interviewed were most unexpected. Employees commented over and over again on the beneficial effect of being able to express freely their feelings and emotions. They appreciated being recognized as individuals who had valuable comments to make, and seemed to obtain a certain "lift" from the interview itself.

REPATTERNING OF GROUP FORCES; PSYCHODRAMA

Individual and group emotional problems are handled in the following way: (1) The individuals are encouraged to speak about their grievances, but then the emphasis is shifted to the objective aspects of the problem by the psychologist's introducing a relevant question. (2) The individual's and the group's suggestions about the best methods of handling the objective problems are asked for. This is at times supplemented by psychodramatic role-playing—e.g., with the foreman playing the role of a worker. The following example illustrates the first two points:

When the psychologist entered the boss's office, the mechanic and the supervisor were standing there in their overcoats ready to quit. The boss explained that they were having some trouble because they did not agree on which machines should be repaired first and that one of the operators was playing them against each other by gossiping with each about the other. The psychologist said that such behavior was common, pointed out that things got twisted up after a few repetitions, and that the hurt caused people if they took such things seriously was more important than what was said. He then told the supervisor and the mechanic that he wanted to talk the matter over with each of them individually and made appointments to do so at their workshops. Thus he got both of them out of their overcoats and back to their work.

When the psychologist saw the supervisor alone, she said that one of the girls who worked under her had complained that the mechanic would not fix her machine. When she faced him with this, he denied it. Then the operator accused the supervisor of lying and said that she had not told her that. The psychologist then asked the supervisor factual questions about frequency of breakdowns. It became clear that the mechanic was very rushed. The psychologist then asked if it would help if he talked to the operators about their attitude toward the problem. The supervisor agreed, pointing out that certain girls were always complaining and were causing other girls to take the same attitude.

The mechanic, in his interview, explained that he had more work than he could handle. He also attributed the irritation to the impatience of the girls and the scarcity of his time, and also thought it would be a good idea to interview the girls.

Each of the girls who had been complaining was interviewed individually, and all agreed that the trouble was due to the fact that the mechanic had too much work to do. Then all of them were seen together, and their suggestions were elicited as to how to relieve the problem. They decided that, when more than one machine broke down at once, the most critical machine in terms of throwing more girls out of work at once should be repaired first.

The mechanic agreed to this plan and to the suggestion that it was the supervisor's responsibility to decide which machine should be repaired first and his job to do the repair. However, he doubted that the supervisor would agree to it.

When the supervisor was seen, she too agreed to the plan, but stated that the mechanic would not accept her decision.

Following this incident, the mechanic and the supervisor, who had until then been constantly bickering on the job, got along well, and the operators, reacting to this, no longer played them one against the other. The mechanic found that he had much less work and more time to tinker around. He installed a system of loudspeakers in the factory and played recorded music two periods a day. The whole shop enjoyed this, and relations became even more pleasant.[2]

There are three aspects of the psychologist's method of handling the situation. (1) Serious emotional problems were involved, and the psychologist took these into account. (2) He did not handle these problems directly but focused the attention of those involved on the realistic problems. (3) Group participation was sought to ensure the acceptance of the final plan. The importance of this last factor is seen in the result of the following experiment by Bavelas (605):

A group of workers who were already producing at a rate well above the plant average met with the psychologist at three weekly meetings. At those meetings they set themselves, by unanimous agreement, still higher production goals. Their production level rose farther as a result of this *group decision.* Another group whose initial production level was lower than that of the first group showed no increase in production after meetings with the psychologist at which no goal was set.

[2] Based on a presentation in K. Lewin, *Resolving Social Conflicts*, Harper, New York, 1948.

In some industrial setups the management is to a large extent at fault in its poor handling of the personnel. Therefore it is frequently necessary for the psychologist to be able to observe managerial officers and to deal with them in order to change their attitudes toward and handling of situations.

An illustration of psychodrama in industry is this: The foreman is trained to handle employees by playing the role of the employee himself opposite another foreman in the presence of observers. This is followed by a discussion of the behavior of both participants. This technique enables the foreman to experience for himself what the employee might feel in a given aspect of the supervisor-supervisee relationship—e.g., when the foreman approaches a worker to tell him that his output is not coming up to expectations. It is also an instructive experience for the observers.

PSYCHIATRIC HELP AND PROJECTIVE-TEST SELECTION FOR THE UPPER MANAGEMENT BRACKET

These procedures consist of employing a psychiatrist for the purpose of treating any high officer of the company in case of difficulty. The consultation takes place on a voluntary basis, but the whole management group is aware of the services available. This method has been followed in some large establishments, particularly where no psychiatrists are otherwise available locally. The other method under this heading is the administration of projective tests to applicants for higher management positions. The test findings are used as one important indicator for the purpose of ascertaining whether the applicant can meet the special emotional requirements of the job. There are no data available on the results of these procedures.

GUIDANCE IN THE EDUCATIONAL SYSTEM

It has been mentioned that youth organizations, such as neighborhood clubs and well-conducted, modern reform schools with trained, adult group leaders are very important therapeutic factors in the prevention and handling of delinquent behavior in children and adolescents. In the following, methods will be discussed that have been developed in the framework of a training organization and which aim at selection, prevention of breakdown, and the earliest possible recognition and remedying of difficulties that arise.

In the majority of case illustrations given for children and adolescents there is some difficulty either in conduct or in level of performance in the school. A brief illustration will be given here to show the intertwining of specific emotional problems and specific school problems. The following is further detail on the case given on pages 326-327.

Apart from conduct difficulties, the main problem of an eight-year-old child was that of penmanship and neatness in writing. His writing of letters and figures at times was so poor that the teacher, with the best of intentions, did not know whether his spelling or his solutions of arithmetic problems were correct. His drawings of fires and gun duels in the play sessions resulted in such confused pictures that anybody looking at them could hardly have made out the content. After a period of treatment, in his attempt to control this rampant aggression, he went in the opposite direction. He pictured houses with every shingle and brick drawn in. In his writing, this was paralleled by his making the letters and figures very small. He felt very proud after he accomplished this, but then felt hostile and disappointed when the teacher commented on the smallness of his lettering. His writing again became disorganized. It was only after the mother, on the therapist's advice, had a discussion with the teacher that the latter understood what was happening and coöperated in straightening out the child's problems.

Schoolwork in general presents the following emotional problems in addition to those discussed in other parts of the book. (See Chapters XI and XXI.) There is a time limit on accomplishment of a task on a minimum level. The examinations are apt to arouse fears of failure and of exposure of weakness and all attitudes and memories about which the individual feels self-critical, guilty, or deficient. Certain subjects are particularly apt to evoke these kinds of reactions, especially if the courses are conducted in a strict way. Much heartache and at times even tragedy can be prevented if the pupil with emotional problems temporarily takes a smaller number of credits and avoids certain subjects altogether.

Gifted children, as a group, have the same gross psychopathological disturbances as the average population, or fewer. In individual instances, however, the giftedness may lead to difficulties in the following ways: The parent may push the child toward exploitation of his special ability. The child may be bored with his environment and with routine school activity; as a result, he may exhibit aggressive conduct disorder, or withdraw, or fail in his studies because of neglect on his part while, at the same time, he does far advanced work on his own. All of these difficulties are preventable. Physical activities and sports are among the best means of maintaining adequate relationship with much less gifted mates. (For problems of mental defect, see Chapter XXI.)

In school counseling, the therapist usually gets the problem case early, referred to him by the school authorities. In college, the student may come for help without having been referred.

ELEMENTARY AND HIGH SCHOOLS

As an example of psychotherapy in primary and secondary schools, we are using the work of the Bureau of Child Guidance of New York City. The children there are referred by school principals, members of the faculty, parents, and agency workers. Retarded children are referred through the director of the Bureau for Retarded Mental Development.

The number of students seen per year ranges from 12,000 to 13,000. During the school year 1944-1945, a total of 12,240 students were seen, with a total of 78,724 contacts; 9369 were new cases. During that year the numbers of cases falling into the various referral categories were: 2662 for conduct problems; 1328 for personality problems; 10,562 for educational problems; 481 for health problems; 496 for family problems; 23 for neighborhood problems; and 101 for other problems.[3] Had facilities allowed, some 15,000 new cases would have been seen.[4]

The therapeutic procedures are adjusted to the individual case. The children are treated by psychiatrists, while social workers work with the parents. If, however, the problem lies in the area of learning, the child is treated by a psychologist. The length of treatment varies from a few interviews to weekly interviews extending over a period of several months. Intensive treatment is not attempted, but both verbal and play techniques are utilized.

Figures on results are not complete, for not all cases are followed up. Over a period of ten years, 22.2 percent of the cases were followed up for six months after termination of treatment. Of these, 77.6 percent showed improvement, 28.4 percent showing full adjustment and 49.2 percent partial adjustment, and 22.4 percent were unimproved.[4]

One of the most important features of the bureau's program is courses given to large numbers of teachers and administrators each year.

COLLEGE

At a small, progressive women's college, it was found that an adjustment rating on a four-point scale based on the student's performance on the Rorschach test at the beginning of the term correlated well with other criteria of adjustment—e.g., with necessity for referral to the psychiatrist in the course of the semester (699). The findings are summarized in Table 7. This study illustrates how the Rorschach or other personality test procedures could be used to single out at the beginning of the semester those students who might benefit by preventive psychiatric help.

Student Counseling. At a large city college, the cases referred for psychological counseling were classified into ten descriptive categories:[5]

1. Student who cannot study, is unable to concentrate;
2. Student who is lonely, cannot make friends;
3. Student who is afraid of examinations, cannot talk in class;
4. Student who is without purpose or vocational aim, a drifter;
5. The habitual evader, obstructionist, complainer;

[3] Children referred for several problems have been listed under each subcategory within which one of their problems falls.

[4] These figures were received by personal communication from Dr. S. H. Peppard of the Bureau of Child Guidance.

[5] This presentation is based upon a personal communication from Dr. Peter Blos, based on his experience at Brooklyn College.

6. Student with a physical defect;
7. Student who is in severe conflict with his family;
8. Counseling problems arising from the war;
9. Psychopath who succeeds in college;
10. Special problems, psychiatric conditions.

In a period of three and a half years, 386 students were seen for a total of 2290 interviews. At one end of the series, 36 percent of these students had only one interview each, taking up only 6 percent of the total number of interviews given; at the other end, 143 students were seen over a period covering from two to seven semesters.

TABLE 7. The Relationship of the Adjustment Rating to External Criteria of Adjustment[6]

Criteria	Adjustment Rating								Totals
	A Adequately Adjusted		B Slight Problem		C Moderate Problem		D Severe Problem		
	N	%	N	%	N	%	N	%	
Seen by Psychiatrist	5	6.5	6	5.5	8	9.5	24	30.5	43
Much Faculty Consultation	4	5.1	19	17.6	29	34.5	37	46.9	89
Committee Rating "p"[a]	3	3.9	1	0.9	8	9.5	5	6.3	17
Adequately Adjusted	65	84.5	82	76.0	39	46.5	13	16.4	199
Totals	77	100	108	100	84	100	79	100	348

[a] The rating of "p" is assigned by the Student Work Committee where maladjustment is described in teacher reports. The maladjustment is usually moderate.

The first step was getting information about the student's problems. Wherever necessary, suggestions were made, and in some cases advice was given to the student. It was usually the parent who first sought out the therapist; in some other cases, he called in the parent. He gave guidance to the college authorities on how best to deal with the student. (See also 158.)

A student had been suffering from a hearing defect since high school, and it became progressively worse. He could not get along in lectures, but managed by copying notes and reading. His mother, who came to see the therapist first, complained that he had no friends and was always brooding, focusing his attention on himself. The therapist obtained objective data on the percentage of the student's hearing loss. It was considerable and had progressed since the time of his

[6] R. L. Munroe, Prediction of the adjustment and academic performance of college students by a modification of the Rorschach Method, *Appl. Psychol. Monog.*, No. 7, Amer. Assoc. Appl. Psychol., 1945, p. 40.

entering college from 58 percent to 73 percent. The therapist then called in the student, who was glad to talk to someone: "I live in a haze. I have built a wall around myself." The therapist brought up the subject of the student's hearing loss. The student had avoided talking to people for fear they would find out about his defect and reject him. He did not remember the percentage of loss, saying it was "about 25 percent," although he had previously been told what it was, and he was uncoöperative about lip-reading. He wanted to do social work, in which listening was the main factor. This desire was interpreted to him by the therapist as a denial of his defect. The student then accepted his handicap and no longer thought of it as a punishment. He noticed that people were nicer to him when he admitted that he did not hear. He became less shy and began to make friends. He gave up his plan of becoming a social worker and coöperated in lip-reading. Nine months after the therapy began, he said, "I don't hate myself about the hearing; if necessary I will get a hearing aid." During a subsequent severe family crisis the boy stood up exceedingly well. He became a clerical worker after leaving college.[7]

The method of treatment was interview therapy. (See Chapter XIV.)

VOCATIONAL GUIDANCE

The majority of adults who come for psychotherapy have had enough opportunity to find out what their occupational abilities and interests are. They may still be undecided as to which of their interests to follow in practice. Some patients have had all of these opportunities yet remain in doubt both as to their abilities and even more as to their interests. A very few have not had adequate opportunities to know what interests them. The patients who have had the opportunities but remain in doubt are usually characterized by indecisiveness and the feeling of insignificance or detachment, so that they cannot take the initiative in or the risk of committing themselves to definite interests. For these individuals vocational guidance is very useful. At times these individuals have been or are in the process of being forced by their parents into an occupation that is not their own choice. The results of the test procedures during vocational guidance then allow them to accept the idea of their abilities and interests or give them firm ground in a sea of indecision and perplexity. Vocational guidance, in the main, consists of the administration of a large battery of tests aimed at determining the individual's actual or potential skills, and a survey of his personality, his life history, and his current economic resources, and should always include a knowledge of the "market"—that is, the opportunity for employment in various occupations. With patients who are perplexed and feel insignificant, the vocational psychologist can be very definite in his recommendations. With the detached persons who do not want to take the risks of initiative, particularly if they are receiving psychotherapy, vocational guidance is best limited to a statement about their skills and un-

[7] Personal communication from Dr. Peter Blos.

formulated interests and practical information about various occupations, leaving it to the psychotherapy to work out the patient's final choice.

A sixteen-year-old high-school boy was referred for vocational guidance after most of his emotional difficulties (temper tantrums, indecision, stammering) improved through psychotherapy. His ideal was a sociable, nonchalant head of an American family who does not exert himself in competitive struggle. This seemed to be a reaction against his father's personality and attainments and the instructions he offered to the son. The patient was administered a battery of tests, including interest blanks, verbal and performance intelligence tests, special aptitude tests, projective personality tests, and a test of stress tolerance (mirror drawing).

The vocation ultimately suggested was engineering, with acoustical engineering as a first choice. This was done with the purpose of utilizing his outstanding abilities, as revealed by the tests, in manual dexterity, insight into good form and balance in art, and capacity for coping with problems involving mechanical principles, as well as good average aptitude in arithmetic problems, recognition of good design, and capacity for visualizing objects in three dimensions. The suggestion was further given that he play a musical instrument as an avocation, as he expressed interests in scientific, musical, and mechanical activities. The emotional problems relating to occupation, on which further work was required, were a high level of aspiration without concomitant drive; the need to play an over-assertive role, based on his need for admiration, with, however, an undercurrent of anxiety; and his tendency to excessive caution and perfectionistic criticism of others.[8]

PSYCHIATRIC SOCIAL WORK

The particular province of the psychiatric social worker is in the functions related to the patient's social adjustment. He may obtain the social history from the patient and his relatives, investigate the home conditions, and help in handling difficulties in the patient's social relationships by clarifying for the family the patient's illness and advising on the difficulties in the home. He tries to determine whether other members of the family have emotional problems of their own and, if necessary, advises them to seek treatment themselves. He may help in the patient's occupational adjustment by enabling him to find work where his illness will not create difficulties or where his co-workers and employer are willing to give him special consideration. He may explain to the employer relevant aspects of the patient's illness. When the patient—as is frequent in the case of emotionally ill children—lives in a foster home, it is the social worker who is in charge of investigating and selecting the foster home and in orienting the foster parents to the problems of the patient. In "intake" work, the social worker interviews whoever applies to the psychiatric clinic in order to ascertain the nature of the problem, whether it falls within the province of the particular clinic, and to orient those who will be involved with further

[8] Personal communication from Mr. Dan Brower.

examination of the patient. With unmarried mothers, the social worker helps the client to make practical arrangements for prenatal care and for confinement. He counsels with her to help her to reach a decision as to whether she wants to keep the child or wants to have it adopted. In case the latter is decided upon, he makes arrangements for adoption of the child. In addition to these functions, which are considered uniquely those of the psychiatric social worker, in some organizations he also performs psychotherapy, usually under the supervision of a psychiatrist.

In modern social work the trend is toward helping the patient to reach his own decisions, in situations where he is faced with a choice, after the implications of the various alternatives have become clear to him.

SUGGESTED READINGS

Mayo's *The Human Problems of an Industrial Civilization* (633) is both excellent reading and a good introduction to its field. Roethlisberger and Dickson's *Management and the Worker* (782) is a more complex presentation of the same topic. A rounded presentation of techniques is given in Maier's *Psychology in Industry* (605). Brodman's *Men at Work: The Supervisor and His People* (124) is excellent reading and very instructive.

On their respective subjects we recommend Lowrey's *Psychiatry for Social Workers* (589), Blos's "Psychological counseling of college students" (101), and Fry's *Mental Health in College* (326).

XIX Somatic Treatment

In recent years, two types of somatic methods of treatment, both of a rather radical nature, have developed. The first of these are the so-called "shock" treatments, including insulin therapy, metrazol therapy, and electric convulsive therapy (ECT). It should be noted here that the term "shock" is a misnomer which has come into popular usage, probably through the erroneous idea that the effectiveness of these treatments is due to some sort of shock, either of a psychological or of a physiological nature, which is dealt the organism. The actual reason for the effectiveness of these methods is not yet known; the theories which are currently most widely held will be discussed below. The other method is the operation known as frontal lobotomy, which involves the cutting of certain pathways between the frontal lobes and the thalamus.

"SHOCK" TREATMENT

All three of the so-called "shock" methods, insulin, metrazol, and electric convulsive therapy (ECT), have in common the inducement of a disturbed state of consciousness. In metrazol therapy and in ECT, this disturbance in the state of consciousness is accompanied by convulsions; in insulin therapy it usually is not. Although convulsions occasionally do occur during insulin treatment, they are usually considered undesirable.

INSULIN COMA TREATMENT

In this form of treatment, the patient is given an injection of insulin sufficient to induce a coma, which gradually develops over the course of a few hours. The insulin injected lowers the blood sugar level and in that way decreases the supply of sugar to the brain, thus causing the patient to lose consciousness. When the coma has lasted from fifteen to ninety minutes, depending on the judgment of the therapist, it is terminated by the administration of sugar or glucose. When the patient comes out of the coma, he is usually in better contact with the environment than he was before. This state of relatively good contact is, at first, short-lived; but, as the course of treatment progresses, the lucid period gradually becomes more lasting. Daily coma treatments are continued as long as the patient continues to improve, but are usually not continued beyond sixty comas (474).

CONVULSIVE THERAPY

Both metrazol and electric convulsive therapy produce convulsions in the patient. These methods are considered equivalents of each other, and, since the use of electric current to induce convulsions was introduced, it has tended to replace metrazol. ECT is more generally preferred because it is easier to administer and because it is less unpleasant for the patient. When metrazol is used, during the short period between the injection of the drug and the convulsion or, if the dosage is insufficient to produce a convulsion, for several hours following the injection, the patient experiences intense discomfort. In the preconvulsion period this consists of a feeling of impending death and sudden annihilation. If no convulsion takes place, anxiety, restlessness, and general discomfort are experienced for a number of hours (474).

It is generally assumed that metrazol produces the convulsion by direct chemical stimulation of cerebral cells; but some workers (187) believe that the convulsion is caused by vasoconstriction due to the drug.

In ECT, electrodes are placed on the patient's head, and an electric current is passed through the brain. This electric current produces a mass stimulation of the cortical areas, which in turn produces convulsive seizures. When the patient regains consciousness, he is amnesic for the treatment procedure. The number of treatments given varies greatly according to the type and the severity of the illness. There may be as few as five convulsions induced, or there may be as many as forty. Following a course of convulsive treatments, the patient may show mental dulling, confusion, memory loss, impaired ability for abstract thinking and for calculation—symptoms similar to some of those seen in cases of organic brain damage. The severity of these aftereffects depends upon the number of treatments received and may not occur at all when only a few "shocks" are administered. They all gradually disappear after the conclusion of the treatment, and rarely last beyond six months (474).

RESULTS

Both insulin coma therapy and convulsive therapy are used in the treatment of schizophrenia, and the latter is also used in the treatment of several other psychiatric disorders. The statistical reports of results in schizophrenics with both forms of treatment show wide variations in the effectiveness of the methods. This is due in part to different handling of statistics by various authors. For example, some authors divide the patients into groups depending on the duration of the illness, while others do not. In addition, criteria for degree of improvement—such as complete remission, partial remission, and improved—differ among the different investigators. Another important factor which affects the results is the number of treatments given. A group of patients that have received only a short course of therapy cannot be compared with a group that have received a long series of treatments.

In the treatment of schizophrenia, the best results with both forms of treatment have been obtained with patients in whom the illness has been of relatively short duration—e.g., from less than one year to eighteen months —and where there has been an acute onset of the illness rather than a long, gradual development.

Various studies on the use of insulin shock in schizophrenia have shown remission rates varying between 50 and 80 percent (364). One study shows a remission rate of 79 percent in patients given intensive insulin coma treatment as compared with remission rates of 10-20 percent in untreated patients, with the quality of the remission higher among the treated patients. A follow-up study based on the same group of insulin-treated patients as well as on a group of patients receiving less intensive insulin treatment showed a remission rate of 55 percent at the conclusion of treatment, 42 percent after one year, 36 percent after two years, and 31 percent after three years. These figures reveal that the results obtained in some cases are only temporary, but even after this length of time the number of patients who still showed improvement was greater than the number of remissions in untreated patients (105, 106, 109).

Aside from the duration of the illness and the type of onset, there are other indicators for a relatively good prognosis with the use of insulin coma treatment. In general, patients with the paranoid form of schizophrenia and excited catatonic patients with hallucinations and delusions respond better than those with other forms of schizophrenia. Patients in whom the disease appears to be largely of a psychogenic nature and those who appear to be dissatisfied with their unreal world are likely to yield better results than are others (474). (See Chapter XXXIV for discussion of types of schizophrenia.)

Studies based on the treatment of schizophrenia with metrazol show essentially the same results as do those where ECT is used. One such study (using metrazol) showed a remission rate of 60 percent in cases of less than one year's duration and of 52 percent in cases of less than eighteen months' duration. An additional 20 percent of both groups showed great improvement. In cases of over eighteen months' duration, a remission rate of 10 percent was obtained, while 37 percent showed improvement (946). The convulsive therapies yield results similar to those of insulin treatment in some acute cases of schizophrenia, like catatonia; in chronic cases, insulin appears to give better results. ECT is more effective in catatonic excitements and stupors than in other forms of the illness, insulin in paranoid, hebephrenic, and simple schizophrenics (Kalinowsky and Hoch [474]).

ECT is most effective in the treatment of depressions. Results reported in depressions of the manic-depressive type and in involutional depressions range from 80 to 100 percent cured. However, patients with a circular psychosis offer discouraging results. Cases of senile and presenile depressions yield results similar to those of the above-reported depressions if the organic changes are not too great. Good results are also reported in cases of psychoneurotic depressions, where the ECT makes the patient better able to use psychotherapy. Some consider this use of ECT controversial. Results in manic-depressive patients of the manic type are almost as good as in those of the depressed type. In cases of involutional psychosis of the paranoid type, improvement is shown in 40-45 percent of the cases treated. In this disorder, the results are better if the illness has been of relatively short duration and if agitated features are present. In other psychoneurotic disorders—anxiety and conversion hysteria and obsessive-compulsive neurosis—results with the use of ECT have been poor. This is true even in patients with a strong schizoid coloring (474).

THEORETICAL CONSIDERATIONS

Many theoretical explanations for the effectiveness of the various forms of "shock" treatment have been set forth. These theories are, for the most part, refinements of one or another of the following more general theoretical ideas: (1) Insulin and electroshock alter the brain metabolism, causing changes in oxidation, and producing either anoxemia or hyperoxemia. (2) They act as sedatives, reducing the over-activity of the nervous system and the emotional pressure behind the symptoms. (3) They stimulate the vegetative regulative centers, particularly the sympathetic division. (4) Some organic changes are produced, especially in convulsive therapy, which imitate frontal lobotomy (see below) to the extent that diseased nerve cells are eliminated. (5) They act predominantly as a form of psychotherapy because the patient is given more attention and is always nursed back into active existence from the helpless state of unconsciousness.

FRONTAL LOBOTOMY

PROCEDURE

Frontal lobotomy is an operative procedure in which nerve pathways between the cortex and the thalamus are cut. There are several variations of this operation involving differences in the size of the incision (differences in the number of fibers severed) and differences in the position of the cut.

These different procedures produce somewhat varying effects. They are used on patients suffering from schizophrenia and severe psychoneurotic disturbances.

EFFECTS OF FRONTAL LOBOTOMY

The most important effects of these operative procedures are in the area of personality change. The different procedures produce varying degrees of personality alteration, but the changes in all types of the operation appear to be in very much the same direction. The operation has been given to some individuals who are emotionally well integrated in order to relieve them from the distress of severe intractable pain. It is perhaps in these persons that the personality alterations can best be evaluated in that one does not risk confusing them with the changes that have already occurred in relation to a mental illness. In these patients no noticeable intellectual impairment has been demonstrated. They do show what may be termed "bleaching" of the personality. They tend to be complacent, with reduced vivacity and emotional dulling. They are not as alert as formerly, and their anticipatory functions show marked impairment. Evaluation of their bodily functions is also reduced. As regards this last point, it is interesting to note that, although the patient's pain persists and he is still aware of it, he is no longer concerned about it, and it no longer appears to distress him as it did prior to the operation.

In mental patients, as in the patients just described, the operation does not change the patient's symptoms, nor does it alter the basic structure of the illness, but it does result in a change of attitude toward the illness and the symptoms. Thus a patient of high intellectual endowment who is unable, because of his illness, to make effective use of his intellectual capacities and is disturbed by his low-level adjustment, if given this operation, may then be able to accept the type of adjustment of which he is capable. Following the operation, the patient no longer demonstrates fear or self-consciousness, and his tendency to evaluate himself in relation to social anxiety is gone. He makes contact with his environment easily. He no longer anticipates failure, and any symptoms based on inferiority feelings diminish. Conflictual situations still remain, but the patient no longer reacts to them. Damage to the personality is seen in inertia or apathy, in decreased planning activity, creativeness, and foresight, and in reduced depth of emotional experience (417).

THEORETICAL CONSIDERATIONS

The theoretical question which arises is whether these operations produce their results directly through the damage to the brain which is involved or whether the personality changes are secondary phenomena stemming from the elimination, by the operation, of anxiety, tension, and self-awareness.

The latter appears to be the more likely explanation when the role of anxiety in the individual's adaptation is considered. "Anxiety is used as an ego regulative function against other drives and if sublimated it performs as creative energy. If all tension and anxiety is cut and self-evaluation becomes indifferent to the individual, the setting of goals, plans, and anticipatory activities change into complacency" (417).

It should be pointed out here that the above described procedures are all of a more or less radical nature and should be used only after thorough examination of the patient and after determination that the patient really needs them. This is particularly true as regards the operative procedures, which produce irreversible organic changes. First and foremost, they should not be used to replace psychotherapy in patients who can benefit by psychotherapy. In some instances—e.g., the use of ECT for neurotic depressives—the technique used should be considered an adjunct to psychotherapy, and its primary purpose should be to make the patient more accessible to psychotherapy.

The use of drugs as hypnotics for narcosynthesis and of penicillin in general paresis will be discussed in their respective places.

SUGGESTED READING

Kalinowsky and Hoch, *Shock Treatments and Other Somatic Procedures in Psychiatry* (474), gives a comprehensive and critical survey of the field as well as the authors' own investigations.

Introduction to Parts V, VI, and VII

CLASSIFICATION OF PSYCHOLOGICAL DISTURBANCES

The classification of psychological illnesses is an important and difficult problem. This is shown by the fact that almost every year special committees of the American Psychiatric Association meet to decide on the terminology and classifications to be used. The general purpose of classification is to enable the therapist to orient himself with respect to the individual who applies to him for help. If he knows a few facts about the patient, he knows what other facts to look for; he can estimate the seriousness of the condition and determine the treatment to be used.

The following points are significant in connection with classifications:

1. All symptoms and modes of handling situations—in other words, character traits—represent characteristic reactions to situations and problems; to use Meyer's term, they are reaction types.

To say that people differ in every characteristic is of course a truism; here we wish to point out briefly *how* these individual differences, particularly in emotion, influence the sick individual's choice of symptoms and make him either more or less accessible to psychotherapy. Their specific role in affective reaction tendencies will be seen clearly in many of the cases which follow.

Various patients usually react to problems in a manner characteristic of them; e.g., one may run away from them, another seek the help of others, another attack the problems directly. One person may use detachment, a second person bursts of temper, as the preferred mode of solving life problems. The first individual will be more likely to have symptoms that express and cover repressed aggression and self-assertion, whereas the second will be more likely to repress feelings of weakness and the like. These two persons will probably have very different symptoms, even though the situation of stress is the same. Furthermore, they present different problems for the psychotherapist. The detached person is much less overt, reactive, and flexible in his emotional reactions than the one who knows how to express his emotions. These detached or rigid individuals are much more difficult problems therapeutically, for they fight off the therapist, refuse to react emotionally, and so insulate themselves that it is difficult to make contact with them.

2. Similar conflicts may lead to a variety of symptoms and reactions. To a considerable extent, however, striking and extremely characteristic reaction types have characteristic and partly specific determinants. In other words, the dynamics of an anxiety attack are usually different—to some extent, at least—from the dynamics of depressive reactions. But in considering specificity, complex determinants should be sought, not one single determinant. For example, many factors which operate in an anxiety attack are also operative in a depressive attack; the feeling of helplessness is common to both and equally important in both. Furthermore, a patient's personality features—his evaluation of himself and of others, his fears, etc.—are important therapeutically, even if they are not specific determinants of the reaction from which he suffers at the time. A patient suffers from attacks of anxiety whenever he becomes angry at the superior who is unfair to him. His anxiety attacks probably represent fears about the consequences of his anger, particularly fear of destruction and injury. However, such factors as need for unqualified dependence, inability to shoulder responsibility, unconscious attitudes of superiority, are all important in evaluating this patient's problems—even in these attacks—and in his treatment.

3. Classifications must not be adhered to too rigidly. Although it is very useful to say that a patient suffers from "anxiety hysteria" or "obsessional neurosis" or "manic-depressive psychosis," none of these labels, no matter how correct, describes the whole patient and all of his significant problems. Patients who suffer from these syndromes always have other complaints and symptoms, which may be in the background, symptoms usually classified under different headings. It should be remembered that the patient has a variety of problems which he attempts to handle in a variety of ways, even if one form predominates. Further, there are maladjusted individuals with many minor symptoms but whose main problem is the fact that they have made a mess of their lives and thus in despair seek help. Moreover, when the symptom syndromes are explored thoroughly, they show many common features. For example, in all of them are manifest disturbances of evaluation of the self (feeling of helplessness) and of the environment (not being loved).

4. Various phases of a patient's complaints and symptoms can be selected as a basis for classification. Most of the classifications are based either on striking symptoms or on the causes of the patient's condition, or on both. Thus the syndromes "anxiety hysteria," "obsessional neurosis," and "manic-depressive psychosis" are based on striking symptoms, whereas "cerebral arteriosclerosis" (hardening of the arteries of the brain) and "alcoholic

psychosis" are classified on the basis of the chief cause of the disturbance. In classifications based on symptoms, other than striking symptoms can also be used; for example, character traits, the patient's characteristic emotional life, and a dominant dynamic principle, such as a search for dependence, are valid bases.

Our discussion will emphasize the following factors, which will often be interwoven: (1) acute symptom groups; (2) causal factors, particularly where there is a specific organic factor; (3) character traits, such as emotional reaction patterns, conscientiousness; (4) dynamic factors.

One of the most important differentiations based on symptoms is that between neurotic (often called psychoneurotic) and psychotic reaction patterns.[1] The main differences between neuroses and psychoses are as follows:

1. Each has its special symptoms, more or less peculiar to it. For example, attacks of anxiety and obsessional thoughts are neurotic symptoms. Delusions of persecution and severe hallucinations are psychotic symptoms.

2. As a rule, the disturbance in the psychoses is much more incapacitating and continuous than it is in the neuroses.

3. The appreciation of reality—the actual perception and evaluation of events and of social customs—is disturbed more profoundly and in a different way in the psychoses than in the neuroses.

4. The relationship with the physician (and with all individuals) is much more elastic in the neuroses than in the psychoses. For this reason the neurotic patient can be influenced much more easily and a permanent cure is more likely.

All these differences are sharply defined in typical cases, but they are quantitative in border-line cases. Thus a neurotic with a very severe compulsion may be far more incapacitated and more difficult to cure than a mild schizophrenic who has no delusions of persecution and only hazy ideas of reference.

The syndromes will be classified further according to the age group—namely, children and adolescents, adults, and elderly people. To some extent, like all classification, this grouping is partly justified and partly arbitrary. Certain problems are present at all age periods, such as problems of interpersonal relations, bodily strivings, and anxiety. Another difficulty with the age grouping is that no sharp line can be drawn; moreover, there are considerable individual differences in maturation and rapidity of de-

[1] The following legal aspects of psychiatry should be mentioned: In evaluating the will of the deceased, the law considers him sane if at the time he wrote the will he knew the natural object of his bounty and the nature and extent of his property. In case of an illegal act, the patient is considered insane if it can be established that he did not know the nature and quality of his act and the difference between right and wrong. This definition is a highly controversial one and is considered obsolete by many investigators. In most states, for the patient to be "committed" to an institution without his consent, he must be certified as insane by two qualified psychiatrists, and in many states, in addition, commitment has to be approved by a judge.

velopment, but even more in the process of aging. Classification by age group is justified, on the other hand, because manifestations of similar emotional problems differ at various age periods. Anxiety is perhaps the most similar in its manifestations at all ages; dependency, hostility, self-esteem, and guilt are quite different. The organic disturbances and psychosomatic disturbances likewise show quite a range. Further, the main life situation of the individual has different accents at differing age periods.

In general, the various disorders will be classified under three main headings: (1) primary behavior, emotional, and psychological disorders; (2) reactions of the total personality to circumscribed bodily disorders; and (3) primary organic disturbances of the brain. The general background and meaning of these three types of disorder were covered in the chapter on psychosomatics (Chapter III). To be sure, this classification is also somewhat arbitrary. It is not definitely excluded that in the tendency toward anxiety states of the psychoneurotic type as against the tendency predominantly toward depression there might not be a constitutional predisposition. Many of the psychosomatic disorders present a definite bodily predisposition, such as allergy, and in gross disturbances of brain histology there is a reaction of the total personality to the diffuse difficulties. The point is that there is no ideal classification. Only one more point will be made here. The psychoses represent a controversial field as to whether they are to be classified as primary psychogenic disturbances or whether they represent a primary organic disturbance of an unidentified type or the reaction of the total personality to diffuse somatic impairment.

SUGGESTED READINGS

For other types of classification see Henderson and Gillespie (402), Thorpe and Katz (930), and Billings (92).

PART V

Syndromes in Infancy, Childhood, and Adolescence

XX Disorders in Infancy

"Infancy" here covers the period before the development of walking and speech, which coincides with the period before sphincter training is seriously attempted. It is also called the period of greatest biological dependency.

The main characteristics of the disorders in infancy derive from the fact that we are dealing with a rapidly maturing organism, the most important task of which is to take care of its bodily and emotional wants in a completely dependent biological relationship. For this reason, interference with the infant's functions in certain limited spheres may have extensive consequences.

REACTIONS TO GENERAL STRESS AND NURSING FRUSTRATION

The majority of infants go through mild disturbances such as disturbed sleep, restlessness, apathy, loss of appetite, vomiting, excessive sucking, excessive crying with rage or with anxiety. These minor disturbances can be due to unavoidable physical illnesses, such as colds, ear infection, or digestive upsets. They represent "emotional behavioral" reactions to the physical discomfort and at times outlast for a while the primary bodily distress and illness.

Some infants, from birth, seem to have an increased tendency to react with the symptoms described to the trivial and everyday problems of living, as to the experience of hunger, to loud noises, to vivid colors, to the interruption of feeding for burping (82, 479).

The mother's attitude toward the infant, as carried over into her handling, may also play an important role. A mother who is affectionate and secure may handle the infant quite differently from one who is hostile or over-anxious. The hostile mother, for example, while nursing the infant, may hold him too roughly or have his head lower than his buttocks or let the nipple periodically slip out of his mouth. The over-anxious mother may be afraid to handle the child and in that way at times deprive him of easy stimulus and affectionate warmth or may, in her anxiety, be too tense and awkward in her movements. Further, there are changes in mood in the life of every adult, and these may carry over into the handling of the infant.

An infant manifested irritability, muscular tension, irregular and labored breathing, and jerky movement whenever handled by the tense foster mother. He stopped crying and ceased to show the tension symptoms when handled by the relaxed psychologist. When in the foster mother's arms, he showed tension symptoms again. This sequence of events could be demonstrated several times.[1]

Excessive sucking and restlessness frequently occur if the infant does not satisfy his sucking need while taking nourishment—e.g., when the hole in the nipple of the bottle is too large. This response has been discussed previously (see page 68). Making the hole of the nipple smaller, and thus enabling the infant to satisfy his hunger and need for mouth activity simultaneously, corrects the condition.

As previously pointed out, apathy and drowsiness amounting to stupor, after a period of excessive sucking, crying, and restlessness, may be the infant's reaction to a nursing frustration of the opposite kind—e.g., to inverted nipples. In such situations the infant's sucking does not lead to adequate relief of hunger, because no adequate nourishment results from the activity. Once the condition develops, it requires considerable handling, petting, and coaxing.

REACTIONS TO EMOTIONAL DEPRIVATION

INCREASED SUBSTITUTIVE PERIODIC ACTIVITIES

Under this heading we comprise increased oral activity (mainly thumb-sucking), genital play, rocking, head-banging, and fecal play. Some of these activities may appear in a mild form periodically in almost any infant. Those situations will be discussed in which they appear excessively, occurring in response to absence of maternal care or bad maternal care. Light is thrown on these phenomena by the following large-scale investigation (889):

A study of three groups of children under one year of age included 16 children living in their own home with their parents, professional and white-collar workers, with devoted but not over-indulgent mothers; 170 illegitimate children living in a nursery where they were cared for by their own mothers; and 63 children living in a foundling home where they were separated from their mothers after three months of age and then cared for by trained nurses, one for about every ten

[1] Based on a case presentation in E. M. Lietch and S. Escalona, The reactions of infants to stress, in *The Psychoanalytic Study of the Child,* Vols. III/IV, International Universities Press, New York, 1949.

children. They were observed for the occurrence of the types of activity mentioned, together with their general responsiveness and developmental quotient. The findings shown in Table 8 were obtained.

The following explanatory note should be added: The genital play consisted of occasional masturbatory activity, either on the penis or on the clitoris, lasting about two or three minutes and occurring two or three times a day. The form of rocking depended on the age of the child. At about three or four months the infant lies on his stomach and raises and lowers his head and arches his back rhythmically. Beginning with six months, he can assume the crawling position and rock back and forth. Beginning with about nine or ten months, he stands in the cradle and bends and straightens his legs rhythmically and forcefully. At the same age he can assume the kneeling position and bounce up and down, striking his buttocks forcefully against his heels. At times, in male children under these circumstances, erection occurs. Fecal play was observed in sixteen of the nursery children studied,

TABLE 8[2]

Group	Genital Play	Rocking	No Autoerotic Activity
Private home	94%	6%	0%
Nursery	13%	51%	36%
Foundling home	2%	7%	91%

in none of the others. In the extreme sense in which it is meant here, it consists of the following: The child takes a small amount of fecal material and carefully rolls it between his fingers into a small pellet and then throws it away. This activity is carried out in an extremely mechanical manner. The child sits among these pellets with a dreamy, withdrawn expression. If, by chance, he should lose one of the pellets while rolling it, he will look for it carefully and smile if he finds it. Occasionally he will swallow one of the pellets.

Extreme Thumb-Sucking and Absence of Response to Other Stimuli as a Result of Almost Complete Lack of Tenderness and Stimulation. An infant was three and a half months old when first seen in the foster home. At this time the pediatrician thought that the infant was deaf. The infant kept her thumb in her mouth throughout the psychological testing and assumed an attitude of stuporous passivity when the psychologist playfully removed it. The child did not smile and manifested no response to visual or auditory stimuli, nor, as a matter of fact, did she respond to any sensory stimulus, even pain. The thumb-sucking was so severe that the child refused food. Although there was no evidence that the child was not deaf, the psychologist doubted that she was. As the psychologist was leaving, she asked the foster mother how the child was, and received the reply, "Well, I'll kill her as I did all the others."

"You killed others?"

[2] Based on figures in R. A. Spitz and K. Wolf, Autoerotism: Some empirical findings and hypotheses on three of its manifestations in the first year of life, in *The Psychoanalytic Study of the Child,* Vols. III/IV, International Universities Press, New York, 1949.

"I killed about twenty-five of my own and some foster children."

"How did you do that?"

"Just my presence seems to be enough. I don't touch it."

"How do you feed it?"

"I introduce the bottle, but I don't touch it."

It was obvious from this conversation that the foster mother was psychotic and suffering from delusions (schizophrenia) and was unable to care for the child properly. At the age of four months the child was transferred to another foster home, which was purposely chosen for over-loving care. By the age of six months the child's performance on the Hetzer-Wolf Developmental Test[3] was normal, and the sucking had declined markedly.[4]

In the responses of this child there was a combination of over-activity—the sucking—with an absence of activity—no response to stimuli—amounting to stuporous passivity when the oral activity was interrupted. The condition of the child was, of course, very serious. The foster mother was correct; the child would have died. The child's response represented an intensified activity in one sphere to compensate for the complete lack of relationship and stimulus in practically all other spheres. This reaction represented quite a different pattern from increase in oral activity as a result of moderate oral frustration.

Head-Banging. In the early period of life, perhaps up to one year of age, the condition may be easily amenable to treatment. If it becomes chronic and survives the later periods, it may be present either as an expression of temper tantrum, representing at the same time the mechanism of aggression turned in upon the self, or possibly as one of the earliest forms of masochistic substitutive gratification. The following case illustrates the symptom:

A ten-month-old infant was brought to an agency by its mother with the desire to give up the child. It was obvious on close examination that the mother had neglected the child, being away from the house at times for several hours and asking the neighbors to look in on the infant. The child at this point showed an average developmental quotient (DQ) but periodically would bang his head violently either against the mattress of the crib or, more frequently, against the side railing, with sufficient violence at times to cause black and blue marks. The child was given to foster parents. The foster mother was over-solicitous and also had been told to give the child a great deal of time and to play with her constantly. In the beginning, the first twenty-four hours, she played with the child whenever the child was not asleep. The head-banging disappeared as a regular phenomenon within forty-eight hours and, following that, returned occasionally in a mild form only if the child was in a state of unusual distress. The DQ rose within two months to a level one month above the child's chronological age.[5]

[3] The Hetzer-Wolf Developmental Test is constructed along lines similar to those of the Gesell scale. (See Chapter XI.) It tests the child's mastery of his body, his ability to deal with stimuli, his social reactions, and his handling of materials.

[4] Personal communication from Dr. Katherine M. Wolf.

[5] Personal communication from Dr. Katherine M. Wolf.

REACTIONS IN WHICH DEPRESSION PREDOMINATES

The syndrome to be described is a reaction of the infant to a sudden loss of the mother (caretaker) after six months of age when the infant has already recognized and become attached to individuals.

The baby was one of the infants in the nursery previously mentioned, where the unmarried mothers took care of their children. The baby always greeted the observer with an immediate smile and gurgling pleasant sounds. She grasped toys offered to her and played happily with them.

"One day when we visited the baby—it was six months and two days old— . . . she was lying in a prone position in her cot, her head lifted, her eyes wide open as if looking for something. She gave the observer a long look at his approach and then the tears started to run down her cheeks. It was impossible to induce her either to a pleasant contact with the observer or to any play with toys. We learned from one of the institution's matrons that for unavoidable reasons the child's mother had been separated from her baby.

"Once aware of this reaction of babies toward separation from their mothers we focused our attention on any other separation of mothers from their children. When separations occurred a substitute mother was appointed for the child. In 45 out of 123 cases this choice was inadequate, the substitution not successful. In these cases the children developed a clinical picture, the inception of which we have described above and which I have called anaclitic depression.

"This depression starts with something that from the adult's point of view one would describe as a 'search for the mother.' Some babies weep with big tears, some babies cry violently, none of them can be quieted down by any intervention. In spite of their negative emotional attitude the babies at the initial stage of their depression cling to the adult. They 'weep on his shoulder.' This stage lasts for 3-4 weeks.

"If the mother does not return, the picture changes. The child lies quietly on its stomach, does not even look up if the observer enters the room, does not play with any toy, does not even grasp for it. It is passive and dejected, has eating difficulties, sleep disturbances, loses weight, and becomes more susceptible to colds and eczema. . . . The whole developmental level drops. Children who had shown previously more than one month developmental advance beyond their age are not capable of age-adequate performances. . . .

"Even more dramatic . . . was another series of observations. Another little girl who had been separated from her mother and had been lying for weeks passive and dejected in her cot, stood up suddenly when the observer came into the room, grasped his hands and then his spectacles, and having grabbed them successfully, notwithstanding the observer's resistance, laughed aloud. Our inquiry into the reason of this changed behavior disclosed that the child's mother had returned 24 hours before. A mental test administered to the child showed that the child had reached a developmental level as high as the developmental level it had before separation."[6]

[6] R. A. Spitz, The importance of the mother-child relationship during the first year of life: A synopsis in five sketches, *Ment. Hlth. Today,* 1948, 7, p. 11.

If the separation of the child from the mother lasts over three months, the child lies with wide-open, expressionless eyes, frozen, immobile face, and a faraway expression, at times engaging in autoerotic activities in the oral, anal, and genital zones. In some children a curious reluctance to touch objects also appears, combined with certain unusual postures of hands and fingers. If the mother returns after three months, the child does not fully recover its former developmental quotient. An interesting fact is that only children who are well treated by their mothers develop such depression on separation. Children who are badly treated by their mothers do not. In sixty-four children, the relation shown in Table 9 was found between the mother-child relationship and depression on separation.

TABLE 9. Mother-Child Relation[7]

	Good			Bad		
	Intense[a]	Moderate[a]	Weak[a]	Intense	Moderate	Weak
Severe Depression	6	11	–	–	–	–
Mild Depression	4	–	3	7	–	4
No Depression	–	–	2	11	2	14

[a] The terms intense, moderate, and weak refer to the strength of the mutual attachment, referring to such aspects as constancy and intensity of interaction.

It is not surprising that the child with the bad mother relationship does not develop a depression. As will be shown, he does pay a price during the period of his stay with his mother. If the substitute mother assigned to this infant takes better care of him than his own mother, the child's general receptiveness and developmental quotient rise. This will be illustrated in the following case, which also illustrates the symptom of rocking.

A pair of twin girls were born to a young unmarried woman while she was in a girl's reformatory. The mother—who came from a middle-class family—was of a social and intellectual level different from that of the other girls in the institution. Following the birth of the twins, the mother had a depressive reaction. Ten days after birth, one of the twins developed an intestinal infection and was sent to the hospital, where she remained until the age of three months; then she was returned to her mother. The mother kept the other twin with her during this period. At the age of five months both twins were tested with the Hetzer-Wolf Developmental Scale. Although their developmental profiles were practically identical, the psychologist noted marked differences in personality. Whereas the child who had been ill responded well to the test, the child that had remained with the mother turned

[7] R. A. Spitz, Anaclitic depression: An inquiry into the genesis of psychiatric conditions in early childhood, II, in *The Psychoanalytic Study of the Child,* Vol. II, International Universities Press, New York, 1946, p. 336.

away from the psychologist and almost refused to respond. The mother remarked, "Nobody should have been exposed to being with me during those three months. This one still suffers." The mother preferred the child who had been separated from her, and treated the other one with alternating acceptance and rejection. The preferred child was much more responsive than her twin, and at the age of eight months attained a DQ of 110. At the same age the other child attained a DQ of 85. At about this age the twin who had remained with her mother since birth developed rocking behavior in response to the mother's alternate rejection and acceptance of her. The mother's ambivalent attitude toward this twin is reflected in the statement she made to the psychologist at one point: "I really only love one person—pardon me—two. The twins."

Later, when both infants were separated from the mother and they were being cared for by a substitute mother, the preferred child reacted with depression, whereas the other twin became more alert and responsive. Their DQ levels underwent practically a complete reversal. The child who had formerly rated high now attained a DQ of less than 90, while her sister attained a DQ of over 110. The substitute mother was an improvement over the real mother for the neglected twin, but was still a disappointment for the favored twin.[8]

REACTIONS IN WHICH RETARDED DEVELOPMENT PREDOMINATES

Sixty-nine children were observed in the foundling home previously described. This institution was conducted with the most hygienic provisions. The mothers brought in their children at birth and stayed with them, as a rule, until the end of the third or fourth month. After that one nurse took care of about thirteen children. The children's range of motility was severely limited to assure supervision. For this reason, as well as for reasons of physical hygiene, the sides of the crib were covered with sheets so that the child's range of vision was limited to the area within the crib and to the ceiling. It was found that up to the fourth month the infants developed well —in fact, as an average, were a month ahead of their age levels. Following the fourth month, the developmental level of the children dropped until the end of the first year; then it averaged four months behind the age level. At a later period twenty-one of the children who had not died and had not been taken out of the institution showed an even greater degree of retardation. They were all undersized and underweight. Of the twenty-one children, ranging in age from two and a half to four and a half years, only five could walk unassisted, only one had a vocabulary of a dozen words, and only one, four and a half years old, used sentences. Eight of the twenty-one children could neither stand nor walk, six could not talk at all, and eleven were limited to the use of two words. Thus these children ranged from moronic to idiotic intelligence. Usually the children varied in behavior from extreme friendliness toward any human being, combined with anxious avoidance of inanimate objects, to a generalized anxiety expressed in blood-

[8] Personal communication from Dr. Katherine M. Wolf.

curdling screams which could go on indefinitely. Some of the children presented a bizarre stereotypy in catatonic motility. (See Chapter XXXIV.) The developmental retardation and the general behavior of the infants could not be influenced in these later stages by prolonged attempts at friendly contact and stimulation (887). These developmental events are dramatically illustrated by the comparative figures shown in Table 10.

TABLE 10[9]

Type of Environment	Cultural and Social Background	Developmental Quotients: Average of First Four Months	Developmental Quotients: Average of Last Four Months of First Year
Parental Home	Professional	133	131
	Village Population	107	108
Institution	"Nursery"	101.5	105
	"Foundling Home"	124	72

The probable explanations for this kind of development are the lack of stimulation, the absence of tender loving care or even of any form of human contact most of the time, and the discomfort attendant on such frustrations, with the resulting general withdrawal from the world.

These factors are then probably responsible for the psychosomatic phenomena, which consist mainly of very much lowered resistance to infections and very high mortality rate. Twenty-seven children (39 percent) of the sixty-nine died at the end of the first year in spite of the fact that the food, the general hygiene, and the physical-medical care were all excellent.

Unquestionably, the retardation of these children developed on a functional basis. If the child were first examined at the age of two and a half or three years, it would no longer be possible to differentiate the condition from idiocy based on organic maldevelopment. This, of course, obviously does not mean that all mental retardation is due to psychogenic factors, but it does mean that one form of it develops on that basis, and in an advanced stage it is irreversible. (See also Goldfarb [355] and Bender and Yarnell [76].)

In a less restrictive situation the reaction of the child to lack of warmth and of adequate stimulation may depend upon constitutional tendencies. Some infants may develop adequately in spite of these lacks, whereas others

[9] R. A. Spitz, Hospitalism: An inquiry into the genesis of psychiatric conditions in early childhood, in *The Psychoanalytic Study of the Child,* Vol. I, International Universities Press, New York, 1945, p. 58.

are damaged severely. Of course, the degree of restriction and deprivation also plays a significant role.

It may be mentioned here that in the not too distant past children born blind or deaf were doomed to feeble-mindedness, because of limitation of sensory stimulation, limitation of their knowledge, and inaccessibility to ordinary techniques of education. With the development of special educational methods, such children can now develop normal or superior intelligence.

Of great interest are also psychological reports on children who had been isolated at an early age and had lived in woods and in caves with animals. In the most famous case on record, the so-called wild boy of Aveyron, we do not know whether the child's ultimate feeble-mindedness was hereditary (genogenic) or due to social isolation. Whether this feeble-mindedness is permanent or not seems to depend on the child's age when social isolation begins. If it starts after speech has developed, it is remediable for a long time after, very likely for several years.

PSYCHOSOMATIC REACTIONS

Some of the symptoms of the digestive organs—such as loss of appetite, vomiting, diarrhea, and constipation—have already been mentioned and will be discussed again later, as will also eczema and asthma. The increased susceptibility to infection and the greater mortality of children with situational retardation of development has been referred to.

Marasmus. This syndrome is characterized by marked underweight of the child, together with wrinkled skin, which gives the infant an old appearance. The children do not gain weight and do not become responsive if they receive only routine care, and eventually they die. The condition used to be not infrequent on wards of public hospitals, but since improved infant care was instituted it has become rare. The following case illustrates the condition as well as its psychobiological background.

The child weighed six pounds three ounces at birth. Both mother and child were thriving when they left the hospital two weeks later. On returning home, the mother found that her husband had suddenly deserted her—the climax of an unhappy relationship. The deep emotional reaction affected her milk secretion; the infant refused the breast and began to vomit. Later he was taken to the hospital, and the mother did not call to see him.

In spite of careful medical attention this baby remained for two months at practically the same weight. He was in a crowded ward and received very little personal attention. The habit of finger-sucking developed, and gradually the child became a ruminator, his food coming up and going down with equal ease. At the age of two months he weighed five pounds. The baby at this time was transferred to a small children's hospital, with the idea that this institution might be able to give him more individual care.

This baby actually looked like a seven months' fetus, yet he had also a strange appearance of oldness. He took large quantities of milk but did not gain weight. With concentrated nursing care the child began to improve slowly. It was possible to introduce the services of a volunteer "mother" who came to the hospital twice daily in order to give him some of the attention he so greatly needed.

As soon as the child's life was no longer in danger, he was transferred to a good foster home in order that he might have still more individual attention. Under this regime his development proceeded well, and gradually he mastered such functions as sitting, creeping, and standing. His speech was slow in developing, however, and he did not walk until after the second year. The general health of this child was excellent at the end of his third year; also his IQ was high on standard tests, but his emotional life remained deeply damaged. With any change in his routine, or in a prolonged absence of the foster mother, he went into a state which was quite similar to a depression. He became inactive, ate very little, became constipated and extremely pale. His emotional relationship to the foster mother was receptive, like that of a young infant, but he made little response to her mothering activities except to function better when she was there. He had little capacity to express affection, displayed no initiative in seeking it, yet failed to thrive without it.[10]

Reactions to partial developmental problems will be discussed in a subsequent section.

REACTIONS TO ORGANIC (CHEMOGENIC AND HISTOGENIC) DISTURBANCES OF THE BRAIN

MENTAL DEFICIENCY

The most important manifestation of general organic brain damage during this period is retarded development. This applies not only to "intellectual" function but also at times to other striking delays. Thus the teeth may appear late, or the handling of the body, which at a later age would be considered an entirely "organic-neurological" problem, in the infant is closely linked with "intelligence" and maturation. Thus the infant may hold up his head late, and sitting, standing, walking, and talking may all be delayed. Also, toilet habits may not be learned or may be learned late.

The cause of such disturbance—in other words, of the diffuse brain damage—may be varied. At times it is a general developmental delay of the brain which never gets fully corrected, and the child remains retarded throughout life. Other disturbances that are not very clear in nature and may lead to these symptoms are microcephaly (small head), hydrocephaly ("water on the brain," large head), and birth injuries which result also in damage to the pyramidal tract and that way lead to spasticity. Less fre-

[10] Based on a case presentation in M. A. Ribble, *The Rights of Infants,* Columbia Univ. Press, New York, 1943, pp. 4-7.

quently there are other factors: severe blows to the head, infections resulting in inflammation of the brain—as in scarlet fever, diphtheria, epidemic encephalitis (see Chapter XXI), and syphilis—toxic chemicals, such as alcohol in continuous large quantities, and lack of the vitamin B complex (nicotinic acid). (See Chapter XXXV.)

In most of these disorders, apart from the developmental lag in the infant's functions mentioned, there may be an uncomfortable quality to the cry, with frequent screaming; there is absence of "intelligent" smiling; or there are hypotonia (flabbiness of the muscles) and apathy. At times, in children who come from institutions and in whom the size of the head is normal, it may be difficult to decide whether the condition is organic or situationally determined, and only continued observation in a favorable environment can decide the problem. Here several other conditions will be discussed briefly.

CONVULSIONS

In most instances, convulsions in infants do not represent gross organic brain damage, and they very rarely mark the beginnings of epilepsy; rather, they are reactions of an as yet irritable nervous system to some bodily disturbance, most frequently infections. The infection at times is of a relatively mild nature, as influenza, or more severe, as whooping cough, pneumonia, or spinal meningitis. The convulsion may occur after a period of extreme restlessness or irritability. At other times the attack may come suddenly, without any warning, and may even be the first symptom of the infectious illness. At times the infant is suffering from tetany (which will be discussed subsequently). If the convulsions are due to infections, they may not be of much significance, and the infants recover completely and lose their readiness to react in this manner.

The convulsions consist either of a sustained contraction of the muscles of the body or of an alteration of flexion and extension occurring rhythmically. The contraction of the facial muscles causes a succession of grimaces, the neck is thrown back, the hands are clenched, the thumbs are pressed into the palms of the hands, and the extremities jerk violently. There is loss of consciousness. After the movements stop, the patient remains stuporous for a while.

TETANY

Tetany consists of continuous or semicontinuous tonic (sustained) muscular contractions and of contractions that occur in attacks. The continuous or semicontinuous are characterized by a spasm of the muscles of the hands and fingers and of the feet and toes (carpopedal spasm). The passing spasmodic attacks are laryngeospasm—called the crowing inspiration, resembling a whoop in whooping cough—and generalized convulsions of the tonic type. There is increased mechanical and electric irritability of the muscles and nerves. Thus, if the face is tapped with the finger at the "motor points," the facial muscles contract. Tetany may be accompanied by general irritability as well as disturbances of digestion. It is caused by a disturbance of the calcium metabolism. The calcium level in the blood is lowered. The condition is due to a deficiency of vitamin D acting through the parathyroid gland.[11] Tetany is entirely curable by the administration of vitamin D.

CRETINISM

Cretinism is due to a deficiency in the secretion of the thyroid gland. It manifests itself early in infancy and varies in severity. The infant suffering from cretinism is easily identified. The skin is dry, edematous without pitting (swollen without retaining the mark of the pressure of the finger), and darker than usual. The tongue is large and does not find enough room in the mouth. The abdomen is large, and the extremities are too short. Without treatment, both the physical and mental conditions continue. The mental condition is sluggishness and retarded intelligence, ranging from complete idiocy to moronity. At the later periods, without treatment, the body appears dwarfed, the head is abnormally large, the neck is short and thick, the eyes are half-shut and the eyelids swollen, the hair is scanty, and the limbs are short and pudgy.

The condition is usually curable if the treatment is started in infancy. The treatment consists of administering thyroid extract. At times the intellectual improvement does not keep pace with the physical, and the person remains mentally retarded. Occasionally neither set of symptoms reacts fully to the treatment.

MONGOLIAN IMBECILITY

The Mongolian imbecile can be identified from birth almost at a glance. The characteristic features are a relatively short stature and consequent underweight; a flattening of the back of the head; poor dentition; a comparatively large tongue, often deeply fissured; small, broad, and stubby hands; laxity of the joints (what is usually called double-jointedness); great sensitivity to extreme heat and cold because of poor circulation; poor speech or mutism. The most characteristic symptom is the peculiar narrowing and slanting of the eyes which has given this syndrome its name.

The cause of Mongolism is unknown. At times it is correlated with advanced age of the mother; the age of the mother is usually over thirty-five. Some damage to the ovum is indicated by the fact that both members of

[11] Tetany is entirely different from tetanus. The latter is due to an infection by a specific germ that enters the body through a dirty wound. It can be prevented by a prophylactic injection of antitetanus serum. Once the condition develops, it is mostly fatal. It consists of violent sustained contraction of the extensor muscles of the body in response to the slightest stimulation.

eight pairs of identical twins were Mongolian imbeciles; no cases have been reported in the literature of identical twins in which one twin was Mongolian and the other was not. There have, however, been pairs of fraternal twins in which one was Mongolian, the other not (Penrose). The condition is at present incurable, and the children usually die by the age of eight or ten.

AMAUROTIC FAMILY IDIOCY

This is a very rare disease. The infant develops adequately up to about the sixth month. Then there is a general regression of all functions such as sitting up and holding up the head. Together with that, the infant becomes very sensitive to noise and starts violently at a sudden sound. He stops recognizing people, and gradually it is discovered that he has become blind. There is a diffuse degeneration of the brain tissue, including atrophy of the retina. As a result of the latter, a cherry-red spot is visible at the fovea (point of central vision). As the name implies, the condition has a tendency for familial occurrence. (See Chapter X.) It is a fatal disorder, and the infant dies within two years.

MICROCEPHALY

The skull of the microcephalic usually has a smaller than average circumference, but the chief features are its cone shape, the receding forehead and chin, and the absence of the usual protuberance at the back of the head. The brain is abnormally small and often shows anomalies of one type or another; for example, the convolutions are simpler, and the cerebellum and cerebrum are smaller. Microcephalics, as a rule, are imbeciles.

HYDROCEPHALY

The obvious characteristic in the appearance of the hydrocephalic is the enormous skull. There is an excessive amount of cerebral-spinal fluid in the ventricles of the brain due to the occlusion of one of the foramina, which prevents its free circulation. Since the skull has a limited capacity, the abnormal quantity of fluid impairs the development of the nerve cells of the brain; the brain tissue is so greatly reduced that there are gross changes in the brain, such as absence of convolutions. The cause of the condition is not known. The mental defects incidental to hydrocephaly may vary in severity; in fact, a few cases have been reported with no apparent defect.

SUGGESTED READINGS

A very readable approach to the field is Ribble's book *The Rights of Infants* (770). For discussion of special problems, see all of Spitz's papers (884-889), the paper of Bender and Yarnell (76), and Goldfarb's papers (354, 355).

XXI Disorders in Childhood

The period of childhood[1] runs from about the age of two until twelve, at which time all forms of activity have made their appearance and increasing social demands and demands for responsibility are made of the child.

In childhood reality-testing is much looser than in later life, and therefore compensatory wish-fulfillment has a much freer sway. For this reason, symptoms like playing with imaginary companions and hearing voices, and a fantasy life which is spoken of as reality, may occur without very serious implications.

PRIMARY BEHAVIOR DISORDERS

It has become customary to classify the primary behavior disorders of children under three headings: (1) neurotic traits, (2) habit disturbances, and (3) conduct disturbances. It should be emphasized again that one almost always sees these disorders in a mixture in the individual child.

REACTIONS IN WHICH NEUROTIC TRAITS PREDOMINATE

Anxiety States. Anxiety states are the most common symptoms in children and in milder form occur in every individual. The reaction of anxiety is as characteristic a feature of the individual's life up to late adolescence as wish-fulfillment is. This is shown by the fact that the large majority of dreams up to that period either are those of simple wish-fulfillment or are nightmares (Despert, Mittelmann).

[1] A somewhat different terminology has developed in child psychiatry from the one prevalent in adult psychiatry. The reason for this is that, on the one hand, certain syndromes that are frequent in adults—e.g., conversion hysteria, compulsion neurosis, manic-depressive psychosis, severe psychoneurotic depression—are rare in children, and on the other hand, such disturbances as enuresis or soiling are common in children but rare in adults. By and large, the terms "neurotic traits" and "habit disorders" correspond to "psychoneuroses," and "conduct disturbances" to "character disorders," in adults.

Anxiety states most frequently occur in the form of nightmares, out of which the child wakes crying, and, in more or less permissive families, runs to his parents', preferably his mother's, bed. Severer manifestations are night terrors. In those the child wakes out of a nightmare and talks about what he saw in his dream—e.g., being chased by an animal or by a man with a knife. At times he is so disturbed that he has difficulty recognizing the individuals of his environment; he finally goes to sleep and is apt not to remember in the morning what happened during the night. The manifestations during the day may consist of attacks of fear of varying severity—as a rule, when being left alone, as, e.g., when the mother leaves, or in response to some happening of minor significance, as, e.g., seeing a harmless insect. The child may be continuously anxious in a mild way, worrying about school, about his parents, about his health, and particularly about being hurt and injured. As in adults, anxiety symptoms may be present as partial manifestations in connection with much graver disturbances—e.g., psychosis. Thus an eight-year-old psychotic girl had the repetitive nightmare of being stabbed in the back by her father. This type of nightmare has a more horrifying and more open quality than the nightmares of children whose anxiety states are essentially of a psychoneurotic type. As in adults, the children's anxiety states are accompanied by bodily symptoms such as changes in heart rate and respiration. In phobia the child avoids certain situations that frighten him. A classic example is the case of Little Hans, who was afraid to go out on the street for fear a horse would bite him (301).

Anxiety symptoms always represent reactions to stress situations: to the mother's leaving, to doing badly in school, to being hurt by classmates, or to being disapproved of by the teacher. It may represent a reaction to a "forbidden" form of gratification of the genital, anal, urethral, or oral type. It frequently represents fear of retribution for hostility strivings in the form of abandonment or of being overwhelmed and injured—often in the genitals—and of being completely deprived, as starved to death and condemned. The child's readiness for anxiety is connected in part with his actual dependence on the adult and with his limited resources for coping with the world.

The most common accent in anxiety is on separation and abandonment. With the Oedipal constellation the fear still includes abandonment and complete frustration, but fear of bodily injury may be present toward a domineering, aggressive mother.

The treatment of anxiety states of the psychoneurotic type in children is usually successful by briefer forms of psychotherapy if the parents can be made to coöperate even to a limited extent. In severer states, as in the case of Little Hans, mentioned above, psychoanalysis is most effective, again dependent on parental coöperation. Difficulties in the school often require contact with the teacher. If the home environment is very bad, foster-home placement can be very effective. Some therapists advocate the temporary use of medication as an auxiliary to psychotherapy in severe cases. Such a drug as benzedrine sulfate, which may lessen the severity of the anxiety and thus make the child more accessible to treatment, may be used.

The following case illustrates an anxiety state in a child, together with the fact that one always finds a complex total picture.

A three-year-old boy was the third of four siblings, with a brother five years and a sister eight years older than he and a sister six months old. In infancy he had a nurse who was an efficient but cold woman, and he was not as responsive as the other siblings. At the age of two he became unhappy when he was told that, unlike his pregnant mother, he could never have a baby. The child's nurses were changed twice at about the time the mother went to the hospital for ten days for the delivery of the youngest child. After this the patient woke frequently at night crying and went to his mother's bed, became very anxious if his mother left the house, and would ask all day long where his father was and when he was coming back from work. He had attacks of low-grade "unexplained" fever (102° F.) and of vomiting and severe abdominal pain, and he would be "all limp" on repeated occasions when his father had to leave for several days in connection with his occupation. He would be affectionate with the younger sibling but at times too vigorously so, so that she would begin to cry.

In a play session he had a bottle filled with milk and first gave it to the baby doll and then nursed on it himself, emptying it and having it refilled five times without being willing to admit that he liked doing this. He also broke some small porcelain plates. None of this behavior had ever been manifested at home. One night he woke out of his sleep with pain in his abdomen and told his mother that his older brother had punched him in the stomach. The older brother confirmed this but said it was a very playful act and at the time the child had not complained. In the subsequent play session the child said, "Daddy-cow punched me in the stomach." The therapist commented on the relevant occasions: "You like the bottle yourself," "Sometimes you don't like the baby," and, "You're afraid of Daddy-cow, and you would like to be with mother yourself." In addition to the play therapy, he was placed in a day nursery with playmates of his own age. His nightmares diminished in frequency. His vomiting, abdominal pain, and attacks of low-grade fever subsided. His remaining symptom was occasional waking from his sleep, with whimpering, when he would join his mother or older sister in bed.

This child had a complex neurosis, with lack of adequate warmth in infancy and excessive dependence on his parents and on older children, with whom he felt small and helpless; he then responded with a depressive reaction (see below) to a blow in his dependent identification with his mother ("cannot have children"); in relation to his father he experienced fear of abandonment, rivalry strivings, and fear of attack, possibly with a fantasy of passive sexual submission; he had repressed rivalry and hostility toward the younger sibling, with revived desire for oral gratification. The child's trust in the therapist as a benevolent and permissive figure was carried over to other relationships. His feeling of equality toward the world around him was accomplished mainly by placement in the nursery.

Depressive Reactions in Children. Depressive reactions in children are very common, although they rarely dominate the picture. Children have a strong readiness to be "heartbroken" when they lose anything to which they are much attached, such as a toy or an animal. Discouragement, feelings of hopelessness, and a feeling that the world is an inhospitable place occur frequently with many children in difficult situations and acompany as transient feelings many of the syndromes. The more marked reactions, nearly always of the psychoneurotic and hardly ever of the psychotic type, occur in response to the following situations:

1. The child is frustrated in his identification with the person on whom he is overdependent. The case given in the previous section, under anxiety states, was an illustration of this. When the boy was told that he could never have a child, as his mother could, he became preoccupied and depressed.

2. The child loses one of the most significant persons in his life, to whom he is deeply attached. This type of reaction is very similar to mourning and to some forms of depression in adults. It is partly analogous to the reaction in infants to their being left by their mothers.

3. The child feels hopelessly mistreated by his parents or by other relatives, is resentful toward them, and is afraid.

A child of six was spending his summer vacation with some relatives and with older siblings. He felt that in all disputes he was put in the wrong, was scolded and humiliated, and did not get candy that was given to the other children. He felt discouraged, wept on his pillow at night, and decided to walk back to his home, which was one hundred miles away. He walked for two hours, and then he returned. This half-act, half-fantasy gave him some consolation, and he tolerated the situation better. When he returned home to his parents at the end of the summer and also met his friends, this mood disappeared.

In severe reactions of this kind the child engages in fantasies of dying, either through an accident or by suicide. The fantasy is accompanied by the feeling, "When they know about this, they will see what they did to me. They'll be sorry."

Three mechanisms are at work in this type of reaction: (a) aggression turning in on the self because of the fear and guilt and the hopelessness of direct attack on the environment; (b) aggression toward the environment; and (c) attempt at restitution in the idea that the environment will relent.

A boy was the youngest of five siblings. His father was kinder to him than his mother and often gave him pennies for candy. He died when the boy was five years old. The family was hard up financially; the mother was upset and considered sending the two youngest children, the patient and his sister, to an orphange for the time being. This she discussed openly in front of the children. They were sent to an orphanage for a month and then were brought home again. The patient became sad, could not play with other children, ate less, and was taciturn. He remained this way for a whole year and then was sent for treatment because he often cried in school without apparent reason. In the interviews and play sessions he was at first disinclined to engage in any activities and seemed obviously depressed. Later, after the therapist initiated various games, they consisted of people being lost in a forest or of accidents in which people were killed. The family proved coöperative. The mother, worried and harassed and working herself, was difficult to influence, but the two older siblings, instead of mostly ordering the patient around as they had done before, became kind and brought him little presents. With the support of the therapist and the two older siblings, as well as of the schoolteacher, the boy got over his depression.

The treatment of depressive reactions is usually successful with brief psychotherapy, particularly because the child easily feels that he has the therapist's love and affection, and that makes up for the loss in the life situation.

Obsessive-Compulsive Reactions. Minor and passing obsessive-compulsive symptoms, such as counting cracks in the sidewalk, the need to step off the sidewalk with the left foot or the right foot, and preferring even to odd numbers, are found in practically all children. These activities are often associated with mild, vague discomfort lest they turn out inadequately or with the feeling that things will go well if the action is carried out successfully, and things will go badly if not. There are three reasons for this kind of behavior: (1) the need to master and overcome the feeling of smallness—the action becoming a test of achievement; (2) an attempt to ward off anxiety and retribution for unconscious hostility or to prevent detection of forbidden acts by rigid regulation and control; (3) propitiation of fate, or forcing fate to come through with the desired event.

In all of these situations there is a survival of magic thinking and of a fusing of situations which do not belong together; e.g., correct counting of cracks may mean passing an examination. Full-blown obsessive-compulsive reactions which dominate the picture are rare in children.

An eight-year-old child's main symptoms were nightmares in response to the school situation and to conflicts with his parents, particularly his father. He also suffered from poor appetite and was assaultive in his behavior with his playmates. At one time, after he returned from summer camp, he presented spasmodic blinking.[2] This child had also a budding compulsion neurosis. He refrained from going to any toilets away from home because they were "dirty." At home, after going to the toilet, he would wash his hands several times, then smell them and wash them some more. His mother was a perfectionistic woman and was suffering from an obsessional neurosis of which the child was unaware.

[2] See pages 333-335 for a discussion of disturbances of motility.

The child's main problems revolved around the problem of aggression and the fear of abandonment. In the relatively mild compulsive symptom, the anal preoccupation was visible, particularly when, at one period during his treatment, he would smell every object that he picked up to play with. The mechanism of reaction formation was present in the excessive handwashing. All of the patient's symptoms cleared up in the course of weekly visits over a period of eight months.

Obsessive-compulsive states of children may clear up spontaneously and be replaced later by entirely different symptomatology.

A twenty-eight-year-old patient entered analytic treatment because of a generalized anxiety and inhibition which manifested itself in almost all spheres of his activity. He masturbated, always with homosexual fantasies in which first there was a violent struggle and finally either he or the other man was overcome. Beginning with the age of four, he suffered from nightmares and an obsessive-compulsive state for two years. He would pray five or ten times a day, mostly for the welfare of his parents, the rest of the time for his own welfare. (He did not have a religious background.) The patient's compulsive symptoms revolved dynamically around his feeling of smallness in this adult world, resentment about domination, particularly over his excretory habits, Oedipal conflict, and fear of injury and abandonment. The excessive piety was an attempt to receive forgiveness by magic means for his aggression and his pleasure striving and thus restore his safety, his self-esteem, and the love of the adult world.

In the adult neurosis there was no sign of compulsiveness in either his character or his symptoms. Apparently he had given up attempts to form intimate relations with men and particularly with women, and instead developed a submissive orientation toward both. This submissive orientation led to the severe anxiety of being overcome and destroyed which then dominated his life. The sexual strivings became the main avenue by which he was trying to solve the problem of helplessness, struggle, and submission.

REACTIONS IN WHICH HABIT DISORDERS PREDOMINATE

Under this heading are included disturbances of the mouth and of the urinary, bowel, skeletomuscular, and speech functions. The disturbances of the various functions have some common dynamic background, which, therefore, will be discussed here. The disturbances of these functions are based on the following dynamic background: (1) All of the functions mentioned have a pattern of tension and relief, with the height of activity accompanied by some pleasure, followed by relaxation. This is obvious in connection with the mouth and excretory and genital functions, less obvious in connection with motility and speech. The result of this is that one function may be substituted for another, at least as regards the tension, relief, and pleasure aspect. (2) The regulation of the function takes place as a result of events in interpersonal relations. This is most obvious in connection with the urinary and bowel functions, also in connection with the mouth function; though less obvious in connection with motility and speech, it is nevertheless present. Obviously, the child is not free to do and say everything his impulses dictate. As a result of this interpersonal aspect, these functions may become the carriers of any disturbances in interpersonal relations. (3) The problem of control or absence of it is common to all the functions. In connection with eliminative functions, originally there is lack of control, they being more or less automatic in nature. When the child acquires control, he may disclaim responsibility for his impulses by reverting to or maintaining a stage of lack of control; e.g., enuresis occurring at night has an involuntary character. Whatever striving is represented by the voiding is therefore not under the child's control. Lack of appetite or vomiting may have a similar implication. On the other hand, the child may use the control acquired as a weapon which is inaccessible to the parent. He may retain feces by not moving his bowels, and the parents cannot make him move them. Motility and speech have the reverse aspect. There is control to begin with, which the child abandons in order to disclaim responsibility for impulses. (4) Any one of these functions may be the expression of a plea of helplessness and the desire to be looked after. This development is facilitated by the fact that, as a manifestation of anxiety, involuntary voiding, defecation, skeletal movements, or inarticulate speech sounds may occur. Further, the adequately controlled function represents being relatively grown up in comparison with the helpless infant. (See also Chapter XI.)

Disturbances of Mouth Function. Disturbances of mouth function include such symptoms as thumb-sucking, nail-biting, loss of appetite, eating difficulties, vomiting, and the desire for odd foods. Whereas the mild occurrence of some of these phenomena is to be expected in the early years of every child, their presence after four or five years of age is definitely a sign of disturbance, although not necessarily a serious one. Oral symptoms are connected predominantly with dependency problems. Any form may also have an aggressive component, although this is more evident in connection with nail-biting or with biting as an attacking maneuver. They can all have a coloring of defiant rebellion against the tyrannical surroundings. The loss of appetite and the vomiting have commonly a strong element of rejection toward emotionally significant persons in the environment. They may all have an element of anxiety, an element of helplessness, and varying degrees of compensatory consolation and substitution. The consolation and pleasurable substitution for oral or general emotional hurts are apt to be most marked in sucking. The coping with the enemy, as well as his destruction, is most marked in biting. Loss of appetite and vomiting easily acquire the meaning of an appeal of helplessness to the environment and, by marshaling its concern, a consoling value.

A five-year-old girl, three years younger than her sister, was bottle-fed and sucked her thumb and then the bedclothes (woolen and later army blanket, cotton and linen sheet) from early infancy on. She dawdled over her meals, refusing vegetables. The mother would scold and spank the child, who would vomit at the height of the excitement. The vomitus at times contained wool and linen shreds. Once, the mother, as a punishment, made the child get into the tub into which she had just vomited. Notwithstanding these lurid features, the mother was essentially affectionate and permissive toward the child, even toward her moderate masturbation. The child's parents were divorced when she was two years old.

The child admitted the mother's complaints only after gentle but direct questioning by the therapist. Then she knew why she had been brought for treatment. She chose two vegetables, from a wide variety offered, which she promised to eat, and the mother agreed to leave the child alone about her eating. The child and the mother were seen five times at weekly intervals. They both stuck by the bargain with occasional relapses. The child's thumb- and wool-sucking disappeared once and for all. No major or moderate psychoneurotic symptom has appeared in the course of fifteen years.

The child's main symptom represented a defiant persistence of oral gratification as a result of hostility toward the mother because of her limited but energetic repressive measures and her separation from the father. The appearance of intense oral activity, practically from birth, made constitutionally strong orality likely. The child accepted the changed mother and the therapist as benevolent and permissive individuals, with an erotically colored attachment toward the latter, possibly as a substitute for the father. This was implied in one of her dreams: She was lying in bed in a room that had a skylight. Suddenly a man resembling the therapist appeared at the edge of it looking in and fired several shots in her direction. There was no anxiety in the dream, and she related it very pleasantly. The offer to choose and reject her food made her feel that she had the right of self-determination. These developments made the defiant oral gratification superfluous.

Reactions in Which Disturbances of Urination Predominate. Most infants with adequate training become dry day and night by three years of age. However, occasional single lapses may occur at night in children as old as eight or ten years, and during the day up to the same age in children who retain the urine too long and cannot find a toilet when the limit of control is approaching. It may also occur in situations of unexpected and severe stress. Enuresis may be nocturnal, the more common form, or diurnal. It may vary from voiding a few drops to complete emptying of the bladder. It is more common in boys than in girls. In most cases, enuresis stops after puberty, but at times it continues throughout life. It may have persisted uninterruptedly since infancy. This type is more common in children of low intelligence who come from poor families, because little attempt is made to train the child and there is lack of easily accessible toilet facilities. Enuresis represents a relapse after a period of established control. This frequently occurs after the arrival of a new sibling, when a foster child is placed in a new home, when a child's family moves to new surroundings and there is a period of shyness and anxiety over the new adjustment, or when the child is caught masturbating and is severely reprimanded. Enuresis may have a sexual connotation as a substitute for repressed genital activity, such as masturbation. This is facilitated by the fact that both activities have, in part, the same executive organ. Because of the involuntary nature of wetting, the individual, via substitution, disclaims responsibility for the guilt-laden and anxiety-arousing genital activity. The reason frequently given for the disappearance of the symptom around puberty is that then genitality takes over more completely. Enuresis may also imply self-magnification, including ambition. Boys are proud of the size of the stream they can produce, and this may be the reason for the greater frequency of the symptom in boys. In girls, penis envy may lead to similar emotional investment of the stream. Enuresis at times shows a tendency to familial incidence, either because of similar emotional constellation in parents and their children, or because of constitutional predisposition to greater urethral eroticism or to greater readiness of certain involuntary muscles to react with spasm. In the latter condition, the child may show an "irritable bladder," with urgency and frequency of urination during both the day and the night (43).

The treatment of enuresis requires attention to events directly relating to urethral function as well as to interpersonal factors. The first category includes the type of toilet training that has been used (severe or understanding) and the toilet facilities available (easily accessible or in a cold and dark place). If any one of these aspects is faulty, it should be corrected. The interpersonal problems include all significant aspects of the child's relationship with his environment, as well as problems of pleasure-seeking, hostility, dependency, and self-assertiveness. The symptom at times responds rather quickly when the child is about four or five, particularly in cases that represent relapses, but in chronic cases the treatment is rather protracted. Success depends, of course, on the total psychopathological picture also. Some investigators advocate taking the child to the toilet every few hours, and also, as part of the total treatment, giving him a red star (or some other reward) whenever he has been dry for a whole day and a gold star if he has been dry for a week. Such measures can be helpful, because they offer satisfaction to the child's desire for affection and self-esteem.

A five-year-old child had been bladder-trained from the age of two. He offered no difficulties for three years. When he was five years old, his mother gave birth to a child, and the boy started to wet his bed again. The enuresis was accompanied by a changed behavior, including refusal to go to sleep and calling his parents frequently after being put to bed; various complaints about minor injuries such as scratches, of which he never used to complain; and moodiness. The child's enuresis lasted for three weeks. The wetting of the bed in this instance represented three points: (1) a request for renewed attention from the parents to the same degree to which he had been receiving it until the birth of the second child; (2) a fear of abandonment and of neglect by the parents, together with resentment toward them, and also a fear and guilt for the resentment; (3) revival of the form of behavior which existed at an earlier period. This represented a statement of helplessness as well as a consoling source of pleasure. There were some sources of insecurity in the family situation. The mother suffered from a physical ailment which necessitated a recurrent absence from the home for hospitalization. There were periodic difficulties between the parents, consisting of irritability with each other because of the father's periodic interest in women other than his wife. During such periods they were irritable with the child also. Nevertheless, the temporary recurrence of enuresis of the type described here may be present in an essentially healthy child in response to the threat which he perceives to himself with the arrival of a new child.

In some instances all of the patient's other symptoms improve, but the enuresis, particularly at night, remains untouched until it disappears spontaneously about puberty. Whether the combination, in such cases, of interpretive psychotherapeutic procedures with conditioning (see page 196) might be effective is an open question. For "irritable bladder" some authors advocate the auxiliary use of atropine preparations taken by mouth (43).

Reactions in Which Disturbances of Bowel Function Predominate. The average child acquires bowel control by the age of two or two and a half, with occasional relapses to about three and, in case of diarrhea, slight occasional lapses up to the age of ten. Soiling either can be continuous from infancy or may represent a relapse in situations of disappointment, stress, and anxiety.

In addition to the fact that defecation is pleasurable, the product itself is of interest to the infant. The child may want to hold on to both of these pleasurable aspects beyond the institution of toilet training or may react too strongly against them. Both developments may appear in combination. The first one may result in an individual's finding the moving of his bowels the most pleasurable activity. The strong rejection of the function may contribute its share to the development of excessive cleanliness and overstrong disgust reaction. The pleasure aspect may be fused with other pleasure functions, such as smelling (see the case illustration of incipient compulsive symptoms in a child, page 326) and genital activity. The proximity of the organs is more obvious in women, but it is also present in men via the perineum (the floor of the pelvis). Sensations from there may be experienced with the function of either organ system. The general attitude most commonly considered as connected with the bowel function is that of disparagement and hostility. The disparagement comes from the restrictive and prohibitive attitude of the environment, which calls the feces dirty. The hostility aspect comes in part from the fact that about the period of established anal-sphincter training children reach a phase of emotional development colored by wanting to do everything themselves, with a tendency to stubbornness. Further, the individual may use this function to express his defiance of the environment because of the way the training itself was handled or because of the general interpersonal difficulties with the person who trained the child. The hostility frequently has a coloring of magic thinking. In other words, "I am angry at so-and-so. If I do this-and-this, it will harm him." (See the case illustration, page 344.) In the child, the normal controlled act of defecation is accompanied by a feeling of accomplishment. This has a positive social orientation. In soiling, the feeling of accomplishment may also be strong but has then a defiant, self-centered quality. The defiant rejection of the environment may express itself more strongly in the withholding of feces, this being the opposite of soiling, although the two are frequently seen in combination. Children may withhold the feces also because they are afraid to go to strange toilets or because of the emphasis the environment puts on bowel movements, ultimately resorting to enemas and suppositories. In such situations the withholding expresses self-assertion and hostility as well as the marshaling of the attention of the environment, together with final submission, substitutive consolation, and enjoyment in the form of combined anal discomfort and pleasure.

The treatment of soiling requires an investigation of the method of toilet training as well as of the toilet facilities. (See under enuresis, page 330.) The treatment of the symptom itself must be part of a total psychiatric procedure, with the discussion of the ebb and flow of the symptom in response to daily events, and the correction, if necessary, of the methods of training. The treatment of uninterrupted soiling since infancy is more easily successful up to five or six years of age, and it becomes very difficult after nine or ten. The treatment of soiling that represents a relapse is much easier than that of the other type. The following is a brief illustration of the difficulty in the treatment of soiling:

An eleven-year-old boy came for treatment because of soiling. He had been toilet-trained and handled pretty rigidly by the mother, beginning with three months. At the age of one and a half he had a relapse, and then the struggle with the mother started. She started to give him suppositories and enemas, to which the child reacted with violent struggle and screaming, but the mother had the child held down and insisted on giving these medications. In general, he was extremely sensitive to what he considered slights—for example, to a change in appointment with the therapist. His drawing covered the whole paper with thick shading; when asked what it represented, he said, "This is poison mud so that everybody is buried." When, in the course of a discussion, his hurt and resentment disappeared, he erased a little square for the purpose, he explained, that "somebody may escape," meaning that he allowed the therapist to live. After several months of treatment, the patient's soiling began to vary in frequency, corresponding to situations when he got angry over some hurt to his self-esteem or disappointment in anticipated affection. In the course of three years, the soiling as well as the patient's other symptoms disappeared. Magic thinking—the equation of bowel movement and feces with violence, e.g., in the drawing—is strongly suggested in this case. The emotional problems resulted from his total relationship with his parents, particularly his mother, and were fought out mainly around the issue of bowel control, which then represented self-assertive defiance, attack, consolation, and substitutive pleasure for loss of love and other gratifications.

Reactions in Which Motility Disturbances Predominate. The disturbances of motility discussed here include delayed development of locomotion, particularly walking, in children who do not suffer from organic disturbances of the neuromuscular system but have been deprived of adequate sensory and interpersonal stimulation. Infantile forms of motility—e.g., crawling or curling up in the intrauterine posture—after the child has acquired more mature forms of locomotion may occur in response to rivalry with a younger sibling for parental affection. More common disturbances in older children are the quick, purposeful-looking movements of groups of muscles. The most common one of these is spasmodic blinking. These may be fairly chronic or may come and go relatively quickly within a few days. Similar movements are sniffling and small movements of the shoulder or of the hands. These are commonly called "habit spasms" or "psychoneurotic tic." They are quite different in treatability and in dynamics from the "organ-neurotic" tic syndrome. "This consists of a series of . . . involuntary movements of gradually increasing intensity and frequency. These usually begin in the upper part of the body, in an upper extremity, shoulder or face, and spread in the course of time to involve the head and neck, trunk, and finally the lower extremities, so that eventually there may be widespread involuntary movements of the entire body, including kicking and jumping, twisting of the head and neck, quick movements of all the extremities, blinking of the eyes, grinding of the teeth, and projection of the tongue. There then appears the involuntary utterance of an inarticulate cry. This in turn is followed by the onset of echolalia [echolike repetition of a phrase or a sentence heard] and echokinesia [imitative repetition of a movement seen], and finally a feature, which, when it appears, is pathognomonic for this disease syndrome, namely the symptom of coprolalia [uttering of obscene words]."[3] The patient is able to stop, whenever requested, the manifestations of the "psychoneurotic tic" syndrome; he is not able to do that with the "organ-neurotic" type. Of course, one finds all degrees of transition between the two.

The blinking of the eyes may represent a desire to look in connection with sexual curiosity and the rejection of the impulse. The uttering of obscene words represents a mixture of oral, anal, and genital pleasure striving, with an aggressive connotation. The movements of the hands and of the torso may signify defense against attack, plea of helplessness through disturbed equilibrium, and an attempt to lean when in a helpless, threatened position. Sudden muscular movements, such as blinking the eyes and

[3] M. S. Mahler and L. Rangell, A psychosomatic study of *maladie des tics* (Gilles de la Tourette's disease), *Psychiat. Quart.*, 1943, **17**, p. 579.

raising the hand in defense, are also reflex responses in situations of sudden threat.

The dynamics of the psychoneurotic tic syndrome differ from those of the organ-neurotic one in two ways. In the former there is apparently a lack of predisposition, and the accent on interpersonal problems is stronger. The individual has not withdrawn so much and has not substituted the motility for more direct coping with the interpersonal problems in fantasy and emotional life. The organ-neurotic type of tic should more properly be considered a psychosomatic disturbance in the stricter sense of the word. There are certain concomitant somatic and psychological phenomena frequently observed in patients suffering from this syndrome—namely, tendency to obesity, increased emotional lability and impetuousness, aggression up to violence, and, in general, increased motor urgency up to the age of five or six. Many authors regard this as evidence of a disturbance of the autonomic centers of the brain stem. The increased impulsiveness may persist or give way to repression or reaction formation, beginning with school age. If the first happens, a hyperkinetic, impulse-ridden picture results. If the second happens, the patient has a diminished general motility. The assumption is that the environmental curtailment of organized motor outlets in the formative phase of these children leads to a pent-up desire for activity and aggression. This development then predisposes the child to the use of the motor system and resumption of infantile motility for the expression and attempted solution of total personality problems.

The treatment of the psychoneurotic type of tic is usually successful (unless it is a part manifestation of a schizophrenic process—see below). The treatment of the organ-neurotic tic syndrome often presents difficult problems. It is of special importance to facilitate channeling of the increased motor urge into differentiated, highly organized locomotor and athletic occupations outdoors. The outlook is more favorable if therapy starts before severe rigidity of the motor automatisms has occurred. An example of a relatively mild psychoneurotic tic syndrome was given in a patient suffering mainly from anxiety symptoms, conduct disorder, and an incipient compulsion neurosis. (See page 326.) Here an example will be given of a patient suffering from the organ-neurotic tic syndrome.

An eleven-year-old boy began at the age of seven to display a series of increasing involuntary tic-like movements, later followed by the uncontrollable emission of inarticulate animal-like noises, and echolalia and echopraxia on occasions of great excitement, as at the movies. He was an unwanted child, and early in the pregnancy the mother tried to induce abortion. After his birth the mother felt, "He must surely be a cripple," and became overprotective, with constant anxieties about his health.

In addition to the tic symptoms, he showed daily elevation of the body temperature to a level between 100° and 101° (on one occasion 103°) and with it an increase in the pulse rate to about 110. Also, at times, nausea with vomiting, headaches, and aches and pains, as well as flushing, sweating, and blanching, were present. These were not explainable by a physical illness. The patient was anxious to please everybody and was compliant both with adults and with children of his own age. He said, "I never say anything worse than 'damn.' Much worse words used to come to my mind when I was angry with my brother, but they don't come any more." The patient's strongest affective drives were directed toward his older brother, who was on the one hand devotedly loved and admired, and on the other hand feared and hated. It was while sharing his bed with his brother that he first began to "throw himself around," and his illness started. Ever since the separation of the two from the common bed when the patient was eight, he displayed a ritual before going to sleep. The door to his brother's room had to be closed because of the patient's fear of a "bogey man" in there. His movements—blinking of the left eye—represented an identification with his brother's friend, who also displayed a tic, to obtain the desired attention from his brother. His echolalia and echopraxia in the movies represented an identification with the masculine hero. He related with interest stories of his brother "and his sweethearts," identifying actively with his big brother and passively with the latter's girl friends. As a result of prolonged psychotherapy, the patient's tics became fewer in number and lessened in intensity, and the echopraxia and echolalia during excitement disappeared.[4]

(See also 268, 269, and 482.)

Reactions in Which Disturbances of Speech Predominate. Disturbances of speech function comprise (1) delayed development of speech, (2) recurrence or prolongation of baby talk, (3) halting speech, (4) excessive, too little, or too fast talking, (5) ticlike explosive utterance of obscene words, and (6) stuttering. Some of these disturbances may occur passingly and in minor degree in every child's life. The early development of speech occurs in conjunction with other critical developmental phases, including the change to solid food and self-feeding, walking, initiating of hand preference, and elimination control. Difficulties in any of these spheres or in the interpersonal relations associated with them may affect the speech function (192). Also a traumatic experience, such as injury to the mouth in an accident or a tonsillectomy, may contribute to the development of the disturbance. Delayed development on the basis of slow maturation of the speech centers will be discussed later. It may occur on a psychogenic basis if the child receives no stimulus from the environment either because he is neglected and therefore isolated or because the parents hardly speak to each other and to the child. The condition may also be present if the opposite obtains—namely, if the child is so catered to that nearly every wish or whim of his is surmised and gratified by the parents; then he simply does not need the use of this additional function to communicate with the world. Prolongation of baby talk or recurrence of baby talk is apt to occur with the arrival of a new sibling. Then it has the same significance in interpersonal prob-

[4] Based on a case presentation in M. S. Mahler and L. Rangell, *op. cit.*

lems and in sibling rivalry as return to infantile motility or enuresis, except that it also has an ingratiating aspect: the child wants the parents' exclusive love and affection, which he feels he lost to the new rival. The prolonged baby talk may also be a result of an overprotective parent who wants to keep the child a baby. Lisping has essentially the same background and dynamics as baby talk except that it is a more circumscribed phenomenon. If based on sibling rivalry, the baby talk and lisping also have an aggressive component. Halting speech is a common anxiety symptom at all ages and occurs very easily up to adolescence. It may be a more permanent phenomenon if the child is shy in general, with all the dynamics of that form of conduct disorder. (See page 341.) Too little talking is predominantly an expression of shyness. Excessive talking may be a compensatory aggressive reaction against anxiety or may represent, regardless of sources, an aggressive attempt at domination and forcing the attainment of things desired. Ticlike, explosive utterance of obscene words has been discussed. (See page 333.)

Stuttering is a disorder which is characterized by a spasmodic repetition or blocking of speech sounds. The stutterer has difficulty enunciating certain words because he cannot articulate the first consonant. In some individuals the stuttering is almost always present; in others it appears only in situations of stress. Any speech sound may cause difficulty, but the ones that are most apt to be troublesome are those that require the greatest articulatory effort, such as *d* or *t*. A person may repeat smoothly by rote, but stutter badly if he has to compose speech. In minor, passing ways it may occur in any child and even in adults. Another type of stuttering consists of fast talking in which the individual gets entangled partly in indistinct pronunciation and partly in spasmodic repetition of the letter sounds. The personality of this type of stutterer is usually different from that of the other type. He is usually an amiable, hail-fellow-well-met, charming individual. Careful studies have indicated that stutterers commonly show other types of disturbance also (192).

In a study of fifty stuttering children, a high degree of motor restlessness was displayed by two-thirds of the group. They manifested a deficiency in fine motor coördinations and manual skills. About half of the children displayed muscular spasms and movements associated with or independent of speech. In the majority of these cases the face was involved. The whole head, arms, legs, and the whole body were involved in some of them. Nail-biting was common in the total group and was very severe in about half of the children (194).

In another study (192) a significant relationship between feeding difficulties and the presence of stuttering was found, as shown in Table 11.

Other neurotic traits found were anxiety and restlessness, compulsive sniffing, enuresis, compulsive behavior, obsessional thinking, thumb-sucking, asocial behavior, and asthma attacks.

From the point of view of etiology, it is important that early, rigid toilet training which involved the use of punitive methods was present in the histories of over half of the fifteen subjects studied (192). The subjects fell into two groups as regards age of onset of the stuttering. In the first group the symptom first appeared between two and three years of age; in the second group attention was first directed to the speech disorder owing to school attendance. The early period of onset coincided with other critical developmental phases (self-feeding, sphincter control), the second with exposure to a less sheltered environment, with more serious consequences for hostile outbursts, and with the necessity of meeting standard requirements.

TABLE 11[5]

	15 Stutterers	%	54 Normal Controls	%
Feeding difficulties	12	80	15	28
No feeding difficulties	1	7	38	70
No information	2	13	1	2

Certain investigators assume that the causal mechanism is a lack of coördination of the impulses from the two sides of the brain (Orton, Travis). Some experiments suggest that nervous impulses to the speech mechanism, and the brain waves in the two hemispheres, are not well synchronized.

The psychodynamics of stuttering is, however, a moot question; hence only tentative interpretations can be made. Speech is a form of self-assertion and an attempt at contact with other individuals. Fear in these situations may lead to a disturbance of this function. The consequent embarrassment may make the stutterer shy and cause him to lose self-confidence. Another factor may be a considerable unconscious preoccupation with oneself, particularly with the bodily function of speech. For the stutterer, speech may have the connotation of a hostile attack and the consequent fear of injury. There may be oral, anal, and genital connotations, either as part of the hostility or apart from it. Forbidden exploratory curiosity may also play a role. Certain words, as illustrated by the case of psychogenic reading disability (see page 344), may acquire sexual, anal, or urethral connotations by implication.

The treatment of stuttering is also complex. There is no doubt that the younger the individual is when he starts treatment, the better are the chances of success. A general survey of the patient's problems and situations of stress should always be made. Although psychoanalysis is not recommended by most investigators, some therapists use it for some cases (97). The method of treatment varies. Some recommend training in breath control during speaking. Others concentrate on easing the patient's

[5] Based on figures in J. L. Despert, Stuttering: A clinical study, *Amer. J. Orthopsychiat.*, 1943, 13, 517-524.

emotional tension while he speaks, the emphasis here being not on clear enunciation but on a relaxed, easy flow of words. Group therapy is also used. Chewing-speaking "games" may be used with children in conjunction with play therapy (191). This involves playing with words and nonsense syllables while chewing gum. Speaking in the presence of a group, all of whom are undergoing speech correction, helps to decrease the embarrassment of the stutterer. Some therapists hold that stuttering may be corrected for periods of time but cannot be cured permanently (239).

REACTIONS IN WHICH CONDUCT DISORDERS PREDOMINATE

Under "conduct disorders" are included all manifestations of the disturbances of the child's general behavior in relation to other people and to objects. Commonly, the term is applied only to disobedient, destructive, and delinquent behavior. However, equally important are opposite forms of general conduct—namely, general timidity and submissiveness, the tendency to get into difficult and disadvantageous situations, and not living up to intellectual potentialities, at times reaching the degree of "affective stupidity." Some form of disturbance of general behavior is almost always present in the syndromes already discussed.

Aggressive Behavior. Under this heading we may include a tendency to attack playmates, destructiveness toward objects, disobedience toward people in authority (including the parents), truancy, lying, stealing, and fire-setting (1002). In some ways such problems come up in every individual's life, and it is only the regularity and magnitude of the conduct that make it pathological. The aggressive behavior may be a continuous phenomenon from early childhood on, or it may appear after a long period of adequate behavior. In its severer form, aggressive conduct disorder is equivalent to delinquency (which will be discussed under disorders of adolescence). The child may be aggressive both at home and in school. The aggressiveness may manifest itself in situations where it is provoked, or it may be displaced from one situation to another. Thus a child who feels hostile toward his feared parents may behave badly in school. A certain degree of aggressiveness is a normal component of every child's emotional life. The increased intensity may be motivated by a feeling of rejection or of humiliation; by the feeling of being dominated and treated unfairly; by various anxieties, such as the fear of being overwhelmed and injured. It may be a reaction against submissiveness and passive and feminine strivings. The various manifestations mentioned then have a defensive and compensatory aspect as well. Lying may be an attempt to escape anticipated punishment. Stealing may be the aggressive taking of what the child feels deprived of: affection, strength, or the missing or threatened male genital. Fire-setting often contains hostility toward the father, with murderous fantasies and an element of self-magnification, along with enjoyment of destruction combined with urethral and genital excitement. Truancy from school is as much an escape as it is an act of defiance; the child is running away from the harsh teacher, from the pain of impairment in learning or some physical deformity. Some of the patients with a history of endless shifts in families have never formed close attachments to parental figures and therefore lack identification and inhibitions and internalization of injunctions. They are impulsive and show no anxiety or guilt (66). In these respects they are like certain types of adult "psychopaths." (See Chapter XXIV.) Still other patients have broken through an excessive burden of ideals and conscience and may engage in some provocative act in order to be punished or to test the person who professes to love them.

The treatment of aggressive behavior requires a correction of the child's actual difficulties. Contact with the environment is indispensable, because children often deny "bad" behavior, and, without information from the environment, the therapist may be completely at sea. If the child develops a fairly adequate conscience, the treatment is much easier. If he is a member of a gang and therefore has considerable secondary companionship and group aggrandizement, the treatment becomes difficult. This will be discussed further in connection with the problem of delinquency. The following is a case of aggressive conduct disorder in whose treatment excessive timidity and self-injurious behavior arose as passing manifestations.

The difficulties of this eight-year-old girl began at the age of two, when she would wake up at night screaming and, on the street, began to run away from her mother. She started to steal at three and had temper tantrums all her life. She was always a poor eater. The mother bottle-fed her until the age of four because she refused any other food. She often vomited. Now she was defiant toward her mother, striking her back if punished, but woke up every night at three A.M. and insisted that the mother sleep with her. Once she kicked both her eighteen-year-old sister and her sister's boy friend in the abdomen. She lied all the time and stole, mostly food or money for it, from relatives and in stores. In school she asked the teacher's help and then got into fights with her; she used vile language and wanted to possess everything the other children had. The mother preferred the older daughter, made scenes before the child's class, anxiously watched her, and restricted her all the time. She said she felt like "putting my foot into her mouth and kicking her."

During the first two interviews in the treatment, the patient behaved timidly, partly because the mother had threatened her with treatment as a "punishment" and partly as "surprise reaction" to the therapist's friendliness, and was frightened over every little mishap, such as dropping a pencil. In response to reassurance she said that the therapist could not possibly like her because she had "a queer nature" and then added that she made her mother scream. Beginning with the third interview, there was a return of the aggressiveness, together with the development of a positive relationship and a conflict between the two attitudes. The aggressiveness returned because the child did not trust a close relationship and was afraid that she would come to grief again. This anticipation of rejection was based in part on past disappointment and in part on her own feeling of worthlessness and guilt. As a result, she engaged in defensive aggressive behavior, which was at the same time testing the therapist as to whether she was really loving and permissive. Had she succeeded in provoking a punitive reaction, she would have proved to herself that her mistrust was justified. The three trends continued for a long time and showed themselves in the following ways: She destroyed dolls, threw clay balls at the therapist, and called her a "nut" because she talked too much, but she admitted that she was afraid of her. She said that she despised her father and called him an "old buck." She would run out into the hall and kick the door of the room where her mother was being interviewed by another therapist. When, one day, the patient's interview had to be terminated earlier, she said that she did not care if the therapist never came back, but in the next interview she sang a song, "Life is empty since you are gone. What is to become of this love of mine?" She admired the therapist's looks; with permission, she put on the therapist's earrings and admired herself in the mirror, and then, as if fearful of competition with the therapist, she took them off and said, "I am too young to wear earrings." She saw a picture in a magazine with the caption, "Can this be the girl no one cared for?" and she said, "Yes, it can." The therapist asked, tentatively, whether the patient felt sorry for the girl who was not cared for. She ran over to the therapist and said she would punch her in the nose. She then asked whether, if the therapist had a little girl, she would care for her. When she received the reply that, if the therapist had a little girl like the patient, she would care for her, the patient laughed merrily and seemed obviously pleased. She said that her mother treated her badly, that she liked her father, and that her father liked her. She said she wished she could have a husband because she liked babies so much and mentioned for the first time that she stole candy from the store. Following a remark by the therapist that the patient's father seemed to be her best boy friend, she suddenly slapped the therapist's face hard. The therapist told her in a kind manner that she must not hurt her and encouraged her to tell why she was angry. Later the patient put her hand on the hot radiator and burned it. From then on, after any expression of negative feeling, she hurt herself in some way (self-injurious behavior). The patient inquired about how babies were born (although she actually knew it) and was satisfied that she would be able to have babies when she grew up. She then played games of being born and of gradually growing up, playing the various stages of growth, such as crying like an infant. As she played being older, she acted out what had actually happened in her life; the father in the fantasy became less indulgent on the request of the restrictive mother. Following this, she became obstreperous in her playing, asked the therapist to reprimand her and tell her what she could or could not do (aggressive, self-restrictive, and submissive behavior as an expression of conflicting longing for love). The therapist handled this situation with understanding and reassurance.

Because of the mother's rejection and restrictiveness, the father's permissiveness, excessive in the beginning, was vital for the patient. When he also became somewhat restrictive, she reacted with anxiety (nightmares at the age of two) and hostility (running away from the mother). The final weaning and, that way, the denial of the protracted demand for milk, representing a demand for affection and oral gratification, further intensified the process. The hostile rejection of the mother manifested itself for a while in the form of vomiting. Following this, the intense conflict of hostility and anxiety is set up about the mother, in which guilt gets repressed and conscience is not allowed to develop adequately. The aggressive, demanding, domineering, taking (stealing) orientation in her behavior becomes her solution. In this process there is also visible the identification with the aggressor: she behaves very much like her mother, and that is how she will tackle the whole world. This then leads to an endless series of vicious circles, by making the whole world rejecting and disapproving. Later she develops the fantasied solution: If she were to marry her father and have children, all her problems would be solved. Thus the Oedipal conflict becomes intensified and, in turn, leads to further intensification of her fear of her mother. This set of circular reactions is cut through in the relationship with the therapist, with whom she learns to develop a loving relationship, with whom she can discuss the feared and forbidden strivings, and whose ideals she then can accept (introject). This development resulted in the disappearance of her symptoms and in the forming of good relations with her family, playmates, and teacher. However, one danger spot remained. The mother's anxiousness and restrictiveness, although diminished, could not be fully resolved. After the child improved, she stopped her own treatment. It is likely that, if the mother has a serious relapse the child will also have difficulties, but will again respond to treatment.[6]

Timidity and Submissiveness. Timid children are rarely brought for treatment, because they cause no trouble to the environment. The timidity may be so extreme that the child is even fearful of approaching friends whom he plays with daily and who are weaker than he. This behavior is often accompanied by a tendency to please and get the affection of playmates and adults through sacrifice and by doing the dirty work. The child, after he overcomes his shyness through the initiative of other children, leaves it up to the other children to decide what role he should play in games. He lets himself "be taken along" on picnics, and then prepares the meals and cleans up while other children go off to play. This is accompanied by the feeling, "I am unattractive and no good; the only way people can love me is if I do things for them." The timid and subservient behavior may be present in all situations or only at home or in school or with playmates. Signs of negative attitudes may be present even with such children, but then the attack comes out in devious ways. Thus the child quietly, pleadingly, but stubbornly asks the sibling for what he considers his rights—although he is actually in the wrong—until the sibling becomes openly aggressive. Other children protest as soon as they feel that the environment begins to take advantage of their quietness and coöperativeness—e.g., when it always sends *them* on tedious errands. The generalized behavior may continue throughout life. Spontaneous changes are more likely to occur if the

[6] Based on a case presentation in Y. Feldman and J. H. W. van Ophuijsen, The case of Miriam Kohn, in *Primary Behavior Disorder in Children: Two Case Studies,* Family Service Assoc. of Amer., New York, 1945, pp. 9-29.

behavior is not present in all major areas of interpersonal relationships. They may occur gradually after entrance to school, particularly if the child becomes associated—although often in a submissive way—with aggressive and unruly classmates. They may occur when the child's self-esteem gets hurt, near puberty, over his "sissy" behavior, and when he feels the new urgency of the sexual problems and the desire to be grown up. They also frequently occur in connection with falling in love and having one's feelings reciprocated and thus having one's worth proved. However, even in all of these instances, in some areas the timidity is retained and gets corrected only after laborious therapeutic work.

The situational background of shy behavior may be a highly traumatic situation in which the child was born and grew up—e.g., severe repression and punitive attitude by the parents. In such situations there is anxious repression of self-assertion and hostility, together with feelings of helplessness, anticipation of rejection, and being overwhelmed by playmates. At other times a frustrating and shameful environmental situation—e.g., illegitimacy, abandonment by the mother, being looked after by a kind but grouchy grandmother—may be combined with a favorable school situation, in which, through compliance and good scholastic achievement, the child feels approved of by the teachers. In such a development there is a strong formation of conscience and ideals overlying the feeling of worthlessness. Other factors possibly contributing are feelings of guilt over forbidden acts of a genital nature. In some cases of premature or difficult birth, the readiness for anxiety and for a feeling of helplessness persists from infancy on, even after the disappearance of the physiological disturbance—e.g., of sensitiveness to noise and easy startle. Some children are very sensitive about their appearance or about some shortcoming or difficulty they have, the shapes of their faces or the color of their hair. This is merely a symptom, then, of an intrapsychic disturbance. Sensitiveness about actual disfigurement or about clumsiness may have a causative force for excessive shyness, in part because of other children's taunts and parental rejection. The condition, in the long run, may, however, have the opposite effect—namely, producing compensatory measures for the organ inferiority (Adler).

The treatment of excessive timidity can be very successful if the environment can be made to coöperate. The permissive contact with the therapist is effective even if the child engages in no aggressive activity in the play sessions. This is particularly apt to happen in children up to the age of ten if the parents support them emotionally when they start striking back in response to playmates' aggressive attacks, and if, further, they report these incidents to the therapist, who can then discuss them with the child. Release therapy is very helpful. If the child has developed a strong self-sacrificing, ingratiating technique, the problem is more difficult. Some cases require full analytic treatment.

Tendency to Get into Difficult, Disadvantageous Situations; Accident-Proneness. The fact that the love of other people may be sought through ingratiating acts, by regularly doing menial tasks for the others and by giving away objects that the child cherishes, was discussed in the preceding section, on timid behavior. This behavior may have considerable compensatory pleasure value. This latter element becomes even more intense in such behavior as asking the other children to tie one to a tree and playing games of pretended torture. Such behavior is not without danger of serious injury. In one instance, while playing being burned at the stake, the dry grass under a boy's foot actually caught fire, and he suffered some mild burns. In more extreme types of games of this kind—e.g., games of being hanged—the victim may actually die if, in an unexpected emergency, the other children get frightened and run away. There may also be fantasies, particularly in girls in their struggle over genital desires, of being tied to a tree and being tortured and masturbated by threatening figures. At times the aggressive, self-assertive aspect manifests itself through an alternate fantasy of being pursued and overcome—e.g., by a cowboy—and the reverse, the girl herself being the aggressor and pursuer and the masculine cowboy who finally sexually overcomes another girl. As an outgrowth of guilt or fear of retribution for hostility or for forbidden sexual strivings, a tendency to actual or near accidents may develop as a passing or repetitive pattern. In such situations the hostility has a more impulsive quality; there is a greater accent on fear of abandonment and helplessness, and on the fantasy of being an invalid and of being cared for.

This type of development, often referred to as a masochistic trend, can be the outcome of situations similar to those in which predominantly aggressive or timid behavior arises. Almost invariably, however, there is fairly strong ideal and conscience formation present, although of a warped and excessive variety, as a rule because of the parents' unreasonableness and because the ideal formation is itself a partial attempt to obtain the doubted love and appreciation.

The self-injurious trend may diminish under circumstances similar to those under which timid behavior diminishes. However, without treatment, much of it is retained as a deep-seated emotional force. Briefer psychotherapy of the type discussed in the previous section may be partially effective. For an adequate clearing up of the trend, psychoanalysis is necessary when circumstances make that procedure possible.

Impairment of Performance (Affective Stupidity, Impairment of Special Abilities). The girl discussed above as an example of aggressive conduct disorder did poorly in school before the treatment started and did well following it. Apart from the aggressive conduct disorder, a child may not make the most of his potentialities. This can be the result of anxieties, psychosomatic disorders, and depressive states. In most cases the environment knows that the child is intelligent. The child's behavior, however, may be so badly disturbed that he gives the impression of mental deficiency. Tests may then still show an exceptionally high intelligence. In other instances even the intelligence quotient, as determined by the intelligence test, may show moronic intelligence at first but a rise after proper treatment —at times combined with major environmental measures—is instituted. Along with a general lowering of the intellectual performance, or separately from it, some special functions may be particularly hard hit—e.g., reading and arithmetic. Functions involving motility may also be impaired, particularly those requiring skillful performance—e.g., sports. (See also the discussions of disorders in infants, page 315, and organic disorders, page 358.) Intellectual impairment may occur as a part of generally anxious, beaten-down behavior representing, in part, a defense against aggression and sexual curiosity. Reading may be particularly impaired because of the teacher's or the parent's accent on it or because, in addition, letters, words, and punctuation may come to represent dangerous fantasies. Reading becomes all the more dangerous to the child who is defending himself against his curiosity about reproduction because, once he can read, he can satisfy his curiosity independently.

If the school work falls down after a period of good performance, there may be a spontaneous correction after a period of time if the child manages to arrive at a different solution of his conflicts, often as a result of change in the environment—e.g., moving to a different school or being placed in a boarding school away from home. If the impairment is general, or if it hits reading particularly and there was no period of good performance, no improvement can be expected, as a rule, without treatment. The treatment is most effective if psychotherapy is accompanied by tutoring and/or remedial reading. The following case illustrates a combination of functional impairment of the intelligence, reading disability, recurrence of wetting and soiling, and behavior disturbances.

An eight-year-old boy had remained for two years in the first half of the first grade without learning to write or to read. He reversed letters or sequences, made meaningless combinations of letters, and used peculiar punctuation marks. Other symptoms were solitary withdrawal from social relationships and wetting and soiling, the latter representing a regression after his mother placed him, at the age of three, in a foster home after the birth of a sister. Both children were illegitimate, but the mother married the father of the second one, and he did not want to take the patient into the home.

In the course of twice-weekly treatment over a year and a half, the patient expressed hatred of his mother, more because she stopped loving him than because of the placement as such. He fantasied burning her up with his hot urine or poisoning her by making her eat his feces, but he also fantasied being a baby, living with his mother, and being tenderly cared for. He regarded reading as evidence of being grown up, but was blocked in his wishes to grow up because of fantasies that this could be achieved only by eating the father to gain his traits in a magic manner. He sometimes explained his mother's desertion as due to her not being Jewish like himself. This was actually not true. The English language must be her language, and he hated her so much that he did not want to learn it. He explained that he tried to turn the English taught at school into Hebrew by writing it backward (reversals). He called his peculiar punctuation marks "Chinese writing," representing words. He had heard that the Chinese tortured people whom they hated, and his Chinese writing, by a magic spell, would cause his mother to be tortured with sharp knives and to be eaten by fierce animals. He once wrote the letter combinations "as ur mor," which stood for the words "ask your mother." It developed that he wanted to ask her (and the therapist, too) to have a baby for him as proof that his love was returned and as an assurance that his mother loved him better than she did her husband.

After he had produced all his imaginary explanations for his mother's having placed him (that she loved girls better than boys, that she stopped loving him when she began to love the man she married, that she was a Christian) and became conscious of his ambivalence, he accepted as the reason for his placement the fact that she could no longer take care of him. He then decided that he no longer needed to hate his mother. Hating his mother, he said, he had hated all women and so had never wanted to do anything his foster mother and his teachers asked of him. Now that he could love women, he would not have any more trouble with school work.

At the age of three, before he developed his neurosis, he achieved an IQ of 95. When tested by the same psychologist at five and at seven, he achieved IQ's of 75 and 74. At the end of therapy, after he recovered from his neurosis, his IQ was again 95.[7]

FUNCTIONAL PSYCHOSIS: SCHIZOPHRENIA

The case described in the preceding section presented withdrawal, magic thinking, and near-delusional fantasies. Some investigators would diagnose that case as schizophrenia. The disturbances were clearly connected with serious environmental difficulties. Frequently such disturbing events cannot be established in cases showing schizophrenic symptoms. Further, psychotherapy, difficult even in cases of the type described, proves to be effective only in a limited way or not at all in the latter type of cases. We will now proceed to discuss the general concept and symptomatology of this latter type of condition.

The symptom complex varies with the level of development. If the process starts in the first two years of life, the development is uneven, and there may be no point at which the child appeared to be normal and then to have

[7] Based on a case presentation in P. Blanchard, Psychoanalytic contributions to the problems of reading disabilities, in *The Psychoanalytic Study of the Child,* Vol. II, International Universities Press, New York, 1946, pp. 163-187.

regressed. There is often evidence of excessive anxiety. There may be no language development at all, but, if there is, it may be lost again or misused as a play pattern. Later the child shows profoundly disturbed object relationships: withdrawal, impulsiveness, hostility, and anxiety, together with characteristic motility patterns (see below).

From three to four and a half years is the most common period of onset. The child then gradually or suddenly loses much of what he has gained, such as speech; he becomes withdrawn; he loses his toilet habits; he may be excitable, engage in unprovoked oral aggression, and show great accentuation of the Oedipal problem; e.g., a boy may become very hostile toward the father, insist on sleeping with the mother, and insist on the father's sleeping in another bed. The child may regain some of the lost functions—e.g., speech—but now distorted by schizophrenic patterning. There may be disturbed sleep, anxiety with phobias, preoccupation with problems of identity, of body functions, and of orientation in space (see below).

Between the ages of six and eleven, in addition to similar symptoms, other phenomena become significant. The tendency to whirling and clinging, motility patterns which are normal up to the age of six, now may become conspicuous. The symptom of so-called "introjected bodies," occasionally appearing even before the age of six, together with hallucinations, becomes conspicuous. The child may speak of "brain bodies," which her bad mother put into her to make her have a baby, or of an Indian or of the Devil in the belly who is saying bad things to her or telling her to do bad things.

> "One young boy, whenever alone, would cry out, 'Every minute, every minute, I can't get it out, a big one, too, Jesus Christ, every minute, it's getting bigger.' He would not explain, but compress his thighs and writhe in his chair and point to his buttocks, and only say, 'There is something in my arms, there is clay—they feel stiff.' "[8]

Beginning with the age of ten or eleven, persecutory delusions, together with hallucinations coming from the outside, appear. The patient suspects that either he or his parents are changed or that other children are against him, partly because of his hostility and anxiety and partly because he cannot identify with them. His efforts to master his motility lead to mannerisms. There is a breakdown in personal habits and the child may truant, wander away from home, and enter strange dwellings, partly to escape, partly to orient himself, and partly to find new contacts and new solutions.

Certain characteristics of the symptomatology are apt to be present at all ages. (1) Some functions are ahead of, and others are behind, the chronological developmental level of the child. This is apt to show up in a wide scatter on intelligence tests. The disturbance of the vegetative functions may

[8] L. Bender, Childhood schizophrenia: Clinical study of one hundred schizophrenic children, *Amer. J. Orthopsychiat.*, 1947, **17**, p. 50.

show through flushing and perspiration or a colorless complexion with blue, cold extremities. He may react with no temperature fluctuation to a severe infection or show an excessive response to a slight illness. The physiological rhythms, such as sleeping, eating, and elimination habits, are disturbed. Menstruation may appear at the age of seven, or there may be delay in its appearance at puberty. There may be considerable awkwardness, or the patient may carry on endlessly with rhythmic and graceful dancing behavior in changing tempos. (2) The patients usually show a difficulty in differentiating their concept of themselves from the rest of the world in a variety of ways. They have a strong tendency to cling to other persons, and, if support is withdrawn while they are leaning, they simply fall into the examiner's lap. This problem of differentiation shows up also in their preoccupation with the peripheral organs of their bodies. They may walk around without shoes and be involved concerning secretions from the mouth and the nose. This problem of clinging, together with a retention of earlier maturational patterns, is present in their motility and in their Bender-Gestalt drawings. The tendency to circular movement is present in their whirling beyond the age of five (see page 131) and in the Gestalt drawings. The separate patterns tend to flow into each other, and they tend to be rotated from the horizontal toward the longitudinal axis. This general tendency to clinging, the flowing of things into each other, together with the tendency to fuse the self with the world and the changeability of reactions, has been characterized by Bender as "plasticity."

At all age periods the emotional conflicts and problems seen in neurotic and also in normal children may be strongly over-accented and at times verbalized with exceptional clarity, because the inhibiting influences which in a sense form part of social reality-testing are seriously impaired.

A nine-year-old child said, " 'I want a hammer to kill my bed. I am mad at it. It won't come to me at night, and I have to go to find it. I am mad at my mother too. She takes food to bed and eats it in bed. . . . I got a gun to shoot somebody's head off and a razor to cut my fingers off. . . . Is that a lady or a man doll? . . . It must be a skeleton. They kill people, jump on your back, and bite you all to pieces. . . . I dreamed a fox was after me. I jumped off the roof, I landed right on my head and got hurt. I like that. When you get hurt and wake up it is beautiful. . . . My mother doesn't love me. She shouldn't have had me. I should have stayed in her guts. I am in my own gizzard. I think I will go back to heaven where I came from.' "[9]

Childhood schizophrenia is "a clinical entity, occurring in childhood before the age of eleven years, which 'reveals pathology in behavior at every level and in every area of integration . . . within the functioning of the central nervous system, be it vegetative, motor, perceptual, intellectual,

[9] *Ibid.*, p. 51.

emotional, or social.' "[10] The pathology therefore has to be thought of as "striking at the substratum of integrative functioning of biologically patterned behavior."[11] The child then reacts with anxiety stirred up by the disturbing phenomena in the vasovegetative, motility, perceptual, and psychological fields. The final picture is a combined resultant of the initial somatic disturbance, the anxiety, and the attempt at coping with the anxiety.

Some of the phenomena described above may be used to illustrate Bender's formulation of the pathology of childhood schizophrenia. The various aspects of the plasticity, such as the difficulty in differentiating the self from the world and the tendency to cling, could be considered to be, in part, determined by the initial somatic disturbance, involving the retention of earlier maturational levels of motility, and thus leading to problems in equilibrium and difficulty in handling problems relating to people. The child then attempts to cope with the resultant anxiety by increasing both his self-centeredness and his tendency to get attached and to cling and to lean. Similarly, some sudden, unconnected, impulsive activities of the patient, best described as "darting," could be considered as representing both an uncontrolled physiological impulse and an attempt to escape from dependency on the mother or from a confining environment or from his own identity and the whole frustrating disorder of the psychosis. This complex tendency was very well expressed in a letter written by a ten-year-old patient to her doctor:

> " 'For the doctor, I am sure I will escape though and go to the real guardian angel hospital meant for all who come here. I, Francine, that is what they call me, was very unhappy there. It was a terrible world. I thought it was a real one but it seems it isn't. I may some day go to the real one.' "[12]

In cases like the one in the previous section, where a clear traumatic situation can be found, the treatment, although difficult, may aim at the full elucidation of the emotional problems. In cases of the type discussed in this section, the approach may be directed at the relief of the anxiety and the consequent symptom formation. There should be, further, an attempt "to help in the integration of the pattern of behavior and the promotion of such identification processes as are possible."[13]

By contrast with adult schizophrenics, "one can often make an unusually good contact with schizophrenic children."[14] They attempt to solve their problems by an excessive identification or interpenetrating relationship.

[10] *Ibid.*, p. 40.

[11] L. Bender, Childhood schizophrenia, *Nerv. Child,* 1942, **1**, p. 138. The presentation of childhood schizophrenia here is based on the formulations of Dr. Lauretta Bender.

[12] L. Bender, Childhood schizophrenia: Clinical study of one hundred schizophrenic children, *Amer. J. Orthopsychiat.*, 1947, **17**, p. 44.

[13] *Ibid.*, p. 52.

[14] *Ibid.*, p. 53.

Withdrawal occurs only after a long period of failure to get satisfaction from interpersonal contacts.

"Six-year-old Martin for a while would eat only what I fed him. He was given an Indian suit in the hospital and would not permit it to be removed for sleeping or bathing except by me. If permitted, he would sit all day in the corner of my office with his thumb in his mouth, and if put out of the room, would be content if only the toe of his shoe could be pushed over the door sill. At such periods the sight of his mother threw him into a screaming panic. Now, at 16, he is still glad to see me (the process is quiescent now) and talks vaguely of his problems."[15]

The prognosis for the disorder of the latter type is poor, even with treatment, if the process starts before the age of two. For the cases that start at a later period it is as good as in adults, which means that from a third to a half will make from a fair to a good social recovery or remission but remain vulnerable. (For surveys of various approaches, see 334 and 335.)

PSYCHOSOMATIC REACTIONS

The term "psychosomatic disorder," in the broadest sense, refers to any disorder in which a correlation can be established between "psychological (including introspective) phenomena" and observable changes in body function. In this sense the easily reversible "psychogenic" disorders—e.g., vomiting—and disorders starting with primary brain pathology are included. In this section the term will be used in the more specific sense—namely, for disorders in the causation of which emotional problems play a major role, while, at the same time, a special somatic factor or predisposition may be demonstrable or be considered very likely.

GASTROINTESTINAL PAIN, FEVER, AND HEADACHE; SUSCEPTIBILITY TO INFECTION

These symptoms may occur as part manifestations in behavior disorders—e.g., in anxiety states. (See the case on page 334.) It has been mentioned that infants, when reacting with depression to separation from the mother, show increased susceptibility to colds and eczema, and that infants in a foundling home, along with general retardation as a result of absence of stimuli and emotional warmth, showed increased susceptibility to infection and increased mortality.

Headaches are not infrequently complained of by children, although they reach the severity of migraines only during adolescence.

ALLERGIC CONDITIONS

Bronchial asthma, infantile eczema, and hives frequently occur in combination in the same child, eczema usually being the earliest in appearance.

[15] *Ibid.*, p. 53.

They have a tendency to familial occurrence and are most frequently based on allergic reactions to certain substances, mostly proteins, which enter the organism either by being swallowed (food) or by being inhaled (pollen, feathers). It is uncertain how regularly psychogenic factors play a significant role in the *onset* of these disturbances, as they undoubtedly do play a role when infants react to separation from the mother both with a depression and with eczema. At other times the condition apparently starts entirely on a chemogenic basis but then becomes patterned into emotional problems. If the condition starts after four years of age, the presence of emotional problems at the time of the onset is very likely. Vasomotor rhinitis and angioneurotic edema will be discussed in Chapter XXX.

Infantile Eczema. Infantile eczema (inflammation of the skin) may start in the first few months of life, reaching its height around the ninth month and disappearing about the middle of the second year. In some instances it continues and may be present in more limited areas throughout childhood and adolescence. In this chronic state the usual locations are the back of the knee and the bend of the elbow, with periodic flare-ups spreading over other parts of the body. When the spread occurs, it usually starts with itching, and the inflammation itself is the result of the scratching. It was found in one investigation that, in the nursery where infants were cared for by their unmarried mothers, those who later developed eczema were characterized by heightened touch and sucking reflexes in comparison with the other infants. Whereas 80 percent of the normal children manifested social anxiety at the age of eight months, only 20 percent of the children with eczema did so. The majority of the mothers of the eczema children were anxiety-ridden, whereas most of the other mothers exhibited infantile, wayward personalities.[16]

It is very likely that the heightened cutaneous and sucking reflexes were the manifestations of constitutional factors. The anxiety of the mothers affected the child either in the form of not enough handling or, if this tendency was compensated for, by anxious handling. The meaning of the relative absence of social anxiety at this period is unclear, because older children suffering from eczema are patently anxious, and, further, anxious mothers in general make for anxious children. It is possible that some other compensatory feature—e.g., hyperactivity—not included in the above observation was present. Eczema becomes entangled with three emotional patterns: (1) fear, particularly fear of abandonment and to a lesser extent fear of disapproval and fear of attack, the skin disorder then further acquiring the meaning of helplessness and being looked after and receiving emotional warmth; (2) resentment, particularly directed toward a stronger person and therefore subject to repression, the skin disorder then further acquiring the connotation of retribution and taking out on oneself what was meant for

[16] Personal communication from Dr. Katherine M. Wolf.

the other person (to scratch); (3) genital excitement, if that is accompanied by fear and guilt, the disorder then acquiring the connotation of substitute masturbation, gratification, and punishment.

The treatment of eczema in early infancy consists, on the physical side, of an attempt to eliminate the protein to which the infant is sensitive, often the protein of cow's milk. The main substitutes nowadays are soybean products. Along with this, soothing lotions and ointments, at times combined with medications that diminish itching, are administered. Almost always a vicious circle develops: the inflammation causes itching, the infant scratches, and that perpetuates the inflammation. To break this circle, it has been customary to tie the child's hands to the crib to prevent scratching. It is not certain how traumatic this is in infancy. It can be very traumatic if it is done after the first half of the second year. A more appropriate method is to put mittens on the child's hands, bandage the eczema, and watch him. The psychotherapy consists in determining and correcting the interaction between the child and the environment. It may take some time for the eczema to begin to respond and for its connection with the varying stress situations to become clear. It is always necessary to treat the mother also, because she herself is very anxious and ready to break off treatment and insist on purely physical procedures. (For a case illustration of infantile eczema, see Chapter XVII.)

Bronchial Asthma. The psychodynamics of bronchial asthma are most frequently centered in the fear of abandonment as a result of hostility. In that case the asthmatic attack has the meaning, psychologically, of fear of suffocation, a cry for help, and an attack of rage. In some children the asthmatic attack occurs almost immediately upon engaging, with conflict, in a game of sexual curiosity. The asthmatic attack then has the meaning of excitement and punishment. (For further description of this syndrome, see Chapter XXX.)

The treatment of asthma consists, on the physical side, of the administration of suitable medication (adrenalin, ephedrine, pyribenzamine) to stop the attack. If a significant offending protein can be identified through skin tests, it should be eliminated, at least temporarily. The psychotherapy of asthma in children is usually quickly effective, at times even in cases that have gone on for as long as nine years without any long interruption.

A twelve-year-old patient suffered from asthmatic attacks, from the age of two up to the age of five, coincident with recurrent quarrels between her parents, ending in divorce when the patient was five. Her attacks recurred three months before the start of the treatment, precipitated by the following events: (1) She got upset when a prematurely born squirrel that was not viable was disposed of during the summer in camp. (2) She was confronted with the problem of sexual maturation when other girls in camp menstruated. (3) She was worried that she would not succeed in the rapid-advance class where she was newly placed. In the interviews occurring once or twice a week over a period of four months, the following topics were discussed: (1) Appearance of the asthmatic attacks in connection with day-to-day events such as anticipation of rejection by boys at parties and resentment toward her brother—e.g., when he left her a note with obscene words, signed, "Your friend, The Killer." She developed an attack while relating this incident in the interview. (2) After considering her mother "extremely fair," she gradually became aware of anger with her because of complete permissiveness toward her brother. She further blamed her for the divorce. (3) Resentment toward her father, who had taken her to see his mistress when the patient was three years old and did not keep his promises about presents for her birthdays. (4) Resentment toward the stepfather, to whom she was also very much attached, and whom the mother had married three years previously. (5) Her fear of her classmates' disapproval and her fear of sex. These had been compensated for by excessive ambition, the taking on of extracurricular activities after school hours.

The patient had a dream that she was bitten by a baby ostrich while nursing it with a bottle. She remarked, "The ostrich behaved toward me as I behave toward my mother." In another dream she was in danger of being eaten up by crocodiles, because she was taking risks her mother warned her against.

The mother also received psychotherapy. The patient's asthma gradually subsided in the course of four months' psychotherapy along with the auxiliary use of pyribenzamine when she had attacks. She gave up her frantic drive for achievement in school. She developed adequate friendships and social life with the girls and boys in her class.

ULCERATIVE COLITIS

Disturbances of bowel function, such as constipation and diarrhea, are common symptoms in emotional disturbances. Diarrhea may be rather distressing in anxiety situations. A more serious disturbance and at times a fatal one is ulcerative colitis, which consists of an inflammation of the colon resulting in formation of small ulcers, with a rise in temperature, bleeding through the rectum, and considerable loss of weight. Psychodynamically, it often starts when the patient feels abandoned by a protector and left prey to the attacker. The diarrhea may further express the fantasy of being an infant and may also represent a substitute gratification and the destruction of the frustrator. Another construction advanced is that the symptom represents the elimination of the hated person, usually the "bad" mother, whom the patient destructively swallowed in fantasy.

The treatment, on the physical side, consists of rest in bed, blood transfusion if there is severe loss of blood, sedatives to ease the pain, diet to avoid irritation of the inflamed bowels, and, at times, operation to secure rest for the colon. Physical treatment alone is unsatisfactory.

Psychotherapy is very difficult and has to be extensive, representing modified analysis. The simultaneous treatment of the mother is indispensable. The condition may flare up after initial improvement if the therapist proceeds too fast or if the mother engages in acts that disturb the child. The cases have to be followed and helped out of difficulties for many years after the condition has cleared up. The following case is that of a patient with ulcerative colitis, arthritis, self-induced infection, and conduct disorder.

The patient was seven and a half years old when she developed ulcerative colitis shortly after her father was inducted into the army. Her mother had always been very critical and strict, letting her cry for hours, had trained her very early, and put much stress upon cleanliness. She had felt protected by her father and now felt helplessly in her mother's power. After the discussion of her anger at and fear of her mother, the symptoms of colitis diminished, and she gained about sixteen pounds after five months of treatment. Two months later, just before her brother's birthday (he was four years her junior) and shortly after her best and only friend moved away from the neighborhood, she squeezed a turtle belonging to her brother, then dismembered it, put stones into it, and buried it. She developed a high temperature and pain and swelling in her knee and wrist,[17] again had bloody diarrhea, and lost much weight. The pain in her joints paralleled her wish to break her brother's bones much as she had dismembered the turtle. She was a disobedient and argumentative patient in the hospital. When the therapist did not agree to her going home right away, she flew into a rage and shouted, "You're a witch, I wish you were dead." When the therapist replied kindly that she understood the patient's feelings and would do everything to make her stay as pleasant as possible, the patient's gloomy face lit up. She began to eat, her diarrhea stopped gradually, her temperature dropped, and soon she was able to go home from the hospital. A month later she had a relapse because her mother, contrary to her promise, had disposed of the patient's dog. In the course of the further treatment the patient's resentment at her parents' sleeping together was discussed, as well as her preoccupation with the genitals of boys and girls, and the way they urinate. She had fantasies that the mother conceives the baby by eating a certain food that the father gives her and that birth was an act of defecation. After some further discussion of her resentment toward her brother, her fear of her mother, her worry that she would make them (magically) sick, and her guilt therefore, she again improved considerably. The patient had another serious illness: an infection of the foot caused by self-destructive picking of the skin. In connection with this illness she realized her hostile longing for complete dependence on the mother, and the mother realized the extent of her own hostility, amounting to death wishes toward the daughter. This finally made a resolution of the fundamental conflicts possible, and the patient has since remained well for several years.[18]

[17] The most common form of arthritis in children is caused by rheumatic fever. Other manifestations of this disorder may be endocarditis (inflammation of the lining membrane of the heart) and chorea (see page 361). Psychogenic factors probably play a role in these disorders only in so far as relapses are concerned, either because the child exposes himself to chilling or because of the secondary emotional implications of the illness. In case of arthritic symptoms, the emotional meaning is the same as here described.

[18] Based on a case presentation in M. Sperling, Psychoanalytic study of ulcerative colitis in children, *Psychoanal. Quart.*, 1946, 15, 302-329.

REACTIONS OF THE TOTAL PERSONALITY TO CIRCUMSCRIBED DEFICIENCIES

These disorders consist of circumscribed primary somatic disturbances in function to which the individual reacts with emotional disturbances. (See Chapter III.)

PSYCHOLOGICAL DISTURBANCES IN PREMATURE CHILDREN

Prematurity implies that the infant is born at a time when various organs of the body have not been developed to the point where they would be at nine months of gestation. The premature infant is therefore exposed to hazards with which he is not yet adequately able to cope. Such children rarely survive if they are born before seven months of gestation. Their heat regulation is particularly vulnerable; hence they are commonly brought up in incubators. They are also very susceptible to infections. They do not have enough strength to nurse adequately; hence they have to be fed with a medicine dropper.

At later periods the children frequently seem to be small for their age and behind in emotional and intellectual development. In addition, they may show difficulties in manipulation, over-activity, impulsiveness, and much distress because they cannot compete with other children of their age.

As the last remark indicates, the manifestations of prematurely born children represent a mixture of direct manifestations of immaturity of their nervous systems, hence over-sensitiveness, and psychological reactions to the disturbed functions, particularly susceptibility to anxiety (366). In a careful study of the incidence of various psychological manifestations in prematurely born children, as compared with a normal control group, Shirley (862) obtained the findings shown in Tables 12 and 13.

Psychologically, prematurely born children require a great deal of patience and understanding in training and discipline, and a great deal of support and reassurance when they react with emotional disturbances. After a certain level of maturity is reached, psychotherapy may be of considerable help.

READING DISABILITY

The child with reading disability is usually of average or superior intelligence, with an IQ of 90-150 or above on individual intelligence tests but rating lower on group tests of intelligence which require reading instructions. Eighty percent or more of the children with reading disabilities are boys (96). It has been mentioned earlier that reading disability may be primarily psychogenic. In the majority of instances, primary organic factors play a predominant role. Apparently 20 percent of the reading disabilities are of the neurotic type amenable to psychotherapy followed by remedial teaching, but about 80 percent will be primarily non-neurotic and able to respond to remedial teaching without preceding psychotherapy (333). The organic etiology may include the following: (1) There may be defects of hearing; a hearing loss of 15 percent or more was found in 30 percent of reading disability cases but in only 11 percent of good readers (332, 678). (2) Very likely, in an important number of cases of reading disability, a delayed or incomplete maturational process of the brain centers connected with reading (angular gyrus of the parietal lobe) is present.

TABLE 12. Characteristics Shown in Test Situations[19]

Age group (6-24 months)	50 Prematures (percent)	50 Controls (percent)
Distraction by sounds	36	6
Throwing toys around	30	6
Banging and slapping toys	20	10
Trembling and shuddering	18	10
Comprehend but refuse to perform	18	8
Seek adult help	22	6
Age group (2½-5 years)	**22 Prematures (percent)**	**22 Controls (percent)**
Very distractible	45	13
Distracted by sounds	18	4
Trembling	9	4

TABLE 13. Characteristics Manifested During Play Period[20]

Age group (2½-5 years)	30 Prematures (percent)	30 Controls (percent)
Remarks about unusual sounds	67	37
Speech difficulties	60	23
Jittery—nervous	83	27
Five or more urinations	27	12

Intelligent children with reading disability are often advanced in their regular classes and yet may be several grades behind in their ability to read. They manage to cover up the deficiency by remembering what is read to them and repeating it with near accuracy in the right context or in response to the right picture in the book. Sooner or later the child is called stupid by his classmates and as a rule is subjected to bad handling by parents and

[19] Based on figures in M. Shirley, A behavior syndrome characterizing prematurely born children, *Child Developm.*, 1939, **10,** 115-128.

[20] Based on figures in M. Shirley, *op. cit.*

teachers. It was found that the parents of a hundred children with reading disabilities were either deeply worried or thought the children lazy and stubborn and scolded or beat the children. The attitudes of thirty-two school principals of forty pupils with reading disabilities were these: Only four realized that the reading disability was the cause of the poor school work. Twenty-eight of them attributed it to low mentality, poor physical condition, and psychopathic tendencies (96). Under the impact of these experiences a child develops the feeling of inadequacy, with hostility and a feeling of rejection. He may largely accept the verdict and react passively with a depressive reaction or may become combative and unruly. Truancy is a common development.

The treatment consists of remedial reading, psychotherapy, and altering the attitude of the environment. All remedial methods require endless patience and kind persistence on the part of the therapist. One of the methods consists of utilizing a number of sensory and kinesthetic functions for the process of reading. The child looks at the word, speaks the word, writes the word, looks at the picture of the object that represents the word, and goes slowly from simpler to more complex patterns. With everybody's coöperation, this method is usually successful. The remedial method is often effective by itself in eliminating all the secondary emotional consequences of the disability. This probably happens because a close supportive relationship develops between the remedial teacher and the child. In other instances, and certainly in all cases of psychogenic reading disability, the disturbances are so complex that they persist, and psychotherapy is imperative.

DELAY IN MATURATION OF THE SPEECH CENTER

A relatively infrequent but serious problem is presented by cases with delay in maturation of the speech center. The condition is not entirely limited to the speech centers, and one may find along with it problems of cerebral dominance or changes of the postural reflexes. The difficulty may show itself in the child's inability to speak as late as four, five, or six years. A severe aggressive type of disturbed behavior toward the outside world, together with generalized anxiety and clinging to the mother, may result. The reason for this development is the child's difficulty and perplexity in communicating with strange adults and children, with the attendant frustrations, disappointments, and mistreatments. The speech may develop gradually, and in the handling of the child it is very important for the parents to give him emotional support, to let him master problems—e.g., locomotion, dressing, eating—in his own way. Ultimately, with the development of speech, other intellectual and learning functions develop, although the child may need help in coming up to par. Also, the emotional problems that persist after the developmental lag is overcome may require psychotherapy.

MOTILITY DIFFICULTIES

Some children are awkward and have difficulty in carrying out skilled motor tasks. They may show disturbances in the postural reflexes[21] and on the Ozeretzky Test. A more serious type of motor disturbance is the result of delayed maturation of the cerebellar pathways. The cerebellum does not initiate movement but plays an indispensable role in maintaining the tone of the muscles and preventing the extremities from drifting off during the assumption of a position and from over-reaching the mark. It also plays an important role in maintaining equilibrium. It is most apt to reveal itself in striking involuntary movements, particularly of the fingers, if the child stands with hands outstretched while his eyes are closed. The environment may be unaware of these difficulties and see only the secondary consequences resulting from the child's anxiety and feelings of inadequacy over failure in comparative motor performance, reinforced by taunts of other children. The effect is considerable dependence on the mother, anxiety and shyness toward other relationships, and the need to be babied. When separated from the mother, the child will reach out and cling to any other available person—adult or child—for similar support (61). Such children require considerable support from the environment and permissiveness in allowing them to handle problems of mastery in their own way (Bender). In so far as the children's anxieties and excessive dependency are interpreted, it should be done with sympathy and the general idea that, the more self-reliant he can be in certain ways, the better it will be for his ultimate welfare.

PSYCHIATRIC SYNDROMES WITH ORGANIC DISTURBANCE OF THE CENTRAL NERVOUS SYSTEM

REACTIONS TO HEAD INJURY

Following severe brain injury, there is loss of consciousness, and after recovery from it or without loss of consciousness there may be delirium (disorientation, hallucinations, usually accompanied by anxiety) or a regression to infantile behavior, with terror or "naughtiness." In the course of a week or ten days the patient may recover from this. The majority of cases with adequate treatment and psychotherapy, including proper attention to the environment (see below), recover without serious damage (63). A small percentage of the children develop epilepsy as a result of localized

[21] If a person is asked to hold his arms outstretched, with his eyes shut, under normal conditions his arms drift apart (abduction) slightly. If his head is turned, under the same conditions, by the examiner, he turns his body—that is, his torso—and both of his arms in the direction of the chin, the "chin arm" rises somewhat, and the other arm sinks slightly.

damage or scarring of the brain and become progressively more disturbed and may deteriorate. Another group shows over-activity, infantile behavior, and an attempt to devour everything. In this kind of behavior there is a reaction of the total personality to the organic damage: the children try to compensate for their inability to have satisfactory experiences, and at the same time they cannot stand frustration.

The treatment in such cases consists of attention to any gross neurological damage, such as paralysis, and, on the psychiatric side, handling of the excessive anxiety and reëstablishment of patterned behavior that meets social demands and is also satisfying to the patient.

It is very important to look at the total emotional picture in the home. The accident at times occurs because the child is not adequately protected or because, as a result of severe emotional problems, he has exposed himself to the accident.

A child suffered two fractures of the skull and was repeatedly admitted to Bellevue Hospital with complaints, made by his parents, of severe habit disorder (enuresis, soiling, nail-biting, hair-pulling, over-eating, genital play with the sister). She showed none of these disturbances on the ward. The social service investigator learned from the neighbors that the child was severely beaten by her parents. She was finally placed with devoted foster parents. On a follow-up examination two years later, aside from some minor disturbances, she appeared to be a normal youngster.[22]

MENTAL DEFICIENCY

The majority of children who present problems of impaired intellectual functioning have organic brain damage. (For psychogenic impairment, see page 343.) The variety of etiologies has been discussed in the section on disorders in infancy (see pages 318-319): Mongolian imbecility, cretinism, microcephaly, hydrocephaly, brain injury, and brain infections, including syphilis. It is important, however, to differentiate in brain injury and brain inflammation between true impairment of intelligence and disturbances of attention.

Three grades of mental defect have been recognized—idiocy, imbecility, and moronity. It must be remembered that originally feeble-mindedness was a legal category which was defined largely in terms of social adjustment.

Idiots are persons so deeply defective in mind from birth or from an early age as to be unable to guard themselves against common physical dangers. An idiot is defined as a person whose IQ is between 0 and 30, and whose mental age in adulthood is two years or less.

[22] Based on a case presentation in L. Bender, Organic conditions producing behavior disturbances: A clinical survey of encephalitis, burn encephalopathy and the traumatic states, in *Modern Trends in Child Psychiatry,* International Universities Press, New York, 1945, pp. 155-192.

Idiots are the only feeble-minded individuals whose condition can be recognized early in life by their physical appearance. The idiot learns to walk and talk much later than is normal, and his speech consists of a few mumbled syllables. A low-grade idiot cannot walk or talk. He is more animal than human in his personal habits, for usually he can do almost nothing for himself. Idiots are usually sterile.

It is in the cortex of idiots only that histological differences from the normal can be detected—fewer cells, different arrangement of cells, etc. No differences have as yet been found in the structure of the brains of morons and geniuses; in other words, little is known about the neurological basis of intelligence.[23]

Imbeciles are persons in whom there exists from birth or from an early age mental defectiveness not amounting to idiocy, yet so pronounced that they are incapable of managing themselves or their affairs, or, in the case of children, of being taught to do so. Their IQ's range from 30 to 50, their mental ages from three to seven years during adulthood.

Imbeciles can be helped by educational measures; for example, they can be taught to take care of themselves, and perhaps even to read a little. But, more important, they can become economically useful in very protected surroundings, for they can do simple, routine, repetitive tasks like rock-breaking.

Morons are usually defined as persons in whom there exists from birth or from an early age mental defectiveness not amounting to imbecility, yet so pronounced that they require care, supervision, and control both for their own protection and for that of others; or, in the case of children, that they appear to be permanently incapable of benefiting from instruction in ordinary schools. Their IQ's range from 50 to 70, and their mental ages from seven to twelve years. They do not differ in appearance from normal children.

One should not think of mentally defective individuals as simply persons with impaired intelligence. As regards their emotional life, they can be rather amicable, as many of the hydrocephalics are, or rather irritable, as many of the microcephalics are apt to be. They may respond relatively well to training, again like many of the microcephalics, or not respond well.

Further, a person who cannot adjust in a complex urban environment may do so easily in a simpler one and even be quite successful. Wallin cites a man whose mental age was only 10.6 years, but who raised a family of nine, all high-school graduates and almost all college students. For ten years he was president of the board of education in the small town in which he lived and was considered by others to be a success.

The following extract from Wembridge demonstrates, more specifically

[23] See, however, L. D. Morgan, Alterations in the hypothalamus in mental deficiency, *Psychosom. Med.,* 1939, 1, 496-507.

than generalization can, how morons think and how they orient themselves in life situations. The questions are from the Binet Tests.

"You recall, no doubt, the standard example in arithmetic which every fourteen-year-old school child is supposed to be able to solve: If two pencils cost five cents, how many can you get for fifty cents? . . . *But neither Flora nor any of her moron friends could master the problem.* We knew they could not because we had asked them. Flora's answer was twenty-five because two into fifty is twenty-five. Her friend Lucille's, on the other hand, was a hundred, because two times fifty is a hundred. . . . It will be observed that all of them knew that *something* must be done in the way of arithmetic, and that their arithmetic was generally correct—except that they could not select the right process to employ. . . .

"It was certainly essential that Flora, out of Chuck's weekly twenty dollars, should save a little for the future. . . . 'If you have twenty dollars a week, and spend fourteen a week, how long will it take you to save three hundred dollars?' Flora, who had a sense of humor, could not at first get past the joke that she should ever save anything. 'A lifetime,' she answered—'and a long lifetime.' . . . The example was written out for her, but she had completely lost the connection, and when she was again reminded, 'But how long a time would it take to save it?' she answered, as if through the telephone, '2025.' What she meant by that we shall never know. . . .

"It is hard, indeed, to discover just what words convey to morons with such a background. Flora when questioned says that 'lecture' means 'getting hanged,' while Lucille says, 'It's the chair.' The fact that the latter's husband is in the penitentiary perhaps explains why both girls should associate the word 'electric.' . . . Words of that abstraction are too hazy for Lucille. . . .

". . . We ask, 'What is pity?' That seems easy: 'You're sorry.' Encouraged, we proceed, 'What is justice?' 'Peace,' answers Lucille, 'I got married by one.' . . . Insure, to Flora, means 'sure,' or 'You get it when you're dead,' or 'They get it at the house,' or 'It's in the company like,' or 'It's when you get hurt.' So much for Flora grasping the insurance principle when some new agent at the door wheedles her out of a first installment, never to be followed by a second! . . .

"Chuck was fond of fables and read them fluently. But the question was: What lesson, if any, did he learn from them? We soon found out. . . . Of the miller and his son who took everyone's advice about their donkey instead of using their own judgment, he said, 'They're so backward, these dumb animals. Too backward, much more backward than human beings.' "[24]

Feeble-mindedness of organic origin often leads to further emotional problems. Although the intellectual function of the child is impaired, he remains sensitive to the name-calling of playmates and siblings. The parents may reject the child or refuse to accept his impairment and then may keep pushing him toward superior tasks, punishing him if he fails. The child reacts with hostility, anxiety, and depression. Feeble-minded children below a certain level of performance are probably happier in institutions.

[24] E. H. Wembridge, *Life Among the Lowbrows,* Houghton Mifflin Co., Boston, 1931, pp. 6-7.

Feeble-mindedness of a moronic level does not predispose the individual to delinquency, but it does allow him to be more easily influenced by others to perform delinquent acts.

The treatment of feeble-mindedness has three aspects: (1) Glandular treatment is effective only in hypothyroid cases (if started in early infancy). Glutamic acid administration has a limited effectiveness in many cases by raising the intelligence quotient at times by as many as ten or twenty points. In some border-line cases this may mean the difference between the child's needing constant supervision and being able to take care of himself within limitations. Its effects last only as long as the medication is continued. When it is discontinued, the intellectual functioning drops to its previous level (18). (2) The correction of any faulty attitude of the environment—e.g., of the parents—is advisable so that it can accept the child's limitations. This is a difficult problem under the best of circumstances, particularly in middle-class families who find it hard to accept even average or dull normal intelligence in their children. It also includes the correction of the emotional difficulties that the child has developed as a result of his difficulties. (3) Finally, it involves an attempt to train the child or adolescent for the kind of relatively simple occupation that he is capable of performing. This, of course, is easier with mental defectives who are not irritable and aggressive and who have a well-preserved sense of responsibility. Those whose intelligence rates them as imbeciles or idiots cannot adjust to extramural environments.

CHOREA

The relationship of chorea to rheumatic fever and endocarditis has been mentioned previously. Chorea consists of involuntary movements which begin in the extremities, particularly the fingers (most marked with the eyes shut), and usually spread to other parts of the body. The movements resemble purposeful ones; so the environment—e.g., teachers—may assume that they are done out of spite (63).

The emotional disturbances are frequently restlessness, irritability, emotional instability, inattentiveness in school work, and "naughtiness." Rarely there may be hallucinations with terror. All of these conditions respond to adequate organic treatment and disappear with the chorea (63). The motility disturbance, together with interpersonal problems, may lead to secondary emotional problems which then may require psychotherapy.

ENCEPHALITIS

Encephalitis is an inflammation of the brain which, unless it accompanies such conditions as meningitis (inflammation of the outer lining membranes of the central nervous system) or abscess of the brain, has a tendency to strike particularly the brain stem. The most frequent cause of it is epidemic encephalitis (when there are epidemics), but it occurs at times as a result of vaccination, measles, scarlet fever, severe burns, or lead poisoning. The discussion here will center on epidemic encephalitis, an inflammation of the brain caused by an ultramicroscopic virus.

The acute phase both in children and in adults is often first manifested by double vision and failure of the pupillary light reflex. Frequently there are somnolence or drowsiness, twitching of various muscles, and pain and rigidity of the neck muscles. Lethargy, if present, is very characteristic. The patient is in a stuporous condition and appears to be sleeping all of the time. For this reason the condition is called "sleeping sickness" or "encephalitis lethargica." The stupor, however, is unusual, for, if the patient is spoken to, he wakes for a brief period and is able to answer questions clearly; then he quickly goes to sleep again. Insomnia may be severe and may appear before the lethargy. Emotional disturbances such as anxiety and agitation are common. The patient may suffer delirium with hallucinations. The acute period may last a few weeks or many months, and it may be fatal.

The chronic condition lasts a long time but does not endanger the patient's life. Sometimes it reappears after the patient has apparently been entirely well for a long period, even several years. The symptoms often follow a recognized acute attack of encephalitis, but the acute attack is sometimes so slight as to be mistaken for a cold. In this case the diagnosis can be made on the basis of the characteristic symptoms and the fact that there was an epidemic of the disease at the time the patient had the "cold" or "influenza."

One of the characteristic symptoms in children is hyperkinetic behavior. The child is restless and very active, and the behavior is unruly and mischievous. Apparently the child cannot control this excessive activity; if he is asked about it, he answers, "I don't know, I don't want to do it, still I do it." He may feel remorseful and self-condemnatory about his behavior.

Either as a result of this constant pressure for activity or possibly as an independent factor, the children are disobedient, destructive, boisterous, and combative. They break furniture and windows, cut things up, and torture animals and other children. Their moral evaluations suffer; such children may smear themselves with excreta, urinate on persons around them, expose themselves, make sexual assaults, steal, use obscene language, or set things on fire. Obviously, such children present extremely serious problems of management at home, with their playmates, and in school, for they may injure others, cause accidents, or completely disrupt discipline.

The sleep may show the so-called "inverted rhythm"; i.e., the child sleeps during the day and is awake at night. The intelligence, as a rule, is normal, but the child does not focus his attention for long periods or study adequately. Tics are common physical symptoms and sometimes appear in attacks, such as forced breathing or a crescendo repetition of syllables. The attacks subside, and between them the functions involved may be normal.

Postencephalitic children are such major problems after an epidemic that special departments have been established for their care in psychopathic hospitals.

In adults the physical symptoms in the chronic stage consist mainly of so-called "Parkinsonianism." This is caused by the localization of the disease in the basal ganglia of the brain, whereby the muscle tonus increases and rigidity results. There is a continuous shaking motion (coarse tremor) in all or some of the extremities. The facial expression is fixed, and the skin is oily. Another symptom common to many cases in the chronic stage is the "oculogyric crisis," in which the eyes suddenly turn upward in a spasm and stay that way for several minutes.

Mental symptoms in the chronic stage may appear with or without obvious physical disturbances. The patient has compulsive and obsessive thoughts, which appear during attacks, usually associated with oculogyric crises. He may show depression with agitation; that is, he is dejected and sad but at the same time restless and emotional, possibly anxious; he may engage in impulsive acts, sometimes with a suicidal intent. This behavior may be the patient's reaction to his physical difficulties as well as to environmental factors which he now finds difficult to cope with because of his physical disability. In rare cases, a postencephalitic patient is unusually happy. Apathy is a frequent symptom. The patient is inclined to sit in the same place, possibly looking out at the street or just staring into space. He may lie for long periods without moving. Delusions and hallucinations are comparatively rare, but occur in some cases. Hallucinations are sometimes tactile, the patient feeling insects crawling on him, or auditory.

There is no reliable treatment for the acute period of encephalitis. Excited patients may be helped by hydrotherapy, and adults with the Parkinsonian condition are benefited by exercise and various forms of medication, with auxiliary psychotherapy.

The irritable and impulsive behavior of children is partly a direct effect of the organic damage, but the reaction to the indistinct physical discomfort, to the struggle with the environment, to punishment, to competition, and to frustration is further insecurity and hostility. For these reasons, considerable reëducation is possible in some cases, and the children are able to master their impulses in part.

Hyperkinetic children can be treated best in sections of psychopathic hospitals especially established for that purpose. With adequate management, reëducation, and proper medication, they may improve sufficiently in behavior so that they can return to their homes.

In the early follow-up studies on children who were treated in psychiatric hospitals, the figures on recovery varied between 42 and 70 percent. On later follow-up studies—about fourteen years after the onset of the illness—the figures varied between 17 and 25 percent (Bond and Appel, Bond and Smith, Ford, Grossman, Heersema, Holt, Kennedy). (See Bender [63] for references.)

SUGGESTED READINGS

A clear and systematic approach through the use of cases is presented in Pearson's book *Emotional Disorders of Children* (726). Bender's book *Child Psychiatric Techniques* (70) is both original and comprehensive. Further recommended are the very readable Pearson and English, *Emotional Problems of Living* (243), Kanner's section on child psychiatry in Strecker and Ebaugh (910), and the child section in Henderson and Gillespie (462). An interesting reading is Abram Blau's *The Masterhand,* Am. Orthopsychiat. Assn., Research Monog. No. 5.

XXII Disorders in Adolescence

Puberty and adolescence present two general problems: (1) sexual maturity, and (2) approach to adulthood, independence, and self-assertion. Both of these have individual, interpersonal, and social aspects. They represent in part old, in part new, issues. The old problems consist of a revival of the attitudes and conflicts around sexuality which have prevailed at various periods before school age—that is, before the latency period. These problems, however, have acquired further additions through the experiences of subsequent years, whether or not there was overt latency. Sexual stimulation and opportunity for hetero- and homosexual activity, with varying emphasis on genital, oral, urethral, anal, or other organ functions, now exert their influence even if the child did not allow himself to react to them during latency, as do, similarly, anxiety and guilt. The child's successes or failures, during the same period, in matching his strength with mates or adults, his ideals, his gratification or frustration of needs for affection, approval, and self-appreciation, influence the new goals and his manner of coping with his conflicts. The entirely new elements in the situation, in both respects mentioned above, are these: The sexual urge is greater, and there are external signs of maturity, both of which make repression more difficult, if not impossible. As regards independence and self-assertion, the group code, in harmony with or clashing with the adult environment, has become more approving and has set up ideals in this direction. All disorders, relating to sexual maturation—e.g., adiposogenital dystrophy—and disorders that influence the appearance of the body and in that way the desirability as a love-object—e.g., obesity—become paramount problems at this period.

PROBLEMS CENTERING IN THE GENITAL FUNCTION

The problem of normal and pathological in connection with strivings centering in the genital function is a complex one, as it is the only biological activity for which there are forms of individual-social integration yet which the individual does not actually have to engage in. A further complication arises from the fact that group customs vary considerably, and the individual's behavior and psychology cannot be evaluated without consideration of his frame of reference. Constitutional differences also play an important role.

There will be frequent references to statistical studies on averages in frequency of various genital activities in men and women at all ages. However, statistical studies rarely reflect the emotional framework and constitutional potentiality of the individual. In the course of psychoanalytic treatment, the individual may shift to an astounding degree from one part of the distribution curve to another. The average frequency of orgasm—a subjective climax in pleasure accompanied by objective manifestations (including ejaculation in the male), and generally followed by relaxation—in the adult male population is presented as 2.34 per week (494). However, a thirty-year-old man, highly successful in his occupation, may come for treatment in alarm over his recently discovered impotence. He has attempted intercourse only with prostitutes twice in his life, never masturbates, and has nocturnal emissions ("wet dreams") once in three months. After protracted analytic treatment, he is able to have intercourse three or four times a night, four or five times a week. Also, the activity resulting in orgasm may shift from homo- to heterosexual activity and from compulsive masturbation to heterosexual intercourse, and may diminish in frequency from six daily to three or four a week, as a result of treatment.

Pathology in connection with the genital function may arise as a result of trauma in connection with the function itself, or the genital function may become the carrier and the attempted solution for the interpersonal conflicts. Most commonly, one finds a combination of both.

REACTIONS OF FRUSTRATION, ANXIETY, AND GUILT; UNTOWARD REACTIONS TO THE DISCOVERY OF THE FUNCTIONS

The discovery of the differences in the genitals is very frequently attended by disappointment on the part of the girl, with subsequent reactions of resentment and envy. Thus a three-year-old girl who used to bathe with her brother suddenly looked at his penis and asked what it was. When told, she exclaimed, "And I don't have any." She was irritable for several days and became angry whenever she was called a little girl. Children of ten console themselves by saying that "it will grow out later" or may give the explanation that "it was cut off." The effect of the discovery on boys is apt to be curiosity, pride, or anxiety, the last implying fear of losing the organ. The last is particularly apt to be present or to persist if there was an environmental prohibition about genital activity. Less frequently, there is disappointment on the little boy's part when he hears that he cannot have a child, like his mother, or that he will never develop breasts like hers. This is more apt to happen if the child is suffering from fears of abandonment by the parents. At times the boy's reaction to mutual exposure is shame and the desire to hide his genitals. This is definitely a pathological reaction based on a readiness for shame and a preference for being a girl. The effect of exposure is strongly influenced by attendant circumstances.

The first experience a girl had relating to the differences in genitals took place at the age of ten when she allowed herself to be tied to a tree and five boys exposed themselves and urinated in her presence. This immediately precipitated a severe anxiety state.

The sexual responsiveness of women goes through a complicated development. Pleasurable experience in response to clitoral stimulation is apparently an unlearned response, whereas the response to vaginal intercourse almost always requires a period of psychological development.

The sex act, when observed, is usually interpreted by young children as a violent assault. A four-year-old girl happened to see the hired man having intercourse with the maid in the barn. She ran to her mother excitedly and said to her, "Joe is strangling Mary." Frequently girls in the prepubertal period, when they hear from each other about intercourse, react with fear and disgust, in part because they are told that a hard object is forced into their body and that it hurts. The disgust has to do with longstanding prohibitive and over-moral attitudes and is thus the result of environmental influences.

The arrival of menstruation can be traumatic, particularly if the girl knows nothing about it and assumes that she has injured herself. It can be disturbing even with proper preparation if anxiety and guilt have developed about sexual functions or if there has been intense hostility toward rejecting parents. The physiological tension that usually precedes the menstrual period contributes to the traumatic effect.

Infantile theories about conception and birth are most abundant and, without correction or with repression of knowledge, may persist into adult life. The commonest are (1) theories of oral impregnation, (2) the cloacal theory, fusing the sex organ with the rectum as a cavity (as it is anatomically in birds), and (3) the theory of anal birth. Their persistence, always accompanied by other conflicts, may lead to fear of having been impregnated through kissing, which may further lead to nausea at the thought of kissing and fear of any intimate contact. This symptom of nausea may be reinforced through the reaction against the idea of injuring the male organ by biting and against another infantile theory—namely, the acquisition of the organ through swallowing.

REACTIONS TO ENVIRONMENTAL ATTITUDES TOWARD THE FUNCTIONS

The most important injurious environmental attitudes toward any of the sexual functions are those of disapproval, threat, and humiliation. These attitudes have considerably diminished in a large section of the population, but nearly every child gets exposed to them either directly through the parents or indirectly through other children. The attitude may start when the child is in infancy and follow him through his whole developmental period into adulthood. Not infrequently, bodily punishment is administered, at least slapping the hand, together with the threat that if the genitals were handled they would be cut off or that masturbation would lead to illness, particularly insanity. The effectiveness of other children's ideas was shown during the treatment of a ten-year-old boy who could not accept the idea that masturbation was not harmful in itself in spite of the fact that he had been reassured both by the therapist and by his parents. He was being told by his playmates that it led to insanity. An equally injurious attitude is the arousal of guilt and humiliation. These become more internalized, spread to the rest of the personality, and become aroused with every recurrent stirring of genital desires. These attitudes may prevent adequate heterosexual maturation and lead to the maintenance or revival of infantile and substitutive strivings.

There are, of course, difficult problems connected with the patterning of the genital function in the social setup, the amount of activity possible, the development of limitations and ideals without injury to the function. These problems come up in connection with the varied experiments and activities of children and preadolescents, with the problem of petting in adolescence, with the problem of sexual outlet in adolescence and adulthood. Adequate patterning can best be accomplished through explanations given at the proper time, with essential approval of the function, yet with clear indication of what is considered healthy and what could be acceptable. The last point has to be decided by evaluating the individuality of the person and the strength of his attachment to the mores of his social group. Thus the general attitude of the upper socio-economic groups, on the whole, is that masturbation is an acceptable premarital sexual outlet, while the lower socio-economic groups tend to reject masturbation as "unnatural" and accept premarital intercourse as the most "natural" outlet for the sexual needs (494). To the individual in conflict, the therapist may indicate that he does not disapprove of the patient's impulses but that the patient has to decide which avenue he will choose. This he can accomplish without fear or guilt if his conflicts are resolved.

TOTAL PERSONALITY PROBLEMS AND THE GENITAL FUNCTION

As previously stated, problems about the genital function may arise as a result of the vicissitudes of the individual in connection with the function itself, which may then lead to problems in other aspects of the total personality. On the other hand, problems may arise through interpersonal relations in self-evaluation or in the need for affection, and these may in turn lead to disturbance of the genital function.

Frustration and the need for love may lead to genital activity as consolation. If the individual is self-sufficient, this results in masturbation; if the individual has a desire for contact, it results in heterosexual or homosexual activity, at times with an otherwise undesired love-object. When there is no love-object actually available, it may be present only in fantasy during masturbation. This may occur at any age.

If there is a general lack of self-reliance and self-assertiveness, the individual will have difficulty in approaching members of the opposite sex. The result may be autoerotic activity, but with fear and feelings of guilt which prevent him from gaining adequate gratification. This is particularly apt to happen in adolescents and adults.

The individual may feel guilty and worthless in general because of parental rejection and blame, intensified by his self-condemnation over his resultant hostility toward them. Then the guilt over the culturally "forbidden" sexual activity will be particularly great. This may happen at any age.

Genital activity may be equated with obtaining unqualified affection and dependence. There is then great vulnerability to the partner's behavior because the condition for gratification is extreme considerateness. There may be a lack of assertiveness and of masculine confidence in the man, resulting in a potency disturbance.

Closely allied with this, genital activity may become entangled in problems of dominance and submission in several ways. The individual may consider the attainment of sex relations a victory, a means of reinforcing his otherwise shattered self-confidence. This may lead to promiscuity or to degradation of the sex object. He may use the sexual activity as a form of submission and ingratiation, together with the offer to be stepped on and the desire to be forgiven and not to be considered a rival. This may then lead to the fear of being overwhelmed and to intensification of all anxieties about the function. Either the victory or the submissive ingratiation may occur in relation to members of the same sex or of the opposite sex. In the former case it contributes to the tendency toward homosexuality. These developments may occur at any age.

Sexual relations may be equated with complete closeness in which all protection is absent. If this is accompanied by a fear of being overwhelmed or by a fear of approaching the opposite sex, the result may be frigidity or impotence. This may occur in adolescence or in adulthood.

If other erotic activities (such as urethral, anal, or oral) acquire the function of consolation, of attack, or of victorious conquest, they may become the strongest objects of longing and thus color sexual activity in the direction of perversion, or they may lead to frustration and frigidity or impotence. This may occur at any age.

Further problems may develop from the cultural attitude of equating strength and victory with masculinity, weakness and submission with femininity. The envy and resentment over the lack of the male organ may get entangled with the resentment and frustration over the limitation of freedom and opportunities for girls and women. A particularly harsh parent of the same sex leads to intensification of the Oedipus complex, and this development in turn increases the fear of the parent and of genital activity. Sexual identification with the parent of the opposite sex may occur if the parent of the same sex has undesirable qualities, lacks qualities for ideal formation, or is altogether absent, and if there is too great a feeling of gratitude, with self-effacement and submission, to the parent of the opposite sex. In sexual disturbances—in fact, in most neurotic patients—all of these problems form mutually reinforcing patterns, with, of course, varying accents in relative causation.

A fourteen-year-old boy suffered from intense conflict about masturbation, which he considered immoral. Since the onset of puberty he had been masturbating about three times a week, as many as two or three times on some days. His conflict was so intense in part because, beginning with puberty, he became particularly "moral," with a religious tendency exceeding that of his immediate environment. He used no obscene words and objected, up to the point of physical violence, to his classmates' using them. He was an excellent student, of superior intelligence, but was shy and self-effacing with his teachers. Although self-assertive with his classmates, he formed a congenial intellectual, but in one respect dependent and submissive, relationship with one of them. He always went to this friend's house and always at the friend's convenience. Two general features were noteworthy in his history. His father was fairly indulgent with all of the children in the family (two older siblings and two younger ones) up to their fourth year and then became very severe. The severity went so far that the children did not feel free to talk at meals out of reverence for him and out of fear of severe physical punishment for transgressions. However, all the other siblings had, in relatively small ways, challenged the father—e.g., by defending themselves against accusations or trying to lie their way out. He never did either. At the age of five and a half he attempted intercourse with a girl of his own age. It was a frustrating experience, but it was made even worse by the girl's talking about it to other children. He was in mortal fear that his father would find out about it. In addition, he felt guilty about the attempt. The full effects of the guilt over the sexual activity and of his consequent feeling of worthlessness, combined with the all-pervading severity of the father, became evident only after the arrival of puberty, in the self-effacement and shyness, the intense conflict over masturbation, the compensatory religious attitudes, and the submissive dependence on the classmate.

SYMPTOMS AND SYNDROMES

Reactions in Which Excessive and Premature Activity Predominates. It is hard to draw the line as to where the term "excessive activity" may be applied. Obviously, in married adults with equally desirous mates, it leads to no difficulty. If a young child engages in regular activity in an environment where most children do, although secretly, one cannot call it, as a rule, pathological, and it is unlikely to lead to problems. In young children, either masturbation or play with other children, in relatively permissive environments, probably has the approximate frequency of three or four times a week. This may show an increase when the child is disappointed or defiant or is preoccupied with problems of conception and childbirth. Another important determinant may be defiance of the parents and, in repressive environments, a defiant reassertion of the forbidden activity, serving also the purpose of reassurance against threatened injury. The last implies that there is fear of retribution, including castration, for the activity; then the activity is again engaged in to reassure the individual of the intactness of the organ and of the existence of the function. This is also often true of compulsive masturbators. Environmental pressure—e.g., by the "gang"—in preadolescence or adolescence may result in excessive activity, although with reluctance and conflict, for the sake of the gang's approval. A relationship, most commonly homosexual, with an adult may likewise lead to excessive activity.

A five-year-old boy was brought for treatment because of his recurrently inducing other children, boys and girls, to engage in sexual play. In the play sessions he repeatedly played games in which accidents occurred. Dolls, representing people, including his parents, were taken to the hospital and their arms were amputated. Both the child and the parents stated that he had been severely scolded when he first engaged in the handling of his genitals and particularly when he first engaged in play with another child. Both parents threatened that "it would be cut off." The activity represented consolation for rejection and for failure in rivalry with a younger sister, defiant reassertion of his activity, reassurance against castration fear, and preoccupation with the Oedipal problem.

The problems that premature and excessive activities can lead to in adolescence are illustrated by the following case:

A fourteen-year-old girl was brought to a physician because of bilateral inflammation of the Fallopian tubes due to gonorrhea. She contracted this through having intercourse with an eighteen-year-old boy, following which she infected a boy of fifteen. She was fully developed sexually by this time, having reached her full height and having fully developed secondary sex characters (breasts, pubic and axillary hair). She had been rather promiscuous for the last year, following her mother's second marriage. Her parents had been divorced when she was one year old, and she lived with her mother, with whom she was engaged in increasing rivalry and of whom she was very critical. A year before, she visited her father with the plan of staying for the summer, but they got into a violent quarrel, and the father asked her to leave. The mother was a superiorly gifted person, who, however, because of her occupation, was frequently away from home. The girl resented this as well as her mother's continued anxiety about her and the continuous pressure on her for superior performance. She frequently stayed with relatives. This was the case at the time the promiscuity started. The girl had enough trust in her mother to turn to her in the current and future difficulties and was brought by her to the physician for treatment. After the girl was cured of the infection, she continued her promiscuity and became pregnant a year later. The pregnancy was interrupted on medical grounds. A year after that, she married, without her mother's consent, an irresponsible young man who deserted her after one month. The mother, with the girl's consent, had the marriage annulled. Her sexual problems and her other difficulties (strong feelings of inadequacy and guilt, considering herself unattractive, anxiety states, superficial relationships with people, erratic performance in her studies) were not straightened out until she underwent psychoanalytic treatment at the age of twenty. The behavior of this girl was determined by a feeling of abandonment (not having a home), rivalry with the mother, sexual preoccupation (the mother's marriage), thwarted positive Oedipal strivings (disappointment in the father's affection), feelings of inadequacy, anxiety, and guilt because of hostility to both parents, and constitutional elements (rapid maturing). The promiscuity was an attempt to solve the interpersonal and sexual problems and problems of self-evaluation, through genital activity and acceptance, although obviously in a defiant, self-debasing, and self-injurious manner.

Some cases of this kind, where an even poorer relationship with the mother is accented by contact with a worse environment, end up in prostitution.

Pregnancy becomes a serious individual and social problem and is particularly apt to arouse some parents' emotional problems and make them vindictive. The unfortunate fate of the adolescent girl then may be: She has gotten into difficulties because of the parents' over-severe attitudes and lack of communication with them and now unequivocally is condemned and forced into a semi-outcast group. Parents, because of their over-severe morality and interracial prejudice, may object to the proposed marriage, institute court proceedings, insist on the girl's being sentenced to a detention home, and in that way force the child to be given out for adoption. With more coöperative parents, the girls come to a social agency, which performs an invaluable service in handling the unmarried prospective mothers, their families, and the child. In modern agencies, as much as possible, the problems are presented to the girls, who are helped to decide for themselves whether to keep the child or to give it out for adoption.

The treatment consists of discussing, with enlightenment, sexual problems, past and current traumas related to them, and interpersonal problems. Brief psychotherapy is often effective in cases where a sexual problem of relatively recent origin predominates or if it is part of a not too severe psychoneurosis. If the condition is of long standing, or if it is part of a severe psychoneurosis, prolonged psychotherapy is required. Problems of pregnancy are most efficiently handled, as a rule, with the help of a social service agency. The problem is difficult with border-line mental-defectives. Because they plan poorly and are not easily influenced, they keep getting into the same difficulties, although otherwise they are adjusting to simple forms of social existence.

Reactions in Which Diminished Function Predominates. Diminished function as a problem rarely causes difficulties with the environment except, in adulthood, with the marital partner. It has been mentioned that in otherwise normal infants in a nursery less genital play was observed than in infants with optimal parent-child relationships in private homes. In early childhood, the latency period, and preadolescence, the complete absence of actual genital play may be the result of a highly supervised environment in which there is no mention of sexuality and in which other children may not engage in sexual talk or play. This complete absence is more apt to occur in girls, in whom, by and large, there is less sexual pressure than in boys. Complete absence of genital activity is not uncommon in pubertal and adolescent girls in some environments. Those women may succeed in repressing all recognizable urges and avoid or repress much knowledge about sexual functions. The environmental repressive process starts in early childhood, as is generally known from psychiatric work and as it has been observed by Kinsey (494). Children of three, four, and five show embarrassment and evasion or shift to other topics when words referring to the function are mentioned. This process occurs not only in children whose parents have gone to college, but even in families who themselves may be in the lower socio-economic groups but who plan to send their children ultimately to college. Complete repression of genital impulses in postpubertal and adolescent boys hardly ever happens, and there is almost always at least nocturnal emission. Boys may refrain from masturbation or heterosexual contact for moral reasons or because of fear of possible consequences. Many of these individuals, men and women, perform adequately after marriage, although many women remain frigid for a long time (494). Hence the average frequency of orgasm in the adult female population of the college group is less than 1.0 per week as against a frequency among the male population of the same group of between 2.0 and 4.0 per week, depending upon age and marital status.

Patients with this type of disorder come for treatment, as a rule, for other reasons than sexual, and the problem is discovered as part of the total picture. They respond well to treatment either of the briefer or of the more prolonged type, as a rule, although frigidity in some women is a very difficult therapeutic problem, even with psychoanalysis.

Reactions in Which Qualitatively Distorted Activities (Including Perversions) Predominate. Under this heading we may include assault, exhibitionism and voyeurism (peeping), passive or active perverted practices (oral, anal, sadistic, masochistic, and fetishistic) with juveniles or adults of the same or of the opposite sex, and incest. It has been mentioned that limited experimental activity in many of these varieties is common in children or preadolescents. As an occasional practice under the temptation or pressure of circumstance, they may occur in adolescence also; but, as a regular occurrence in the postpubertal period, they are pathological, although the individual may accept them and feel comfortable about them. A preference of preadolescent boys and girls for the company of their own sex is common, and the former tend to be contemptuous of the opposite sex. Intense emotional involvements with older women—e.g., teachers—in adolescent girls, which may have a sexual coloring, are largely attempts to break away from the parents, form new ideals, and "be a grown-up" while leaning on a new source of support (207). Actual incest after puberty is rare. It occurs either in very poor socio-economic settings or in very badly disturbed parent-child situations. The various forms of activity discussed in this section are considered legally "delinquent" manifestations, but their significance and treatability are entirely different if they are part of a psychoneurotic picture than if they are part of a total "delinquent" pattern (see below).

"In the course of a five-year study of boy sex offenders and their later careers, . . . the significant discovery was made that primary or so-called true juvenile sex offenders are curable. . . . The cases included all male sex offenders, with the exception of the feeble-minded, who were studied and treated at the Children's Court Clinics of New York City from 1928 to 1934 inclusive."[1] Among the 250 cases in the study, only two boys were so fascinated by their perverse practices, along with other manifestations, that they could be considered "homosexual" in the sense of drivenness for this form of gratification. All other cases were motivated by momentary impulse, imitation, seduction, force, curiosity, or desire to gain the favor of older gang members. The boys, at the time of the initial sex offense, were between seven and sixteen years old. Even among the offenders who displayed other delinquent activities, all adult sexual failures occurred among those who were postpubescent at the time of the original Children's Court treatment, indicating that the prepubescent of this group responded better to redirection. The therapy in this series consisted of the *exposure* of the children's "offenses" to their families and of proper sexual reorientation.

The effectiveness of this "brief psychotherapy" under the above conditions, although exceptional in its extent, certainly illustrates the modi-

[1] L. J. Doshay, Male sex delinquency and community responsibilities, in *Modern Trends in Child Psychiatry,* International Universities Press, New York, p. 125.

fiability at this age period of these genital activities; usually more extensive treatment is required. Environmental correction, straightening out home conditions, and having the offenders join supervised boys' clubs are important elements in the treatment. It may be advisable in all cases to give a somewhat longer treatment. This becomes necessary in patients who have more serious psychoneurotic symptoms or who have engaged in these activities for a longer period of time.

AGGRESSIVE CONDUCT DISORDER: DELINQUENCY: CRIMINAL BEHAVIOR

The problem of delinquency and criminal behavior is in its own way as complex as some of the problems of genital behavior, partly for similar and partly for different reasons. The laws regarding both vary from culture to culture and vary in the same culture with the passage of time. What is perhaps even more important, the mores—that is, what is considered desirable, what is disapproved of, what is permissible and winked at, how serious an offense is considered to be—also vary. Going over a twenty-mile speed limit while driving is considered in quite a different light from the simplest kind of theft. The discrepancy between the attitude of the large majority of the population and the violent though irregular law enforcement during prohibition is perhaps the most striking example on the national scale. Further, in most children, attitudes and problems psychologically related to what ultimately may be considered delinquency or crime are a part of normal development. The extent of aggression—e.g., toward rival siblings and also toward the parents—in impulse and in fantasy gets very close to murder. Also, the wish to possess everything desirable, with the resultant forceful appropriation or even stealing, occurs in most children's lives. The problem of the regulation of these impulses and their socialization is a very important feature of normal development. For these reasons the evaluation of delinquent and criminal behavior has to be done on the same basis as that of sexual "delinquency"—namely, with a background of the group mores and the relationship of this behavior to the individual's total personality. It should be remembered, of course, that there is a strong overlap between sexual and delinquent and criminal behavior in two ways: many forms of sexual behavior are in themselves classified as delinquent or criminal, and the aggressively delinquent or criminal groups also have characteristic sexual mores.

The term "delinquency" applies to children up to the age of eighteen. The term "criminal behavior" applies to individuals above that age. The following discussion will center on adolescents, with consideration of children and adults as well. Delinquent behavior usually includes stealing, assault, murder (at times considered criminal even in the "delinquent" age), willful destruction of property (breaking, fire-setting). Such behavior may occur regularly or on special occasions. It is customary to classify delinquents into three groups: (1) individuals who have grown up in contact with a delinquent minority group (as, for example, in slum areas) and have adopted the customs, mores, goals, practices, and ideals of their respective groups; (2) individuals who engage in delinquent or criminal behavior as the dominant form of solution of their interpersonal conflicts (one might call this the psychopathic type); and (3) individuals who engage in delinquent or criminal behavior as one of the symptoms of a severe psychopathological condition, neurosis or psychosis. It is debatable whether and to what extent the first—i.e., identification with the delinquent group—can be considered pathological. The decision is difficult because, in slum areas, children are frequently exposed to serious traumas of rejection, neglect, broken homes, and brutality and sexual traumas on the part of parents, siblings, and playmates. The second group—namely, those whose delinquent behavior is a predominant solution for problems of the total personality—is definitely pathological. The third group—those whose delinquent or criminal behavior is one expression of psychopathology—comprises, among the neuroses, compulsive stealing (kleptomania) and, among the psychoses, assault or murder as a result of delusion of persecution in paranoia and occasionally in schizophrenia, and assaultiveness in the manic phase of manic-depressive psychosis. Certain forms of sexual behavior can easily clash with the law. They fall into all three groups if they are committed under certain circumstances or if they are of a certain nature and quality. Delinquent or criminal behavior frequently appears in combination with other psychopathological manifestations.

Twenty-five consecutive white male offenders between the ages of sixteen and twenty who were accused of offenses ranging from purse-snatching to murder were studied. It was found that eleven showed neurotic traits such as suicidal attempts, depression, excessive shyness, and anxiety; fifteen showed excessive use of alcohol; and five showed homosexuality. Twenty-one showed one or several of these manifestations (8).

Seduction or attempts at seduction of minors can occur as a result of senile psychosis or general paresis or as a regular practice in individuals who have solved their emotional problems mainly through this type of behavior. Assault may be the result of identification with the minority delinquent group or, again, a special form of solution of individual problems. Homosexual behavior in semipublic or public places may be the regular solution of individual problems, but it occurs in some individuals only in special situations of stress. The crime of passion, killing out of jealousy, should be considered in most groups at present as the result of an acute psychopathological state grafted onto chronic personality problems. Lust murder may be the result of the solution of personal problems or part of a psychotic state. If it is the former, it is a syndrome difficult to classify, for it goes far beyond neurosis and yet the individual presents no psychotic features. It may be closer to the dynamics of psychopathy or severe addiction, with the accent on sexuality and aggression. Fire-setting as a dominant manifestation probably belongs in the same group. These conditions are difficult to treat, in part because in new situations of stress a relapse may occur, and in general the patient's relapses have a tendency to revert to the same manifestations as in the past, with grave consequences.

It is of very great importance that individuals belonging to the second group gradually become part of the first group through identification. This development introduces important new factors into the dynamics of delinquent and criminal behavior. These new factors are the following: (1) stimulus effect—the examples of the other members of the group increase the desire of the individual for delinquent activity and diminish whatever repression might be directed against it; (2) relief of fear—the delinquency-directed impulses are made more intensive and more daring by the apparently fearless planning and execution by other members of the group; (3) relief of guilt—unconscious guilt is relieved because the group leader and other members plan and do things first; (4) reinforcement of self-esteem, of feeling of accomplishment through group approval and group ideals; (5) defense against the effects of group-alien influences, accomplished in several ways: (a) by segregation and group hatred, achieved by avoiding contact and by disparaging and hating members of other groups with other goals and ideals; (b) by depersonalizing symbolization—group-alien people are considered not individuals, but simply symbolic representatives of the value system of the out-group which is to be rejected and fought; (c) by taboo against code-dangerous identification: the group members may love other individuals but must never "identify" with them—in other words, may be attached to them emotionally but turn against them as soon as their delinquent code and their relationship with the gang is questioned (759).

As regards the psychopathology of delinquent behavior, the most obvious fact is that of aggression, hostility, and defiant breaking of rules and laws. The special forms of activity have special connotation. The initial motivational background may also vary. As regards the relationship of guilt to delinquent and criminal behavior, three constructions have become prevalent: (1) The individual since childhood has felt deprived and is aggressively seeking what he wants with very little or no feeling of guilt (Aichhorn, van Ophuijsen). (2) The individual is suffering from a very severe sense of guilt and acts so as to invite punishment and that way obtain relief (Freud, Alexander, Healy). (3) The individual has developed a good conscience and ideals; for a variety of reasons, they become too intense, and in defiance, or as a reaction against them, he engages in aggressive delinquent activities (van Ophuijsen).

There is commonly, accompanying delinquent, and often criminal, behavior, a strong belief in invulnerability, with the conviction that the activity will not be discovered or, if it is discovered, that the perpetrator will succeed in escaping the consequences. This attitude may be based on individual self-magnification and on group identification. The successful carrying out of the delinquent activity increases the self-magnifying attitude, partly because of the satisfaction going with it and partly because it now serves to confirm, through reality, the magic belief in invulnerability.

The genetic dynamic motivational background of delinquency, when it represents a solution of personal problems, may be the following: (1) Initial spoiling and granting of all desires, followed by excessively severe repressive measures. The combination results in an essentially guiltless, demanding attitude, with a feeling of resentment and unfairness about the later restrictions. (2) A purely permissive attitude, as a rule, does not lead to aggressive delinquency, but it may lead to irresponsible delinquent behavior like stealing and forging checks. It may lead to aggressive delinquency if the group exposure is very strong and if no restrictions, conscience, and ideals develop from the parental side. (3) Being deprived of affection, together with being criticized and rejected as against a more favored sibling. The dominant attitude here is also an aggressive, demanding one, with conscience and ideal formation. An example of this kind of development was given in connection with the aggressive conduct disorder (see page 338). (4) An early frustration in identification and ideal formation because of disappointment in the parent of either sex through the discovery or assumed discovery of parental transgression in matters of sex or honesty or mistreatment of the other parent. In the latter case, the hostility is first of all directed in the delinquent activity toward the disappointing parent. It may also be directed toward the parent of the opposite sex because this parent may be blamed by the child for the behavior of the other parent. In such instances conscience has developed, and as a result guilt may be strong, but either it is defiantly thrown over, or the aggressive act may represent the attitude, "The world isn't any good, nobody is any good. The world mistreated me. I am no good." Thus the aggression is directed as much toward the world as, in a self-degrading manner, toward the self. In such situations the motivation may have a strong sexual coloring, and it may represent a hostile, defiant act, with simultaneous or subsequent guilt and the desire to confess and be punished. The act then, under certain circumstances, may be committed in a foolish manner so that the individual is caught. The act—e.g., stealing—may be a substitute for the guilt-laden "internal" act—e.g., masturbation—which is not carried out.

One may add to this that in some instances the conscience and ideal formation proceed adequately and the child is able to master his conflicts with his parents until, partly in connection with the advent of puberty, partly in connection with the desire for self-determination and to be a grown-up, and partly in connection with the feeling that the parents demand too much and are unfair, the ideals are defiantly repressed and disregarded. It may be mentioned here that in some instances delinquent activity may be engaged in as a result of the need for self-assertion and to show fearlessness, partly as a process of growth or as an over-compensatory measure against feeling of inadequacy and too great a dependence on the parents. Unless the environmental conditions—here, mainly, the attitude of the parents—are bad, such forms of behavior are not tenacious.

The various forms of delinquent behavior may have special dynamic determination. Thus stealing is apt to represent acquisition by hook or by crook of what was otherwise denied—such as affection and love—or it may represent attempts at restitution and reinforcement against threatened frustration or of a threatened organ—e.g., the genitals. In assault and in hold-up, the element of aggressive, forceful acquisition of the same gratifications is accented. In stealing cars, the element of individual power and self-magnification may have special accent. In rape, the aggressive forcing of sadistic sexual gratification is evident, as well as vengeance for rejection suffered at the hands of the opposite sex. In homosexual assault the same elements may be present toward the same sex.

REACTIONS TO BEING CAUGHT AND TO LEGAL PUNISHMENT

These reactions include (1) defiant resentment, with the conviction of escape and resumption of career; (2) fear and guilt; and (3) a shattering of omnipotent self-confidence and group reliance. The reactions may start with one of these and then swing over into another. New group ties may be formed in the direction of gang psychology, previously discussed, and may reinforce the subject against fear, guilt, and the collapse of self-reliance. At other times the frustration going with imprisonment, as well as the fact of being caught, precipitates a serious overt psychopathological disturbance. An important determinant of this reaction, apart from the collapse of the belief in magic omnipotence, is that the world now looms all-powerful and is ready to wreak vengeance on the helpless criminal. One way in which some prisoners try to cope with the situation is either the wish to be insane or actually trying to pretend to be insane. This further complicates the problem. Probably depending on the intensity of these feelings, as well as on the patient's previous personality, several dominant forms of syndrome pictures come into evidence: (1) The Ganser syndrome, or syndrome of approximate responses (replies and actions). This is characterized by the individual's giving somewhat foolish replies, which give a strong impression of malingering; e.g., he is asked, "How much are two and two?" and he answers, "Three," is asked, "How many legs has a sheep?" and answers, "Five." The patient seems somewhat perplexed at the same time. It is particularly difficult, at times, to decide with this syndrome, whether the patient is simply malingering. It is, however, a syndrome that occurs in a hysterical type of psychoneurosis also, in which the patient certainly is not malingering. This may be accompanied by relatively childish and naïve, semidelusional statements. (2) Depression, which has the essential characteristics of a severe depression of the psychoneurotic type, with a border-line psychotic coloring. The patient, as a rule, does not have severe retardation and poverty of thinking, but the depression is continuous, with no smile occurring at any point in the interview. (3) Schizoid symptoms, with suspiciousness, persecutory delusions, and hallucinations. (4) True psychoses, particularly of the schizophrenic type. The difference between this and the previous one is that the picture is not changeable and the patient may not recover at all or only after a long period of time. The diagnosis of prison psychosis is always difficult, and frequently there is disagreement between equally well-trained psychiatrists examining the patient. There are two difficulties in the diagnosis. One is that there are no simple "objective" tests, like reflexes, for psychopathological disturbances, and the motivation of the prisoner to avoid punishment is very difficult to leave out of consideration. Secondly, prison psychoses represent situational reactions and occur in a very special kind of situation and therefore almost invariably present atypical features. The duration of the imprisonment is also of importance, because some prisoners, who give a strong impression of malingering a few weeks after imprisonment, may present an unquestionably psychotic picture several months later.

The problems presented by feeble-mindedness (because of the easy influencibility) and by the postencephalitic syndrome (because of the hyperkinetic behavior and the impairment of inhibitory forces) have been mentioned. In the following, three cases will be described to show the various types of problems and developments discussed.

When first seen, the patient was twelve years old. He presented the picture of adiposogenital dystrophy (see page 37). He had been restless as an infant, and overactive and destructive since he was first able to crawl around. He was a disciplinary problem in school. He was abusive to his mother and exposed himself and masturbated in her presence. He had a voracious appetite, bit his nails, and wet his bed. He made good contact with the examiner, but he was unable to stop handling objects on the examiner's desk for more than a minute. He would give an apologetic look when he caught himself engaging in this restless activity, only to start again a few minutes later. The father, the dominant member of the household, had some understanding for the boy but beat him violently. The mother, who suffered from anxiety and conversion-hysterical symptoms, hated the boy. In the course of a year's medical treatment the endocrine symptoms cleared up and disappeared. Psychotherapy at weekly intervals with the patient and about once or twice a month with the parents in the course of another year and a half was not of much help except that the patient developed a good attachment to the therapist, trusted him, and wanted his approval. His behavior got worse in that, together with other boys in his neighborhood, he stole tires and, later, cars. He was arrested and paroled three times. After the first two occasions he was convinced that he could continue with this activity and that everything would turn out all right. After the third occasion the judge asked the father whether he wanted to have the boy paroled. The father consulted with the therapist, who was in doubt himself whether it would not be more advisable to have the boy sent to a correctional institution. The father told the boy about this. He now was really frightened and felt guilty. He made a strong plea to the judge to give him one more chance and said he realized that, if he were caught once more, he would be a fourth offender, so that a parole would not be granted. The judge paroled him. Soon after that the patient took a job and remained the only wage-earner in the family during the 1929 economic depression.

The chief determinants of this patient's delinquent behavior were his hyperkinetic drive, rejection by the mother, the over-severe father, Oedipal strivings, and sibling rivalry. Contact with the gang was the final determinant of the behavior in the adolescent period.

Two brothers, one twenty and the other twenty-two years old, held up a messenger who was carrying money in an elevator. They both were armed with five revolvers. They were pursued by a policeman, who shot one of them, whom we shall call John, in the knee. He fell to the ground. As the policeman leaned over him, he shot and killed the policeman. He was taken to a hospital for treatment of his wound, and, when he recovered from that, he was taken for psychiatric observation because of his behavior. The other brother, George, was captured without being wounded but was severely beaten over the head. After a period of imprisonment he too was sent for observation to the psychiatric hospital. Both of them were repeatedly examined very carefully, and the conclusion arrived at by several psychiatrists with considerable experience in the field was that they were malingering. Another psychiatrist, who examined them in the prison several weeks later, was of the opinion that John was suffering at the time from a Ganser syndrome with reactive depression. He looked sad and gave few answers, and those he gave were approximate answers of the type described. When asked to put a key into a lock, he put his finger into a hole. When asked what happened to him, he began to weep, and said, "They took my sword away." At this point George presented the picture of schizophrenia of the catatonic type. (See Chapter XXXIV.) He gave no replies, did not look at the examiner, and, when his extremities were moved, either resisted or retained them in the position in which they were placed. During the trial this brother, while sitting in the courtroom, would defecate in his trousers and try to eat his feces. Both of the brothers were sentenced to death. In prison, awaiting execution, both of them presented the picture of a catatonic stupor. They were mute, lay on the cot without moving, did not attend to their bodily needs, and had to be fed artificially. A committee of three psychiatrists appointed by the governor examined them and came to the conclusion that they were psychotic.

The life history of the two brothers was very instructive. From early childhood on, the history was full of incidents of the following kind: Having been abandoned by one of the parents, they lived with relatives who were alcoholics or petty criminals. They committed minor offenses in childhood and preadolescence and had been sent to reform schools. They continued with worse offenses and ended up with the final venture. These two cases illustrate the fusion of interpersonal problems and traumas continuously from early childhood, including identification with older people having delinquent and criminal orientations, and exposure to gang practices. They illustrate the problem of diagnosis of psychiatric states following capture, fear of imprisonment, fear of punishment, and the collapse of the magic omnipotent reliance on the self and on the group, when they felt that they would be crushed by retribution.

The treatment of delinquency and criminal behavior, as an all-round problem, is as complex as its cause and evaluation. It is obviously a problem of sociology, economics, and individual psychology. The discussion here has to be limited to the psychological problems of the individual. The treatment is always a difficult one. It is easiest in the cases in which the delinquent or criminal behavior is of short duration and is part of a neurosis, but not of a psychosis, and is not of the type that we considered to be related to addiction—e.g., pyromania. It is further easier if the treatment is instituted early in life—i.e., in childhood or adolescence (see conduct disorder, page 338). The more involvement there is secondarily with gangs, the more difficult the treatment becomes. The first phase of the treatment consists of the establishment in the delinquent of a strong attachment to the therapist, often expressed by the phrase that the therapist makes himself "indispensable" emotionally for the delinquent (Aichhorn, van Ophuijsen). This attachment is based on the feeling that the therapist is kind, that he is ready and able to give the delinquent emotional satisfaction, often in actual helpful ways. One technique is this: The therapist lets the delinquent know that he is very well informed about the details of the type of life the delinquent leads and knows even more about criminal methods than the delinquent himself (Aichhorn). The delinquent is profoundly impressed and is amazed at the fact that the therapist is not utilizing this knowledge for criminal purposes but pursues socially acceptable goals. Finally, the point comes in every treatment when the delinquent has to recognize painful emotional problems. If his attachment to the therapist by then is strong enough, he is willing to go into this difficult work instead of breaking off the treatment. If the group ties are strong, this individual contact alone is not sufficient, and activities and identifications through group ties in the therapeutic direction become necessary. Thus it was found that, five years after treatment, 88.2 percent of 1000 delinquents showed no improvement (353). Another study revealed that 70.2 percent continued their criminal careers (856). "Especially in camp settings, preferably of the all-year-round type, it can easily be observed that some youngsters are ready to surrender group psychological resistances toward the person who is part of the group life."[2] Similar therapy can be accomplished in modern schools for problem and delinquent children in which there are well-trained and skillful adult leaders. All of these methods, of course, work predominantly with children and adolescents. In all modern cities, there are psychiatrists, psychologists, and social workers attached to juvenile courts, and a serious attempt is made to handle the psychological problems with the naturally limited facilities. In many less well-conducted reform schools, there is a difficult problem, because the therapeutic effect may be outweighed by the effect of reinforcement of the delinquent group code.

PSYCHOSOMATIC DISORDERS

OBESITY AND ANOREXIA NERVOSA

These two syndromes are greater problems in women, and the second, anorexia nervosa, as a rule represents the swinging over of obesity into excessive dieting, with extreme weight loss and emaciation, during adolescence. Of the two, obesity is the more common problem; anorexia nervosa is relatively rare.

The difference in sex plays no role as regards the reaction to obesity in childhood (discomfort over being called nicknames), but it does so beginning with adolescence. This is, in the main, culturally determined. In the Spanish and Italian cultures and, up to recently, even in central European countries, the ideal for women was definitely on the plump side. In some primitive cultures the acme of beauty is reached by women so obese that they are hardly able to walk. Because of the prevalent preference for slim figures, the feeling of being devalued and rejected, with the subsequent internalization of this feeling, becomes paramount in the adolescent and adult woman. For men the degree of obesity has to be much greater before this orientation becomes strong, and even then it never reaches the same intensity.

At times obesity is facilitated by an identifiable endocrine disturbance—e.g., lessened function of the thyroid (as in adiposogenital dystrophy; see page 37) or pituitary gland. At other times it is due to a constitutional factor of unknown nature. It has been found that mice of an obese strain retain isomeric carbon in their fat cells longer than those of the nonobese strains. It is not clear how frequently such a factor is present in stout individuals.

The common psychological factor in obesity is the utilization of eating for consolation and substitute gratification. Frequently, added to this, is an aggressive component in reaction to the rejection and frustration suffered.

[2] F. Redl, The psychology of gang formation and the treatment of delinquents, in *The Psychoanalytic Study of the Child*, Vol. I, International Universities Press, New York, 1945, p. 376.

This development would be natural enough in childhood and would be a continuation of the excessive sucking (and biting) described in infants in response to frustration. The environmental reaction to obesity then supervenes, and this happens to some extent even in childhood, when a child is called "Fatso" or "Slim"; not infrequently the child also shows clumsiness and difficulty in competing in sports. With this, the excessive eating acquires the further meaning of consolation for hopelessness, along with aggressive self-debasement. The patient is saying, when the problem is fully developed, "I cannot succeed with anything. I cannot get what I want. I might as well wallow in an orgy of eating." Now, in many cases, a vicious circle is set up. The patient eats excessively in order to compensate for frustration, and gains weight, and the obesity now becomes a source of further feeling of worthlessness and defeat. The patient continues to over-eat in order to compensate for this. By an extreme effort of will he may stop his excessive eating and lose weight, but the process starts up again in the face of new frustrations. Many individuals succeed in pulling out of the circle eventually, whereas others may get deeper and deeper into it, become depressed and hostile in addition, and fail in their studies and in social contact. Others develop a clowning, facetious compensatory attitude.

The devastating development for some patients is the physical consequences of the impulse. The patient eats for consolation, but the process does not stop when he decides to stop eating. It has turned into excess weight; the patient gets more than he bargained for, which requires hard application and self-deprivation to remove. This the patient cannot tolerate, because it has the meaning of the renewal of the frustration from which he originally sought consolation. In addition to these dynamics, genital and anal elements usually get added. On the woman's part, the obesity, and with that the over-eating, may come to mean rejection of the idea of being a desirable woman. It may represent for both sexes the fantasy of pregnancy, particularly through oral impregnation. Anal and urethral preoccupation may enter as a result of the greater amount of elimination during the bout of over-eating and the periodic bowel disturbance, such as cramps and mild diarrhea. The anal preoccupation may further acquire consolation value in itself or may get fused with the impregnation and pregnancy fantasies and may further lead to a degradation of the food consumed.

When obesity swings over into anorexia nervosa in adolescence, it usually starts with very strenuous dieting, attended, as a rule for a short period of time, by the same struggle. The patients go to the other extreme, stop eating adequately, and lose weight far beyond the average for their age and height. When the weight loss has gone on for some time, the patients usually become irritable, hostile, and uncoöperative, and it may be very difficult to reach them emotionally. The condition can be fatal because of the extreme weight loss or intercurrent infections. Often the condition is very close to schizophrenia.

The essential steps in the shift start with an intense reaction against the obesity because of the environmental attitude, as the patients see it, and the resultant self-depreciation. The patients further feel that they will now lose out also in sexual contact in its interpersonal and physiological aspects. The old drive toward eating persists, and the only way the patients finally succeed in overcoming it is by complete repression of the desire for food. Partly because the rejection of food still means the old trauma, partly because they have retained their sensitivity to frustration and failure, and partly because of the weakening effect of extreme undernourishment and the new form of unattractiveness, the patients feel unconsciously that they have jumped from the frying pan into the fire. This probably explains their irritability, uncoöperativeness, and tendency to withdraw.

It is not always clear why some people manage this swing-over from obesity to anorexia. It may be correlated with two factors: a somewhat better ability to tolerate frustration in general via inhibition, and events in their lives—e.g., a gastrointestinal upset—that enable them to use rejection of food and loss of appetite as a form of coping with a frustrating environment.

In both obesity and anorexia nervosa there are not infrequently disturbances in function of endocrine glands, as illustrated by disturbances of menstruation. It is probable that these phenomena are due to the metabolic disturbances caused by the obesity or malnutrition, as is the arterial hypertension observed at times in obesity in late adolescence and adulthood.

Anorexia nervosa is not always preceded by obesity, and rarely it may occur in men also.

The psychiatrist is apt to see only the more severe cases of obesity and anorexia nervosa. Many less severe cases appear to clear up spontaneously. The problem of the person who likes to eat and who becomes somewhat plump—as, for example, the woman who is approaching the menopause—is an entirely different one involving different psychodynamics.

The treatment of severe cases suffering from either condition is difficult, of anorexia more so than of obesity. It is perhaps easiest in the rare cases that one catches as they are in the process of swinging over from one into the other. In both conditions the first aim of psychotherapy is to elucidate the interpersonal problems as well as the problems of self-evaluation and the genetic vicissitudes in relation to organ functions. Soon, in the course of the treatment, dieting becomes a major problem, and the familiar vicious circle, in obesity, and the unequivocal plea of having no appetite, in anorexia, move into the center. Perhaps it is best to treat the severe cases in a hospital for a while so that they are not exposed, to quite the same extent, to the vicissitudes of daily existence, and so that, when they themselves want to restrict their food intake or to increase it, as the case may be, the burden of carrying out the decision and regulating the circumstances does not fall on them. In the course of psychotherapy, for a long period the accent has to be on current events and reactions; otherwise the over-eating gets completely out of hand and ruins the therapy. For a long time the patient's reaction to the obesity has a tendency to move into the center of the discussion, and, in addition, the patient has the tendency to maintain that if she could lose weight and keep her weight down, she would have no other problems. Many patients who come for treatment for psychoneurotic conditions have over-eating or loss of appetite with underweight as a problem. In many of these cases the metabolic problem does not take the center of the stage and gets cleared up with moderate stress and strain when the time becomes ripe for it. Occasionally the obese or the anorexia patient develops a psychosis in the course of treatment. This does not make the situation hopeless, but the intramural stay then has to be a rather prolonged one. Both conditions may still clear up eventually, although the patient will retain serious possibility of relapse. Patients with identifiable endocrine disturbances—e.g., adiposogenital dystrophy—should receive glandular treatment. Dieting in general may be facilitated by drugs that reduce the sensation of hunger—e.g., dexedrine sulphate.

A seventeen-year-old girl applied for treatment because she felt unhappy, was overweight, and began to fail in her studies. When she was one year old, her mother had had to go away for a year because of tuberculosis, from which she recovered. During that period the patient ate very badly and lost weight, but later she started to eat excessively and had been overweight since. She started to struggle with the craving for food at the age of fourteen. She was of superior intelligence and, with some weight loss, also exceptionally attractive. Yet she thought of herself as dumb and unattractive. Her attitudes revealed themselves in a repetitive dream in which she saw elephants (her obese self) and clowns in a circus procession (self-disparaging facetiousness) while she was looking on (attempt at detachment). The patient was three years younger than her sister, whom the mother had always preferred. All her life she turned to her sister for support and ideals, but the sister, up to adolescence, always rejected her. Following that, periods of kind treatment alternated with scolding criticism and attempt at domination. The sister, for some time, had been popular with men and had had intimate relations with them. The patient was both envious and censorious of her sister's activities. It also turned out in the course of the treatment that the patient had been stealing, mostly clothes, since the age of five, but she had never been caught. Throughout her school career she cribbed in examinations, but also was never caught. She had a dream in which she was eating a long piece of meat and felt nauseated. In connection with this she related an episode of oral seduction by an older boy when she was six. Parallel with the clarification of this material and the straightening out of difficulties in her family, the patient's craving for food disappeared, and her relationship with boys and girls became adequate.

A seventeen-year-old girl came for psychiatric treatment because of anorexia nervosa. She was very close in age to her sister, less than one year her junior, to whom she looked so similar that they used to be considered twins. Up to puberty she used to be overweight. At the age of fourteen she began to diet and started to be thin, at the same time feeding her sister, who was now starting to be chubby. The patient wanted to be completely different from her sister. At the beginning of the treatment the patient was thirty pounds underweight. On the Rorschach test, she saw a beautiful fat leaf in the first card and called card V an ugly thin leaf, "the opposite of the leaf in the first card." In card X she saw a clown who was putting a pillow on his stomach to make himself appear fat (self-debasement, thinly disguised pregnancy fantasy). She saw in card III "twins who are emptying garbage." Again the self-debasement, the accent on the mouth function, and the degradation of food (garbage) are quite obvious. The very poor form in some of these responses, together with the use of color symbolism in other responses, indicated a schizophrenic process. Soon after the onset of the treatment the patient stated that she was not eating at home because the food was poisoned, probably indicating dynamically a fear of retribution for her own death wish toward her sister. The patient was hospitalized and received insulin shock treatment along with psychotherapy. She recovered from her psychosis, gained thirty pounds, and was able to hold a job effectively.

SUGGESTED READINGS

On the psychology of adolescents of both sexes, see Peter Blos's *The Adolescent Personality* (100); on the adolescence of women, see Helene Deutsch, *Psychology of Women,* Vol. I (207). For a sociological approach, see Havighurst and Taba (395). A very readable book, as well as a classic, is Aichhorn's *Wayward Youth* (17). For an up-to-date handling of the problem of criminology, we recommend Bromberg's *Crime and the Mind* (127). For a survey of sexual behavior and problems, Kinsey, Pomeroy, and Martin (494) and Hoch and Zubin (421) are recommended.

PART VI

Syndromes in Adulthood

XXIII Character Disorders

WHY THE PATIENTS COME FOR TREATMENT

There are several ways in which a patient comes for treatment: the patient himself feels that he is sick because he is suffering and is in need of help; somebody else points out to him that he is having difficulties, and he accepts the opinion after more or less of a struggle; he is in complete disagreement with the opinion of the other person but comes for an interview "just to see" and then may continue with treatment or may stop. The patient may be a source of trouble to himself and to others yet lack all insight into this obvious fact. If he is seriously psychotic, he may be forced to accept hospitalization. If, however, he has retained the main features of his contact with reality, there is no way he can be persuaded or forced to accept custody or treatment.

The large majority of patients who come to outpatient clinics and to private offices nowadays do *not* present a predominant set of crystallized symptoms, such as psychogenic paralysis or obsessive thoughts. They present some symptoms that are classifiable in this manner, but these are of peripheral importance. The majority of patients come for treatment because they feel distressed, unhappy, and, at times, discouraged and alarmed. They feel that they have made a mess of some situation, have failed to achieve something they strongly desired.

Such disappointments and failures may be an inability to get married following a list of broken informal or formal engagements; difficulty with some activity, ultimately leading to partial failure in career or in finishing creative work; being jilted; falling out with friends or with the family; death in the family or among friends; some physical illness of the patient or of some member of the family, with complete or partial recovery but a persistence of the emotional stress and strain.

How do we classify these people? First we have to realize that no clear-cut rigid classification is possible, because individuals are unique and different. In each individual a habitual mode of perceiving, reacting, evaluating, feeling, and acting develops, the integrated sum of which is usually referred to as character. If one considers a large sampling of patients who have come for treatment, one becomes aware of the fact that they show certain individually predominant character traits or trends—in other words, habitual ways of dealing with life situations—which ultimately got them into difficulties. In the following, we will try to classify the various character types on the basis of these individually predominant traits. Sometimes these traits show only slight intensity, and the individual is very close to what anybody would consider, for practical purposes, normal; but some situation has developed which would mean a major stress for anybody and is particularly calculated to disturb the equilibrium of the person involved. At other times the character disorder or the trait is so intense that the individual is guaranteed to get into trouble sooner or later. There is a measure of relationship between the character disturbances and the syndromes to be discussed in later chapters. There is a tendency for certain character types to develop certain symptoms. Then the symptom simply represents a much greater intensification of the same dynamic problem that the individual was struggling with previously. At other times the symptoms have many qualities and special dynamic features which make them appear to be a new way of attempting to grapple with life problems, or they represent reactions to altogether new problems.

We will now proceed to discuss these various trends as they appear in individuals in whom they overtly predominate. All of these predominant traits involve, on close examination, all major motivational spheres of the individuals. For the sake of convenience we will group them around the foci of the main manifestations in interpersonal relations, handling of the self, and substitution of things and ideas for emotional experiences.

TRENDS PREDOMINANT IN INTERPERSONAL RELATIONS

TENDENCY TO DEPENDENT-SUBMISSIVE AND TO DEPENDENT-DEMANDING ATTITUDES

The dependent tendency shows itself as the need for emotional or authoritative support in most situations, as difficulty in making independent decisions and taking on responsibilities, and as the dread of loneliness. The dependent-submissive trend goes with ingratiating and self-effacing behavior; the dependent-demanding person can vehemently demand appreciation and affection. These features may be accompanied by an optimistic or pessimistic view of the world, either of them at times out of keeping with the individual's achievements and position. Closely allied to this is the feeling that success can be achieved only through a favorable stroke of luck, that sooner or later fate will strike back and everything will collapse.

These trends lead to difficulties in the following way: the desire for love and attention may be so great that the requirements cannot be met for long, and the patient, through his behavior, destroys the relationship which first put him into "seventh heaven."

The current dynamic background of these trends is the feeling of insignificance of the self and an intense over-valuation of the power of the other person. The hostility resulting from the patient's disappointment in the other person is repressed in the submissive orientation but is overaccented in the dependent-demanding trend. The submissive trend may appear also as an attempt at expiation of guilt, in which the benefactor forgives the aggression and transgressions of the person, restores him to worth, and gives him affection. In the dependent-demanding trend this guilt is projected out on the supportive person. Genetically, the feeling of smallness was always present as a result of a cruel and rejecting environment, or it was established after a period of self-assertive self-reliance in early life as a result of changed conditions which fill the child with fear of abandonment and injury. Or the child was kept dependent by an overprotective mother. The pessimistic outlook is apt to be present particularly if, before the age of six, the patient lost one or both parents and has been shifted from relative to relative or to institutions. The granting of all wishes by the parent without the development of adequate inhibitions, at times followed by severity in the fourth or fifth year, is more apt to result in the dependent-demanding trend.

A woman twenty-six years old, a very successful musician, showed her *self-effacing dependency* in her relationship with her teacher, from whom she kept on taking lessons, commuting to her from different parts of the country, and accepting all of her, at times, very biased opinions. She was also very sensitive to people's opinions. She showed her *labile emotionality* in connection with her sensitiveness to people's opinions: she was anxious before a performance and elated even after minor success, would feel hurt and sad over somewhat unfavorable notices, but in the end always blamed herself and felt that she should have done better or should have been more diplomatic and attentive to the people by whose actions she felt hurt. Her *compulsive rigidity* was visible in her tendency to systematic procedures: she kept her house very orderly, catalogued everything, kept lists of minute possessions and of letters she received and letters she sent out. Serious difficulties started almost immediately in her marriage to an architect. The difficulties resulted from a mutual beatific and passionate attachment. Her *dependent-demanding* and *suspicious-hostile* trend came into evidence. She felt unloved if he did not draw her into the conversation in company, if he spent one hour away from her, or if he read in her presence. She created heated scenes over such alleged slights and demanded that he live up to his promise that they would "never leave each other" (apparently not even for one hour) and that they would "lead a life in common." Her mistrust had a distinct paranoid tinge when she suspected him of affairs with women and with men if he received people individually when she was not in the house or if he visited other people. If he questioned the necessity for her cataloguing things, she felt deeply hurt. For a period of time he was very considerate and tried to behave in a manner which would allay her hurts, anxieties, and suspicions, but soon he began to find the situation intolerable. She entered upon psychoanalytic treatment, in which she presented a mixed picture. Her emotions were highly elastic; she responded most of the time to interpretations. The sources of her resentment, anxiety, and sadness could be elucidated and the condition relieved. Her need for contact, with some tendency toward dramatization in this, was quite evident. Her suspicions of her husband could also be traced and their unconscious motivational background elucidated to her. However, the dependent-demanding trend, permeating her whole emotional life in relation to her husband, proved to be impervious to therapeutic attempts. She refused to consider it in any way pathological and, while accepting its current and genetic background—her disappointment in her mother, exploitation by the parents as a musical prodigy, disappointment and guilt over early seduction—she idealized it and said, "If I cannot have the kind of relationship with my husband that we promised each other, I'd rather have none." Actually she almost threatened suicide when he suggested divorce. Eventually, however, she accepted his decision in a more or less submissive manner, at the same time holding on to her "ideals."

This patient was prevented from a breakdown through the treatment, without, of course, a fundamental change in her personality being accomplished. This latter effect might have been achieved if she had entered treatment because of occupational difficulties; that way she would have been forced to recognize that her difficulties lay within herself—an extremely difficult hurdle for her to clear. As it happened, she could blame her husband and cling to her illusory goals.

TENDENCY TO MISTRUST

This tendency shows itself in a readiness to take offense and to assume that individuals are inimical and are willing to go out of their way to injure the subject. There is, further, a tendency to take events in a personal way if such an interpretation is at all possible. This suspicious, distrustful orientation may be combined with a tendency toward anxious withdrawal or, more frequently, with hostile reactions, with carrying a "chip on the shoulder." The individual may be quite emotional and illogical about the interpretation of events in the described manner or may reason with tenacious logicality. There may also be a tendency toward dramatic display of injuries suffered. Such individuals get into difficulties because of unhappiness they bring upon themselves by shifting from one place to another in order to escape "mistreatment," or harm their own advance through hostile attitudes, or alienate spouses, employers, and friends. Symptoms developing are usually paranoid delusions. Dynamically the trend is motivated by a conviction that the world is hostile, based on the experience of severe rejection in early childhood, along with fears of retribution for hostile impulses, which are also projected onto others. It may be reinforced by repressed homosexual impulses turned into their opposite and projected out onto the environment: "I do not love you, I hate you. I do not hate you, you hate me."

TENDENCY TO DOMINATE

This tendency manifests itself through the need to have the unquestioned decisive voice in all situations. Closely allied is the need always to be right, to be unquestioningly respected. Opposition to any of these needs is met most commonly by resentment amounting to temper outbursts or by a tenacious, insistent reasoning, which may be carried out with great acuity but always leads to a foregone conclusion. The trend may be combined with generosity. The person, while dominating, wants to carry everyone's burden on his shoulders and also wants to retain control. The husband may refuse to give his wife a weekly allowance, but insist upon generously disbursing money for each individual expenditure. The subject himself may get into trouble if his domination is finally challenged, either by one of his children or by his mate's falling in love with somebody else. Such situations may lead to an intensification of the subject's resentment or to a state of depression or anxiety. Business difficulties which shatter the individual's conviction in his position may lead to similar symptoms. Genetically, this tendency may arise out of an unremitting position of dominance which was challenged—e.g., by sibling rivalry—but was victoriously handled by the individual; or the person was dominated by one of the parents or by a sibling and then later acquired the tendency through the mechanism of delayed identification with the aggressor. In current dynamics the tendency may be motivated by self-doubt, fear of being deprived, and fear of being dominated, for such people's view of the world is that one dominates or is dominated. They can be sure of affection only if they feel they have the whip hand. The trend at times accompanies homosexuality.

TENDENCY TO DETACHMENT AND SELF-SUFFICIENCY

This trend is characterized by an unruffled emotional existence, due to considering events unimportant, and by idealization of the detachment. This frequently is combined with a reluctance to lean on anybody and with having to meet all situations with one's own strength. It has two varieties. In one, the attachment to persons and events is almost fully retained, but the individual underplays the importance of them to himself. In the other, the *need* for contact and for success is intense but covered by heavy layers of repression, contempt for the environment, and a tendency toward aggrandizement of the self. These individuals get into difficulties when they meet a critical situation in which they would need another person's support. They do not admit this need, and, in addition, the other person may by then be alienated. The support is not forthcoming, and that creates an emotional crisis. Individuals of the second type described may gradually shut off all contacts and then be overwhelmed by the unconscious feeling of isolation. The symptoms that the first type is apt to develop are anxiety state and work inhibition; of the second type, schizophrenia.

The dynamic aims of the tendency toward detachment are the prevention of rejection and domination in intimate relationships and the forestalling of retribution for hostility. There is a substitute satisfaction and self-reinforcement from the idealization of the detachment. In the first type, genetically, the contact with other individuals was never sufficiently disturbed to cause withdrawal; in the second type, it was disturbed very early.

A moderately successful artist had suffered from anxiety states as a child up to the age of twelve. He was sickly as a child; his mother had preferred his two older brothers and had left his care to his nurse. His infantile anxiety state started after it became known to him, at the age of five, that his nurse was going to return to her home country. He had a close relationship with his father, who expected unquestioned acceptance of his opinions and at a later period threatened to cut off all financial allowance at times of disagreement. The patient developed an attitude of *detachment*, with ideas of self-sufficiency beginning at the age of fourteen. He was convinced that he could handle in this manner all rivalries—which he said did not matter much to him—all problems of achievement—he said he did not care much about success or failure—and also his relations with women and with his friends. He had an enormous working capacity and could be at his art twenty hours a day without much emotional contact with his wife, who was also an aloof person and sexually frigid. She give birth to a girl after two years of marriage. This child was the only person from whom the patient did not feel detached. When his second one-man show received some favorable notices but also some which were strongly critical, he expected consolation from his wife without openly showing his need. The wife was not even aware of his need, and, on top of this, she engaged in a flirtation with another man. The patient was hardly aware of the connection between these events and his "upset," mounting to distress and fear that he would never be able to work again. It soon became clear in the course of the treatment that he had an insatiable need for success and recognition. Not only that, but whenever anybody else got good reviews he felt, irrationally, that he had failed. Thus, emotionally, he had to be the only good person in his field. Further, along with unconscious submissive homosexual strivings, he had need for unqualified love and had always managed to have at least one close friend of each sex. The lack of consolation from his wife at the time of his partial success as an artist represented a catastrophic disappointment of his need for affection and of his self-magnifying self-sufficiency.

TENDENCY TO SELF-SACRIFICE

This tendency involves recurrent exertion of great effort for others for advantages denied to oneself or regular giving away of money that the individual could use to better advantage. The activities of self-sacrifice may be carried out more frequently for individuals who are more or less failures. These actions are combined with the feeling that the individual is rescuing others from misfortune or that he has no right to deny anyone anything, together with uncertainty as regards "rules of conduct," inasmuch as there are endless variations in them all over the world. The individual usually has a feeling of elation when he behaves in this manner, but the tendency leads to trouble for the following reasons: He meets with ingratitude on the part of the person for whom he sacrificed; the woman who sacrificed to rescue the man, with the hope of love or marriage, is jilted; the individual is in constant difficulties because he deprives himself of things he needs for existence; and, lastly, he may get the gratitude but lose interest in the person, whom he has over-valued up to this point, and then have conflicts over severing relations. The dynamics of this kind of behavior may be motivated by ingratiation on the basis of anticipated rejection and feeling of worthlessness or by guilt. In the latter instance, the self-sacrificing behavior follows regularly a period of hostile, destructive, and debasing actions. Or the individual feels certain of acceptance only by someone whose gratitude he has obtained; he feels he has let someone down in the past—e.g., a parent—and now tries to remedy the situation by rescuing others in difficulties. This latter aspect may have a sexual coloring and may be in part an attempt to save the Oedipally desired parent from the Oedipal rival.

A woman thirty-five years old had had four unhappy love relations. The first one was with an alcoholic whom she "rescued" and cured of alcoholism in the course of two years at the cost of time, money, and nursing care. Then he wanted to marry her, but suddenly she could see only his bad qualities, although up to that point she had idealized him. Two of the other relations were with married men who had difficulties with their wives, were unhappy, and were "confiding" in her. She set out to "rescue" them, but they did not have the decisiveness to go through with a divorce. The fourth one was a struggling writer whom she helped financially for several years and who then fell in love with somebody else. After the fourth incident she felt that she had made a mess of her life, was afraid she would never get married, and was unable to work; she decided to seek psychiatric help. The treatment was prolonged but successful.

TRENDS PREDOMINANT IN THE HANDLING OF THE SELF

TENDENCY TO EMOTIONAL LABILITY

The tendency toward labile emotionality shows itself in readiness for fleeting and strong emotions. The emotion experienced may not be a direct one, but some kind of change may occur—e.g., anxiety in the place of anger. The individual may easily get into a turmoil of resentment, fear, unhappiness, and tears. At times labile emotionality is connected with a tendency toward dramatic affect: the emotional display is greater than would be indicated by the intensity of emotion actually felt.

Such individuals get into difficulties either because they themselves are unhappy over the constant turmoil or because their emotionality and dramatic display wear out the environment. The symptoms they are most likely to develop are the psychoneurotic anxiety states (anxiety attacks or phobia), conversion hysteria or impaired potency in men, and frigidity in women. Dynamically, the lively emotionality represents not only a retention but also an intensification of the constant reaching out for human contact. Correspondingly, one of the dominant fears connected with this tendency is the fear of abandonment or absence of full human contact, and conversely the patients believe in the full remedial effect of human contact. The sexual problems connected with this trend represent a fear of genital function but with the retention of the desire for it; genital function may be strongly tied up with the desire for interpersonal contact and the desire to be taken care of, or, if the dramatic quality is accented in the tendency, then with the idea of sexual desirability.

TENDENCY TO INHIBITION

This trend shows itself in a feeling of constraint, shyness, and timidity, and in difficulty in asserting oneself. These phenomena may be present even in such minor situations as asking a soda clerk for a glass of water after he has filled the order proper. There may be the same difficulty in expressing positive feelings as negative ones. This tendency is motivated mainly by anxiety and caution; the individual feels small and vulnerable. A secondary feeling of safety is established through avoidance of open expression of impulses. Genetically, the feeling of smallness usually arises in a highly repressive environment (see Chapter XXI), often accented by guilt over forbidden genital activity. Individuals showing this trend are apt to get into difficulties because their anxieties become pervasive and seriously interfere with their capacity for working and for making friends. They may have strong repressed resentment over being taken advantage of or over being left out of social situations. The trend is likely to lead to symptoms of anxiety, depression, or masochism.

TENDENCY TO RIGIDITY

The tendency to rigidity is characterized by the need to handle life situations always in an identical way. This general tendency may be combined with excessive idealism. Then the individual himself follows strict precepts of conduct and applies them in his dealings with other individuals. The rigidity may be combined mainly with ideas of cleanliness and orderliness, as in "housewife's neurosis." The woman then requires that every ashtray should be in its proper place, everything free of dust, and all clothes hung up right. Executives at times illustrate the combination of rigidity and "efficiency": the smallest articles on the desk have to be in perfect order, stamps put on in exactly the proper place, all allegedly on the basis of efficiency.

Some rigid individuals set up "rationality" as an ideal. Emotionally they are likely to lack fleeting reactions, and, when under pressure, their impulses may come out in a rationalized and displaced manner. Thus a woman who represses her anger at her husband because she believes in "undisturbed relationships" may instead become anxious over her child because he does not keep his room clean enough; she may then maintain that this is important for his character development. The rigidity may lead to indecision, in part because the individual cannot decide which of two different modes of procedure is more appropriate in a given instance.

Rigidity may lead to difficulties because it arouses the resentment of the environment. Further, situations arise in which rigid methods of behavior prove ineffective. This is threatening to the individual and leads to anxiety, indecision, and self-doubts. Dynamically, rigidity is the attempt to cope with anxiety through rules. In case of combination with idealism, there are coping with guilt in the same manner, making the problem impersonal, moral self-magnification, and, at times, self-sacrifice. In case of orderliness and efficiency, there is also gratification from the results achieved. Rigidity is close to the mechanism of reaction formation, and genetically the trait is often traceable to conflicts revolving around sphincter training. Then desire for gratification and interest in the product are replaced by their opposites—namely, excessive cleanliness, parsimony (disinclination to give), and excessive orderliness. Hence this combination of traits has been called "anal character." It is worth pointing out that interpersonal aspects between the parent and the child play a role in this also. The child transforms his opposition to the parental request into an excessive acceptance or, in a measure, into a caricature and remedies his own helplessness by rigidity. In the idealistic type of solution, the experience in school of getting approval and affection at times becomes crucial for the development.

A thirty-year-old woman was successful as an art critic but was unable to do original painting in spite of sustained attempts. She was highly idealistic, with *rigid* standards of well-verbalized artistic integrity which she demanded that her husband, a writer, live up to also. In her discussions of ideas and methods she could never consider that she might be wrong in any of her approaches. She became critical of her husband and accused him of having "sold art down the river" when he once wrote a humorous novel. Well-polished *over-valuation of ideas,* with its loss of spontaneity and need for perfection, paralyzed her creative efforts and was also alienating her husband. When she discovered that he was being unfaithful to her, she decided to get a divorce but was unable to carry out her decision and became depressed.

She had always felt that her parents preferred her sister and her brother. She was disappointed in and hostile to her mother. She felt a strong kinship with her father, who over-valued standards and ideals, but felt disappointed in him because he was "taken in" by her sister. Her feeling of disappointment, however, was repressed. She was envious of the male. She had an intense unconscious need for free emotional expression and was tied to her husband because of his demonstrativeness and emotional intensity.

TENDENCY TO ACTIVITY AND CONTACT WITH THE WORLD

This tendency is characterized by activity in too many enterprises and contact with too many people. Individuals with this trend are frequently exuberant, but some constantly experience pressured anxiety. In some individuals of this kind, mood swings (alternation between elatedness and mild depression) are present (cyclothymic personality). These individuals may experience difficulties as a result of the chronic discomfort stemming from too many undertakings or because nothing they undertake is quite satisfactory because they "scatter their shots." Their excessive and pressured activity may create situations which alienate people who are important to them. The cyclothymic individual may constantly, during his exuberant periods, undertake many things which he is unable to complete because he becomes depressed and apathetic. Patients with this trend may develop psychoneurotic depression, chronic states of fatigue ("neurasthenia"), or manic-depressive psychosis.

Hyperactivity in these people represents a rushing into external contacts in an attempt to escape from the necessity of facing their inner problems.

TENDENCY TO SENSUALITY

Some individuals must have gratification of physiological needs—in most cases, oral and sexual—and become distressed if this is not forthcoming. Successful satisfying of heterosexual needs may be indispensable for their feeling of worth. Anxiety is channeled into fear of frustration (of starving to death, if oral gratifications are primary). This trend may lead to difficulties because of limitations in sexual success or because the gratifications tend to decrease even in case of success. In those in whom eating is of primary importance, gastrointestinal difficulties and obesity may result. The latter represents greater difficulty for women than for men because it decreases their attractiveness. The symptoms which are likely to develop include obesity (in the "oral" group); perversions, homosexuality, and the tendency to get into compromising situations (in the "sexual" group); and addiction (in both groups).

Dynamically, this type of behavior represents reassurance against strong fears of frustration. Existence and the feeling of worth are equated with physical satisfaction, which then consoles for and reassures against other failures. These patterns are apt to develop in individuals who, as young children, were exposed to a generally inhibiting, restrictive environment in which some sensual gratification was freely allowed and was fostered by the parent or offered by a sibling or friend.

A forty-year-old man was very successful as an industrial designer and sculptor. His whole life was characterized by a series of successes in which he tired of the field or the circumstances under which he attained success and afterward changed to some allied activity. In addition, he engaged in a great many enterprises, such as art-collecting, writing projects, bookstores, traveling. He was always active in four or five undertakings at a time. Many of these undertakings were conducted by people who seemed to have talent but who somehow never made adequate use of it. To these he gave generous advances, and, more often than not, they did not carry out adequately the work assigned to them. Thus the trend toward *activity,* and the generous, helpful, though ill-advised, trend toward *spending,* characterized his mode of existence. His generosity was not confined to material objects, but he was generous, as well, in giving emotional support to others. To this should be added the strong *need for sensual gratification,* which, in his case, also had, most of the time, a highly aesthetic quality. He became restless and moody if he had to postpone sexual gratification, felt tired and irritable whenever hungry, and cultivated the connoisseurship of drinks, although only infrequently becoming drunk. He could be lost in the sensual enjoyment of textures of materials, such as highly polished wood, and in the contemplation of works of art. He finally got into difficulties through the combination of two developments. One was that, finding these multifarious activities less and less gratifying, he wanted to restrict himself to sculpturing, which he could have done successfully had he been able to tear himself away from all the projects and had he been willing to incur the financial losses involved and abandon the supportive spending. For all this, however, he did not have the decisive self-assertion. The other developments were the difficulties that arose with his wife. He had been her adviser and financial supporter in her art photography. This relationship was "giving and supporting" and was very important to him. Now she became not only independent, but also financially more successful in her undertaking than he in his. His new mode of living, that the withdrawing from his activities would have entailed, clashed with her desires, but again he did not have the decisiveness and self-assertiveness to carry through. He was not aware of his hostility toward her or toward the other people from whom he wanted to withdraw his support nor of his conflicts about self-assertion. Instead, he developed a serious anxiety state which gradually incapacitated him for his work, and he was afraid of going insane and of suddenly collapsing and dying. When he began treatment, the conflicts mentioned were easily elucidated, and he responded quickly, as his emotional life was open, outgoing, and *labile.*

His parents had separated when he was two years old. He lived with his mother in poverty. He slept in the same bed with his mother until the age of eight, on one occasion exploring her sexually. He left his mother in order to continue his schooling, and she died while he was away. When she died, he experienced a great deal of guilt over having left her. His constant activity represented a search for the happiness which he missed in life, first in his relationship with his mother. His spending and giving of support were attempts to ensure his being loved, as well as attempts to undo his repressed resentment and atone for his desertion of his mother. His need for sensual experience was an expression of his search for complete, unalloyed happiness and a way of allaying his fear of frustration and starvation.

TENDENCY TO BOASTFULNESS AND SELF-CENTEREDNESS

Some individuals constantly seek the limelight, try to make themselves the center of attention, solicit praise, and are boastful. Trouble results when they cannot live up to their proclaimed abilities, which had been accepted by others at face value. Frequently they antagonize others by their constant self-promotion. When they develop symptoms, these most commonly take the form of depression or anxiety. This pattern may develop through identification with a boaster—e.g., the father—either along with the receiving of constant praise or after having been constantly belittled by the boaster. In the latter case, persons with this tendency have a deep-seated feeling of insignificance, which they are constantly reassuring themselves against.

TRENDS EXPRESSED THROUGH THE SUBSTITUTION OF THINGS AND IDEAS FOR EMOTIONAL EXPERIENCES

TENDENCY TO ACCUMULATE

The tendency to accumulate may be manifested on a major scale, in which case the individual accumulates wealth, leads a narrow life, spends little, and enjoys in life only the idea of his accumulated wealth. There may be a tendency to spend money, but on things that can be accumulated—e.g., books, pictures, or stamps. On a less extensive scale this tendency may be expressed through the careful building up of a bank account or the unwillingness to discard, e.g., old clothes. Individuals with this trend get deeply distressed if they lose their possessions; or their lives become so narrow that they are abandoned by persons close to them. Their symptoms are most likely to take the form of depression, compulsion, or obsessional thoughts.

The trend is based on things and possessions replacing interpersonal ties and physiological gratifications. The amassing of possessions guard against the fear of impoverishment and frustration into which all other fears are translated. The formula is: "If I have this-and-this much money, I am secure." This pattern may develop through the receipt, as a child, of lavish gifts which are coveted by a rival (frequently a sibling) or through early deprivation, especially in a situation where some other individual does have the things which the subject lacks. In the latter case, the subsequent behavior represents identification with the possessor. The development of the tendency may be related to early sphincter training, in which case it represents a caricature of the parental request (to retain the feces) and a defiant protection against being deprived.

A man thirty-five years old had worked himself up from very poor beginnings in a very extensive and successful career as a contractor. His mother had been the dominating member of the family. The patient idealized her and obediently accepted her decisions in spite of the fact that some of his brothers and sisters (there were altogether six siblings) had rebelled repeatedly. The patient married when he was twenty-one and had four children. He had an intense need to apply himself to all aspects of his business even after he was highly successful and had to *accumulate* larger and larger reserves in excess of what his undertaking required. His views could never be questioned in the family, and he was given to temper outbursts if he was crossed. He reserved most of the responsibility of the financial management of the household for himself and did not encourage his wife to manage on a weekly or monthly allowance. His wife fitted into this pattern with her own dependent, self-effacing personality. With this manner of management, and with the accumulation of his financial reserve, he *dominated* his environment. He was not ungenerous, however. On the contrary, he would give his wife and the other members of his family unexpected expensive gifts, always tipped people generously, and supported some of his relatives out of his own initiative when they were in need. He was deeply moved and pleased by their respect and gratitude. Thus he showed the tendency to *spend* along with the trend to dominate and accumulate.

When his wife, as a result of psychoanalytic treatment for her asthma, became self-assertive and insisted on having some say in the finances, asked for a monthly allowance and rights in deciding about entertainment, and refused him sexually when he was high-handed, he became deeply upset, thought that all his success was worth nothing, had murderous and suicidal dreams and impulses—but entered upon psychiatric treatment himself. The treatment was successful not only in relieving his immediate suffering but also in effecting a fundamental change in his whole personality structure.

TENDENCY TO OVER-VALUATION OF IDEAS

This tendency shows itself by the attempt to replace experience, action, and emotion with ideas in order to escape anxieties connected with the former. The idea that thoughts are omnipotent is apt to be present by implication, and there is a great deal of self-magnification associated with the worship of intellect. Sexual curiosity and sublimation may contribute to the dynamic background. The tendency to over-value ideas may be combined with shy inhibition, detachment, or rigidity. The combination with detachment or with an odd kind of sentimentality may give the personality of the patient a distinct schizoid flavor, particularly if the ideas accented represent a close philosophical questioning and an elaboration of values.

TENDENCY TO GIVE AND TO SPEND

When this tendency is prominent, the individual spends money lavishly on himself and on others, not thinking of the future and therefore often spending beyond his means. It is often combined with general helpfulness and readiness to take charge of crises that threaten others. Such a person is very generous when he has the means and may expect others to be as generous with him when he himself is without means. He becomes disturbed when he runs out of excess money to spend, particularly if others do not live up to his expectations of return generosity or gratitude. He may get into debt. The symptoms which are most likely to develop in persons with this tendency are depression, alcoholism, and gambling.

Dynamically, this tendency represents the desire to obtain affection or respect through gifts. If such individuals spend money mainly on themselves, they do so in order to reassure themselves against feelings of insignificance. When the tendency is combined with the expectation of generosity by others, it reflects the individual's desire to see the world in terms of everyone's generosity to everyone else and the denial of hostility and threat in interpersonal relations. The tendency is likely to develop in persons whose parents are excessively generous or, on the contrary, extremely niggardly with material gifts. Also, if the parents "buy" the child's affection, expecting affectional returns for material gifts, the child is likely to develop this trait. It may be accented by the method of sphincter training if the child defecates —gives gifts—upon request and receives gifts as a reward. Passive-dependent expectations of being taken care of as in infancy may be prominent in those who expect reciprocal generosity from others.

TREATMENT OF CHARACTER NEUROSES

It used to be said that patients with "character neuroses" were more difficult to treat than those with clear-cut syndromes, one reason for this being that the former did not consider themselves sick. However, with modern developments, even the treatment of patients with clear-cut symptoms is predominantly an investigation of conscious and unconscious trends, and the exploration of the special "meaning of symptoms" plays a restricted role. The exploration of trends, defenses, and strivings of patients suffering from "symptoms" runs into the same resistances that patients with predominant "character neuroses" offer. The patient's accessibility to treatment depends on the nature of the predominant tendencies, particularly on the degree to which they influence the patient's elasticity of reaction, his readiness to form and maintain attachments, the tenacity of his goals and illusions, and the rigidity of his existing orientation. The patient's life situation—whether it is a difficult and unchangeable one or favorable and changeable—is also of great significance. Some patients with qualitatively less accessible character disturbances give better results in treatment than those with easily accessible disturbances but with difficult life situations. It might be said of most of the trends described that a limited degree of them is favorable for the treatment whereas an excess degree is unfavorable. The ideally accessible patient is the one with labile emotionality, because the reaching out for human contact is strong, reactions and connections are easily visible and can be conveyed to the patient, and the patient is ready to accept the interpretation. On the other hand, if this trend is intense, the situation is something like writing in sand: the patient has no self-reliance, and there is very little to build on. This general statement applies also to patients with dependent orientations. With the overtly dominant trend, it is difficult to evaluate at first how deeply it permeates the patient's emotional life and how tenaciously he will cling to it. One may find in the overtly hostile patient or in one with schizoid overvaluation of ideas or in rigid patients who always have to be right and have to dominate the scene, all of which are difficult trends to handle, that underneath there is a strong need for contact and closeness. This may appear in the treatment in a fleeting way or by implication; but, once gotten hold of, it leads to loosening up and to accessibility of the individual.

SUGGESTED READINGS

For various approaches to character types and problems, we recommend the respective sections in Fenichel's book (267), Horney's *The Neurotic Personality of Our Time* (431), Reich's *Character-Analysis* (761), Jung's *Psychological Types* (473), Adler's *The Neurotic Constitution* (10), and Sheldon and Stevens' *The Varieties of Temperament* (858).

XXIV Psychopathic Personality

The term "psychopathy" is used here to refer to conditions in which the main pathological manifestation is in the individual's action and behavior, and is based on his inability to experience certain interpersonal, social, and moral values. The following features are characteristic to a greater or lesser degree of the varieties of patients grouped under this heading: (1) Lack of adequate attachment or labile emotional attachment. The individual has no strong and lasting feelings toward anybody and, while professing love and affection and considerateness, engages in acts that cannot help hurting the other person's feelings. The psychopath may obtain special privileges from a superior and then use against him the very fact of having granted privileges contrary to rules. (2) Lack of responsibility or labile responsibility. Psychopaths may marry but feel none of the obligations which most people feel toward mates and children and then may desert their families without adequate provocation. They are likely to walk off their jobs without warning or explanation. (3) Absence of or inadequate remorse after the act committed —e.g., in the above illustrations, desertion of family or walking off the job. This absence of adequate remorse is often combined with rationalized justification of the act, including putting the blame on the other party. (4) Tenuous hold on truth. In the examples given above, the individual may make up a completely untruthful story. At times, even without such a practical advantage as self-justification, he may make up lies or half-truths. (5) Impulsiveness. The lack of responsibility and the absence of strong ties, combined with the absence of a sense of moral values, result in relatively unexpected and unplanned acts. These acts may consist of walking out of a situation of responsibility or of a sudden flare of anger and destructiveness. (6) Inability to tolerate stress. This difficulty may concern a state of frustration or situations in which difficult effort has to be sustained or minor hardships are imposed by another personality. Thus, in case of financial need, stealing or forgery or the appropriation of the valuables belonging to another person is easily enacted. Violent temper outbursts or attack on a harassed and therefore irritable leader may occur with complete disregard of the necessities of the situation. For example, during an operation, a surgeon's assistant walked out of the operating room because the surgeon made sarcastic comments. (7) Repetitive behavior. The actions and attitudes of the type mentioned keep recurring over prolonged periods. They may be present from childhood on or may start about adolescence or in adulthood. In the latter cases, pathology is not absent in the earlier periods but may not have the described form until later. In some individuals, repetitive behavior is present even under the best of circumstances, and it is characteristic of them that the difficulty they get into—e.g., being caught and forgiven or being caught and punished—does not prevent its recurrence. In other patients, the behavior appears only after a turn in life situations. As long as a man works in a prosperous business for his father, he gets along well. If the father retires and the man has to run the business himself, he may start getting into difficulty.

Dynamically and genetically, the types of origin discussed under conduct disorder in children and under delinquency in adolescents can be recognized: (1) The individual, through rejection and deprivation, never developed adequate attachment to and identification with the parents or substitutes; he lacks the fundamental qualities of closeness and internalized ideals. Added to this is the hostility over the experienced disappointments, the feeling of worthlessness, and the fundamental mistrust of people's affection; the individual then decides to get, by hook or by crook, what he feels was or is being denied to him, or he impulsively rages against the frustrator or the figure in authority. (2) The individual was first indulged and was therefore not confronted with the problem of having to develop inhibitions for the sake of acceptance; then ensued a period of excessive severity in handling, against which he rebelled, developing no adequate identification and restriction, and feeling he had been treated unfairly. If the restriction never occurred, the individual regards the world as owing him the same indulgence as he originally received, and he attempts to obtain it by the same means he used with his parents. (3) In some respects the individual has a strong need for acceptance and a sense of guilt, but this is not constructively integrated with his total personality. In so far as guilt and the feeling of rejection are aroused, they get translated into irresponsible acts, either to obtain what the individual wants or in order to be detected and punished. The relative accent on these dynamics varies with the type of psychopathy. We can conveniently differentiate four general groups: (1) the irresponsible and charming, (2) the hostile and rebellious, (3) the inadequate and ineffectual, and (4) those who repeatedly commit antisocial acts.

THE CHARMING, IRRESPONSIBLE TYPE

Patients in this category form a fairly well-defined group. They are persons with pleasant manners and ease of contact, who can gain the confidence, interest, and affection of people in whom they are interested. People can become quite devoted to them and are ready to view their difficulties as due to ill treatment by the outside world and give them the devotion that they assume they need. Some of these psychopaths shift from one promising situation to another but do not carry through consistently on anything. Others manage to complete their training in highly complex and intellectual occupations but still keep acting in the irresponsible and at times highly questionable manner previously described. Some of their acts may be patently selfish in the sense that they satisfy their pleasure while hurting other people, but some are foolish in that they involve risks far in excess of what they can gain. They may act as impostors, charlatans, gamblers cheating at cards, or confidence men. Some of them are quite successful according to some worldly standards because they mix genuine accomplishments with unscrupulous practices and charlatanry.

A man of thirty-five lived mainly on money collected in the way illustrated by the following incident: He inspired the confidence and devotion of a student who was working his way through college and borrowed several hundred dollars—the student's total savings—on the basis of an invented story that his wife was pregnant and sick and needed hospital care. He finally told the student that he had borrowed the money on a pretext, and he still retained the student's affection for a long time, although he never returned the money.

If they have talent—particularly of the artistic type—which they can utilize with fair consistency, and if they can live in a world where rules of conduct are rather elastic and eccentricities are allowed or even expected, psychopaths may be able to lead genuinely full and successful lives. Frequently, psychopaths of this type become alcoholics or drug addicts.

THE HOSTILE, REBELLIOUS TYPE

This type of psychopath is quick to take offense, ready to be dissatisfied with conditions, and given to outbursts of rage. This tendency may result in acts of aggression ranging from the verbal to the physical, in the sudden throwing up of a situation, in the actual wrecking of a plant or of machinery, or in stirring up general dissatisfaction and rebellion on the part of others of the same station as the psychopath. The cause he espouses, of course, may have valid grievances. The surly, hostile psychopath can be just as shiftless as the charming, irresponsible type, and he may go from job to job, getting into fights and quitting. The violence in psychopathy can be directed toward the self also and may unexpectedly lead to suicide. Those of this type justify their grievances and invent stories and lies in the same manner as the charming type. Like the charming kind, they may combine alcoholism and, less frequently, other forms of addiction with the general personality make-up. Many merge by gradations into delinquents and criminals. Some authors

(163) limit the term "psychopath" to people who cannot fit into and cannot identify with any group, but obviously that depends upon the degree of irresponsibility. (See the case on page 412.)

An illustration of this type of psychopathy is a nineteen-year-old boy with the following history: His father died when he was four years old. He had a sister three years his junior. His mother remarried when he was five. The stepfather had a one-sided partial paralysis and was disparaging, sneering, and contemptuous toward the boy. The boy played truant from school and engaged in minor thefts, for which, however, he was never caught. He had frequent violent fights. When he was thirteen, he beat up his stepfather because, he said, the stepfather made a "pass" at his sister. He beat him so severely that the stepfather was blinded in one eye and died a year later. The mother was always very censorious of the boy and said that she wished she had never given birth to him. He left home at fourteen and worked at odd jobs. He joined the navy at sixteen, giving an incorrect age. When his true age was discovered, he was discharged. After again working at odd jobs, he joined the army, where he got into trouble in the following way: He became friendly with a girl before he went on his furlough. When he returned, the girl told him that she had changed her mind about him. He replied, "You'd better watch out. Some girls have been found dead around here." She reported his threat to the police, and he was arrested. In the course of investigation it was discovered that he had been in the navy and had not stated so on his army enlistment papers. As a result, he was discharged from the army. After some odd jobs and some violent fights, he joined the air force but was discharged from it because, again in connection with some trouble, it was found out that he had withheld information of his having been in the navy and in the army. All this only increased his mother's criticism of him. At one time, while living with his mother, he was working in a cafeteria. He started a fight with a man who "made a crack" about his mother. In rage because the owner tried to stop the fight, the patient broke up the place.

THE INADEQUATE, HYPOCHONDRIACAL TYPE

The psychopath of this type is inclined to lead a parasitic existence, expecting his family or friends to help him out, and is apt to be complaining and indignant. In describing his "injuries," his stories are often falsified and at times are completely fabricated. Such individuals frequently have multitudinous physical complaints—e.g., pains in the back, in the limbs, joints, or chest, and other minor ailments—for which there is no adequate organic pathology. When they do become physically ill, they exaggerate the intensity of their illness. A cold in the head is reacted to as if it were pneumonia, and they expect to be treated accordingly by others. Their physical complaints are used as a basis for not working. Some of them try to work for short periods, but do so ineffectually, without adequate expenditure of effort, and let others carry the major burden of work.

The various types of psychopathy described can appear mixed, so that periodically the same individual can be charming and confidence-inspiring, then surly and resentful, and then complaining, dependent, and parasitic. Furthermore, other types of disturbances may be included—e.g., the unscrupulous, cold, calculating individual or the repetitive embezzler who is neither charming nor obviously rebellious. Many of those in the "inadequate, hypochondriacal" group are border-line schizophrenics or suffer from hypochondriasis.

THE REPETITIVE COMMISSION OF ANTISOCIAL ACTS

The fourth type of psychopathy is characterized by the repetitive commission of acts which grossly clash with the accustomed social values and/or the law—e.g., rape. What differentiates this group from the other three psychopathies or from delinquency and criminal behavior is that the total personality picture frequently does not show the general disturbances mentioned earlier. The questionable actions may be experienced by the patient as an impulse against which he struggles but which he finally carries out. Some of these disturbances were referred to as "manias"—e.g., kleptomania or pyromania. A more modern term is "compulsive stealing"; but the act has rather different qualities and dynamics from compulsive actions. (See Chapter XXVII.)

Some of the most common of these acts are stealing, arson, sexual crimes, assault, and murder. The patient derives no significant material benefit from any of these acts, but he experiences various degrees of satisfaction and relief; however, guilt and self-punishment follow later. The objects stolen are not of much use to the thief, or they do not have to be obtained through theft. Thus a very wealthy person may be a shoplifter who takes only low-priced objects. Sometimes a person steals objects which have sexual significance for him; for instance, a man may steal women's gloves although he can afford to buy them; in any case, he obviously cannot use them for their ordinary purpose. At times, in kleptomania, the meaning of the act is easily visible. Thus a girl who was abandoned by her mother may steal women's articles of clothing that are always too large for her but might possibly fit her mother. Stealing these articles means, "I have my mother."

These conditions differ from the compulsive thoughts in compulsion neurosis in one very important respect: Patients in the latter group have thoughts of violence which make them extremely uncomfortable but which they never carry out.

Rape, Lust Murder. Rape at times is part of the individual's total mode of living—e.g., in adolescent delinquency. In some instances, however, it is a relatively circumscribed disturbance quite out of keeping with the individual's life pattern. He may be a married man with children, engaged in a regular occupation, at least externally without gross disturbance, and adequately providing for his family; yet he may get information about apartments and at the time some woman is alone get in under a pretext and commit rape.

Lust murders are of a similar type. The individual may be a responsible man in his occupation, and then it may be discovered years later that he had lured women to his home and then killed them and buried them in his cellar.

DYNAMICS

The discussion of dynamics applies to the general traits and to the first three types described, with accent on inadequate attachments in the charming, irresponsible psychopath, on hostility in the surly, and on helplessness, with infantile coloring, in the inadequate type. The last show lack of responsibility and inadequate attachment but do not present impulsiveness and the need for immediate gratification. The "manias"—with the exception of compulsive stealing, which in accessibility to treatment is close to neurotic reactions—are less well understood. Perhaps their dynamics are similar to those of the other psychopathies, with the difference that the more successful inhibition, repression, and social conformity in their general mode of living increases the need for a break-through in a circumscribed region. With the satisfaction attained through the commitment of the act, psychopaths of this fourth type can again accept repression and conformity in their total conduct. The satisfaction obtained in the act is often a symbolic one, along with increase in the sense of power; e.g., the fire-setter has a feeling of grandeur when he sees the flames bursting high, and the man who assaulted or killed another feels all-powerful because he has vanquished his adversary.

The problem of predisposition in the psychopathies is a moot question, and predisposition originally was assumed to be the sole causative agent. Hence the condition was called "constitutional psychopathic inferiority." There is little doubt now that the condition in some instances is brought about predominantly by life experiences. Other cases are suggestive of a predisposition either in the sense that severe stresses lead to this type of disturbance instead of others or that in addition there is an increased vulnerability to certain types of psychic stresses. Electroencephalographic findings are of special interest. They show a higher percentage of abnormalities in aggressive psychopaths—children or adults—than in the normal population and, further, a higher percentage of such abnormalities in the families of children with aggressive conduct disorder than in the general population. Some authors conclude from this that aggressive psychopathy is possibly due to early encephalitis or is related to epilepsy. Anticonvulsant drugs are used therapeutically, on the latter assumption. Other authors (Kennard) consider these disturbed encephalographic patterns as manifestations of anxiety and therefore quite different in significance from the characteristic epileptic pattern. Some authors have found the administration of ephedrine preparations therapeutically useful.

THERAPY

The treatment of psychopaths is notoriously difficult for three reasons: (1) The superficiality of the emotional attachment and the tendency to disparage are manifested toward the therapeutic situation; as a result, there is little leverage with which to maintain the relationship when the psychopath would have to go through the painful recognition of his problems. (2) There is little or highly tenuous insight. (3) The problems, instead of being elucidated, are apt to be acted out impulsively.

Nevertheless, therapy can be effective. In children and adolescents with aggressive conduct disorders, if the individual's life situation is still easily changeable, psychoanalytic therapy and/or management of the group and of the home situation may lead to success. One illustration of this has been given under aggressive conduct disorder in children. Therapy can be effective in the adult if, in spite of his psychopathy, the patient has successfully completed an occupational training and has sufficient need for attachment, self-criticism, and guilt to make a strong enough therapeutic relationship possible. A brief illustration of this kind will be given.

A man twenty-eight years old, highly regarded as an industrial personnel adviser, appropriated a hundred dollars from money collected for a gift fund. The embezzlement was not discovered. It was a small amount in relation to his salary, and the risk he ran of being discovered was ludicrously great by comparison. He had many fleeting affairs with women, on impulse, often with the wives of his friends. He never got into serious trouble, but again he was running foolish risks. Without his needing to do so, if the woman was much attracted to him and insisted upon continuing the affair, he would let her rent and pay for a room in a hotel.

His parents' marriage was his father's second marriage, and there were several much older half-siblings. His father was in business and had several times narrowly escaped being convicted for illegal practices—for example, committing arson in order to collect fire insurance. As a boy, the patient frequently played truant from school, always cheated at examinations but was never caught, and, with his superior intelligence, received high marks. He ran away from home at about the age of fifteen, took a job as a salesman, used make-up to appear older, and was quite successful. He engaged in several dubious financial transactions but either was not caught or was forgiven because of the large volume of business he brought in. He married at the age of twenty-one, after a month's courtship. Surprisingly, and this is quite in contrast with his psychopathy, he had had no sex relations before his marriage. His wife was frigid, and he was upset because of her lack of responsiveness.

Soon after he joined the army, while he was in Burma, he lived for several months with a seventy-year-old woman. On his transfer to China, he sold army equipment on the black market but was never caught at it. After his release from the army, he decided to go back to study and attended a technical college. He both studied for and cheated at examinations, getting high marks. In addition, he was active in student organizations and was elected president of one of them. His popularity with the students and with the dean finally led to the dean's recommending him for the job of personnel worker.

His marriage survived. His wife was devoted to him in spite of his impulsiveness and unreliability. They had three children, to whom he was at times unnecessarily derogatory and sarcastic. The wife went for treatment because of an anxiety state and eventually asked the patient to go for treatment also. Although his behavior in the treatment was characterized by constant restatement of the opinion that nothing was wrong with him and that the treatment was all "baloney," it soon became evident that he had a constant concern about what the analyst thought of him, felt anxiety when he arrived for the session, and even had fleeting attacks of fear, of feeling "small" on the couch when he had to relate a particularly crass incident over which he expected disapproval. Meanwhile, his wife had lost her anxiety state and had become sexually responsive. He soon began to make such remarks as, "What am I doing these things for? Why do I run around with other women? My wife is more devoted and more satisfying than any of them." With the leverage of his attachment to the analyst, his self-criticism, and his improving relationship with his wife, it was possible to work out the current and genetic dynamics of his psychopathy, and the treatment, which lasted for two and a half years, was successful in changing his orientation and behavior.

SUGGESTED READINGS

Cleckley's *The Mask of Sanity* (163) is both dramatic and enlightening. The respective chapter in Henderson and Gillespie (402) is recommended, as is also Bromberg's *Crime and the Mind* (127).

XXV Reactions to Shock, Threat, or Bodily Injury (Traumatic Neuroses)

The syndrome occurs after any event which is interpreted by the individual as a sudden threat to existence—usually, a close approach to death. Such a trauma seems to demonstrate to the individual that his confidence in himself and in his ability to handle the problems of life, his picture of the world as a safe place that he can count on, are false, that in reality he is entirely helpless to control the forces of life, and that the world is an extremely dangerous and fearful place. The condition arises most commonly after accidents and, in its severest form, as a result of experiences in war. Hence it is often called "shell shock" or "war neurosis." (See Chapter XXXII for further discussion of war neurosis.)

The symptoms are various, for there are many forms of traumatic neurosis. Characteristic of milder cases, however, are irritability, excessive perspiration, trembling of the hands, sensitiveness to noise, dizzy spells, tics, nausea, and sometimes vomiting. The patient tires easily and his efficiency is generally impaired; it sometimes disappears almost entirely. In more severe cases—shell shock, airplane accidents—there may be various paralyses, speech disorders, disturbances of walking, severe attacks of dizziness, confusion, fugues, sometimes even convulsions. The patient may not be able to walk, talk, or feed himself. Perhaps most characteristic of all are the dreams; they are terrifying nightmares in which the patient repeats the original traumatic experience again and again, or is annihilated in one catastrophe after another, or is repeatedly frustrated in many ways.

It must be emphasized that the symptoms are the result, not of physical damage, but of the disruption of the personality. These symptoms are seen in physically wounded individuals, but they occur in exactly the same form in people who are unharmed physically.

Probably everyone has at some time experienced a mild temporary traumatic neurosis—the result of an automobile or train accident, a fire, in fact of any event that brings to mind the possibility of death. Although the symptoms here are the same as those found in the "abnormal" cases, they last only a few hours or days, whereas the latter may persist for years or even permanently. Why one person shakes off the experience quickly while another succumbs completely is not known.

A middle-aged woman driving an automobile at night was hit head on by another car that suddenly swerved to her side of the road. The other driver had fallen asleep at the wheel. Amazingly, neither driver was hurt, although both cars were smashed. The woman was not even bruised.

A few minutes after she got out of the car, she was overtaken with such violent trembling and weakness that she collapsed and started weeping. Later this was succeeded by a mild but persistent nausea, which came whenever she looked at the wrecks. She had the strong impulse to flee from the situation but was able to control herself.

She could eat nothing until the next evening, and she spent a sleepless night thinking about the accident and what it meant. She had been driving for twenty years and had never had an accident because she was a very careful driver. But what did her care avail her if her fate was not in her own hands? She felt very foolish in having been over-confident, and she was extremely perturbed by the thought that her existence was a matter of mere accident. She relived the accident again and again, particularly the moment before the crash when she had expected to die.

For almost a week thereafter her sleep was disturbed by recurrent nightmares, which slowly calmed down toward the end of the week to frustration dreams in which she tried again and again to build a house which collapsed repeatedly. She would wake from these dreams trembling and perspiring. During this period her work suffered. She was extremely jumpy; a sudden noise made her gasp and made her heart beat rapidly.

She recovered almost completely without help from anyone, and was able later to laugh at the episode. No change in personality was noticeable. She was a little more likely to jam the brakes on suddenly and completely if anything untoward happened while she was driving. Beyond this there was no change in her driving.

PSYCHODYNAMICS OF REACTION TO TRAUMA

While this syndrome has been known for a long time, only a few authors (Rivers, Freud, Kardiner) have studied its psychodynamics. Rivers interpreted it as a way of dealing with repressed emotions. This is not incorrect but is certainly incomplete. Freud was so impressed with the character of the dreams of shell-shocked soldiers that he reorganized his whole theory of psychoanalysis. He had thought that all dreams were wish-fulfilling, and that, more generally, all reactions were pleasure-seeking; but this is obviously not so in the traumatic neurosis. This discussion is largely based on Kardiner's studies of the psychodynamics of these reactions.

Because of his evaluation of the world as a threatening place, the traumatic patient's vital physiological and psychological functions become inhibited, partly to protect himself from further hurt. The inhibitions are usually concerned with those activities which were related to the traumatic event. Thus the patient is unable to carry on activities which he resorted to in the traumatic situation or any activities that resemble them. At the same time he avoids situations which remind him of the traumatic one, such as accidents or near accidents. When he is faced with such a situation, his symptoms become acute. There is no substitute for walking, standing, sleeping, or eating, the functions that are inhibited or destroyed in traumatic experiences. The individual is deprived of the fundamental abilities upon which rest the most primitive feelings of self-esteem and security. Hence it is easy to understand why he perceives the world as overwhelmingly hostile and dangerous and himself as helpless. This is the meaning of the catastrophic dreams. In fact, we may think of the traumatic neurosis as an actual catastrophic breakdown. Furthermore, the patient feels resentful toward the world that threatens him; as a result, he fears counterattack. He may revert to childlike mechanisms and in severe cases may have to be cared for like an infant. This type of device, together with the care received, gives him a measure of security but perpetuates his helplessness.

TREATMENT

Milder cases improve with weekly interview therapy. Sedative medication is also helpful. In severe instances the patient has to be seen more frequently and over a longer period. He must be made aware of the fact that he has an altered conception of the world and of himself, and that this change originated with the traumatic experience. The reflexly defensive character of the syndrome must be demonstrated to him, and he must have a clear understanding that, in this, the syndrome defeats its own ends. Depending on various factors, the condition may last a few weeks or may be partly permanent.

SUGGESTED READINGS

One of the best readings on traumatic neurosis is the chapter on dreams in Freud's *New Introductory Lectures on Psychoanalysis* (308). A penetrating but complex discussion of the problem is Kardiner's *The Bio-Analysis of the Epileptic Reaction* (582). It would be interesting to compare these with Goldstein's concept of catastrophic breakdown (357, 358).

XXVI Reactions in Which Neurotic Affects Predominate

ANXIETY HYSTERIA

Fear (or a similar emotional state, such as concern, worry, anxious anticipation) is one of the commonest psychopathological symptoms. Often this state and its accompanying discomfort are low in intensity, but they may be almost continuous. The patient may feel concerned, worried, or afraid about practically everything, important and unimportant. A woman may be continually afraid that her child or her husband will become ill or have an accident. In other instances a patient vaguely anticipates considerable trouble and misfortune even though there is little justification for it; for example, a mother expects her child to develop pneumonia although he has only a slight cold, or a person suffers a slight scratch and worries about blood-poisoning. In such cases the fear may be fairly intense. It may be even more intense periodically if, because of some slight bodily discomfort, the patient thinks that he has tuberculosis or heart disease.

There are other cases, however, when the individual is suddenly thrown into a state of intense fear which lasts a few minutes or even less and then subsides. This is known as an anxiety attack. Such attacks are frequently the predominant complaint of a sick person. They may occur several times a day or once a week or even less often.

These attacks are extremely disquieting. During one the patient may be afraid of dying, "going insane," or having heart disease, tuberculosis, or cancer. In still other instances he is gripped by anxiety without knowing why. He may feel that the walls are closing in on him, that he is a small thing in a gigantic, threatening world, that he is trapped in some place—e.g., on a boat, with no possibility of getting off—or is alone on a great height, with the huge world around him. The fear may be coupled with the desire to jump out of the window.

Anxiety attacks are often accompanied by bodily manifestations, such as palpitation, rapid heart rate, pain around the heart, difficulty in breathing, feeling of suffocation, nausea, perspiration, coldness of the extremities, need to urinate or to defecate, dizziness, choking sensation (lump in the throat), bodily tremors, sudden weakness, belching, need to clear the throat, or headaches. These symptoms may be manifest even when the patient has no conscious feeling of anxiety, or the anxiety attack may be accompanied by a disturbance in only one organ, such as difficulty in breathing or palpitation.

ANXIETY ATTACKS AS REACTIONS TO STRESS SITUATIONS

A patient who was under analysis had no cigarettes to offer a visitor at his home. He put on his hat and started out to get some. His wife asked him where he was going and, when he told her, said, in a hurt and angry manner, "We decided to save money; don't go for the cigarettes." The patient's feelings were varied and largely unconscious; he felt that she was dominating him, he was ashamed at being scolded before the visitor, and he became angry at her; but he went for the cigarettes. While he was out, he began to have difficulty in breathing; it continued, but he controlled himself until the visitor had left. He and his wife then had some further discussion about expenses, whereupon he began to have considerable difficulty in breathing, became very anxious, and feared that he was dying. Still later he had a fantasy that he would hang himself in the bathroom and that his wife would be grief-stricken when she found him dead in the morning.

The patient's anxiety attack thus had as its most immediate source the fear of the consequences of his anger: "I became angry at the person upon whom I am absolutely dependent, and by being angry at her I endanger my whole existence." He then expressed his helplessness, and his anger as well, in the form of the anxiety attack, as if saying, "I am helpless, have pity on me"; and also, "See what you have done to me."

Attacks of anxiety do not represent a sort of foreign body in an individual who is otherwise emotionally well. Detailed study always shows that he has other disturbances also, in interpersonal relations, in his work, in the functioning of various organs. The locus and extent of these disturbances may vary considerably from one patient to another. The personality make-up of these patients likewise varies; for example, they may be conscientious and ambitious or careless and irresponsible. Most frequently their general emotional make-up shows considerable elasticity[1] and is outgoing. They are apt to respond emotionally to most situations of either stress or pleasure, although this may not show in their behavior.

In a study by Welch and Kubis (962), the rate of conditioning and the stability of the conditioned response (psychogalvanic reflex) were studied in a group of twenty-two normal subjects and twenty-four patients who presented a clinical picture of anxiety. The nonconditioned stimulus was the sound of a buzzer; the conditioned stimulus was a nonsense syllable. The patients required a fewer number

[1] That is, they react emotionally in accordance with various situations, instead of sailing through all situations with no reactions, or always reacting to everything in only one way, such as rage.

of trials to respond with the psychogalvanic reflex to the nonsense syllable, and there was a tendency for their responses to persist longer than in normal subjects.

PSYCHODYNAMICS OF ANXIETY ATTACKS

The fact that anxiety attacks occur in response to important events in the patient's life and that various bodily functions may be disturbed makes it clear that the individual's whole personality and its functions are involved in such an attack.

1. The anxiety attack is the closest approximation to the catastrophic state which most patients anticipate unconsciously. The patient's self-evaluation is chiefly a feeling of helplessness; the catastrophic expectation is chiefly injury and abandonment. The injury may concern the entire body or one part of it; the unconscious expectation of injury to the genital organs is common. It may also take the form of complete paralysis, of being immobile while destroyed by uncontrollable forces. The abandonment which the patient fears and experiences in his attack may embody complete loss of love and emotional isolation, or the refusal of all help and protection where vital needs and physical safety are concerned. A vital need which the patient commonly experiences as being threatened is the obtaining of food. For example, he may become angry at someone. If he considers himself helpless and the other person all-powerful, he may unconsciously fear that the other one will deprive him of food, even though consciously he recognizes this to be a ridiculous idea. Food here is equated with love and help. Fears of catastrophic humiliation, disapproval, and condemnation may also be present in the anxiety attack; but injury, abandonment, and the withdrawal of love usually predominate.

2. In the anxiety attack the patient experiences an intense emotion openly. In so far as the attack partially represents a near-catastrophic expectation or experience, it has no goal; almost always, however, there is also a definite goal. By means of his anxiety attack the patient emphasizes his helplessness and unconsciously appeals for help. Thus his chief method of dealing with the threatening situation is an open, dramatic appeal for help. This is why anxiety attacks are most frequently a predominant complaint in people whose emotional life is adaptable, changeable, nonrigid, and open. However, this is not always so, for occasionally these attacks are almost the only overt emotional manifestation in individuals who otherwise are detached and attempt to repress all their emotions (1008).

3. Insight into the emotional factors leading to the anxiety attack is always inadequate, for repressed emotional factors are always connected with it, the most frequent ones being anger and hostility. The patient may be entirely unaware of any resentment in certain situations, and he may reject the idea that he is angry; but he has an anxiety attack. Only after considerable therapeutic work will he realize and acknowledge his anger.

Other impulses which may be completely repressed are submission, sexual impulses, superiority.

In so far as the patient is afraid of the consequences of these impulses, he is, as a result, really afraid of his own impulses.

4. Revivals of earlier forms of behavior and reactions (regressive phenomena) are often observable in anxiety attacks, or in the patient's attitudes which are connected with or lead to these attacks. The need and desire to obtain reassurance and safety by being fed or completely cared for, as by a protective parent, are frequent. Such a patient is often found to have been particularly anxious as a child, to have had anxiety attacks at an early age, and to have expressed his conflicts and tried to obtain parental help by means of them.

TREATMENT

Shorter treatments, such as a series of interviews, can be very effective with patients whose dominant complaint is anxiety attacks, particularly if their general emotional reaction pattern is open, not detached. The patient may experience considerable relief after the first visit; if he continues treatment after the most distressing symptoms disappear, there is often marked improvement in other functions. For example, his work may improve; the woman who was unable to love her husband may find that she now is able to do so. Occasionally, partial frigidity disappears, particularly if, as a result of treatment, there is open discussion between coöperative mates.

Psychoanalytic treatment is also very effective for these patients. A very remarkable change can often be observed in their work, in their interpersonal relations, and in their organic functioning. One man, who was of the passive type, who preferred masturbation to intercourse with his wife, and who was afraid to show initiative and ambition, attained normal potency and a healthy emotional attachment, and became one of the best-liked men in his field, after analytic treatment.

Patients with longstanding anxiety attacks who in general are strongly repressed emotionally or whose life circumstances are very unhappy present difficult therapeutic problems. Psychoanalysis can be effective here also, although the results may not be as brilliant as in the case just cited. Group therapy is also partially effective.

REACTIONS IN WHICH FEAR OF A SPECIAL SITUATION PREDOMINATES (HYSTERICAL PHOBIA)

Hysterical phobia is characterized by an overwhelming fear of special situations, such as closed or open spaces, heights, subways, animals, the dark. Most people have relatively unimportant fears of this type, but in some individuals these fears become so intense as to be overwhelming.

PHOBIC SYMPTOMS AS REACTIONS TO STRESS

Like the anxiety attacks just discussed, the phobia represents a definitely patterned reaction to stress. Once the reaction pattern is fully established, it is more difficult to see the connection between it and the stress of daily events than in the case of anxiety attacks. There are two reasons for this:

1. The phobic patient unconsciously disconnects the reaction from the stress causing it; he (or she) reasons as follows: "I am afraid only of going out on the street; I fear nothing else. My fear is something with which I have nothing to do; it is entirely beyond my control. The reason for my fear is not that I want to leave my husband because of the way he treats me; it is not true that I want intimacies with other men because I am angry at him or because I need a more affectionate and dependable mate. My fear is the completely unsubstantiated fear of going out on the street. I am an invalid, and I must be helped."

Thus the patient can be said to displace or project the fear of an impulse or of its consequences onto an external situation. This displacement at times takes the form of symbolization. Thus being alone on a height or in any high place may come to represent abandonment, with the threat of catastrophe. For example, a man may have a disagreement with his father which is not immediately followed by fear; that may, instead, appear later when he is going up in an elevator in a tall building. If he is working in a high place, he becomes utterly unable to work. The true reason for his inability is completely hidden; he knows only that he cannot work in a high place. In some phobic reactions, particularly in children, large animals may represent the father or the individual of whom the patient is afraid.

2. The phobic patient attempts to prevent the occurrence of the dangerous situation. Thus the woman mentioned above develops fear, not after attempting to flirt with strange men, but before going out on the street. This means that the connection between stress and fear is further hidden.

In reality, the interaction between the patient's unconscious attitudes and the activities of his daily life constantly renews his emotional reaction pattern of disappointment, anger, and feeling of helplessness. It is this fact, together with his tendency to prevent situations of stress and to blame the external situation instead of his reaction, which maintains the phobia.

The general personality make-up of the patient with phobic reactions varies; but it usually shows the same outgoing and elastic emotional traits as that of the patient with anxiety attacks. If the phobic reactions have lasted for some time, the patient usually becomes more rigid emotionally, and generally fearful and anxious; he tends to shut out of awareness all emotions except those that are entirely approved of.

Patients with phobic reactions often have either fleeting or continuous disturbances in various organic functions—headaches, dizzy spells, gastrointestinal troubles, etc.

PSYCHODYNAMICS OF PHOBIA

The patient's self-evaluation is chiefly helplessness; his catastrophic expectation is of injury and abandonment, as in anxiety attacks.

The purposive aspect of the phobic reaction is stronger than in anxiety attacks. The displacement is strong, and the connections between the situation of stress, the hidden impulses, and the subsequent reactions to these impulses are hidden. The patient's statement of helplessness and appeal for help are likewise stronger. The patient who is afraid to cross the street or ride in the subway can often do these things if he is accompanied by someone close to him; his dependence is thus safeguarded. Sometimes another unconscious purpose may be detected in a phobia. In subtle ways the patient can express hostility if he wishes, and thus obtain vengeance on and domination over the individual whom he forces to be at his side. Thus the wife who forces her husband to be with her in this manner secures his help and at the same time tortures him.

A patient with phobic reactions attempts to cope with certain problems by carefully avoiding them. As we shall see, this tendency to systematic and carefully controlled behavior is not as marked as it is in patients with obsessional reactions, but it is definitely present.

TREATMENT

The treatment of phobic reactions is more difficult than that of anxiety attacks, particularly if the condition has lasted for some time.

Psychoanalytic treatment often has brilliant results, especially when the patient is of the outgoing emotional type. However, this treatment may present difficulties if the patient is unable to come to the therapist's office by himself, but must be brought by someone else. His phobic symptoms may become worse during crucial conflict situations and his behavior toward his escort be objectionable. If, because of his own conflicts or antagonism, the escort refuses to coöperate or becomes pugnacious, the patient may not tolerate him. Because the patient's external circumstances are therefore more significant than they are in the case of anxiety attacks, direct contact with the patient's relatives and with his environment may be indispensable for the therapist. Often enough, such difficulties interrupt the interviews or even make them impossible. Institutionalization may be necessary for such cases.

A girl of twenty-five was afraid to be alone at home (claustrophobia) and to go alone more than one block away from home (agoraphobia). These conditions were of one year's duration when she applied for treatment. She occasionally had mild spells of dizziness and was often constipated.

From early childhood the patient never felt that she was loved for her own sake, that she had any strength within herself. Her attachment to her mother was strong, but she felt that her mother did not really care for her, but used her against her father. Her attitude toward her father was likewise split. She wanted his affection, but she felt that by accepting it she would lose more because she would be deprived of her mother's affection. She felt fairly secure in school and worked well. Her mother's death, when the patient was sixteen, was followed by a period of depression because she realized for the first time her absolute need of the support that she had lost, and also because of her guilt at her previous hostility toward her mother. In the years that followed she achieved a fairly satisfactory relationship with her father. She stayed home to keep house. She had more of his affection than before, but at the same time she could dominate him by forceful insistence on household routine and thus satisfy whatever resentment she had toward him. She formed no attachments with young men because she unconsciously anticipated trouble similar to that she had experienced with her parents. Furthermore, she was afraid of new relationships because she would have no protection. She was afraid of the genital function because of her insecurity, the idea of submission and domination, and the fear of being injured in retribution for her anger toward men (first experienced toward her father). When she was twenty-five, the father developed pneumonia. His illness represented a serious threat to her both because his death would deprive her of needed support and because of her guilt and consequent fear of retribution and abandonment resulting from her resentment toward him. His passing contact with another woman at the resort where they went during his convalescence aroused the daughter's fear that he might marry this woman, and she would thus be abandoned by the one person on whom her whole existence depended. When he returned to business, his leaving the house represented a constant renewal of this threat of abandonment, and she developed her phobia.

This patient received interview therapy for six months, during which time she improved about 50 percent. Further improvement was impossible because the father really did not want her to become more independent of him; for example, he never wanted her to go out in the evening. He would not consent to her being given psychoanalytic treatment.

REACTIONS IN WHICH (PSYCHONEUROTIC) DEPRESSION PREDOMINATES

This type of reaction is characterized by the feeling of sadness and discouragement, which is present most of the time although lifting for brief periods. Most patients with character disorders who come for treatment feel perplexed and helpless, but the patients being discussed here are more deeply discouraged; they look downhearted. The patient may have suicidal thoughts, but he really does not consider suicide. He feels fatigued, lacks adequate drive, and feels that he is a failure. There is some difficulty in concentrating, which may result in impairment of work where sustained effort—as in studying—is required. This may have as much to do with preoccupation with his feelings of sadness as with actual difficulty in thinking. Weeping spells are common and may occur on slight provocation. He may suffer from loss of appetite or may eat excessively in order to compensate for feelings of loss of love and abandonment.

The neurotic type of depression differs from the depressed state in manic-depressive psychosis (see Chapter XXXIII) in that the individual does not have delusions and is able, on appropriate occasions, to smile. It is usually not accompanied by loss of weight or by constipation, as is psychotic depression. At times the depression is accompanied by obsessive thoughts. There are some border-line cases which verge on a psychosis, either manic-depressive or schizophrenic. (See Chapter XXXIV.)

Neurotic depressive reactions most commonly occur in persons with elastic emotionality, except in cases of prolonged mourning. It occurs most frequently in women. While it does occur in men, they are less willing to give in to it, and the reaction is apt to be masked, showing itself mainly through fatigue.

This reaction may be precipitated by disappointment in a love relationship, the death of a loved one, or frustration in some important goal-seeking activity, such as not getting a job which the patient feels is important for his future career. Dynamically, the feeling of loneliness is dominant and is accompanied by feelings of abandonment and hopelessness. The last very often turns into the feeling that some lack in the individual himself leads to failure. At times, aggression, directed toward the self, plays an important role. The symptom includes an appeal of helplessness. In childhood these patients frequently experienced rejection and abandonment (at times through death) by the parent. There may be a close relationship to the mouth and/or the genital functions. The former is seen in the patient's eating behavior: food represents affection, and the loss of appetite is symbolic of the rejection of the (disappointing) love object; over-eating, on the other hand, represents a substitute for the (unobtainable) affection. The relationship to the genital function is present in two ways: (1) the rejection may be taken as a punishment for forbidden genital activity; (2) the genital function represents complete care and complete acceptance by the other person.

A woman of twenty-four came for treatment because of weeping spells which began shortly after she came to New York, a strange environment for her, to work. She had difficulty in making friends and felt lonely. Her parents had wanted a boy and felt disappointed when the patient was born. Her mother would bargain for her affection, expecting special demonstration of gratitude whenever she bought the patient something—e.g., a new dress. The patient was exceedingly shy, being too timid to approach her playmates when she saw them playing on the street. Although she had overcome her shyness to a large extent by the time she reached adulthood, she still had difficulty in making social contacts. When she was a child, she occasionally had fantasies of growing old and dying. At about the age of nine she began to have extensive fantasies, which continued throughout her adolescence but were considerably diminished afterward. These were romantic in theme and had a masochistic quality in that they usually involved a near breakup in the love relationship. She became fat in early adolescence and was therefore unattractive. At the age of eighteen she started to lose weight. During this period she fell in love, but, after several months' courtship, the man decided he did not want to marry her. She reacted to this with depression and had weeping spells over a period of about six months.

TREATMENT

The psychoneurotic type of depression usually responds well to brief psychotherapy and particularly to psychoanalysis. The depression may lift very quickly, but passing recurrences in the course of the treatment are not infrequent. Fundamental change in the patient's orientation—e.g., a giving up of stubbornly held illusory goals—can be accomplished but is at times a long drawn-out process.

In very severe psychoneurotic depressions a few electric convulsive treatments, three or four, may be helpful in hastening the patient's recovery and making him more accessible to psychotherapy. Some consider this use of "shock" treatment controversial. Where phobic anxiety is present, the use of ECT is definitely contraindicated, as it may intensify the anxiety.

SUGGESTED READINGS

See Chapter XXVII.

XXVII Reactions in Which Obsessions and Compulsions Predominate

In obsession and compulsion neuroses, the patient's chief discomfort arises from thoughts which he does not accept yet cannot avoid, and from actions which he cannot resist. He may consider them silly and ridiculous, or exceedingly painful or humiliating, and shrink from them in horror. If he attempts to resist the compulsion, he becomes extremely uncomfortable and may even suffer a violent anxiety attack. He may be incapable of any sustained or constructive activity because the major portion of the day is devoted to compulsive acts.

Doubt and indecision may be an important factor. The patient may become vacillating, hesitant, and so uncertain of himself that he is unable to make any decision (abulia). In some cases this completely incapacitates him for any normal activity, such as business or education.

Such a patient may have a terrifying thought which he attempts to counteract by a specific action. For example, if he thinks that he has picked up some germs on his hands, he may feel compelled to wash his hands. In fact, hand-washing is one of the most common compulsive acts; it may be carried to such an extreme that the hands become irritated and painful. Similarly, if he thinks of killing someone or of someone's death, he may fear that this will cause that individual's death; he thereupon is compelled to utter a word or phrase—"God save Mother," for example—or to make certain definite movements with his hands, such as folding them in prayer.

Compulsive actions are manifold. The patient may be unable to sleep unless his pillows are arranged in an apparently senseless way; he may have to return to his house several times to assure himself that all the gas jets are closed or that no windows are open—this in spite of the fact that he checked them carefully before he left the first time. Compulsive acts may interfere with the patient's work, or even endanger his life: a pianist had to interrupt his playing frequently to wash his hands, and an army officer had to stop frequently to look for papers in his pocket, even if this meant holding up an attack he was leading.

Minor compulsive thoughts or acts are rather common in many people. The above description applies to cases in which the individual is definitely disturbed, if not incapacitated.

A variety of personality features is encountered in obsessional reaction types. Some of them, among which are the following, occur relatively more frequently and can be assumed to have some relationship to the dominant symptom.

1. Extreme orderliness, together with excessive cleanliness, stubbornness, and stinginess (Freud). The tendency to arrange and put things in order, when accompanied by an emotional conviction of the usefulness of this behavior, may be of some social value, but it may be annoying to other individuals and seem quite ridiculous to them. One of the most common examples is presented by those housewives who expect everything in the house to be spotless all the time, and who feel that every chair, napkin, book, and ashtray must *always* be in its proper place. Such patients have no insight into the pathological aspects of these character traits. This is well brought out by the amusing story of the university librarian who was hurrying so much that he bumped into a member of the faculty. His eyes gleaming, he explained that every book but one was now safe in the library stacks and he was hurrying to take that one away from the person who had it.

2. A strong idealistic trend, with great conscientiousness and tenderness and considerateness toward almost everyone. These features also are fully approved of, and they have very useful social aspects, but they are carried to extremes in patients. The patient may expect himself and others to be motivated only by idealistic impulses, never to become angry but always to settle everything by reasoning, always to treat everyone considerately, and always to understand and forgive. His emotional reactions may be quite definite and outgoing, but usually there is also considerable emotional rigidity.

The above character traits are often combined with their opposites, and the picture then becomes exceedingly contradictory. On the one hand, the patient is clean and orderly; on the other, he at times neglects his duties or keeps part of his life in a disordered state. Thus his house may be spotlessly clean, but in a closet he may keep a disordered pile of old, filthy rags. The considerate and conscientious patient with high ideals may engage in irresponsible acts and be openly unfair and cruel. He may be annoyingly overlogical in some respects, and in others be completely ruled by superstition.

Patients whose dominant symptoms are obsessional reactions are usually also troubled by disturbances in various organic functions such as elimination, appetite, and eating, may have spells of dizziness, headaches, etc. The exact relation of these bodily symptoms to obsessions and compulsions is not known; a reasonable assumption is that they are, in part, products of great physical and psychic tension.

PSYCHODYNAMICS OF COMPULSIONS AND OBSESSIONS

The obsessive-compulsive personality attempts to achieve security by arranging his world in an orderly, regular way that he can count on, so that nothing unexpected can happen. He attempts to live by rules and regulations rather than by spontaneous decisions.

In spite of his self-devaluation, the patient with obsessional symptoms may attempt to establish close relationships with other individuals. He may, however, be irritating because of his rigid manner, his insistence on perfection of function and achievement, and his need always to be right.

The patient's dominant reaction to difficult situations is one of hostility, disparagement, humiliation, and degradation. His major fear, expressed in the obsessional symptom, is of being completely enslaved, injured and destroyed, and morally disapproved of. The tendency to and the expectation of hostility, the tendency to humiliate others and the expectation of being humiliated, explain the fact that obsessional thoughts most frequently are thoughts of violence, such as killing, shooting, and cutting the throat, and thoughts of dirt, such as excreta, germs, and infection.

The patient's chief ways of dealing with his impulses and anxieties are: (1) Reaction formation (see page 93). This explains how a patient may at the same time have thoughts of violence and ideals of excessive tenderness. (2) Displacement (see page 96). The patient's main conflict situation may be the feeling of being dominated or humiliated by his wife; he may show exceeding tenderness toward her but also have obsessive thoughts of cutting his children's throats. (3) Persistent and rigid thought and behavior patterns. These are the most obvious symptoms. (4) Regressive phenomena are often observable as part of the patient's total reaction to stress. These consist chiefly of the revival of childhood attitudes, reactions, and fears, particularly in connection with anal functions and, more specifically, with bowel movements. Often these childhood attitudes were already pathological, having risen in response to over-severe parental discipline and its attendant conflicts. Thus the child may have used his bowel function (holding back or soiling) as the only means of asserting himself against, expressing his hostility to, or obtaining attention from, his parents (Kardiner).

TREATMENT

Patients with predominantly obsessional complaints often respond well to treatment, particularly if they have an emotionally outgoing personality. Interview therapy is especially effective when the complaint is chiefly obsessional thoughts and not compulsive acts, and when the symptoms have not incapacitated the patient for work. The first signs of improvement are usually the less frequent recurrence of the obsessional thoughts and their decreased ability to disturb. Under continued treatment these thoughts may eventually disappear almost entirely. However, they are likely to return when a new situation of stress confronts the patient, but renewed treatment will put them under control more quickly.

Psychoanalytic treatment can achieve excellent results with patients whose major complaint is obsessional thoughts or compulsive actions. However, it may fail when the condition is longstanding, when the patient has become almost completely incapacitated, when his whole life revolves around these thoughts and actions, and when, in addition, he is emotionally rigid. Analytic treatment presents one difficulty, but this can be overcome. The patient may be inclined to doubt every interpretation the analyst makes, and to advance logical reasons against them; or he may agree to the interpretations but have a detached emotional attitude toward them. Unless both of these reactions are themselves analyzed, the patient will be untouched by treatment.

Patients suffering from severe compulsion neurosis of many years' duration which has not been relieved by protracted psychotherapy may derive benefit from topectomy, a form of frontal lobotomy (see Chapter XIX) in which a small amount of cortical tissue is removed.

A thirty-year-old man applied for treatment because of disturbing thoughts that he would cut the throat of his child, his wife, or his mother. He considered himself utterly contemptible and worthless for having such thoughts, was in constant dread of carrying them out, and even contemplated suicide. At times he would not dare to touch a knife.

The patient was the oldest of five siblings. His mother was incredibly unfair and cruel toward the children. For example, she would tie the patient to a chair and let him watch while the rest of the family ate, or promise him a dime to clean the house, but give him a whipping instead of the dime because she found some nook in which there was dust. The patient's father, a mild-mannered man, occasionally made the mother treat the children with less severity.

The patient, an ambitious child, wanted to go to high school. His father saw no purpose in it; his mother, however, was in favor of his studying and was willing to forgo what he would earn if he were working. He was always a good student. This was the only activity for which his mother did not punish him, but she never praised him either.

When his father died, the patient interrupted his studies to earn money to support the family, but continued to educate himself by reading and attending courses. He was a good worker, had intelligent ideas, was charitable and fair. He was a peacemaker; he never swore, never abused anyone, and never lost his temper. His mother had prevented all her children from marrying. However, after one son's suicide, she raised no objections when the patient married a fairly sensitive and intelligent woman, who had difficulties in her home. One reason for his marrying her was to help her. The two had much in common and were deeply in love at the time of marriage; they had a child a year later.

The patient was active in organizing his co-workers into a union, and he was to be elected a delegate to the union conventions. However, he refused the offer because his wife became depressed at the thought of his being away from home for such long periods. Not long after this, in the fifth year of his marriage, his compulsive thoughts began. He never went out alone in the evenings, though he liked to attend political meetings, visit friends, and go bowling. Although his wife would not openly object to his going out, she would become depressed. He also gave up all his labor union activities.

The patient often had headaches and burning sensations in his forehead; these usually appeared in situations when he should have become angry. He had a slight difficulty in breathing, and palpitations of the heart; these usually arose when he was afraid or should have been afraid. The connection between these organic disturbances and their underlying cause became clear during analysis because the disturbances appeared whenever the patient spoke of certain incidents or the analyst made various comments. Thus the compulsive symptoms predominated in this patient, but some organic functions were also disturbed.

When the patient came for treatment, he said that his relationship with his wife was perfect and that he had no criticisms of her. His attitude toward his mother, he said, was one of understanding; he realized that she had treated him and all her other children badly, but he forgave her because she had known no better. Only by day-to-day observation could the therapist be certain and convince the patient that he felt considerable resentment toward and conflict about both his wife and his mother. The therapist could then make clear to him that he felt that his wife dominated him, was unfair to him, and had interfered with his career and his ambitions; in other words, his compulsive thoughts were particularly intense whenever he stayed home to prevent her from becoming depressed. He was also shown that because of his high ideals and his need of her approval he did not permit himself to feel angry or to acknowledge his anger; instead, he felt that he had to take her burden upon himself and sacrifice himself for her happiness, for, if he did not do this, or if he became angry, he felt utterly worthless. He also realized eventually that he was very resentful toward his mother, that he had not actually forgiven her for her treatment of him.

The patient improved considerably after one year of analytic treatment. His condition then remained stationary until his wife agreed to be treated. At the end of three years the patient had recovered completely.

SUGGESTED READINGS

A comparison of this and the preceding chapter with the corresponding ones in other textbooks of abnormal psychology or psychiatry is valuable: Henderson and Gillespie (402) and Rosanoff (791) are suggested.

For more general reading, the following are recommended: Freud's *A General Introduction to Psychoanalysis* (310) and his case histories (304); the relevant chapters in Fenichel's *Psychoanalytic Theory of Neurosis* (267), in Menninger's *The Human Mind* (639), and in Janet's books (455-457).

XXVIII Reactions in Which Disturbed States of Consciousness and of Memory Predominate

Amnesia, somnambulism, fugue, and double personality—the symptom groups to be discussed in this chapter—are characterized by the following:

1. The individual undergoes extensive dissociations of consciousness; some activities are considerably affected while others may remain unchanged.
2. The complex activities which remain enable him to carry on very complicated performances, such as locomotion, contact with other individuals, and the execution of various tasks, without any apparent loss of efficiency.
3. The four symptom groups differ from each other in the degree to which consciousness and memory are disturbed and the extent to which complicated tasks are possible.
4. Strong psychological forces in the patient—conflicts, anxieties, situations of stress—are responsible for his loss of identity or disturbance of consciousness. However, other strong psychological forces make him *want* to retain or regain knowledge of his identity or integration of consciousness; these are the forces which eventually result in breaking through the dissociation.

These four conditions are usually called "dissociation" because the unity of the individual may be disturbed and several different and nonassociated processes go on simultaneously. The best nonpathological examples of dissociation, in addition to those given below, are the phenomena of automatic writing, crystal gazing, and hypnosis. In hypnosis, for instance, there seem to be two different levels of memory. A subject awakened from a deep trance will remember nothing that happened during the trance. But, if he is put into a trance again, then he will remember. Girden's work on conditioning under curare (347) is of interest in this connection.

A conditioned reflex was established so that a specific isolated muscle of one hind limb contracted to an auditory stimulus while an animal was under the influence of curare, a drug that paralyzes the gross musculature of the body. It was found that, upon recovery from curare, the CR (conditioned reflex) established in one hind limb during the drugged condition was now suppressed, and that it reappeared only upon recurarization. If a CR was then established during the normal situation in the other hind limb, it became suppressed when curare was injected, and it reappeared only in the normal state after recovery from the drug.

These two systems of behavior to a single stimulus (bell) were thus mutually antagonistic or *dissociated* from one another; one appeared only in the curare state, the other only in the normal situation.

AMNESIA (LOSS OF IDENTITY)

As we have seen, every psychopathological reaction has aspects of which the individual is unconscious; these aspects frequently concern the memory of definite events, which may have occurred at any time in his life. In the syndrome to be described here, however, this disturbance of awareness concerns a special aspect of his existence and becomes the predominating problem.

A person thus disturbed suddenly forgets his name; he does not know who he is. As Abeles and Schilder put it, "The subjects forget their own identity. To one's own identity belongs the connection with a specific social structure. One has relatives, friends, a place where one works and another where one lives. But one's name and the address are symbols of one's identity. In everyday life one identifies people by these criteria and they identify themselves in this way."[1]

Usually patients cannot remember either their name or their address, although there are rare cases in which only the name is forgotten. In some cases they forget practically everything about their past; they become perplexed and agitated, alarmed and depressed; they wander about the streets trying to discover their identity, and finally ask someone for help, usually a policeman, who takes them to a hospital. Some patients cannot recognize even their own name if they are identified, and they may not recognize near relatives.

Once in the hospital, the patient's memory for recent events is usually good. He may do well on memory tests, and his perception and judgment may be functioning well. In some cases, however, his evaluation of objects around him may be disturbed.

The amnesia lasts from three hours to a month (Abeles and Schilder). The patient may recover his memory spontaneously, in some cases when he

[1] M. Abeles and P. Schilder, Psychogenic loss of personal identity, *Arch. Neurol. Psychiat.*, 1935, 34, 587-604.

hears a name or sees an object which reminds him of his identity. In many cases hypnosis has been found the speediest means of bringing patients out of their amnesia. Amnesia rarely persists for years.

PSYCHODYNAMICS OF AMNESIA

The loss of identity is a reaction to situations of conflict and distress, which may vary considerably in nature and all of which accompany anxiety. They may be economic—financial reverses, unemployment, impending poverty—or sexual, or largely interpersonal, as, for example, hostility toward a particular individual.

The amnesia represents the patient's attempts to find a way, even if a poor one, out of conflict. The desire to escape the distressing situation is quite obvious. Having forgotten his identity and his circumstances, he is prevented from returning to them; thereupon he shuts his whole conflict out of awareness. The amnesia is sometimes, literally, a lifesaver, as in the following case.

A man married against his family's wishes. He lost his job and was forced to appeal to his family for support. An uncle gave him some money, but warned him he would get no more unless he divorced his wife. On the way home the patient was held up and his money taken from him. He decided to jump into the river. But on his way to the river he forgot who he was and where he lived and that he was married; nor could he account for his being in that locality. He became perplexed and alarmed and asked a policeman for help. He was taken to a hospital and, one day later, recovered his memory of these incidents and his identity under hypnosis.

Even before his economic crisis, this same patient had had occasional dizzy spells and mild attacks of palpitation and depression. His father had been very severe, and his mother extremely emotional. He had been on bad terms with them from early childhood, and broke with them completely after his marriage. His life in general was characterized by alternate periods of rebellion and self-effacement.

SOMNAMBULISM

In somnambulism the patient attempts to carry out an act which he unconsciously desires but which inhibition prevents him from doing in the waking state. The somnambulistic acts are probably connected with dreams, which, however, are almost always forgotten, just as are the somnambulistic episodes themselves.

The patient usually goes to sleep as usual, and then, without waking, but with his eyes either open or half open, gets out of bed and does various things. Spontaneously, as a rule, he goes back to bed later, sleeps through the rest of the night, and has no recollection of what happened. These patients usually avoid obstacles, and, probably because of the absence of fear, some have a better sense of balance than when awake; others, however, suffer injuries. Thus a young man, in climbing out of a ground-floor window which was at some distance from the ground, fell and dislocated his shoulder. Patients usually hear when they are spoken to, and will stop their activity on command. Violent stimuli, such as shouts or being held down, force the patient to awake.

Patients who suffer from somnambulism usually have other symptoms; the total personality is disturbed. Somnambulism first appears, most frequently, during puberty; in many cases there are only one or two episodes, after which it disappears. Individuals in whom somnambulism appears during puberty sometimes have severe conflicts which arise in connection with the increase in the genital urge, particularly with masturbation.

A thirteen-year-old boy would get up in his sleep and walk to his parents' bedroom, open the door, and attempt to get into their bed. If they asked him what he wanted, he would either murmur unintelligibly or walk on toward the front of the house. If they said, "Go back to bed," he would turn round, go to his own room, and sleep until morning.

This boy was strongly attached to his mother. His father, whom he had always been afraid of, was idealistic, but strict and demanding; he never showed the boy any affection. The latter's attitudes toward his father were so strongly repressed that he never became consciously angry at him, although he was frequently severely punished. He was often in a state of severe conflict about masturbation, felt worthless and guilty, and feared discovery and disapproval. As a result of this fear, he became markedly fatigued. Unconsciously he longed for his parents' affection and approval and at the same time felt strong hostility, particularly toward his father. One by-product of this situation was that he became excessively religious.

Walking into his parents' bedroom was an unconscious way of satisfying impulses which were totally repressed in the waking state.

FUGUE

The patient with a fugue reaction unexpectedly engages in a series of complicated but apparently normal acts which usually take him far away from where they started. He suddenly finds himself in a strange place without knowing how he got there, but he usually knows who he is, although in some cases there is also amnesia. His activities during the fugue may vary. He may simply wander off or go on a hike or buy a railroad ticket and go off on a journey or spend all his money on shows, drinks, etc. The fugue may last from a few hours to several days and may be recurrent in some patients.

Fugue is a reaction which occurs in response to a difficult situation of stress, partly as an escape (fugue means flight). For example, patients suffering from severe anxiety attacks walk down the street, suddenly feel frightened, and then start to run, as if they were running away from their own fear. There is no amnesia in such a reaction, but it contains the germ of the fugue.

The patient's activities during fugue often have a wish-fulfilling or compensatory aspect. Thus, in addition to running away from the situation of stress and escaping conflict and anxiety, the patient by his activities satisfies certain needs or consoles himself in his plight.

The following case, which presents a combination of amnesia and long-continued fugue, illustrates these points.

J. F., aged fifty, was admitted to a hospital, complaining of complete loss of memory and identity. He was supposed to have left a town in Pennsylvania and to have arrived in New York a week earlier, but remembered nothing that had happened before this. His memory of events of the past week in New York was hazy. He had some recollection of going to see "a lot of shows." His knowledge of general current events was almost nil. He declared that his mind was a complete blank.

When his sister and a niece visited him the next day, he did not recognize them. He even said that he could not speak his native language, although he evidently knew it. He denied understanding the most basic conceptions of everyday life. When asked if he recognized his face in the mirror, he said, "My face looks strange—it does not look natural." On the fourth day in the hospital the patient recovered with the aid of hypnosis.

His history showed that he considered himself a "mental healer" who helped people by "hypnotizing" them. Several months before his illness, a girl he was treating in an effort to make her reform her way of life accused him of having sexual relations with her. He was arrested and fined $500. On the day of the onset of his illness he had been near the Union Station and had suddenly gone to New York on an excursion he saw advertised.[2]

The situation of stress from which this patient sought escape is obvious. The compensatory elements—the attempt to console himself by "going to shows" and "having a good time in New York"—are also clear. The disturbance of his whole personality structure is made even more obvious by the occupation in which he engaged.

That criminal activities may occur in fugues is shown by the following case:

"A young man committed murder in what appears definitely to be a state of fugue. He killed a taxi driver, took possession of the taxi, later disposed of it, and disappeared. He was not apprehended until six years later, during which time he had led the life of a very honest worker, married, and lived happily and peacefully with his wife under an assumed name. While vaguely aware that a crime had been committed, he was completely amnesic as far as the act itself was concerned. A prolonged study of the case, lasting many months, revealed an unusually complicated life. Ever since childhood the boy had been interested in mechanical things.

[2] M. Abeles and P. Schilder, *op. cit.* This is a shortened account of the case.

He had wanted to drive the family automobile which was forbidden to him. The family had always imposed their decisions upon him as to studies, career, or anything else. When one day it was announced that the family had decided that he was to study medicine, he became low in spirits and was found that evening tinkering with the carburetor of the family car. Now, while serving a life sentence in prison, he is one of the best, most industrious, and most capable automobile mechanics of the institution. His life was a mixture of a great desire to settle down and a peculiar truancy. The whole crime was reconstructed as a sudden impulsive acting out of the murder of the taxi driver. Incidentally, a great part of the man's amnesia of the crime was cleared gradually in a piecemeal fashion during the course of many interviews."[3]

DOUBLE PERSONALITY

The following phenomena are observed in so-called double personality: From birth on, the individual, like any other person, has a name, a general mode of behavior, interests, associates, and friends, and he speaks a certain language. Suddenly, however, he becomes convinced that he has a different name and different interests; his whole behavior changes; even his knowledge of his language may become limited. While in this condition he has no conscious knowledge of his name and of the various aspects of what he previously considered his own life. He behaves essentially normally, and the people around him do not realize that anything is amiss. Thus, under his given name, a man may have been a professional man, such as a priest, a lawyer, a teacher; under his second name, he may enter an entirely different occupation, such as opening a store, but still function essentially well.

After many weeks, months, or even years, the individual may, apparently spontaneously, remember who he is. He has no recollections of the intervening period, and is surprised and puzzled at finding himself in his present situation.

Cases have been reported of individuals who, while under observation in a hospital, changed alternately from one "personality" to another, or even rotated among "several personalities."

Like amnesia, somnambulism, and fugue, double personality represents an escape reaction to situations of conflict, distress, or dissatisfaction, or a revolt against one's own unsatisfactory personality, in favor of a completely different type of character.

The following case has been reported by Erickson and Kubie (251).

"For over a year a twenty-year-old college girl, quiet, reserved, and well poised, had suffered secretly from constantly recurring fears that the icebox, kitchen, college laboratory and locker doors had been left open. . . ."

This girl (Miss Damon) volunteered to serve as the subject of some experiments in hypnotism. Later she spontaneously showed some dissociative phenomena.

[3] G. Zilboorg, Some sidelights on the psychology of murder, *Journal of Nervous and Mental Diseases,* 1935, **81,** 442-444.

Erickson at once suggested that she might like to try automatic writing (an excellent technique for investigating dissociation). The writing, however, was scrawly and illegible. It was in the course of discussing it that the second personality was discovered:

"After the subject's hand had completed the last bit of automatic writing . . . the investigator quietly slipped the sheet of paper from under her hand, leaving a fresh one in its place with her hand still holding the pencil. This was done without attracting her attention. She continued her task of deciphering the writing, finally declaring aloud that she could make out only the words 'trance,' 'will,' 'my,' 'catalepsy,' and 'ever,' and expressed much amusement over her inability to read more, asking laughingly, 'Did I really write that nonsense?' Both the investigator and his assistant replied affirmatively and in the same amused tone. At the moment the subject was leaning forward over the desk and her hand was out of her peripheral vision. As the verbal reply was given to her question, her hand was observed to write 'No,' of which Miss Damon remained unaware. Immediately the investigator asked, as if speaking directly to the subject, 'What do you mean?' and while Miss Damon puzzled over what he meant, her hand wrote 'Can't.' Again speaking as if to Miss Damon, the question was asked, 'Why?' to which her hand replied, 'Damon doesn't know these things.' "

There followed a series of oral questions seemingly directed to the subject; she was bewildered and confused because of their unintelligibility, but her hand wrote appropriate replies. These questions and their answers, continuing from the last one above, are quoted verbatim to show the definition of this second personality.

"Q: Why?

"A: Don't know, afraid to know.

"Q: Who?

"A: D (Damon).

"Q: Who does?

"A: Me.

"Q: Me?

"A: Brown.

"Q: Who?

"A: Me–Brown–B.

"Q: Explain.

"A: D is D, B is B.

"Q: B know D?

"A: Yes.

"Q: D know B?

"A: No. No.

"Q: B part of D?

"A: No. B is B; D is D.

"Q: Can I talk to B?

"A: Are. . . .

"Q: What do you want?

"A: Help D.

"Q: Why?

"A: D afraid.

"Q: Do you know what D is afraid of?

"A: Yes; D no.

"Q: Why?

"A: D afraid, forgot, don't want to know. . . .

"The secretary then read the questions and her answers were shown to Miss Damon. She attended carefully with a look of increasing understanding, finally remarking, 'Why that really must mean I have a dual personality,' and then was greatly startled that her hand emphatically wrote 'Right.' Recovering her poise, Miss Damon asked, 'Can I talk to you?' 'Sure.' 'Can you talk to me?' 'Yes.' 'Is your name really Brown?' 'Yes.' 'What is your full name?' 'Jane Brown.'

"Throughout the investigation, the Brown personality was found to be literally a separate, well-organized entity, completely maintaining its own identity, and differentiating to a fine degree between Brown and Damon. Brown was capable of entering into spirited arguments with the investigator, his assistant and with Miss Damon, and of expressing ideas entirely at variance with those of Miss Damon. . . .

"Brown was found to maintain a highly protective attitude toward Damon, shielding her, demanding special consideration for her, offering encouragement, distracting her attention, deliberately deceiving her, and employing various other protective measures."

In brief, images were finally brought to D's consciousness that evoked the repressed memory of a traumatic experience that had occurred at the age of three. Her symptoms disappeared, and over a period of years have not returned.[4]

TREATMENT

We have said that the patient sometimes breaks through the dissociation spontaneously. If spontaneous recovery does not occur quickly, hypnosis or waking suggestions in repeated interviews help to bring him out from his immediate condition. However, because he usually has general personality problems, he should then be given prolonged interview therapy. Psychoanalytic treatment is valuable if the patient is analyzable and coöperates. But he must be watched; the symptom may recur in crucial conflict situations because he may attempt to act out his conflicts instead of solving them.

SUGGESTED READINGS

Of great value are Janet's *The Major Symptoms of Hysteria* (455), M. Prince's *The Dissociation of a Personality,* Abeles and Schilder's "Psychogenic loss of personal identity" (1), and Erickson and Kubie, "The permanent relief of an obsessional phobia by means of communications with an unsuspected dual personality" (252).

[4] M. H. Erickson and L. S. Kubie, The permanent relief of an obsessional phobia by means of communications with an unsuspected dual personality, *Psychoanalytic Quarterly,* 1939, 8, 471-509.

XXIX Reactions in Which Bodily Complaints Predominate

The symptom syndromes to be discussed in this and the following chapter are characterized by various distinct neurotic reactions. Differentiation of these reactions is based partly on the character of the complaint, the possibility that physiological or structural disturbances can be either demonstrated or assumed, and the emotional and ideational reaction pattern accompanying the bodily complaint. On this basis, the following can be differentiated: (1) conversion hysteria; (2) hypochondriasis; (3) neurasthenia; (4) sexual disturbances; (5) organ neuroses with structural change. The last will be discussed in the next chapter.

It is particularly important that this type of patient should have adequate and, if necessary, repeated physical examinations, for only in this way can the relative importance of organic factors in symptoms and complaints be determined. The neglect of the emotional causes is, however, as serious as the neglect of possible physical causes.

CONVERSION HYSTERIA

The term "hysteria" has been and, to a lesser extent, is still used to cover a wide variety of disturbances. Furthermore, different authors use it to describe various manifestations. Thus Janet uses the term "psychasthenia" to refer to phobic reactions, whereas Freud uses the term "hysteria." A certain type of amnesia and double personality are frequently referred to as hysteria.

The term "conversion hysteria" was coined by Freud to convey the idea that in situations of conflict and stress the patient, instead of having a purely "psychological" symptom, shows an observable change in an organic function. In other words, the "psychological" conflict is "converted" into a bodily disturbance. Why this is more common in some individuals than in others is an unsolved problem. Often the organic disturbance, which at this stage is entirely psychological or functional, was first an actual structural disturbance; for example, the patient with hysterical coughing spells may first have had bronchitis.

Many of the symptoms to be described still occur as predominant complaints in some cases, but such patients are comparatively rare—one may work in a mental hygiene clinic or a psychiatric ward for many years without encountering a single case of "hysterical convulsions" or "hysterical blindness." Such conditions were probably more frequent about fifty years ago; because of the way in which they were treated by both society and physicians, they lasted longer and were more continuous.

SYMPTOMS

Disturbances of Autonomic Functions. The disturbances of autonomic functions are either entirely or partly involuntary. Among this type of symptoms are a "lump" in the throat, a "choking" sensation, belching, hiccoughing, coughing spells, clearing the throat, difficulty in breathing (particularly the inability to take a deep breath), loss of appetite, vomiting, nausea, frequency of urination, constipation, diarrhea, cold and clammy extremities, excessive perspiration, headaches.

Sensory Symptoms. Sensory symptoms are observable in the functioning of the sensory organs, such as those of touch and sight. Thus anesthesia (loss of sensation), hyperesthesia (excessive sensitiveness), or paresthesia (exceptional sensations, such as the "pins and needles" feeling) may be manifest in the tactile sense. It is characteristic that, in contrast to organic disturbances, these sensory disturbances do not follow the anatomic distribution of the nerves; moreover, they respond quickly to suggestion. In one type of this disturbance, "glove" or "stocking" anesthesia, the patient feels neither touch nor pain in the area of the limb like that covered by the gloves or stockings. Another form of sensory disturbance is the loss of sensation on one side of the body. This nonfeeling area stops exactly at the midline, whereas, in disturbances of sensation that are due to such factors as a hemorrhage of the brain, the transition from the nonfeeling to the sensitive part of the skin is gradual.

In hysterical blindness, the eyes and the optic nerves are entirely normal, but the patient cannot see. In some cases, testing the field of vision shows that the patient "sees" the object only in the center of the normal visual field. This is called constriction of the visual field. Janet was the first to observe that patients whose field of vision was constricted almost to a pinpoint, in direct testing, were able to engage in complicated activities, such as ball playing. In other words, in actual activity, they used the complete visual field.

Motor Symptoms. Motor symptoms are manifest in the muscles that are under voluntary control, and consist of excess and unusual movements, continuous contraction, or complete limpness with paralysis.

If the hysterical paralysis or contraction remains for many years, there may be a secondary wasting or shortening of the muscle. The paralyzed limb is usually cold and bluish even in the early period, if the condition is continuous, and secondary disturbances may appear in the skin and nails.

In one form of disturbance, called astasia abasia, the patient is able to sit, but can hardly stand or walk. Both the reflexes and the reaction of the muscles to electric stimulation remain normal.

Tremor (shaking) is of relatively frequent occurrence. A generalized twitching of the muscles (hysterical convulsion, "hysterical fit") may also occur. The patient falls to the ground (without injuring himself), and his whole body shakes; but, in contrast to the epileptic, he neither bites his tongue nor turns blue in the face. In epileptic convulsions the pupils cease to react to light, whereas in hysterical convulsions the light reaction is present and other reflexes remain unchanged.

In aphonia the patient is able to talk only in a whisper; in mutism he is unable to utter any sound. These conditions usually occur suddenly, usually immediately after a fright or a few days later. They can be differentiated from organic conditions in the following ways: there is no sign of inflammation of the larynx and throat, and the voice is not hoarse (differentiation from laryngitis); furthermore, the vocal cords can be seen to be completely separated on expiration and well together on inspiration (differentiation from organic paralysis).

These bodily symptoms, with the exception of the anesthesias, are usually accompanied by corresponding local physiological changes. Even though these changes sometimes cannot be determined with certainty, they can be validly assumed to occur. For example, in hysterical paralysis the arm hangs limp and the muscle tone is diminished; in a hysterical spasm the muscles are actually contracted. Probably, when the hysterical patient complains of pain in the heart region, there is actually some change in the circulation. In dizziness there is probably some real change in the circulation in the brain.

PSYCHODYNAMICS OF CONVERSION HYSTERIA

The personality type most commonly found in conversion hysteria is emotionally outgoing and elastic.

The patient's self-evaluation tends to be one of helplessness and infantilism. He is afraid to shoulder responsibility. He longs for emotional closeness, but is frightened by it. The main catastrophic fear is of rejection, abandonment, injury, and, frequently, bodily frustration.

The bodily symptoms represent reactions to situations of stress. This can be demonstrated as easily in conversion hysteria as in anxiety attacks, provided the symptoms have not yet become continuous. They appear during or after situations of stress and disappear after the stress subsides. The emotions with which the symptom is correlated are often entirely unconscious, particularly anxiety and anger. The patient also expresses his helplessness, punishes himself, and seeks forgiveness, love, and support with the symptom. It is, at times, predominantly a defense against distress by avoidance and exclusion (blindness: "I do not want to see the cause of my misery").

Often the symptom has an additional disguised gratifying and ameliorative function. For example, the patient wants to gratify a need arising in a pleasure-seeking organ, but this gratification occurs not in the organ where it is normally experienced, but in the organ where the symptom arises. Thus, instead of sexual excitement and gratification, the patient may complain of frequency of urination, which is for him both painful and pleasurable.

There is usually abundant fantasy behind the symptom. Thus weakness of the arm may mask fantasies of murder, of being hurt, of being tied and injured. The sexual function is often involved in these fantasies.

TREATMENT

Patients with conversion hysteria are usually very good subjects for psychotherapy, particularly if the symptoms have not been of long duration. The more serious symptoms are easily controllable by suggestion or hypnotic techniques; for lasting cures, psychoanalysis is very effective. If there is not enough time for this more thorough technique, a series of interview discussions in which various combinations of partial techniques are used usually gives good results.

A forty-year-old pianist complained that, when he tried to play music which was particularly soft and slow, his arm became rigid. This happened only when he was performing publicly in an auditorium, not when he practiced alone. Before the symptom occurred for the first time, however, he had had attacks of anxiety in the auditorium. He was ambitious, but his symptom seriously interfered with his playing.

The patient always smiled in his contacts with people; at times he felt anger but did not express it. He never insisted on his rights. He preferred prostitutes to his wife, and masturbation to intercourse. He often felt very tender toward his wife, but at other times he was aloof. He rarely slept well.

His parents got along very badly with each other, his mother constantly threatening to commit suicide. When he was about eight years old, she suggested that he learn to play the piano, and he proved exceptionally talented. His father died when he was thirteen years old, and he became completely self-supporting when he was about nineteen. He had had mild attacks of anxiety ever since his father's death. They became more incapacitating when, at twenty-five, he found that he had to continue to support his mother. He married at the age of twenty-seven upon his wife's initiative—he told her that he was not in love with her.

His unconscious resentment toward his mother, his wife, and other people created feelings of worthlessness and helplessness. The manner in which he behaved toward them led to the fear of discovery and of retribution and abandonment. His playing in public represented to him a situation of exposure and of threat. In the course of two years of psychoanalytic treatment the patient was entirely cured of his main symptom, his relations with his wife became satisfactory, and he grew normally self-assertive.

HYPOCHONDRIA

The term "hypochondria" is often used very broadly to mean any preoccupation with, or fear or anxiety about, one's body and its functions. We shall distinguish between the hypochondria that occurs with anxiety (which is discussed elsewhere) and pure hypochondria, in which no anxiety or fear is found, but only a tremendous absorption with the bodily processes (Freud).

A definite type of personality is usually associated with such hypochondria. The individual may seem to have ordinary social contact with others. Psychologically, however, he is soon found to feel completely isolated, to be interested only in himself, without any identification or sympathy with others.

The patient may complain of pain in the back, uncomfortable sensations in the back of the head, the stomach, the chest, the genitals, or, for that matter, anywhere. Or there may be no complaints, in the literal sense, but rather a cheerful, interested preoccupation with his digestive functions or excretory processes.

Some authorities place in this group all the vast army of health and diet fiends—people who drink mineral oil as others do beer, who decide suddenly to live only on nuts or cabbage, or who shun tea or coffee as they would poison. Only some of these are true hypochondriacs; most are merely victims of false information or fallacious theories.

PSYCHODYNAMICS OF HYPOCHONDRIA

The symptoms themselves have, as usual, several meanings or purposes. The patient solves his problems by increasing his social detachment; a compensatory increase in interest in himself endows him and his organs with an increased significance, which gives him a certain pleasure and feeling of protection. Second, the symptoms are in part a very direct and bald expression of suffering. That is, they are, in effect, pleas for attention, help, love, and respect. Third, they are, in part, self-punishment and expressions of guilt, arising perhaps from masturbation, from the patient's unconscious or conscious hatred of others, from his perception of his own selfishness, or from other sources.

TREATMENT

The treatment of the hypochrondriacal patient is usually difficult because he does not easily establish a good rapport with the therapist. Furthermore, it is difficult to convince him that his complaints are products of psychological stress and that they have purposes. He clings to his symptoms and is loath to admit that they are not what they seem.

Long-continued interviews, in which the patient is convinced of the therapist's interest and affection, can be helpful. Psychoanalysis is probably necessary for complete cure, and even here success cannot be counted on.

A college student complained of extensive gastric disturbances, indigestion, "weak" stomach, belching, aches, and many other symptoms. Questioning showed that he had made a full-time job of studying his eating, his digestion, and his eliminative processes. For instance, he had menus made up for a month in advance in which everything was weighed to the ounce. He always cooked his own meals, because he would not entrust this important task to his mother.

He spent several hours each day using muscle exercisers, breathing according to a special system, and reading medical books.

The problem that brought him to the psychologist was his relation to his fiancée. Questioning revealed that she loved him intensely but had angered him by disparaging his symptoms. He apparently did not love her at all, but intended to marry her because "everybody gets married." He had broken off with her without any feeling of loss, even with relief. He now wanted to know if marriage was necessary to health.

It took some time to convince him that he needed psychological treatment, and this was possible only after a very detailed examination by a medical specialist showed negative results. He never really made contact with the therapist, and no results were being obtained by interviews; therefore he was sent to another therapist, with whom he got along a bit better. However, when he was instructed to give up his pills and laxatives, he never returned.

NEURASTHENIA

The term "neurasthenia" was once used to describe almost any psychopathological condition. Later it was limited to conditions characterized primarily by continuous fatigue. Many individuals suffer these complaints in a minor degree; in fact, temporary fatigue and exhaustibility are among the most common of all symptoms. In neurasthenia, however, they are predominating. Because of their continuous character, it is often difficult, except in the advanced stages of treatment, to make clear to the patient their connection with situations of stress and conflict.

PSYCHODYNAMICS OF NEURASTHENIA

The symptom, of course, has also ameliorative, defensive, and goal-seeking aspects. It wins pity, attention, and sympathy, and brings an illusion of being wanted and looked after. There is often an element of sheer pleasure in the laziness, sloth, and sleep justified by this fatigue. The condition sometimes centers about unsolved sexual problems—for instance, in young people, about conflict over masturbation. It sometimes occurs in people who are chronically stimulated sexually with no ultimate satisfaction. Probably, however, it is most common in the so-called "nervous housewife" who is neglected by her husband and children.

Prolonged feeling of fatigue may be accompanied by a lowering of blood sugar. The outstanding features then are apathy, aimlessness, and a repulsion against the routine of everyday life. Attacks of extreme weakness, tremulousness, sweating, and dizziness may occur. The lowering of the blood sugar in these conditions is considered psychogenic. The psychological picture represents a reaction of disappointment and defiant, self-incapacitating refusal to be active: "I cannot have what I want; I will not play any more."

TREATMENT

The first recommendations should be the obvious ones of attempting to ameliorate the precipitating situation—in the example above, securing love in a legitimate way, raising self-esteem by actual achievement, bringing about amelioration of the family situation. Only if these are impossible or prove to be ineffective should extensive character reorganization be attempted. Interview therapy can be of considerable value. Psychoanalysis is ordinarily entirely successful.

If there is a lowering of blood sugar, some authors advocate the administration of atropine to break the vicious circle of fatigue, the resultant disappointment in oneself, and guilt. Relief of the patient's symptoms may increase his hopes and make him more amenable to psychotherapy.

A gifted and ambitious engineer complained of continuous fatigue and pressure in the head. He excelled in his work, but felt seriously handicapped because he became easily exhausted. At times he needed eleven hours of sleep, but he slept badly. He complained of frequency of urination, frequent constipation, and impaired potency. His complaints started during puberty, with intense guilt reactions to sexual impulses and masturbation, for which he was brutally punished and threatened.

The patient's father was strict and at times brutal, particularly in his sexual discipline. He was frequently away from home when the patient was a child, and during such periods the mother was very close to him; however, she always had the father discipline the lad on his return. The boy was disappointed in both parents; he felt betrayed, particularly by his mother, and he feared severe corporal punishment from his father. The patient was completely relieved during three years of psychoanalytic treatment, during which the etiology and dynamic meanings of his symptoms were made clear to him.

DISTURBANCES OF THE SEXUAL FUNCTION

Disturbances of the sexual function are extremely common and, at one time or another, are present in most psychopathological reactions. Although the patient frequently does not mention them to the psychotherapist because he considers this aspect of his functioning entirely adequate, it often becomes obvious that his estimation of this phase of his life is not correct, just as he fails to estimate accurately his interpersonal relations and his behavior in friendship and in work. Other patients, however, appeal for help chiefly because of disturbance in this field. These patients sometimes assume that their difficulties are limited to sexual ones; but closer investigation always shows clearly that other aspects are also involved.

The discussion of this subject could be limited to disturbances in the functioning of the organs, but this would make the survey too narrow. There are customs, laws, ideals, and limitations which are accepted by the group as a whole and by its individual members. Therefore disturbances of the sexual function usually involve one or more of the following: (1) disturbance of the organic function itself, (2) disturbance in the functioning of related organs, (3) disturbance in the circumstances under which the organic function is exercised, and (4) deviations in the choice of sexual partner.

The evaluation of the sexual function depends on the individual patient—on his outlook, his whole personality, his immediate situation, his social environment. The healthy pattern for the adult in our society includes the ability to form a close emotional relationship with an adult of the other sex, and the desire to engage in the sexual act with objective and subjective adequacy—that is, with emotional acceptance of the function and adequate duration and satisfaction. In the following discussion not only the actual functioning of the individual but also his conscious and unconscious fantasies must be kept in mind.

IMPAIRED POTENCY; FRIGIDITY

"Impaired potency" is usually applied to sexual disturbances in men; "frigidity," to sexual disturbances in women. The disturbance may appear in any or all phases of the function, or in any or all situations. There may also be considerable individual differences, depending on the behavior of the partner. As a rule, if the partner is loved and behaves tenderly and considerately, the disturbance is less. In other cases it may appear in just those situations in which there is attachment to the partner and the partner is emotionally outgoing. Usually, however, the function improves under conditions of security and happiness.

The characteristics of frigidity and impaired potency are as follows: (1) All desire may be absent; the function, or even the thought of it, may be repellent. In the latter instance the exercise of the function may be accompanied by other organic disturbances, such as nausea or vomiting. (2) In the man tumescence may be inadequate, or the climax may be reached too quickly. In rare cases he may be unable to reach a climax; or the function, even though objectively adequate, may lead to inadequate subjective satisfaction. (Even such "biological" functions may be culturally determined; in some primitive societies there is no sexual climax.) (3) In the woman there may be either complete absence of gratification or a slight gratification without the ability to reach a climax.

Dogs with experimental neurosis induced by the conditioning method may show frequent and almost constant erections reactive to the environment and particularly to the specific signals formerly connected with food. Further, in normal dogs the conditioning environment has no effect upon the onset and duration of erection in response to normal sexual stimuli. Neurotic animals exhibit premature ejaculation in that the duration may be decreased to one-third of the animal's normal performance (330).

Once the sexual function is adequately established, it may continue even after the sex glands have ceased to function. Thus the woman may continue to function after menopause, and the adult man whose testes have been removed because of disease may suffer no impairment. The following case, reported by Rowe and Lawrence (807), illustrates both this point and the extreme care necessary in deciding how physiological factors lead to psychological disturbances.

The man's testes had been removed bilaterally for medical reasons. The man lost all interest in his work, lost his ambition, became apathetic, and returned to his native village. There he fell in love with a woman who reciprocated his feelings. She knew of his condition but was willing to marry him. He found himself to be potent, his ambition and efficiency returned, and he took up his former occupation.

The clinical and experimental observations indicate the complexity of the interrelationship between physiological and psychological factors.

THE INDIVIDUAL'S ATTITUDE TOWARD THE DISTURBANCE

The individual may be deeply disturbed by the symptoms for many reasons. His self-esteem may be badly damaged because he considers himself worthless and inadequate, or feels that something is profoundly wrong with him, that something essential is lacking in him. In our society, self-esteem, especially in the male, depends in part on sexual adequacy. He may feel that his happiness is threatened because his relationship with his mate is endangered. Other such individuals have a remarkably detached and philosophical attitude toward the disturbance. They rationalize it on the ground that the whole function is a nuisance and of no importance; they may even say to themselves that they want to be self-sufficient and that autoerotism is more satisfactory. More detailed examination shows that most of these individuals are concerned by the disturbance but repress this attitude and try to compensate by rationalization and a philosophical outlook.

The emotional attitude with which disturbances of the sexual function are most closely correlated is fear in its broadest sense. At times partly consciously, or largely or entirely unconsciously, the individual is afraid of failure, rejection, injury, and humiliation. He is afraid to assume responsibility or to become emotionally close to anyone. These fears involve his whole evaluation of himself and others. Here an early attitude of disapproval of and guilt toward sexuality in general, as well as parental fear of sex which is internalized by the child, plays a significant role.

A patient related the fact that her mother made her feel very guilty as a child if she even mentioned anything pertaining to sex. At a somewhat later date she heard such remarks from her mother as, "Women are just pleasure-toys for men," and "That man ought to be sent to jail for killing his wife with too many children." The mother told the patient when she was a child never to be alone with boys because something frightful would happen to her.

The dominant goal aspect of impotence or frigidity is avoidance and defense: "This action isn't taking place at all; I'm safe from danger," or "I don't have this organ at all," or "I'm not really part of this affair and therefore am doing no wrong."

The defensive aspects are often the result of other general attitudes involved in the function. The woman may want to gain the man's protection through complete dependence and submission, humiliation, and pain. But this desire leads to the fear that what she is asking for will actually happen—she will be humiliated and injured. To save herself from that fate, she develops frigidity. Often attitudes of hostility are also involved; they may be entirely unconscious or appear in fantasies. The individual is afraid of their consequences because he does not want to help the mate, or feels guilty, or fears counterattack. Impotence or frigidity may develop a defense against these fears.

Disturbances may arise partly as a disguised expression of the desire to frustrate and humiliate the mate: "I did not grant you what you wanted," or "I remained aloof." These attitudes may be almost entirely unconscious. All such expressions of hostility injure the individual himself as well.

TREATMENT

In the prevention and treatment of sexual disturbances, proper enlightenment about the problems of sexuality, marriage, and pregnancy is important. It is not merely a question of imparting proper knowledge; such enlightenment also imparts reassurance, permissiveness, or approval, which leads to a lessening of fear and guilt. However, the adult who has a definite disturbance needs more than this. Symptomatic improvement, particularly in men, may be secured by interview therapy and suggestion. In interview therapy the patient's entire mode of existence has to be discovered; in other words, the treatment deals with the whole individual, not merely the symptom. The treatment of severe frigidity is, as a rule, more difficult than that of impotence, although the latter can also be extremely difficult. The best results with impotence and frigidity can be obtained through psychoanalysis.

OTHER DISTURBANCES OF THE SEXUAL FUNCTION

Disturbances of the sexual function may have other forms, among them being (1) sadism (infliction of pain) or masochism (enjoyment of pain); (2) fetishism (substitution of an inanimate object for the mate); (3) perversion (substitution of other organ functions); (4) exhibitionism (self-exposure) or voyeurism (looking as the ultimate aim); (5) nymphomania or satyriasis (excessive desire, promiscuity, insatiability); (6) homosexuality (choice of individuals of the same sex).

These behavior patterns can sometimes be observed in a very clear form, as when the individual consciously desires rather severe pain and injury, or wants to inflict it. It is difficult, however, to draw a sharp line, for often the pain or injury is emotional rather than physical, the partner being humiliated and tortured by words and behavior. In other cases this desire appears in fantasy but never in any action. Some of the above terms—"masochism" and "sadism," for example—have been extended to include tendencies on the part of the individual which do not include the sexual organs. To avoid misunderstanding, it seems best in such instances to speak not of sadism and masochism, but of the desire to hurt, to humiliate, to submit, etc. These sado-masochistic attitudes may, of course, be present in connection with any kind of function and in any kind of situation. However, sexuality is a common means of expressing them.

All the above behaviors may have the individual's full and conscious approval if the circumstances are relatively favorable for their practice, and he may, in general, function well. However, other people who engage in them disapprove of themselves to a greater or lesser degree, at times very intensely, even when circumstances are favorable. This disapproval is almost always accompanied by the desire to change, an essential element in helping the individual overcome the practice. This type of disapproval must be differentiated from that involved when the patient gets into legal difficulties; for in some extremely severe conditions, not only are there no qualms of conscience but even murder may be committed in a state of ecstasy.

The practices arise in two ways: (1) Various conflicts and problems appear whenever the sexual drive is activated; these are expressed in and solved by these practices. (2) Similarly, conflicts and disturbances which appear in various other situations are reflected in and solved by practices in the sexual sphere.

As in all other reaction patterns, these practices are interrelated with the patient's total personality, his evaluation of himself and of other people, and other emotional attitudes or modes of behavior. The general disturbances in self-esteem and in security feelings, the various fears and psychological reactions, are essentially the same as those described in the discussion of potency. There is always fear of failure, of responsibility and closeness, of abandonment and injury, of the organ function, and of both sexes, particularly the opposite sex. There is usually special emphasis on some one type of catastrophic expectation in connection with the various practices; and the compensatory, ameliorating, or goal-seeking elements in these reactions are particularly definite and characteristic.

In sadism the dominant fear is of being injured, to which, of course, is always linked the expectation of humiliation, domination, and frustration. The ameliorative formula is: "If I engage in violence, I am safe; I can reach my goal safely. With this I avenge myself also, and thus I obtain satisfaction and I triumph."

In masochism the chief fear is of abandonment, neglect, or rejection. Against this is a strong hostile reaction, with the fear of counterattack: "I offer to submit and to be hurt, and in that way I'll be forgiven and I won't be abandoned."

Fetishism is characterized by a fear of rejection and humiliation by the opposite sex. The individual safeguards himself through a full mastery of an inanimate object. There is also frequently a strong tendency toward self-degradation; for this reason shoe fetishism is particularly common.

In exhibitionism the chief fear is of insignificance and humiliation, the self-exposure representing a sort of aggrandized "showing off." In voyeurism the fear is of frustration and disapproval; the activity (almost always secret) represents partly a stealthy, partly a defiant, way of attaining the limited goal, for it frequently brings a feeling of power over the one being looked at.

Promiscuity may be based on various types of fears and have varying compensatory aspects, such as self-degradation, abandoning one's partner instead of being abandoned, blaming another for one's own deficiencies, or searching incessantly for love and affection from a distance. Self-aggrandizement is a common factor, particularly in men. In insatiability, the dominant fear is of frustration; the attempt is to secure more and more gratification, as if it might all suddenly be lost.

In homosexuality the dominant fears may be of abandonment and rejection, humiliation, being vanquished in competition, and being frustrated by the opposite sex. The compensatory aspects may be self-aggrandizement and self-sufficiency (fantasy of belonging to both sexes); submitting to and being completely looked after by a less dangerous partner; dominating, humiliating, and inflicting pain on a less dangerous antagonist; being free of any possibility of progeny; looking after another individual as if saying: "This is how I ought to be taken care of."

Some element of defiance and hostility is also present in all these reactions: "I will do that which is forbidden."

These reaction patterns often contain regressive elements and are frequently recurrent continuations of phenomena which were first manifested in early childhood. In many cases elements of the reaction pattern first appeared in actual situations in childhood. Thus, in shoe fetishism, the kind of shoe to which the individual is attracted is usually found to be that worn by an adult to whom he was emotionally close as a child.

Many of the practices described here appear for a short time during the life of a great many people.

Kinsey (494) reports that 37 percent of the total male population of the United States has some homosexual experience leading to orgasm between adolescence and old age; 8 percent are exclusively homosexual for at least three years during that period; only 4 percent are exclusively so throughout that period. The fact that much homosexual behavior is experimental in nature or due to temporary environmental factors, is short-lived, and tends to drop out with increasing maturity, is seen in the following figures given by Kinsey: Among 20-year-old American males, 4.9 percent are exclusively homosexual; among the 25-year-olds, 2.9 percent are exclusively so; at the 45-year age level, this figure has dropped to 1.8 percent.

These practices become permanent only if they are linked with the basic psychopathic reactions—if they acquire a special significance in relation to conflict, anxiety, and meeting problems. Therefore it is best to apply the various terms—i.e., "exhibitionism," "homosexuality," etc.—only if these practices are actually engaged in and are compulsive and exclusive—that is, if the individual is driven to this activity, and if it is the preferred or only way of achieving satisfaction. The recurring fantasies and impulses that many people temporarily engage in may have determinants—emotional reasons and purposes—similar to those concerned in the actual practices; at other times the determinants are different. In either case there are very important differences, from the point of view of the individual's total adaptation. To put it more simply, exactly the same behavior which is called normal if it occurs in a healthy person is called sick if it occurs in a neurotic patient, because the behavior has different meanings and different motivations.

A patient who complained of anxiety attacks, trembling of the hands, periods of discouragement, and some minor compulsive acts was frequently troubled by homosexual fantasies. It was soon established during treatment that these fantasies appeared in two situations: (1) Whenever he had to face an individual who was stronger and more brilliant than he, or who had a superior position. In this instance the homosexual thought meant, "I am willing to submit to you in any form you want me to; only don't injure me, don't disapprove of me, and don't abandon me." (2) Whenever he felt rejected, or when he was too shy even to speak to a woman to whom he was first attracted. Here the thought meant, "I can't find love and gratification from women because I am too helpless, too weak, and too much afraid of them. Perhaps I could have love from men, whom I fear less. I must have some love and some gratification."

Similar reactions are found in many people who have homosexual fantasies and are greatly disturbed by them. The difference between fantasy and actual practice in the individual's total adaptation is as follows: The person who has the fantasy but does not engage in actual practice has found other ways of coping with his conflict and anxiety. For example, he may have sadistic fantasies, but in actual behavior he may be tender with his wife, may have potency disturbances, and may have a complacent and serene outlook on life, refraining from ambitious undertakings. These characteristics take the place of actual sadistic behavior. That is, they are symptoms of repressed sadism; it is repressed because of serious inner objections to the actual practices, such as need for self-esteem or approval, the attempt to avoid secondary anxiety, the desire to maintain ideals.

Profound changes may occur in the person's outlook and total adaptation because of new situations of stress; they may be the result of chronic situations, or of external circumstances which make one form of solution preferable to another. Under these circumstances he may begin any one of these practices at any period of his life; for example, a man may engage in homosexuality after rejection by women.

The injection of sex hormone into the healthy, sexually functioning animal increases his or her sexual activity in a significant percentage of experiments. Passing homosexual activity, such as mounting another male, or, conversely, lordosis and quivering of the ears if mounted, can be observed in male rats if they are hyperexcitable as a result of hormonal injections or if they were previously frustrated and no member of the opposite sex is available (54). Some features of passing homosexual behavior can be observed in monkeys on the part of both the dominant and the submissive male or female. Thus the submissive male monkey may assume the female copulative position toward the dominant male, and the dominant male may mount the submissive male (616). At times the female animal that is otherwise submissive to the sexually responsive male becomes dominant, and the sexually desirous male becomes submissive.

A man and a woman, both of whom had had serious personality problems all their lives and passing homosexual experiences in adolescence, were married. They got along fairly well until the wife became pregnant, a fact which greatly disturbed both of them. The wife had a miscarriage, left her husband, and became homosexual. The husband, feeling rejected, also became homosexual. This solution was easy for both of them because they moved in a social group in which homosexuality was relatively common.

The man came later for treatment. He had an intense feeling of worthlessness because of his sexual life; this was aggravated by the fact that he had not been attracted by women for five years, although he attracted them.

The treatment of these conditions is difficult and involved. In general, a person can be enabled to change these practices and become sexually adequate only if he is strongly dissatisfied with this aspect of his existence, if he has an intense desire to change it, and if the practices have not continued for too many years. If he is satisfied with this phase of his life and wishes to continue it, there is no reason why any therapist should insist that he change, as long as he does not harm others. If the patient is dissatisfied with his sexual practices, it depends on the degree of his dissatisfaction, and on the therapist's judgment as to how much can be expected of the patient, whether the therapist will aim at "curing" him or merely enabling him to live at peace with himself. In any case, the treatment always involves the whole individual, not the symptom alone. Almost the only ultimately effective treatment is psychoanalysis. If the patient is dissatisfied with his practices, the effectiveness of this treatment, in the experience of one of the authors, is more the rule than the exception.

SUGGESTED READINGS

Comparison should be made between our treatment of these disturbances and the discussions of other authors. In addition, we recommend in Freud's *A General Introduction to Psychoanalysis* (310) the portion on hysteria and Janet's *The Major Symptoms of Hysteria* (455). A very readable book on neurasthenia is Meyerson's *When Life Loses Its Zest.* For a good approach to the subject of sex, see Levy and Munroe (552), Wexberg's *Psychology of Sex,* and the book by R. L. Dickinson (209). For more complex discussion, see Kinsey, Pomeroy, and Martin (494), Hoch and Zubin (421), and the related chapters in Fenichel's book (267).

XXX Reactions in Which Organ Neuroses Predominate: Psychosomatic Disorders

In the various illnesses discussed in this chapter, the patient's chief complaint is a disturbance in the functioning of an organ or part of the body. Examination in all cases discloses definite structural or physiological changes; and, *in some cases*, the onset of the complaint as well as its severity is shown to be correlated with the patient's emotional reactions to certain distressing situations, or to his general character structure.

Various personality types and various conflict situations are found in the same type of organ neurosis. As a rule, however, certain personality types and conflict situations show a higher degree of correlation with particular types of organ neurosis. Ulcers of the stomach and duodenum are relatively common in the hard-driving, ambitious personality (22), as is also an anger response to conflict situations (675). The personality type in which repressed anger predominates is particularly common in high blood pressure (19, 820). Evidently a multiplicity of factors, psychological and organic, may determine a special type of neurotic organ reaction. Deutsch (203) assumed the following determinants in the case of asthma: (1) physical illness in childhood (e.g., whooping cough or bronchitis) during a period of emotional conflict; (2) parental attitude during this period concentrated on the child's illness (the mother being particularly concerned); (3) current conflict and situation of stress for the adult (e.g., the wife separating from the husband). (See also 223.)

The following example illustrates the multiple nature of conflict situations which may precipitate and maintain psychosomatic disorders.

A patient regularly got colitis attacks under three circumstances, with emotional stress characteristic for each: (1) Whenever he was overworking, driven by uncontrollable ambition. One might say that under these circumstances he was straining with all his effort. (2) Whenever, urged by his ambition, he undertook a task, particularly public presentation in a new field, for which he felt he was not adequately prepared and in which he therefore anticipated failure and exposure. One might say that under these circumstances he feared exposure in the performance of his function and also pleaded helplessness like an untrained infant. (3) When, because of feeling of sexual inadequacy and damage, he was stirred to homosexual fantasies, including that of swallowing the erect penis for the purpose of self-restitution.

The following study is an example of a careful approach to the problem of specific personality traits associated with specific psychosomatic disorders:

Fifty consecutive patients, found on physical examination to be suffering from hypertension, were examined, along with two control groups, for the presence or absence of certain personality traits. The latter examination was done without the examiner's knowing whether the subject was a "hypertensive" or a control. Statistically significant degrees of association were found between the presence of hypertension and "obsessive-compulsive behavior" ($r = 0.44 \pm 0.10$) and "subnormal assertiveness" ($r = 0.38 \pm 0.10$). No such association was found for the control group. This study shows that there is a measure of specificity of personality traits for certain psychosomatic disorders, but this is far from being exclusive (369).

Patients may suffer from two or more psychosomatic disorders simultaneously, or from a psychosomatic disorder and a psychoneurotic or psychotic reaction simultaneously. At times one observes an alternation between a psychotic state—e.g., depression—and a psychosomatic disorder—e.g., bronchial asthma.

The following experimental observations afford a good introduction to the discussion of the relation between organ neuroses and anatomical changes.

Several patients suffered from periodic attacks of small blisters around the mouth *(herpes labialis).* It was found that these attacks followed reactions to situations of stress. These patients were hypnotized when they were free from blisters, and severe, emotionally traumatic events (for example, death of the fiancé) were discussed with them. After the trance the patients always developed blisters.

The experiment was carried further. The contents of the blisters were transferred to the eye of a rabbit. The fact that the rabbit developed small blisters and then ulcers on the cornea proved that the contents of the blisters contained germs. (The germs that are responsible for *herpes labialis* have not yet been identified, but the infectious nature of the condition can be proved in this way.)[1]

The subject is put into a deep hypnotic state. His skin is then touched with some object (e.g., a pencil), and the suggestion is given that the object is a red-hot iron. There is an immediate circulatory change, and some hours or a day later a blister forms at the site where the burn was suggested. This blister, on microscopic examination, shows the same histological changes as a blister actually caused by a burn. The course of healing is also the same (219). Such experiments are not successful with every subject who is put into a deep hypnotic state.

Obviously, the germs in the herpes blister in the first experiment were

[1] R. Heilig and H. Hoff, Über psychogene Entstehung des Herpes labialis, *Med. Klin.,* 1928, 24, 1472.

not created by hypnosis; they were present in or on the body. The hypnotic experiment created some change in the function of the body concomitantly with the reaction to stress; the blisters were the result of these two factors. This general principle is probably the pattern for all organ neuroses that will be discussed. Although in the first experiment an identifiable agent (germ) was involved, in most situations the bodily factor is not clearly known. For this reason, in discussing psychological factors in organ neuroses, it should be understood that other factors may be operating which remain to be investigated.

DISTURBANCES OF THE GASTROINTESTINAL SYSTEM

PEPTIC ULCER

A peptic ulcer is a small wound which develops either in the stomach itself or in the duodenum, the portion of the bowels immediately below the stomach. The patient complains of recurrent pain in the upper abdomen, usually when the stomach is empty; the taking of food usually relieves the discomfort.

Psychosomatic Experiments on Emotions and Gastric Function. Mittelmann and Wolff (675; see also 24) have conducted experiments on normal individuals, on individuals with anxiety states, on those whose chief bodily symptom was a burning sensation in the stomach, and on patients with peptic ulcer. In control observations, the subjects were urged to relax while lying on a comfortable couch in a quiet room, and the finger temperature, the gastric secretion (obtained through a nasal catheter), and the stomach motility (registered by means of a swallowed inflated balloon) were recorded. After an initial period of relaxation, emotional stress was induced through the discussion of emotionally charged life situations. The predominant emotional tone of these experiments was anxiety, anger, and embarrassment. Many normal controls showed a decrease in the secretion of hydrochloric acid on days of greatest relaxation. During active discussion the secretion increased. At times, this increase was preceded by a temporary decrease. Bile was also regurgitated from the duodenum during excitement and stress.

In the most striking experiment, on a patient suffering from peptic ulcer, the following phenomena were observed: During a period of moderate but continuous anger, the secretion of hydrochloric acid was high and stomach motility increased. During periods of more intense anger, peristalsis increased still further; the hydrochloric acid secretion first dropped and then rose to its previous high level. After the period of most intense anger, blood appeared in the contents of the stomach. This last indicates that circulatory disturbance may occur during active periods of stress. There was a circulatory disturbance in the extremities also, as indicated by a fall in finger temperature.

In a subject who, as a result of an operation, had an opening of the stomach in the abdominal wall, extensive observations were made on the correlation between emotional reactions and gastric function. During panic reactions there were a temporary paling of the mucous membrane of the stomach and diminution of secretion and of peristalsis. During anger and anxiety there were an increase in the same functions and a blushing and swelling of the mucous membrane. In such a state the mucous membrane was easily injured. If the mucus was kept away from a wound in the stomach wall, the wound did not heal but developed into an ulcer (990, 991).

These experiments illustrate beyond question that emotional disturbance —i.e., anger, anxiety, embarrassment, and shame—may be correlated with disturbances in the functioning of the stomach. The experimental disturbing stimulus and its duration closely resembled the disturbances to which the subjects were exposed in their daily lives. The experiments also illustrate the widespread and complex changes in the body involved in a reaction to distress in connection with significant life situations. There was change not only in the functioning of the stomach, but also in finger temperature, respiration, blood circulation, etc.—in a word, in the whole body, as well as in the whole psyche.

The α index expresses the percentage of α rhythm in, let us say, a two-minute run of the electroencephalograph (EEG). This is fairly constant for a given individual. The term "dominant" α rhythm was applied to runs in which from 75 to 100 percent of the waves are of the α type. By evaluating the subject's dreams as indications of his bent for "activity" or "passivity," a correlation could be established between high α index and "passivity" on the one hand, and low α index and "activity" on the other (823). It was found that 71 percent of a hundred patients with peptic ulcers and 60 percent of forty-five patients with bronchial asthma exhibited "dominant" α indices. The incidence of dominant α index in unselected "normals" is 20 percent. In both of the above conditions, reactions to frustrated dependency longings play an important role in the dynamics of the illness (810, 811).

These are significant findings, but on further investigation the problem of the relationship of EEG type to personality traits will probably turn out to be more complex.

The following case illustrates clearly an ulcer complaint that appeared under stress and was correlated with the patient's character traits and emotional needs. Once the ulcer is established, it is maintained and reinforced by the stresses and strains of daily existence.

An electrician, thirty-five years old, a conscientious, rather hard-working, and ambitious man, had been suffering from duodenal ulcer for five years. He was devoted to his wife and his three children. He enjoyed the company of his friends and was interested in labor problems. Outwardly he always maintained good poise and calm. Careful discussion of his life history and of the circumstances under which his complaint started revealed the following: Frequently his work took him to another city for prolonged periods. During such periods he visited his family about once a month and sent money home regularly. While away from his home, he sometimes had relations with other women. When he was about thirty years old and away from home, he met with a serious accident in which a leg and an arm were broken. He was removed to the hospital and recovered fully. However, the next time he had to be away from home, he began to have pain a few hours after meals.

He was the oldest child in his family. His father, a good provider and a rather dutiful and strict man, died in an accident when the patient was five years old. The boy supported his mother and his three younger siblings practically from the age of fifteen. His younger brother was the mother's favorite. The patient's mother also died in an accident, as did one of his sisters.

In spite of the patient's predominant ambition, poise, and excellent performance, it was found that he had a strong, unconscious need to lean and depend upon others. This need clashed with his ideals and self-esteem. Furthermore, beginning with his relationship to his parents, he had always unconsciously expected rejection in all close emotional relations. He was in conflict about being away from his wife and family. His accident, together with guilt feelings because of his relations with other women, threatened his emotional dependence upon his wife. ("If she knew what I had done she would condemn me, repay me in kind, and abandon me.")[2] This resulted in anxiety and resentment. This emotional constellation was correlated with disturbance of the stomach, and each time he had to be away from home it was revived.

After psychotherapy was begun and dietary measures were taken, the patient's complaints lessened considerably, and he came to be almost entirely free from symptoms. Then a disturbing event occurred when his wife suffered an attack of appendicitis and had to be operated upon. She was reluctant to undergo the operation, but the patient reasoned with her without anger or rancor, and persuaded her to submit; he handled the situation with considerable poise and in a very sensible manner. During this period, however, his ulcer symptoms returned in full vigor because of the conflict situation, which was characterized chiefly by anxiety and the fear of losing her psychological support. Because of his unconscious outlook, this, of course, was accompanied by anger.

COLITIS

Colitis is characterized by frequent bowel movements or constipation, accompanied by pain and a discharge of mucus and blood. If the condition continues long enough, ulcers appear in the colon (ulcerative colitis). Colitis may be caused by a variety of agents, such as infections or dietary indiscretions; all these factors must be excluded before a case can be diagnosed as colitis attributable chiefly to emotional causes.

Some experimental observations are available on the influence of emotions on the activity of the colon (226). X-ray observations show that the emptying time and the tonus of the colon change concomitantly with emotional conditions. The colon may become spastic (extremely tense) or atonic

[2] Where there is such an unconscious fear of retribution, an accident like breaking a leg strengthens the fear, for the accident itself is unconsciously regarded as retribution.

(completely relaxed) in periods of emotional stress (24). Mucous colitis was correlated with resentment, anxiety, and guilt in fifty-three out of fifty-seven cases studied and is to be considered a psychosomatic condition (972). So is ulcerative colitis if no serious primary infection is present. A common stress situation is that of frustrated dependency, with hostility and suicidal trends (178). The emotional formula in psychogenic diarrhea may be, "I am giving of myself to the world; I deserve to be looked after"; in psychogenic constipation it is, "I am not receiving love and care; therefore I will give nothing to the world." Ulcerative colitis is a very serious illness and may end in death. The treatment is dietary and medicinal. Psychotherapy may be effective. (See also disorders in childhood, page 352.)

In the psychotherapy of ulcerative colitis, a method worked out by Lindemann is based on determining what person the patient lost, either actually or intrapsychically—i.e., the person died or rejected the patient. The therapist then attempts to replace this lost person for the patient, partly by "role-playing"—that is, behaving in some respects in a manner similar to that of that person; e.g., if he was firm, so is the therapist; if he was very kind, so is the therapist. Secondly, the patient is brought into contact with another individual who can play in his life a similar emotional role as the lost person. (See also childhood disorders, page 352.)

A man of fifty-five, an efficient carpenter, had symptoms of colitis. He had always been headstrong and rather aggressive, and inclined always to dominate the situation. His wife was completely obedient to him and accepted his verdict in everything. His father's character had resembled his own, and his mother had accepted all his father's verdicts. The father was rather strict with the patient and punished him severely when he rebelled, as he often did. He finally left home, chiefly to get away from his father. He later became reconciled with his father, but he himself adopted a similar behavior. When he was about fifty, he found it difficult to maintain his earning capacity and his position in his trade. Although he was not hard up financially, the situation enraged him, and it was during this period that his bowel movements became too frequent and finally colitis developed.

This patient had felt dominated, insecure, and unfairly treated in his relationship with his parents. His relationship with everyone else had the same qualities as that with his parents. He solved his conflicts chiefly by assuming a dominant, overbearing, ambitious, superior, self-centered attitude. This carried him along fairly well until his age and the economic depression made it impossible for him to maintain such an attitude successfully. The preference for younger men threatened his whole security system, his method of solving life problems. It was the threat to his over-valued picture of himself that aroused his anger and his anxiety.

DISORDERS OF THE RESPIRATORY SYSTEM

BRONCHIAL ASTHMA

Bronchial asthma[3] is characterized by attacks of difficulty in breathing during which the patient practically has no control of it. An examination during the attack shows characteristic wheezing sounds over the chest and certain characteristic blood changes. The attacks are caused by an involuntary contraction of the bronchial muscles. This spasm interferes with the respiration during both inspiration and expiration, but particularly during expiration. This contraction of the bronchial muscles is mediated chiefly through the vagus nerve. The muscles are relaxed and the attack is terminated by an injection of adrenalin, which increases the tone of the sympathetic system.

Asthma attack is correlated mainly with attitudes of anger and hostility, particularly toward a dependency figure (mother or her substitute) and the resultant fear of abandonment (295). The asthmatic attack itself frequently represents the equivalent of an attack of rage (Dunbar) or a stifled cry for help (Saul). In thirty-seven of fifty unselected asthma patients emotional factors were significant in the maintenance of the illness (595).

Psychosomatic Experiments on Respiration. Comprehensive experiments on the correlation between emotions and respiration were conducted by Finesinger (272). He determined the respiratory curve and the amount of oxygen consumption (basal metabolic rate) of several patients, first in a period of relaxation. They were then asked to think of something disturbing, and the respiratory curve and the basal metabolism were recorded. He found that, during disturbed periods, respiration became more frequent and deeper, the inspiration-expiration angle grew sharper, and the oxygen consumption rose considerably. (See also 80, 199, 200; for a case illustration, see page 351.)

VASOMOTOR RHINITIS

Vasomotor rhinitis consists of congestion of the nasal mucous membrane and of the conjunctivae of the eyes; there is a thin, watery secretion from the nose, together with sneezing and with itching of the eyes. The personality types may vary. The common stress situation is that of frustrated dependency longing, directed particularly toward the mother or mother substitute. There may also be strong sexual curiosity relating to the function of reproduction and a desire to look and smell. The result of the conflict may be congestion of the nasal mucous membrane, with damage to both olfactory and visual perception (979, 821, 427). (At times sinusitis

[3] Asthma and vasomotor rhinitis are allergic disorders. See pages 349-352.

develops on a similar emotional background because the circulatory disturbance leads to lowered resistance to infection.)

Daily observations of nasal functions and structures, including changes in circulation, swelling, secretion, evidences of obstruction, and pain, were made on groups of healthy and sick persons. Daily records were made of the subject's life situation, attitudes, dominant emotional reactions, fantasies, and dreams. It was found that abject fear and dejection and disgust were associated with pallor of the nasal mucosa and decreased secretion; on the other hand, anxiety and resentment were associated with redness and swelling of the mucosa, increased secretion, and obstruction. Weeping, as well as the feeling of being on the verge of tears, was associated with pallor, extreme swelling of the nasal mucosa, profuse secretion, and obstruction, with complaints of difficulty in breathing (427).

FREQUENT UPPER RESPIRATORY INFECTION

By this term are meant frequent colds, sore throats, laryngitis, and bronchitis. The psychogenic factors may operate in these conditions through reducing the patient's resistance to infection or by making him expose himself more or less unwittingly to chill as a self-destructive act. The characteristic conflicts may be over olfactory curiosity and fear of retribution through abandonment or attack, as symbolized by choking (427, 819).

PULMONARY TUBERCULOSIS

The tubercle bacillus may cause chronic inflammation in any organ of the body. The most common site is the lungs. Reactions to life situations may lower the resistance of the individual to this infection (459, 460). Reactivation of the inflammatory process just at the time of planned discharge from the sanitarium is not an uncommon observation. Fear and reluctance to leave a sheltered environment may be factors in it. At times the onset and the recurrence of the illness seem correlated with a largely unconscious, defiant, self-destructive refusal of the patient to commit himself to a course required by an actual and internalized authority (usually the father figure).

Psychotherapy may be a useful adjunct in the treatment, which is mainly adequate food and rest, general hygiene, and, recently, the use of antibiotics—e.g., streptomycin.

SKIN DISORDERS

The skin disorders that are connected with personality problems are excessive perspiration of the armpit and of the extremities, with thickening and sensitiveness of the soles of the feet, warts, acne, itching, urticaria, and dermatitis. These disorders have been identified as psychosomatic either because they start or become worse during stress situations or because they improve or are cured by psychotherapy, at times of the hypnotic type.

Warts disappeared as a result of suggestion in 78.5 percent of 179 checked-up cases (Bloch). Many of these patients had been suffering from warts for months or even years and then suddenly lost them within from two to twelve weeks after treatment (916).

The two disorders that will be discussed in greater detail are urticaria and dermatitis, both of which, as well as itching (658, 666) and angioneurotic edema, can be grouped under the allergic disorders. Angioneurotic edema is a transient swelling of the skin without pain or redness, occurring most commonly on the face and on the back of the hands.

URTICARIA

The symptoms of urticaria are a fleeting rash and a swelling and itching of the skin. The relation of this disturbance to emotional disturbance has been known for some years. A recent study by Saul (821) demonstrates this relationship. (See also 223.)

A patient who was being treated psychoanalytically had twelve attacks of urticaria, all of which could be connected with a previous acute frustration of her strong desire for warmth and affection in her engagement. There were, of course, more than twelve frustrations, and Saul attempted to discover why no urticaria resulted from these others. His conclusion, based on very plausible evidence, was that, if weeping occurred after frustration, urticaria did not appear; i.e., urticaria is a result of unreleased emotion in frustration, and weeping represents such a release. He reports at least one startling confirmation of this hypothesis. A traumatized woman who wept incessantly developed an urticaria of the whole body when forced to stop; the urticaria disappeared when she was encouraged to weep again.

The following case shows how the symptoms are connected with emotional problems and fantasies.

A gifted mathematician, who was under psychoanalytic treatment, agreed to his wife's desire that they have a child, although he had resisted it for years. He had never admittedly applied himself whole-heartedly to anything, and he never became fully attached to anyone. He married because he felt that his wife was a good worker and no financial burden would fall on him. In general, he was a dependent individual, but he followed a philosophy of detachment and self-sufficiency. His decision to have a child was based partly on his improved outlook but to an even greater extent on his desire to show the analyst that he was entirely well and completely independent of him. The latter was obvious from the fact that he said nothing of his wife's pregnancy until the analyst deduced it from the patient's dream.

At the time of his wife's delivery, the patient went into a serious anxiety state. His general reaction was: "I'll have to take care of her now, I'll have to assume the burden of the children, and I'll have to submit to their domination. Actually, I am helpless and enslaved, and I ought to be looked after without being dominated.

In fact, I ought not to be the father, I ought to be the child." The emotional constellation was chiefly anxiety, anger at being entrapped, a feeling of helplessness and enslavement and rebellion. In several dreams the patient threw a woman and a child into a rocky, turbulent stream and himself fell into the stream. He dramatized these emotions with urticaria. The patient, of course, had many other symptoms during this time, such as nightmares, periods of complete inability to work, the desire to sleep twelve or thirteen hours at a time, and sometimes considerable irritation with his wife in the hospital. All of these symptoms were connected with his emotional crisis.

ECZEMA

This condition is an inflammation of the skin characterized by itching, redness, and often formation of small blisters which are scratched open and lead to oozing. If the condition is chronic, the skin becomes thick. Of course, special types of infection and the presence of irritating chemicals—e.g., gasoline—must be ruled out. Secondary infection may occur. The condition has been named neurodermatitis, emphasizing the "nervous" origin, and atopic dermatitis, emphasizing the allergic aspect. Individuals suffering from it frequently, although not invariably, have had infantile eczema (see Chapter XX) or have other allergic manifestations also.

The emotional factors that play a role are (1) desire for closeness and emotional warmth, the skin reaction then representing the anxious realization of the fantasy of being cared for through the symbolism of warm fondling; (2) aggression directed toward the self (scratching); and (3) erotization of the skin.

The following case illustrates briefly the possible complexity of the dynamics as well as the combination of several psychosomatic disorders in the same individual.

A woman with aggressive, outgoing personality was suffering from arterial hypertension and later, in addition, from periods of psychoneurotic depression and anxiety. When she was five years old, she had itching of the feet, probably connected with rivalry with her younger sister. When she was fourteen years old, she developed a generalized itching lasting twenty-four hours after seeing a thief sneak out of her house with her mother's jewels and after the mother became "hysterical" and screamed. At the age of fifty-one, when she was disappointed in the coldness of her husband, she decided to spend the summer at the house of her sister, with whom she had once been in rivalry but with whom she was now on friendly terms. A passing, dry, erythematous (red), scaly eruption appeared on the webs of her fingers when her husband visited her and they had some clashes. This skin eruption had a background of resentment and a desire for aggressive use of the hands.

The next summer, the patient went away for two months and decided she would not return to her husband. Now a similar eruption appeared on the back of both of her hands, her face became swollen (angioneurotic edema), and there was a redness of the eyes and a thin, watery discharge from the nose (vasomotor rhinitis).

Her physician advised her to return to her husband. This she did, and she became depressed, but the eruption on the back of her hands disappeared. She entered upon analytic treatment, and she again decided to leave her husband because he declined to coöperate by going for treatment himself. Concomitantly with the fear of loneliness, her angioneurotic edema and the dermatitis on the back of her hands reappeared, the latter in a more severe, weeping form. The skin eruption was an anguished cry of fear, an expression of feeling of debasement, and an attempt to obtain love and care.

As other allergic disorders, eczema also responds well to briefer psychotherapy or to analysis, particularly if the acute manifestations are handled medicinally as well (adrenalin, ephedrine, antihistaminic drugs, soothing local applications). The effect of the treatment at times is very rapid, at other times it is prolonged and interspersed with hectic periods.

ENDOCRINE DISORDERS

EXOPHTHALMIC GOITER

Exophthalmic goiter is characterized by irritability, restlessness, bulging of the eyes, excessive perspiration, loss of weight, rapid heart rate, trembling of the fingers, and enlargement of the thyroid gland. Oxygen consumption is considerably increased, indicating a rise in basal metabolism. The physiology of the condition is not entirely clear, but it is known that not all the symptoms are caused by the over-functioning of the thyroid gland. Bulging of the eyes does not appear in a healthy individual who takes an excessive amount of thyroid substance.

It is difficult to state whether an emotional factor is always involved in the syndrome in human beings. Conrad (167) and Mittelmann (659) found that the condition followed an emotional crisis with a probability of ninety-three out of a hundred cases. (See Chapter III.)

Deutsch and Kauf (204) observed that during emotional stress, which may be largely unconscious, pulse rate and metabolism rise. They hypnotized subjects and tested their pulse rate and metabolism. After a control period they suggested harrowing experiences to these subjects, at the same time recording pulse rate and metabolism; there was a rise of about 27 in the pulse rate and of approximately 20 percent in the metabolism. The suggested harrowing experiences were of this type: They told a woman who was much attached to her mother that her mother was lost in a forest during a storm. They told this woman that after waking from the trance she would forget the experience, but that these emotions would recur when the experimenter took a handkerchief out of his pocket. They found that her metabolism and pulse rate rose under these conditions, without conscious anxiety and without her knowing why. Such experiments show that anxiety and other distressing emotional states are correlated with change in basal metabolism.

Since the use of iodine as a preparation for the operation, surgical removal of a large part of the thyroid gland is a most reliable way of treating the condition, with additional psychotherapy. In the last few years, two forms of medication have become effective. One is thiouracil, and the other is radioactive iodine. Thiouracil must be administered over a protracted period; radioactive iodine is given just once. The difficulty with the latter is that the exact dose required is hard to determine. Psychotherapy in the management of the patient is particularly important with medicinal treatment; otherwise he does not carry out instructions, becomes easily disappointed in his physician, and is constantly exposed to emotional stresses.

DIABETES MELLITUS

Diabetes mellitus is a condition characterized by deficient functioning of the internal secretion of the pancreas. The psychogenic factors play a role in two ways: (1) They increase the blood sugar level, possibly through the effect of other glands of internal secretion that oppose the pancreas—e.g., the adrenal medulla. (2) Because of defiance and feelings of futility, the patient may not carry out the medicinal (insulin) measures and may develop acidosis and go into a diabetic coma (131, 794).

DISORDERS OF THE CARDIOVASCULAR SYSTEM

HIGH BLOOD PRESSURE (ESSENTIAL HYPERTENSION)

Opinion differs on the normal upper limit of the systolic blood pressure in a relaxed individual; some consider 140 the limit, but no authority considers a pressure above 150 anything but high. The most important aspect, however, is the diastolic blood pressure, because that is determined mainly by the condition of the smaller blood vessels. For the diastolic pressure, the upper limit of normal is 90. The person with continuously high blood pressure may have no complaints, or he may complain of headaches and dizziness. Primary physical disturbances, such as inflammation of the kidneys or hardening of the arteries, may be responsible for this condition. In some instances, however, as in essential hypertension, no such factor can be found, but the presence of strong emotional influences can often be established.

Normal people who are apprehensive—e.g., students before an examination—may have a higher than normal pressure. The blood pressure in animals rises during rage or fear (150), and normal human beings who are extremely angry likewise show a rise (522).

The significance of anxiety is illustrated by accidental observation of the kidney function of two subjects who got into acute states of anxiety while the circulation of the kidneys was being measured. The renal blood flow was decreased by about 40 percent, and there was an increase in blood pressure. It may be mentioned that a diminished blood flow in the kidneys liberates a substance which raises the blood pressure (872).

There was an explosion, followed by extensive fire, in a chemical plant in Texas. The blood pressures of all the employees of the company had been previously recorded. Following the explosion, a number of the employees with previously normal blood pressure readings developed sustained elevation of the systolic and diastolic blood pressure.

The emotional constellation most frequent in patients with essential hypertension is anger, often completely repressed, mingled with anxiety and depression.

Alexander (19) regularly recorded one patient's blood pressure before and after each analytic session. It was high when he was in a disturbed emotional state, but was at or near normal when he was emotionally calm. (See also 987.)

This patient was self-conscious and had a vivid sense of inferiority, but at the same time he was ambitious to excel and to do perfect work. His overt modesty and compliance put him under extreme pressure and created intense inferiority feelings in him. The patient would never contradict his superior; he would follow his suggestions and accept blame while talking with him, but after he left the office he would be filled with self-contempt and would say to himself: "You should have answered; you should have said no! You are no good and you never will be any good." This self-deprecatory attitude usually became so unbearable that he would want a drink, for alcohol dissipated his sense of weakness and inefficiency. Furthermore, drinking during the day represented an act of rebellion in that he was indulging in a forbidden activity. He also was promiscuous sexually at such times; this was an expression of rebellion against his wife. Otherwise he subjected himself to all the requirements of the marital state.

As a child, the patient had had outbreaks of extreme rage which he later completely forgot, but which were recovered in the analysis. His father, an object of fear and hostility to the boy, thought it his duty to break the lad's aggressive spirit and rebelliousness, and made a point of teaching him how to be a loser. When the patient was about eight years old, his father began taking him out to the golf course, beating him at the game repeatedly, and trying to make him like to be beaten. The patient remembered his senseless rage when he was beaten in any competitive game (19).

NEUROCIRCULATORY ASTHENIA

Neurocirculatory asthenia, a syndrome which has also been called disordered action of the heart, soldier's heart, and effort syndrome, is characterized by rapid and labile action of the heart (over eighty beats per minute), difficulty in breathing, often with feelings of faintness and dizziness, and cold extremities. The condition is essentially an anxiety state, particularly aggravated by exercise. The patient is afraid of physical effort, constantly anticipates it, and, in this sense, is constantly engaged in it. Physical effort comes to represent aggressive behavior, with the attendant anxiety. The condition responds well to psychotherapy.

Irregular heart beats may also occur in association with anxiety states (903).

RAYNAUD'S SYNDROME

Raynaud's Syndrome is characterized by attacks of blanching and/or cyanosis in some of the fingers and, less frequently, in the toes. It is frequently accompanied by pain. It is due to a spasm of the blood vessels. The attacks are precipitated most commonly through cold, but emotional factors may also play a decisive role. A combination of both factors induces the attack most frequently, as can be shown in experimental investigations in a constant temperature room. If the temperature of the room is moderately low, a discussion of stressful life situations induces a drop in finger temperature, and a characteristic attack occurs (674). Under favorable circumstances, the disorder responds well to psychotherapy. In some cases, surgical removal of the sympathetic nerve supply to the upper extremities is effective.

MIGRAINE

Migraine consists of periodic severe headaches, usually on one side, which are frequently accompanied by nausea, vomiting, constipation, or diarrhea. In more severe cases, the patient may have spots before the eyes and uncomfortable sensations on one side of the body. The attack may last from a few hours to several days. The attack is mediated through a spasm of the blood vessels supplying the respective organs, particularly the meninges of the brain.

Migraine usually occurs partially as a reaction to situations of stress. As a rule, patients suffering from these attacks are unusually ambitious and preoccupied with achievement and success. They are often perfectionists, to whom efficiency means a great deal; they are orderly to an extreme. A disturbance of the sexual function is common, manifesting itself in frigidity and disgust (614).

A married woman of thirty-three had migraine of six years' duration; it had been growing worse in the last six months, attacks occurring once or twice a week. The illness had its onset with growing domestic tension, culminating in her husband's sister coming to live in her home. The sister quarreled continuously with both the patient and the patient's husband. The latter had been unemployed for four years. The family was on relief; and the patient, besides keeping house and caring for two children, supplemented the family income by peddling stockings. She was a meticulous, "fussy" housekeeper. "When I am home I don't sit down for five minutes. I always find something to do. I've got a worrisome nature; and besides, having a man around the house seven days a week, you can't keep your house 'just so.' "

The patient was a tense, anxious, driving, and ambitious woman who was thoroughly dissatisfied with her lot and looked on her life as miserably lacking. Despite an unusually small income, she gave her children advantages that could come only from good management. Notwithstanding concern for her family's welfare, her relations with her eldest daughter were bad. The child had temper tantrums, was obstinate, and seriously distressed her mother. On one occasion the child precipitated in the mother a frenzy of murderous rage. "I wished she were dead. I started to undress her. I wanted to murder her. I wanted to kill her dead nude. It ended by my having an hysterical crying attack."

The patient had been the youngest of seven children and had been considered a timid, bashful, obedient child.

At the age of eleven many responsibilities were loaded on her, primarily the care of her sister's babies. This, and the oppressive influence of a dominating father, caused her to resent her home life bitterly. She grasped the first opportunity for marriage, explaining, "I married my husband just to get away from home." Her sexual and married life were unsatisfactory.[4]

DISTURBANCES OF THE GENITOURINARY ORGANS

DISTURBANCES CONNECTED WITH MENSTRUATION

Three groups of conditions connected with menstruation have varying degrees of psychogenic factors: (1) changes in the amount of menstrual flow, (2) emotional stress preceding or during menstrual flow, and (3) painful menstruation.

Changes in the Quantity of the Menstrual Flow. Temporary delay in menstrual period is not infrequently seen as correlated with stress situations. Of rarer occurrence is "false pregnancy" (pseudocyesis), in which the woman does not menstruate for many months, together with enlargement of the abdomen due to accumulation of gas. There is an excess of gonadotropic (pituitary) and a diminution of estrogenic (follicular) hormone (with persistence of the corpus luteum), as in pregnancy (691). The psychogenic background of the disturbance is a fantasy of being pregnant—that is, the desire for a child. However, desire for a child accompanied by such phenomena is a total personality reaction, and pregnancy represents a desperately desired fulfillment of the role as a woman or the idea of self-sufficiency, possessing everything within oneself, including the male organ ("narcissistic" desires), and the desire to be looked after.

Premenstrual or Menstrual Tension. Premenstrual tension is the more common of the two. It consists of moodiness, irritability, and, in more severe reactions, anxiety states. As a rule, the symptoms disappear when menstruation begins. In other instances, however, the symptoms continue or become intensified during menstruation.

If the symptoms are severe, they represent total personality reactions. The dominant features are (1) reaction to an unlocalized (hormonal) tension, and (2) rebellion against the feminine role and increase in anxieties about interhuman relations as symbolized by the feminine role. At times the hormonal level is excessively high or remains high when it ought to decline (77).

Dysmenorrhea (Painful Menstruation). The pain in dysmenorrhea is

[4] H. G. Wolff, Personality features and reactions of subject with migraine, *Arch. Neurol. Psychiat.,* 1937, 37, 895-921.

cramplike in character and is due physiologically to increased contractions of the uterus occurring mainly on the first day of menstruation. The physical condition at times shows an under-developed uterus. Psychologically, there may be fear of the feminine role and, particularly, an equating of menstruation with being attacked and injured. The symptom often improves or disappears in the course of psychotherapy. Medicinal treatment consists mainly of analgesics and sedatives.

DISTURBANCES OF THE URINARY FUNCTION

Enuresis occasionally continues into adulthood. Even if the enuresis stops, urgency and frequency of urination may continue in the adult. (See Chapter XXI.) The bladder disturbances in adulthood can be of two types: more commonly, frequency and urgency and, less frequently, retention of urine in the bladder. The former is associated with an increased tension, the latter with a relaxation of the bladder masculature. It has been possible to demonstrate experimentally the increase in the intravesicular tension during reactions of anger and anxiety in patients suffering from the former condition and a low tension in the latter group, particularly in states of apathy and depression (906). All of these conditions respond to psychotherapy, but at times the symptom yields only after prolonged treatment.

DISORDERS OF THE SKELETOMUSCULAR SYSTEM

ARTHRITIS

In chronic inflammation of the joint, the emotional stress may exert its effect through muscle pull, disturbances of circulation, and violent, jerky, or strained movement, which may damage the lining membrane of the joint. The frequent psychopathological constellation is conflict over the use of the extremities for aggressive and sexual purposes, resentment over constrained motility, and an impulsive way of dealing with conflicts. It is difficult to state how much of a role the psychogenic factors play. The new drug that produces a dramatic improvement is one of the hormones of the adrenal cortex.

SUGGESTED READINGS

Good introductions to the field are Hinsie, *The Person in the Body* (414), and Maurice Levine, *Psychotherapy in Medical Practice* (450). Dunbar's *Emotions and Bodily Changes* (226) covers the field encyclopedically. A more concentrated, briefer presentation of the field is Mittelmann's article (665). Weiss and English, *Psychosomatic Medicine* (960), is easily readable and comprehensive; Alexander and French's *Studies in Psychosomatic Medicine* (22) is more complex. For detailed studies, see various issues of *Psychosomatic Medicine*.

XXXI Reactions in Which Alcoholism and Drug Addiction Predominate

The use of chemical substances such as alcohol and opium can be considered pathological only (1) if they are used in excess, if the individual cannot do without them, and if they have deleterious effects, and (2) if their use is disapproved of by the group. In a sense, the second point is a special instance of the first, for, if a person uses a substance which the group disapproves of, he almost invariably does so because he "craves" it and cannot be deprived of it, and he invariably uses it in large quantities.

The following discussion will center chiefly on the pathological aspects, but the effect of a moderate use of these substances will also be mentioned. Essential to an understanding of the whole problem are the patient's psychological problems which lead him to use the substance, the physical effects of this substance, and the psychotic reactions which result. In these psychotic reactions, the direct toxic effects of the substances are combined with the psychological reactions, attitudes, and conflicts characteristic of the individual (663).

PSYCHODYNAMICS OF ALCOHOLISM AND DRUG ADDICTIONS

The fears that are characteristic of addictions are of unbearable humiliation, particularly after failure, and of complete submission and destruction, especially after the individual has sought relief from anxiety through homosexual submission. This catastrophic threat is closely approximated psychologically in alcoholic hallucinosis.

In addition to these fears, several other factors combine to make the habitual use of a substance a major problem. External factors are important. For example, contact with groups which drink heavily or use drugs gives a person an opportunity and inclination to do likewise. An individual faced by conflicts, unhappiness, and anxieties may attempt to cope with or escape them through the narcotic or intoxicating effect of these substances. A special bodily responsiveness to the substance or special psychological constellations are probably responsible for his adopting this special solution.

The most commonly used intoxicant is alcohol. Its use has the following "ameliorative" effects: (1) Alcohol gives the individual pleasure through the use of the mouth and the taste. This in itself has a consoling value and may compensate for other pleasures or satisfactions that he is not able to obtain. (2) The narcotic effect of the alcohol enables the individual to forget his fears and stresses. In the state of drunkenness, the external world is excluded. The intoxicating effect further enables him to indulge in satisfying impulses which he ordinarily struggles against. Thus alcoholic belligerency may serve the purpose of expressing his hostility toward various people, and sexual desires which are ordinarily inhibited may be satisfied. (3) The elation which may accompany alcoholism enables the individual to feel positive joy and satisfaction that he is otherwise unable to attain and which helps him to forget his difficulties. Probably both self-debasing and self-aggrandizing tendencies are concerned when a person tends toward chronic alcoholism. (4) The individual's companions are like himself; they drink. This companionship compensates him for his rejection by and the loss of the love of other people. It is often quite characteristic of this alcoholic relationship that it lacks "closeness" and "warmth." As a matter of fact, the individual is afraid of close relationships because he fears rejection. The barroom relationships do not demand too much from him, and he receives from them just as much as he wants. (5) Alcohol induces defiance and self-assertion, and raises self-esteem. The drinker says, "I have the courage to defy prohibitions and authority. I am somebody. I am worth something. I cannot be dominated." (6) Profound desires for self-effacement, submission, self-debasement, and withdrawal from the world, ordinarily repressed, may appear because the alcohol diminishes inhibitions (833). (See also psychopathy, Chapter XXIV.)

Some patients periodically change the drugs they use, replacing opium by cocaine or marijuana by alcohol. The dynamics are similar, but social attitudes and actual circumstances limit the use of the substances other than alcohol. This implies either that the dynamic forces making for their use are stronger, so that they override the opposing forces of guilt and fear of detection, or that the self-destructive tendencies are more intense—provided the individual belongs to a social group that essentially accepts the prevailing injunction against their use. If the individual belongs to the criminal group or a group with a less strict code of behavior—e.g., jazz musicians—then one of the dynamic factors is conformance with the group. The use of hypnotics (barbiturates) or of bromides has, in the main, an anxiety-relieving effect and none of the disinhibiting effects nor the forms of social contact that go with the use of the other substances. Addiction to hypnotics starts most frequently on the basis of the use of the drugs for insomnia, along with their use during the day to allay anxiety and restlessness. Bromide intoxication starts with the use of the drug for "nervousness."

PHARMACODYNAMIC EFFECTS

In sufficiently large doses, the acute effect of all the substances is a sedative and hypnotic one; at times, depending on the individual and the substance—e.g., alcohol—this occurs after an initial period of disinhibition and euphoria. This latter effect has much to do with the anticipation and with the social setting in which the consumption occurs. The other effect of large enough doses is ataxia. With the recurrent, repetitive use, the disinhibiting, euphoric effect increases and lasts longer, in part because the individual learns the amount necessary to reach and sustain the euphoric state.

The following brief statements apply to the substances other than alcohol. Addiction to the *opiates* is most serious of all, in part because of the withdrawal symptoms at the time of the attempted cure. These symptoms are restlessness, yawning, cold and hot flashes, excessive nasal secretion, feeling of suffocation, vomiting, diarrhea, profuse perspiration, tremor, feeling of despair and of threat of violence, and, at times, complete collapse, sometimes causing death. If no drug is administered, the symptoms disappear within from seven to ten days. At any time during this period, if the drug is administered, the symptoms disappear within a few hours. Withdrawal can be effected with much less discomfort through the administration of insulin.

Dogs have been experimentally addicted to morphine by regular injections. When the injections were discontinued, they exhibited symptoms similar to those exhibited by human beings during abrupt withdrawal.

Marijuana (hashish, "reefers") differs from the opiates in that it creates no increased tolerance and is free from withdrawal symptoms. It is used mostly in the form of cigarettes. In some individuals, it causes only physical discomfort, such as fullness in the head and palpitation, whereas in others it produces anxiety or euphoria, talkativeness, flight of ideas, and impulsive behavior.

There are no withdrawal symptoms associated with the discontinuance of *cocaine*. The chronic use of *barbiturates* and of *bromides* leads to forgetfulness, confusion, lassitude, delirium, ataxia, and speech disturbance. The most important withdrawal symptom in barbiturate addiction is convulsions. This occurs in individuals who have never suffered from epilepsy. The diagnosis of bromide intoxication is based, apart from the history, on finding a high bromide level in the blood stream.

The number of responses elicited on the word-association test in the same individual without alcohol was smaller, but the responses were of a distinctly superior quality, more logically associated with the stimulus. For example, to the stimulus word "butter," normally such response words are produced as "cheese," "bread," "yellow." After a glass or two of whiskey is taken, the stimulus word "butter" may evoke such responses as "bitter," "flutter," "butterfly." These findings can be interpreted in the following two ways: (1) that alcohol diminishes the efficiency of the subjects in responding relevantly to a test of association; (2) that alcohol produces relaxation in the subjects, this being apparent in the ease of production of a larger number of "nonsense" responses. Finally, some inhibited subjects respond freely and with qualitative improvement only with alcohol because of release from self-consciousness; this is apparent in the occasional individual who shows qualitatively improved production.

Cats with experimental neurosis induced by the conditioning method respond again adequately to stimuli after ingesting a small amount of alcohol (630). This phenomenon may parallel the relaxing effect mentioned in the inhibited human subject. However, what obviously happens in alcoholism is this: with the quantity of alcohol increased, the repressed emotional disturbances overwhelm the subject.

Fifty million persons in the United States use alcoholic beverages. Six percent (or three million) of this group become excessive drinkers. Of the six percent, one-fourth (750,000) become addicts (999).

Dipsomania. The patient with dipsomania indulges in excessive drinking periodically. He drinks to such an extent that he is not able to pursue his normal work, and he gets into trouble and may be injured. The period of drinking may start quite involuntarily—a cocktail with friends may initiate it—or it may begin voluntarily after a period of struggle against it. Between periods of drinking the patient behaves apparently well, but careful examination will bring forth personality disturbances. The periodic drinking is a reaction to situations of stress. (See also repetitive commission of antisocial acts, Chapter XXIV.)

A gifted and fairly successful writer had periods when he drank heavily. They would occur anywhere from every three to every eight months and would last from two weeks to a month. He would get into trouble. He would wander away from the house and turn up in a hospital with a fractured rib, without knowing how he broke it. He would neglect his work, fail to keep appointments, and fail to live up to his contracts. He would become belligerent, get into fights, and be beaten up. Several times he attempted to forge checks, but they were not accepted.

The patient's drinking bouts always occurred after a disappointment, either with a friend or with his work. During his free periods, he worked quickly and wrote voluminously; he had a good market for his material. After many years of drinking, his work began to deteriorate, the periods of drinking grew much longer, his hands trembled, and he showed signs of chronic alcoholism. He would spend the money that he earned on drinking, and then would beg his friends for money to buy food for his wife and child. Frequently, when he was drinking at home, he shouted abuse to men whom he heard talking and who he said called him obscene names. He accused his wife of infidelity and threatened to kill both her and his child. He refused all psychotherapy, and nothing could be done for him.

(Chronic alcoholism will be discussed under alcoholic psychoses, in Chapter XXXV.)

THE TREATMENT OF ALCOHOLISM AND OF ADDICTIONS

The treatment of alcoholism has two aspects: the treatment of acute drunkenness with coma and the prevention of a return to excessive drinking.

A person who has drunk so much that he remains unconscious more than one day is exposed not only to the effect of the alcohol but also to autointoxication and hence to the danger of developing disease infection. For this reason the stomach is washed out and an enema given. Frequently the individual revives as a result of the enema. If he is able to swallow, he is given coffee; if not, caffeine is injected into the muscles. Sedation, a high-caloric, vitamin-rich diet, and fluids are given (854).

The ease and effectiveness of the treatment of alcoholism depend (1) on the total psychopathology of the individual, including the presence and nature of other symptoms, and (2) on how predominant a role the alcoholism plays in the total adjustment pattern. The patient's complaints and reasons for coming for treatment are not always a reliable guide in this respect, although it can be said in general that it is much more frequent to find "alcoholism" not the predominant problem in individuals who apply for treatment because of alcoholism than to find alcoholism the predominant problem in individuals who apply for treatment for other reasons. In many patients who come for treatment either way, one finds drinking bouts occurring which are characterized by open aggressive behavior otherwise not manifested. These patients may be suffering, in addition, from anxiety states, impotence, and depression. They respond well to psychotherapy, particularly of the psychoanalytic variety. If "alcoholism" is associated with schizophrenia or psychopathic personality, the problem, of course, is more difficult.

The conditions in which alcoholism is the main symptom present a difficult problem for treatment.

The treatment of chronic alcoholism requires the complete cessation of drinking. This can be done gradually within seven days, but it is impossible if the patient remains at home, for he will sneak out and buy liquor.

It is very difficult to prevent the recurrence of chronic heavy drinking after the patient leaves the hospital. This can be accomplished with certainty only if his whole personality can be rebuilt so that his reactions to problems and difficulties change and he copes with them differently. Surprisingly enough, some people who have been heavy drinkers for as long as thirty years can stop suddenly. Other individuals are benefited by a thorough discussion of their problems, their personalities, their reaction patterns. Psychoanalytic treatment has proved successful in still other cases. None of these methods, however, has thus far been successful in every case.

The most effective treatment in chronic or recurrent alcoholism is the procedure developed by the association Alcoholics Anonymous. It is predominantly of the group-inspirational and supportive type, although an aspect of self-analysis is not missing. The prerequisite for the effectiveness of this treatment is: "We admitted we were powerless over alcohol—that our lives had become unmanageable; came to believe that a Power greater than ourselves could restore us to sanity."[1] In way of practical steps, when the first of these statements prevails, either the patient turns to Alcoholics Anonymous for help, or he accepts the services of the organization, which sought him out on somebody's recommendation. They speak with the individual whenever he wishes to discuss his problems and ask him to attend meetings in which problems are discussed by fellow alcoholics who have stopped drinking—"Made fearless and searching inventory of ourselves."[2] The effect is frequently quite dramatic and lasting. Unfortunately, no statistics are available. (See 932.)

Two methods of treatment that have been used as auxiliary to psychotherapy are conditioned reflex treatment (see Chapter XIV) and antabuse. Antabuse is a chemical compound which has the effect of producing an increased concentration of acetaldehyde from alcohol ingested. The patient, after a preliminary study as to sensitivity to the toxicity of the drug, is supposed to take it in tablet form for a year. While the drug is taken, consumption of alcohol has such unpleasant effects (flushing, vomiting) that the expectation is he will refrain from it permanently after one year's abstinence. This form of treatment, however, is controversial: some patients stop taking the drug, others take the drug yet use alcohol, and the effect in some individuals is so toxic as to cause serious damage.

The treatment of all the addictions involves withdrawal of the drug, which can be done gradually or abruptly. In barbiturate addiction it should be done gradually to prevent convulsions. In opium addiction it can be done either way. If the abrupt withdrawal is used, morphine is given in rapidly diminishing doses, and codeine is administered. For all of them hospitalization is required. Psychotherapy and the correction of the patient's socio-economic status are indispensable for a lasting effect. If the patients are followed over a long period, relapses are found to be common. Of course, one should remember that relapses may occur in any type of emotional disturbance, and the patient has a tendency to suffer a relapse to the same condition for which he was treated.

SUGGESTED READINGS

It is useful to see the treatment of this topic in other textbooks. For a psychoanalytic approach, see the related chapter in Fenichel (267) and the later article of Simmel (864). We recommend, as a thorough and interesting study, Karpman's "Female alcoholism," *Journal of Psychopathology Monograph,* 1948.

[1] *The Twelve Steps,* Alcoholics Anonymous.
[2] *Ibid.*

XXXII Reactions to Conditions of War

War conditions entail new types of stress situations for almost all people, civilians and military personnel alike. As in all other conditions of stress, the individual utilizes all the adaptive techniques at his command, but in a certain number of persons these techniques will prove to be inadequate. ". . . The underlying basic hazards to the soldier [were] (1) separation from home and anxiety regarding family (this [was] especially important for the British, French and Russian soldier, who [might] have his family injured in the course of civilian bombing by enemy planes); (2) fatigue; (3) discipline; (4) monotony; (5) loss of liberty; (6) strange surroundings; (7) change of diet; (8) change in attitude toward authority; (9) change in the psychology of the peace-loving civilian to becoming a 'killer' of the enemy; (10) fear of personal injury or deformity."[1] In combat situations, the person is faced with realistic dangers of death or mutilation, and inadequacy on his part—such as inefficient functioning due to fatigue or anxiety—may prove to be fatal. In these situations, many servicemen break down who might otherwise have led relatively normal, effective lives. In individuals whose adjustment was already tenuous, a psychopathological reaction which was already latent and which might have occurred sooner or later under less unusual life circumstances may be precipitated. In civilians who find themselves under enemy attack, as when cities are bombed, the same realistic dangers exist. Then, however, the additional stress of being helpless in the danger situation and being unable to fight back or to defend oneself is present. In the following discussion, emphasis will be placed upon neurotic reactions in service personnel.

It might be of interest, first, to survey the size of the problem of psychopathology in service personnel. As an example of this, United States Army figures will be quoted. The American army during the Second World War

[1] S. B. Wortis, Some aspects of military neuropsychiatry, *Trans. N.Y. Acad. Sci.*, 1945, pp. 167-180.

was composed of 11,367,989 men and women. During the course of the war, there were 918,961 neuropsychiatric hospital admissions. This comprised 6 percent of all hospital admissions. During the same period, 256,134 persons were discharged with the diagnosis of psychoneurosis. These statistics are not completely valid for several reasons. Some person were admitted to the hospital more than once. Some patients on medical and surgical wards were suffering primarily from emotional disorders. These statistics do not include patients seen at outpatient clinics and those who were diagnosed as cases of operational fatigue, combat fatigue, or combat exhaustion but who were suffering from neurotic reactions and whose condition cleared up quickly, before further study and more definitive diagnosis could be made (641).

BACKGROUND AND GENERAL DYNAMICS OF PSYCHOPATHOLOGICAL REACTIONS IN MILITARY SERVICE

Although the psychopathological reactions may occur at any point during an individual's military career, there are certain situations which have proved to be more difficult to adjust to than others. These situations will be briefly described, and how they are likely to lead to breakdowns will be discussed.

ADJUSTMENT TO MILITARY LIFE

In entering military life, the serviceman is called upon to adjust to what may be for him an entirely new type of life situation. Frequently this is his first prolonged period away from home. He is expected to give up certain mature modes of behavior and goals. He is no longer an independent individual able to decide upon his goals and the techniques for achieving these goals. He must accept group goals which are set for him (defeating the enemy) and has little or no choice as to what he as an individual is to do to achieve this. He tends to lose his individuality and become merely a cog in a machine, and his own needs are ignored in favor of military requirements. He may get lost in a jungle of red tape. He is usually drafted and assigned to a particular branch of the service (infantry, artillery, etc.). Malassignment is not infrequent and leads to a good deal of frustration in that the soldier feels that his capabilities are not being properly exploited. In general, he must learn to obey orders without question, and certain needs are supplied for him without any special effort on his part. He is clothed and fed. Certain immature, dependent personalities may find military life more comfortable than civilian life. More mature individuals are able to give up their independent patterns of behavior because they recognize the necessity for this in order to attain a goal which they approve and accept or because of strong feelings of identification with their country—i.e., patriotic feelings—or, later, with their group (combat unit). Others, who have attained a mature adjustment but in whom this is somewhat tenuous, may or may not be able to adjust to military life. Some more specific aspects of military life may prove to be especially threatening to certain individuals. For example, a person with a strong latent homosexual tendency may find living in close association with men threatening and may break down as a result. Others, in whom these tendencies are well sublimated, may find this type of life gratifying. Conflicts over authority and over competition are aroused. In general, it can be stated that people who break down early in their military career have already developed adjustment patterns which are relatively rigid and inadequate and make them more liable to psychopathological reactions under conditions of limited stress.

INITIATION INTO COMBAT

When the serviceman first experiences combat, he is usually meeting realistic dangers of this type for the first time and has as yet experienced little drain on his physical and emotional resources. When an individual breaks down early in the course of his combat experiences after having experienced only minimal stress, his psychopathological reaction is usually based upon previous pathological trends, and the nature of his reaction is usually related to his "precombat" personality organization. Under these circumstances, three main types of reactions have been observed: (1) The pathological reaction is based on an intrapsychic conflict involving a strong sense of duty—he wants to do his job, and he does not want to let his buddies down—and deep-seated feelings of insecurity. The stress of combat intensifies his feelings of insecurity and leads to anxiety, which becomes incapacitating and prevents him from carrying out his assignments. Because of his sense of duty, his failure results in feelings of guilt, self-condemnation, and depression. The individual may develop any type of neurotic symptom. (2) In this group, the conflict is primarily between inner feelings of insecurity and the desire for self-preservation on the one hand, and the realistic dangers on the other. As in the first group, underlying insecurity feelings are quickly intensified by combat experiences, and anxiety results. However, these people lack a strong sense of duty. They are likely to seek out the medical officer quickly at the first sign of anxiety in the hope of being removed from combat on medical grounds. (3) In persons who have had difficulty in adjusting to group life, to authority, and to coöperative work with others, the stress of combat may intensify these difficulties. These people are frequently more distressing to those who must work and live with them than they are to themselves, and they may not recognize their emotional disturbances (370).

PROLONGED AND SEVERE COMBAT STRESS

Prolonged and severely stressful combat experience saps the individual's resources both physically and emotionally. Fatigue and tension pile up in the ordinary course of fulfilling military duties. As the individual becomes increasingly tense, he is apt to be restless and to suffer from insomnia. He may lose his appetite, feel too tired to eat, and he is particularly apt to become intolerant of an unvaried menu and of food prepared in an unappetizing manner and may prefer to go hungry rather than eat the same dull, uninviting food. Thus replenishment of energy may become increasingly less adequate. After harrowing combat experiences—seeing his close friends killed and severely mutilated, having a near-fatal experience—nightmares in which combat experiences are relived may occur and disturb his sleep, and what sleep he gets is therefore less restful for him. As friends are lost in combat, the love formerly felt for them is replaced by concern over the self. As his resources become depleted, the individual further manifests increasing interest in his personal welfare, and along with this his passive-dependent needs become intensified. This revival of more immature strivings has already been facilitated by the initial requirements of adjustment to military life. (See page 477.) As he begins to make more and more demands for gratification of these needs upon those around him, they, who are going through the same process, are less and less able to meet his demands. He tends to become increasingly intolerant of the deprivations of military life, which now become actual frustrations for him. This further increases self-interest. As the individual's attachment to the group is thus weakened, he begins to feel guilt over his destructiveness—which was up to now acceptable to him because of his attachment to a group which not only sanctioned it but considered it necessary—and to fear retaliation from the enemy. This produces an increased expectation of injury and death. Thus a gradual attrition of the resources of the total organism occurs, and each new situation of stress becomes proportionately more difficult for the individual to face and to cope with. The individual then feels increasingly helpless, and the dangers he faces loom larger. This arouses anxiety, which comes into conflict with his remaining feelings of attachment to the group, his ideals, and his sense of duty. The anxiety thus aroused may interfere with efficient functioning in situations where accuracy may mean the difference between life and death. In addition to the external dangers he faces, the soldier now has to face the dangers arising out of his own (real) inadequacy.

In this setting, emotional breakdowns may occur in persons who can be considered essentially healthy individuals. These reactions may be of any type. Usually they do not fall into any clear-cut diagnostic category; patients are more likely to present mixed pictures, with several different symptoms. Whereas the initial reaction may be clearly related to the precipitating stress situation, as time goes on, and particularly after the patient is removed from the combat area, the picture tends to change. The patient may recover rather quickly, with only a brief period of rest out of the immediate combat zone, or he may require vigorous psychotherapy. If he does not recover rapidly and there is delay in instituting psychotherapy, the symptomatology and behavior change and become more closely linked with the soldier's "precombat" personality and conflicts and his previous habitual manner of solving conflicts. Still later, if a cure is not effected, the illness may take on yet another, chronic form (485). Upon investigation, it is frequently discovered that the breakdown occurred in a stress situation which was related to and aroused internal conflicts similar to those that first arose in the patient's early life (370).

RETURN TO NONCOMBAT DUTY AND TO CIVILIAN LIFE

Upon removal from combat after successful completion of a tour of duty, the serviceman, under average circumstances, was returned either to noncombat military duty or to civilian life. In this process he was frequently separated from his combat unit, with which he felt a strong identification, and had to revive old attachments and identifications which previously existed in civilian life and form new ones in his new surroundings. At the same time he was expected to give up the standards and morals adopted during combat life in favor of older ones he had formerly accepted. This transition took time and was not always accomplished smoothly. Now that he was no longer required to subjugate his own needs and feelings to the requirements of the group, the anxiety, hostility, and passive-dependent needs which developed during the course of his combat experiences and which remained masked because of the exigencies of combat life made themselves felt in the form of intense demands for gratification. The intensity of these depended upon the level of maturity the individual had previously attained, the severity of trauma experienced during combat, the intensity of disturbance created by separation from the group, and the amount of gratification and frustration he found in life after separation. These passive-dependent demands were frequently of such an intensity as to be practically impossible of gratification. The resultant frustration led to anxiety, irritability, and depression because of a feeling of being unloved and unappreciated. This conflict was intensified when the individual was unable to accept his passive-dependent needs because they came into conflict with his ideals of maturity and of masculinity. Then, when people in his environment did attempt to gratify his needs to some degree, he found their behavior unacceptable and threatening to his already tenuous equilibrium. Thus the frustration arising from external sources was intensified by that arising from internal sources. Concurrently, the anxiety aroused during combat, which was to a large extent repressed at that time, appeared on the surface. The formation of new attachments and the reëstablishment of old ones at times became difficult, because the returned man regarded the people he now came into contact with as potentially hostile for three reasons: (1) their inability to satisfy his needs made them appear hostile in his eyes; (2) this led to counterhostility, which frequently aroused fear of retaliation; (3) expectations of aggressive behavior from others carried over from his combat experiences. He was also faced with the problem of controlling his readiness for aggression, which was released during combat.

On the basis of their emotional reactions, the returned servicemen tended to fall into four groups: "(1) Those whose . . . reactions originated overseas, but who are now undergoing a successful and spontaneous process of 'unwinding,' 'uncoiling,' 'cooling off' or 'decompression.' (2) Those with neuroses which originated overseas, but which persisted with unabated severity, sometimes becoming progressively worse. (3) Those who develop new conflicts, due to failure of adaptation to the home environment, because their personalities have been altered by overseas experiences. (4) Those who show a recrudescence of former anxiety states, or who develop them for the first time owing to apprehension concerning new duty assignment or fear of their future."[2]

WOMEN IN MILITARY SERVICE

During the Second World War, women were incorporated into the various military services to carry out many noncombat duties. Up until that time the only women in military service had been nurses. As concerns adaptation to military life, the stresses undergone by women were to a large extent similar to those undergone by men, but there were some stresses which were unique to women and others which were experienced more keenly by women than by men. Their motivation in entering service was, of course, different from that of men in that their enlistment was voluntary.

Most women in military service entered the armed forces for patriotic reasons. In addition to these reasons, however, there were many other, partially conscious and partially unconscious, motivating factors. Among these were the desire to attain a degree of freedom and independence that many women were unable to attain in civilian life; identification with a specific male person in the army, such as a father, husband, or brother, or an unconscious masculine identification; protest against the feminine role; a need for a sense of security, which was derived from the fact that certain needs would be cared for by, and the individual could be dependent upon, authority figures; the hope of making a successful adjustment in a new environment after attempts at adjustment in civilian life had failed; expected gratification of sublimated homosexual impulses; and the opportunity to express femininity by doing an important job within a woman's capacity and by seeking out masculine company.

Among the special stresses experienced by women in service were the giving up of typically feminine pursuits and interests, including the niceties of civilian life, feminine and individualized clothing, and the opportunity

[2] R. R. Grinker and J. P. Spiegel, *Men Under Stress*, The Blakiston Co., Philadelphia, 1945, p. 345.

for carrying out beauty routines. In this regard, nurses were in a somewhat different position from that of other servicewomen in that they were continuing in their civilian career, which is accepted as a particularly feminine profession. The lack of privacy implicit in barracks life was particularly difficult for women to adjust to, as were the regimentation and discipline of military life. In civilian life the average woman is much more independent in her role as home-maker than is the average man in his work. In service, social contacts with men were restricted by considerations of rank. At the same time the presence of a very small number of women in a masculine society created many problems. Frequently a great deal of pressure was brought to bear upon them by the men with whom they came into contact. These created conflict, which was intensified by feelings of loneliness (641).

TYPES OF PSYCHOPATHOLOGICAL REACTIONS IN THE ARMED FORCES, AND THEIR DYNAMICS

Many of the psychopathological reactions occurring in servicemen differ little in their manifestations from those seen in civilians during peacetime. The dynamics of these reactions are also similar to those of civilian psychoneuroses in several respects. In other respects, however, differences are observable. Rarely, if ever, in civilian life is the individual faced with the realistic dangers over a prolonged period and the deprivations and frustrations which the soldier must face in combat. The specific choice of symptom may show a clear relation to the conflicts specifically related to the combat situation. For example, a pilot who develops an impairment of depth perception cannot continue to fly in close formation. He thus can be honorably removed from this situation, with only a minimal amount of guilt. Whether the patient experiences free-floating anxiety or develops a conversion symptom may be related to his already existing tendencies to develop one type of symptom rather than another. On the other hand, the type of symptom which develops may be a result of its effectiveness within the military situation; e.g., a soldier may attempt to conquer his anxiety and continue in combat, but he cannot do so in the face of a disabling physical symptom. Although pathological reactions may develop gradually, they usually occur in response to a specific combat experience or in response to a change in the total situation which requires a readjustment on the soldier's part—e.g., return to a noncombat status. The reason why the patient broke down at this particular point in his military career was, in part, his generally weakened capacity to respond adequately to stress situations. However, the specific nature of the situation which precipitated the breakdown was usually such that it aroused old conflicts within him. The death of an officer (father figure) may represent the fulfillment of a death-wish toward a father substitute and lead to strong guilt feelings and depression.

Because of the large overlap between war neuroses and civilian neuroses, it will be well for the student to refer to the discussions of the various types of civilian neuroses in the course of reading the following material. In this presentation, repetition will be avoided as much as is feasible, and the discussion will be limited to brief descriptions of the syndromes as they are most likely to appear in the war neuroses and to those aspects of the dynamics of these pathological reactions which are most intimately related to the military situation. The reactions to be described rarely occur in pure form; rather, each patient characteristically presents symptoms which fall into several categories. One symptom usually dominates the picture, however, and the diagnosis is based on this dominant symptom.

COMBAT EXHAUSTION, COMBAT FATIGUE, OPERATIONAL FATIGUE

These terms are used interchangeably to describe a condition characterized by increasing irritability, sleep disturbances, and startle reaction. The irritability is seen in the soldier's tendency to over-react to relatively mild stimuli. He may react with intense anger and experience impulses to physical violence in the face of what would ordinarily be only a minor annoyance. His emotional control becomes generally impaired, and emotional reactions such as weeping may be easily aroused. While opportunity for sleep is usually limited during combat, soldiers suffering from combat fatigue are unable to sleep when such opportunity arises, and, when they do fall asleep, their sleep is disturbed by nightmares and sudden, involuntary starting or leaping up. The startle reaction is seen in a tendency to jump and to carry out defensive movements such as cringing upon hearing sudden noises, no matter how slight, and sometimes in reaction to sudden movements and the sudden appearance of light.

This type of reaction is closely related to the drain of the individual's resources resulting from the stress of combat. It is usually a temporary reaction, and the soldier may quickly recover from it when removed from battle and allowed to rest, or it may prove to be the first stage in the development of a pathological reaction and may change into a more clearly defined clinical entity (370).

ANXIETY STATES

Anxiety reactions to combat stress are extremely frequent in military personnel and cannot be considered pathological unless they reach a point where they interfere with the individual's efficiency in combat. As long as the soldier is able to continue functioning in combat and attempts to control his anxiety, anxiety remains a normal reaction to a danger situation.

If the individual feels he is unable to remain in combat upon experiencing relatively mild anxiety, his behavior is an outgrowth of a characterological problem. Such a person probably has a weak sense of duty and may not have formed close attachments to other members of his military unit and therefore does not feel a need to stand by his buddies (see page 478). Usually, however, the soldier does make some efforts to control his anxiety. He may not succeed, however, or may be only temporarily successful. In that case the anxiety may simply increase in intensity to a point where it interferes with his carrying out his military duties, or other psychoneurotic symptoms may develop. Usually, when he fails in carrying out his duties, he feels guilty because he has let his buddies down and has not lived up to the standards he has set for himself, and he reacts to this with depression.

The anxiety reactions may be of varying intensity. The patient may experience vague, generalized fear, or he may become "nervous" and "jumpy," showing increased sensitivity to sudden or loud noises. He may become shaky with circumscribed or general tremors. His hands may shake so that he cannot take aim, or his whole body may shake so that he is unable to carry out any voluntary activities effectively. He may manifest panic reactions or may freeze in moments of danger. In more severe cases the patient may become stuporous or develop mutism or amnesia. The amnesia may be only for the precipitating traumatic experience, or it may cover large areas of the patient's past.

Dynamically, anxiety states represent an expression of the patient's feelings of helplessness in the face of overwhelmingly powerful and dangerous forces from which he cannot legitimately escape and which nothing he can do is sufficient to halt, while his defensive behavior is inadequate to protect him from death or injury. These feelings of helplessness increase in intensity as the soldier sees his friends die as a result of enemy action and when he himself experiences a close brush with death.

REACTIONS IN WHICH HYSTERICAL SYMPTOMS PREDOMINATE

Conversion Symptoms. The organs affected are usually those which are essential for the particular type of combat the soldier is engaged in, as in the case of the pilot mentioned above (see page 482), who suffers impairment of his depth perception. The symptom effectively resolves the soldier's conflict between his desire to flee from danger and his need to remain and face it. The secondary gain in these cases is obvious. Just how effective a physical symptom can be in resolving such a conflict is clearly brought out in the case of a soldier who suffered a physical symptom which was not based on emotional causes. When he first arrived in the hospital, this soldier was extremely tense and shaky; he looked apprehensive, and his speech was tremulous. When his bandages were removed, he took one look at his gangrenous feet and lay back and relaxed. For the rest of his hospital stay he was carefree and happy (174). Some patients manifest the *belle indifférence* typical of civilian patients with conversion symptoms, while others do not.

Phobic Symptoms. In general, phobic symptoms have two modes of onset: (1) There may be no definite trauma, but the individual is unable to cope with a preëxisting anxiety due to unconscious conflicts which were already present in civilian life. A particular aspect of the combat situation may arouse these conflicts, and a phobia results. Thus combat may arouse and give reality to a fear of death which has been present since childhood. A person who has never had much trust in other people's capability may develop a fear of a combat situation where his activities must be guided by other people's observations and instructions, but may be able to carry out missions where he is given more freedom in planning and making decisions. (2) The phobia may be related to a definite traumatic experience. Here the individual attempts to repress the experience. The repression is not completely successful, and, where it fails, the phobia appears. Thus one or two limited aspects of the traumatic situation may come to represent the entire danger situation to the soldier, and he develops a fear of this condition. If the soldier is able to avoid the phobic situation, he may be able to continue in combat. His phobic reaction may spread, however, to other parts of the combat environment, in which case he cannot remain in combat (370).

Amnesia and Fugue States. The patient may be amnesic for the traumatic event which precipitated his emotional breakdown or for the crucial incidents which occurred as part of the entire traumatic experience. This occurs frequently in soldiers even when other symptoms dominate the neurotic picture. In other cases amnesia is itself the major symptom and usually covers a greater area. The soldier may forget all of his combat experiences, may not remember or recognize military friends and acquaintances, and may even forget much of his precombat history. In fugue states the patient may suddenly become disoriented, not know where he is and what he has been doing, and wander away from the battlefield.

In these reactions, the danger situation and the anxiety resulting from it have become unbearable, and the patient represses them completely, effectively denying their existence.

PSYCHOSOMATIC REACTIONS

As has been pointed out before, the reaction of any individual to the stress of prolonged combat is a complex psychosomatic one in which all aspects of the total organism are involved. Physiological dysfunctioning is a "normal" concomitant of this total reaction. Anxiety equivalents, of course, are common phenomena. Some soldiers, however, develop psychosomatic symptoms which are expressions of unconscious attitudes and which interfere with their successful performance of combat duties. These reactions frequently subside when the soldier is removed from the stressful situation. At other times, however, they continue. It is frequently difficult to separate the emotional from the physical causative factors in the development of the symptom. Any one or several organ systems may be involved. Grinker and Spiegel (370) point out that the most common psychosomatic symptoms observed in American soldiers during the Second World War were those involving the gastrointestinal system.

Gastrointestinal Symptoms. Many different types of gastrointestinal symptoms were observed. These include vomiting, anorexia, abdominal pains, diarrhea, and peptic ulcer. Those symptoms involving hyperactivity of the stomach, as seen in hyperacidity, hypermotility, hypersecretions, and peptic ulcer, expressed the patient's attempt to solve his conflicts by being loved and taken care of through being fed. Many of these men had an intense desire for milk, some requiring it as their sole diet, as in early infancy when all their needs were taken care of by their mothers. In those soldiers who developed peptic ulcers, examination revealed that their adjustment prior to induction was that of the classical "peptic ulcer personality" (650). (See Chapter XXX for discussion of peptic ulcer.) Nausea and vomiting were often the sole expression of hostility toward officers and superiors. This reaction corresponds to the gagging of the angry infant. Loss of appetite (anorexia), accompanied by a feeling of a load on the stomach, frequently expressed guilt feelings and depression, with self-condemnation, over the death of a close friend. Here the death either represented the fulfillment of unconscious hostile wishes directed toward the friend, or the patient felt that in some way he was responsible for the friend's death: had he in some way acted differently, had he been there at the time, had he not ordered this person to do the thing which resulted in his death, he might still be living. The patient feels unworthy, that he has no right to live (to eat, to sustain himself), and the anorexia represents a self-punitive attitude. Diarrhea may be an expression of anger, fear, or restitution. As an expression of anger, the feces are considered dirty and uncontrolled, and excessive defecation takes on the meaning of an act of disparagement toward others. As restitution, it represents atonement for guilt: "I am giving of myself, I am giving something that is of value to me, I am complying with your wishes." Diarrhea is particularly apt to develop in people of shut-in characteristics in whom feelings of inferiority are compensated for by a rich fantasy life (650).

Cardiovascular Symptoms. In neurocirculatory asthenia (see Chapter XXX) there are unconscious rebellion against discipline and, of course, fear of injury and of loss of life (665). This syndrome is most frequently found in dependent persons who, in the past, always avoided giving vent to their aggressiveness and tended to withdraw from situations in which their aggressive impulses were aroused. The aggressive activity required of them in combat is a particular strain on such people (650). Hypertension frequently results from unconscious conflicts over unexpressed aggression. (See Chapter XXX for a discussion of the dynamics of hypertension.) Heart palpitations are primarily an anxiety equivalent.

Other Psychosomatic Reactions. Many other types of psychosomatic symptoms are seen in soldiers, including dermatological symptoms, joint and muscle symptoms, frequency of urination, nocturnal enuresis, headaches and vertigo, chest symptoms, and impotence. They may occur as the chief symptom or may be secondary to other types of reactions. Dynamically, they all are reactions to the anxiety aroused in combat, and many of them involve conflicts over the expression of aggression.

Delayed and Disturbed Convalescence. As has been mentioned, the development of disabling physical symptoms due to any type of causal factors results in the soldier's being removed from combat and its attendant dangers, thus removing him from the anxiety-arousing situation and relieving his anxiety. When the patient begins to recover and his return to combat becomes imminent, his anxiety is again aroused and may cause delays in convalescence. His symptoms may remain after their physical basis has disappeared; he may develop new symptoms, which are either psychosomatic or conversion symptoms; or old symptoms associated with previous illnesses may be revived. Personality disturbance may have been present in such patients prior to their illness, or it may be manifested for the first time after the onset of the illness (125).

DEPRESSIVE REACTIONS

Depressive reactions in combat personnel are almost always accompanied by anxiety. The usual sequence of events is that the soldier first experiences anxiety and attempts to control it. When he fails and is removed from combat, he reacts with feelings of guilt and unworthiness, and depression results. Even after successfully completing his combat duties and being returned home, the soldier may experience guilt feelings over having deserted those who must remain in the fight, or, still judging himself by the values and standards of combat life, he experiences guilt feelings over the life of relative luxury and comfort which he now leads. Unconscious hostility, often based on preëxisting life patterns, felt toward a comrade who was lost in combat results in guilt feelings in that the patient feels in some way responsible for the death. These feelings may be rationalized in that the patient says he might have saved his comrade. For example, even though he had been ordered by a superior to bail out of a disabled plane, he feels that he should have remained to help a friend who was unable to bail out.

Actually, that way both would have died, yet the patient continues to blame himself. Guilt may be experienced over aggression released during combat, particularly by individuals who had always had strong unconscious conflicts concerning their hostile impulses. In general, depressive reactions involving strong guilt feelings were most likely to occur in persons who had always set high standards of performance for themselves and reacted with self-condemnation when they failed to live up to these standards.

Depressive reactions may occur in response to frustration of passive-dependent needs. This frustration is particularly likely to be felt acutely upon separation from the combat group, when the patient is deprived of emotional support he received in his relationships with other members of the group, and, upon return home, when family and friends are unable to satisfy the intense passive needs which have been fostered by the combat stress.

The patient, twenty-five years old, was an Army Air Force captain suffering from depression. His commanding officer had rotated the assignment of flight leader among the best men in the squadron. On his twenty-fifth mission the patient had been assigned to lead the flight. His friend, who had been flight leader on other missions, had pulled up and was flying wing to wing with him. The patient could have ordered him back into formation or could have yielded the lead position. He did neither. Suddenly the friend's plane went up in flames. Although feeling badly depressed, he successfully completed his tour of duty. He refused promotion to command of a squadron. He was reassigned to a job in the United States, which he liked very much, but his depression, accompanied by severe startle reactions and battle dreams, continued. He tried to decrease his anxiety and depression by drinking, but the only result was an increase in anxiety. He found it impossible to forget his experiences.

In the first pentathol interview, the patient spoke of his friend, Joe, who had died on his twenty-fifth mission. He said amid tears and sobbing that his friend was a "nice boy," that he hoped his death had not been his (the patient's) fault, that perhaps he should have chosen a safer target (although the choice had not been up to him), and that his friend should have remained in formation.

Then, in a conscious state in the same interview, he went over the incident again, just as he had done under narcosis. Then he talked about another boy, who crashed on a low-level flight, maintaining radio silence according to instructions although he was in need of help; yet the patient felt he should have helped him. Then he told of feeling bad about killing Germans. The interview was ended by the therapist's telling him that he had assumed a responsibility for the death of Joe that did not seem to be based on fact.

In the next interview the patient talked about his father, who was very kind but strict in his attitudes. If, as a child, the patient did not live up to his responsibilities, the father would look pained and say, "This was your job," and then do it himself. "It was worse than a spanking." He was always on very good terms with his father.

He then said that his commanding officer was an exceptionally strong leader who went on the most dangerous missions himself, a man who was fair and expected everyone to do his job.

The therapist pointed out that the commanding officer was like the patient's father; that the patient was now punishing himself for what he considered his failure in carrying out his responsibilities; and that this was the result of guilt feelings which must be due to negative attitudes. The patient then said that he had always been ambitious and told of competitive relationships with men in the past. The therapist explained that victory in such competitions unconsciously meant to him the destruction of other persons. The patient related under pentathol that he and Joe were jealous of each other and were fighting for the job of leading the flight.

He then began to talk of episodes in his squadron overseas that he thought were funny and amusing, and then he said, "It is silly for intelligent people to let things bother them the way I did." His ego now had confidence in its strength and could dwell on the past without anxiety. Nine months later the patient was still well and functioning as a successful pilot in this country.[3]

AGGRESSIVE AND HOSTILE REACTIONS

The aggressive impulses may be largely suppressed, and only the tension resulting from the effort to control them may be manifest. Hostile attitudes toward persons in one's environment may result in irritability, defiance of authority, belligerence, and readiness to fight on the slightest pretext. In some cases the openly aggressive behavior only appears when the patient's inhibitions are released while drinking alcohol.

The large quantity of poorly controlled or uncontrolled aggression in such patients may be due to the release of aggressive behavior in combat and to the soldier's inability to reinstitute his former control mechanisms. The hostility may have been mobilized in situations where the morale of the group suffered. If large losses have been suffered by the military group, the aggression toward the enemy may be intensified, or aggression may be directed toward military superiors who are accused of incompetence or lack of concern for the welfare of the men. Officers who are over-strict disciplinarians or who show favoritism and unfairness in handing out promotions and awards are likely to arouse hostility in their men and impair the morale of their units. Old, unresolved conflicts concerning aggressions are restimulated in the combat situation. In the setting of the increase in passive-dependent needs which takes place under combat stress, aggressive impulses are intensified by the frustration of these needs. At the same time the personality has returned to a stage where anger is expressed directly to supporting figures who have rejected or failed to support the individual. Overtly aggressive behavior is most likely to occur in individuals who have always had difficulty in controlling their aggressive impulses and whose aggressions were easily aroused and expressed with relatively little provo-

[3] Based on a case presentation in Grinker and Spiegel, *op. cit.*

cation, such as persons with psychopathic tendencies. (See Chapter XXIV for a discussion of psychopathic personality.)

A twenty-year-old gunner had tremendous hostility to the army, his parents, his fiancée, and all civilians. He had enlisted in the army with eagerness to fight and had enjoyed his training and early missions. On his twenty-first mission, some planes peeled off and returned to the base before reaching the target. This left him as the tail gunner in the tail ship of the remaining formation. As they approached the target, they were jumped by twenty-five German fighters and also received tremendous attacks of flak. His ship was badly damaged, and he suffered minor flak injuries to the buttocks. No punishment was meted out to the crews that had fallen out of formation, a lack of justice which made the patient intensely angry. He became profuse in the use of profanity in outbursts against them. After six days of drunkenness he returned to flying, but finally had to be grounded because of alcoholism and aggressive outbursts. He then had an affair with a woman older than he.

He told the psychiatrist that he was brought up to be a decent boy, not a criminal. He felt the army had ruined him, and he often cried in self-pity. Thus, from an independent, courageous soldier, he regressed into a crying child who wanted to go home to his mother. This was precipitated by his feeling deserted and unprotected by the weak leadership of the officers. The support provided by a strong group ideal disintegrated, and he had to seek within himself for strength. This he could not find, for something had happened to his own ego ideals: "I used to be a decent boy, not a criminal." He found it now absolutely necessary to have a strong external authority to hold him in line. This patient's regression had gone so far that he could no longer be retained in the army.[4]

PASSIVE-DEPENDENT STATES

As has been pointed out before, most servicemen, after a period of severe combat stress, tend to experience an intensification of their passive-dependent needs. The extent to which this occurs varies. (See page 479.) In most instances the soldier gradually readjusts himself to peacetime living and returns to a more mature level of personality organization. Individuals who, prior to combat service, lacked self-reliance may retain their intensified passive-dependent needs after discharge in spite of brief psychotherapy. They manifest a desire to return to some supporting figure in their past environment, such as mother, wife, or "buddy." They wish to have all their needs taken care of by others. If permitted to do so, they would remain in bed until noon or later, and may resent having to go to the mess hall for their meals if they are in the hospital and would prefer to have all their meals brought to them in bed. Frequently they have a strong desire to drink milk, and some even reject all other forms of food. This parallels the extremely passive state of infancy, when all their needs were gratified by people in their environment.

[4] Based on a case presentation in Grinker and Spiegel, *op. cit.*

CHARACTEROLOGICAL PROBLEMS

Many people with previous mild character disorders (see Chapter XXIII) experience an intensification of their problems during the course of their military life. Persons who have always had difficulty in adjusting to group living and coöperative work are almost invariably under a strain under such conditions. If they are lucky and are assigned to a job where they can work relatively independently of others, they may get by with little increase in their personality problems, but, in combat, the drain on their resources is bound to result in some intensification of their difficulties. In persons with psychopathic tendencies, the relative inability to identify with a group and group goals and to form close interpersonal relationships with their fellows is likely to result in poor motivation, and they become disciplinary problems, being reluctant to submit to military rules and regulations. When they do complete a tour of combat duty, the easy expression of aggression which has been fostered by combat remains uncontrolled and is likely to lead to antisocial behavior. Persons with immature personalities are particularly apt to experience an intensification of passive-dependent needs and to be unable to regain their former level of adjustment (see above). In addition, they are the men who are least able to endure prolonged combat stress and who are most likely to seek "out" when the going gets tough. (See page 478.) Men who are inclined to be suspicious are likely to become more so under stress of combat, especially if things progress badly. They tend to accuse others of inefficiency, poor planning, etc. Overt paranoid symptoms appear in some of these men. The patient projects his own hostilities, which have been intensified by combat, onto those around him and sees the world as a hostile place where everyone is against him. Some single out certain individuals in their environment as being particularly hostile toward them. At times retaliatory aggressive behavior is manifested.

PSYCHOTIC-LIKE STATES

Psychotic-like states can be distinguished from other war neuroses by the degree of loss of control over impulses and the severe impairment of reality-testing which occurs. Complete disorientation as to time and place may occur, but orientation for person usually remains intact. Thus, while fully conscious, the patient may reëxperience a traumatic combat situation, believing himself to be on the field of battle, hearing battle sounds, and seeing the enemy around him. He may begin to fight off hallucinatory figures. A similar sort of reaction is seen in many combat veterans upon awakening from battle dreams. This differs from the psychotic-like reaction, however, in that their behavior is stimulated by the combat dream; it disappears, and the patients quickly become reorientated as they regain full consciousness. In the psychotic-like reaction, the patient has become incapable of differentiating between past and present reality. On the other hand, these reactions can be distinguished from true psychoses in that the patients improve rapidly as they are removed from the battle area, and the psychotic-like manifestations quickly disappear with brief psychotherapy.

Paranoid reactions may also reach a psychotic degree. In these patients, as well as in individuals with psychopathic personalities, poorly controlled aggressive impulses may become of homicidal dimensions. These are frequently due to the returnee's tendency to confuse his present friendly environment with the past hostile (combat) environment (370).

A radio-operator was shot down over enemy-occupied territory on his fifth mission, but evaded capture and returned to his base after a month. He complained of sleeplessness, nightmares, depression, loss of appetite, and tachycardia. His most disturbing symptom consisted of illusions that he was back in combat. When he shut his eyes, or at night in the dark, he actually felt himself to be in combat or eluding the Germans. It took a few minutes for him to orient himself after opening his eyes.

His symptoms had become much worse since his return home. He became depressed because his girl friend had become friendly with another serviceman. He asked her not to break off with this man, who was going overseas; the patient did not want him worried when he got into combat. He spent the early part of each evening with his girl so that she could be with the other man for the remainder of the time. It became apparent that a great deal of his depression was related to the repressed hostility which he had toward his rival. He had never been able to express any hostile competitive attitudes. The symptoms of his combat neurosis were due to repressed aggressions toward the Germans, a repression that was not completely successful because free anxiety dominated the picture.

Psychotherapy was directed toward helping him to accept the normal nature of his aggressions, and his anxiety and depression decreased. He was able to verbalize negative feelings. He recovered completely from the illusion of being in combat. He developed courage to send for his girl and her mother, and an understanding was reached that after the war they would get married.[5]

PSYCHOPATHOLOGICAL REACTIONS TO INJURIES

Physical injuries resulting from combat are, of course, frequent. While all patients suffering from such injuries react to them emotionally, in some individuals these reactions must, to some extent, be considered pathological. In some individuals with amputated limbs, for example, hysterical symptoms such as coarse tremors and intractable pain occurred which were not the result of stimulation of nerve-endings due to improper healing of the stump. Many persons with head injuries showed no psychological manifestations other than those directly referable to tissue damage. Others, however,

[5] Based on a case presentation in Grinker and Spiegel, *op. cit.*

showed reactions similar to those found in civilian traumatic neuroses, with depression and anxiety symptoms prominent features of their reactions (650).

CHRONIC FORM OF TRAUMATIC NEUROSIS

The psychopathological pictures so far described represent the individual's attempts to master the anxiety and conflicts aroused in the traumatic situation by recourse to techniques that he has found more or less successful in dealing with conflicts and anxiety throughout his life. When these attempts fail, the symptoms in which they are expressed tend to disappear, and a different picture is seen. The patient continues to react to his environment as if it contained the same dangers as were present in the traumatic situation, avoids any situations which in any way resemble the traumatic situation, and gives up all or most of those adaptive techniques which were relevant to the traumatic situation. The symptoms that result are due to the individual's attempts to make a new adjustment with his now limited resources, but they retain also the dynamics of the old emotional conflicts (485). (See the more detailed discussion of traumatic neurosis in Chapter XXV.)

"When originally seen, the patient complained of a strange symptom in both lower extremities, extending up to the umbilicus. He was subject to feelings of numbness, pain and cold, but more especially to sweating from the waistline down to the toes. This sweating, he said, was continuous, especially at night. When he was asked how old this symptom was, he said at least seven years. Among his other complaints were marked irritability and instability of temper; he became aggressive and pugnacious very suddenly and without sufficient cause. He also suffered from spells of transient blindness, which lasted anywhere from five to fifteen minutes. Attacks of vertigo were among his symptoms. His sleep was disturbed continually by the usual dreams of drowning, being run over, or receiving electric shock. In some dreams he was the aggressor.

"When inquiries concerning his traumatic history were made, he denied ever having suffered a serious shock. Then he casually stated that he was on board the U.S.S. *President Lincoln* when she was torpedoed. He was asked to narrate the details of this accident, which were in substance: He was in the kitchen gambling with several of the mess attendants when he heard a shot. This he interpreted as due to target practice and continued his game. Several minutes later there was another shot, and then another, the last one a distinct explosion. At this, all of the men ran upstairs. The command was given to take to the lifeboats, and he realized the ship had been torpedoed. It so happened that some of the lifeboats were disabled and there were not enough to go round. At all events, the patient and about eight other Negroes were obliged to take to a raft. He described the sinking of the ship, his lack of trepidation at the sight, and the absence of panicky sensations. He said this was due to the fact that the retreat to the lifeboats and the rafts was very orderly, and the ship did not sink until some hours later. At this point in his recital the patient became rather excited and began to swear profusely. His anger was aroused chiefly by the incidents connected with the rescue. They were in the water for a period of about twelve hours when a destroyer picked them up. Of course priority was given to the officers in the lifeboats. The eight or nine men clinging to the raft were allowed to remain in the water. They had to wait for six or seven hours longer until help came. In describing his feelings while in the water, the patient emphatically denied having had any panic or fear. However, while narrating these incidents, it was quite clear to me that he was very disturbed. The disturbance he acknowledged. He said that his telling of the story made him fearful. I made him revive many details of the story that had a harrowing effect on him.

"The similarities between the symptoms he complained of, in the form of sensations and sweating from the waistline down, and his story of being submerged in cold water up to this level were pointed out to him. He admitted that when he allowed himself to close his eyes and think of his present sensations, he still imagined himself clinging to the raft, half submerged in the sea. He stated that while clinging to the raft, his sensations had been extremely painful ones and that he had thought of nothing else during the time. He also recalled the fact that several of his companions had lost consciousness and were drowned. It was quite obvious that, to a large extent, the patient owes his life to the concentration of attention on the painful sensations occasioned by the cold water.

"The symptoms represented, therefore, a hallucinatory reproduction of the original sensation of being submerged in the water. Concerning his remaining symptoms, it is of interest to note that he developed many of the secondary symptoms of traumatic cases that are epileptoid in character. The spells of transient blindness used to come on specific occasions, for example, when he saw something in the nature of violence. Thus the patient was out walking one day and witnessed an automobile colliding with a train. He became maddened with excitement, was blinded for ten minutes, and was taken home in a state of extreme agitation. He alleges that it took him four months to recover from the effects of this incident, although the danger did not directly concern him. During these four months, he was obsessed by a vision of the accident. He had, in fact, a profound reaction to violence of any kind. He could not witness others being hurt, injured or threatened. Prior to his service, he had never had fears or phobias of any kind. He had been an employee of a railroad company and had seen a very bad wreck without serious consequence to his state of mind. In fact, he himself had assisted in extricating people from the wreck. He was also extremely sensitive to loud noises. This was very remarkable, because he had heard very little shellfire during his naval career—yet he shared this secondary reaction with patients who had come from the zone of active fighting. He would yell or scream on a sudden call or other abrupt noise. He was troubled by the violence of his reaction to these stimuli. He claimed that he felt like suddenly striking people, and that he had become very pugnacious to his family. He remarked: 'I wish I were dead. I make everybody around me suffer.'

"He had the usual disturbing dreams, but his memory for them was poor. However, he might start from his sleep several times during the night.

"Of great interest is the fact that in the lower extremities he had no objective sensory disturbance whatsoever. His reactions to water were quite typical. He did not like sea-bathing, and whenever he had attempted to go into the water since his return from service, he became nauseated and vomited. He treated his lower extremities most tenderly. He protected them with all kinds of ointments and wore warm stockings in all seasons."[6]

It can be seen from this case that the breakdown occurred in the face of a traumatic situation which was realistically overwhelmingly dangerous to the patient. The fact that other factors in the situation, aside from the realistic dangers, contributed to the breakdown is also demonstrated. Thus the patient resented the fact that the officers were the first to be rescued while he had to wait several additional hours before being rescued. It is likely also that this situation mobilized unconscious resentment against the majority group and that he felt that the long delay before rescue was in part due to discrimination against him because he was a member of a minority group.

PSYCHOTHERAPY OF WAR NEUROSES

THERAPEUTIC AIMS

The aims of psychotherapy during wartime were conditioned by military needs and limitations. The chief aim was the return of the patient to combat if at all possible, which is in keeping with the final goal of the total war effort—namely, to defeat the enemy. If return to combat duty was not possible, return to noncombat duty became the goal. If neither of these was possible, the patient was discharged to civilian life after brief psychotherapy, the aim of which was to remove the patient's more disabling symptoms as far as possible. The result of this was the return to civilian life of many men with psychopathological disorders, the responsibility for their care lying with civilians or with the Veterans' Administration.

The psychotherapeutic aspects of military psychiatry can be divided into two parts: (1) prophylaxis, where the purpose was to prevent the occurrence of incapacitating psychopathological reactions, and (2) treatment after disabling neurotic symptoms were formed.

PROPHYLAXIS

Here the aim was to increase the individual's tolerance of stress. This was the responsibility of the general medical officer attached to the group or unit. Important for this were the maintenance of good morale and the increase of motivation. Education as to the purpose of the war was found to be helpful in increasing motivation. Good leadership was found to be an essential factor in maintaining morale, so that education of officers as to the role of the leader in a group was important. The medical officer fre-

[6] A. Kardiner, The bio-analysis of the epileptic reaction, *Psychoanalytic Quarterly*, 1932, 1, Nos. 3 and 4, 375-483.

quently acted as a liaison between officer and enlisted personnel. For this reason, as well as for others which will be touched upon below, it was necessary that he know the men in his unit fairly intimately. He could listen to their "gripes" and, if he found that they were well founded, try to persuade the officers to modify the situations giving rise to complaints if this was possible. He was, of course, responsible for the general health of the men in his unit, which was an important factor in their tolerance of stress. It was up to him to estimate the amount of stress each man could endure without crippling effects, to remove him from combat at least temporarily, if possible, when this point was approaching, and, at the same time, to keep him in combat as long as possible before his limit of endurance was reached. He had to be alert to the first signs of behavioral change which indicated a beginning pathological reaction in order to arrest and mitigate it. When such signs began to appear, he could recommend an environmental change (sending the soldier to a rest camp or to kitchen duty for a week), or he could give him psychotherapeutic interviews. In these interviews the medical officer attempted to help the patient understand the nature of anxiety and the fact that it is a normal reaction to stress and to help him understand the function and purpose of an ineffective or crippling mode of handling his anxiety. He encouraged the patient to abreact his traumatic experiences—that is, to relate them while reëxperiencing his emotional reactions in a nonthreatening, relatively permissive setting. He could attempt to modify the patient's motivation, either by stimulating the patient to make more demands upon himself if he appeared to be using relatively mild anxiety as a means of being removed from combat or by enabling him to be less demanding of himself, to accept his anxiety reactions, and to reduce the guilt feelings resulting from his feeling that he was proving to be inadequate. The latter was accomplished by the therapist himself accepting and expressing understanding of the patient's anxiety reactions and resultant inefficiencies. He could, to some extent, gratify the patient's dependent needs by being a sympathetic, supportive person in his contact with him. This type of psychotherapeutic handling was frequently sufficient to maintain the serviceman in combat.

PSYCHOTHERAPY AFTER DISABLING NEUROTIC SYMPTOMS HAVE FORMED

After disabling neurotic symptoms had formed, and particularly after they had become bound to the patient's precombat modes of handling stress and early conflicts, a more intensive psychotherapeutic approach became necessary. The therapist attempted to give the patient emotional support, which was of vital importance in the face of the patient's intense passive-dependent needs. At the same time, in the hospital management of the patient, some demands were made upon him (he had to make his own bed, was occasionally asked to help the nurse in carrying out ward duties), so that he was not encouraged to give in completely to his dependent desires. Release of repressed material relating to traumatic experiences, together with abreaction, was important. The therapist helped the patient to gain insight into the relationship between his current reactions and his past behavior patterns and the historical derivation of these patterns. By means of a permissive and accepting attitude, he attempted to decrease the patient's feelings of guilt and worthlessness and the self-punishing attitudes resulting from his actual or felt failures and from repressed hostilities. The patient was desensitized to his memories of anxiety-producing situations by repetitive recounting of these experiences, while the therapist helped him to distinguish between past danger and his present safety and between the real world and his inner anxieties. The patient was reëducated to use more effective methods of compromise between his dependent needs and the limitations of reality. At the same time his attempts to regain a more mature level of adaptation were encouraged, as was his reintegration with a group with supportive relationships and good leaders.

Treatment of the chronic conditions is the same as that for civilian forms of traumatic neurosis (see page 416).

OTHER THERAPEUTIC TECHNIQUES

Along with brief psychotherapy, other therapeutic techniques were used, usually as adjunctive procedures. One of the most important of these was narcosynthesis. In this procedure the patient was administered a hypnotic drug (sodium pentothal) in sufficient quantity to produce narcosis, but not enough to put him to sleep. In this state of semiconsciousness the patient was able to revive repressed memories of traumatic experiences, and abreaction took place. When the patient regained full consciousness, it was necessary that he be aware of what took place while he was under narcosis in order to integrate the uncovered material into his conscious thinking, so that he could understand the relationship of the incident and the emotions aroused by it to his current difficulties. Some psychiatrists used hypnosis in order to obtain similar results. Suggestion was used in order to obtain immediate relief from symptoms, particularly in patients with conversion symptoms. This was sometimes done by means of direct suggestion through hypnosis or while the patient was in a relaxed state or indirectly by such techniques as application of an electric current to the affected organ. Procedures aimed at the improvement of general health were important. Included in this were such things as sedation in patients who were too tense and could not sleep and in those whose sleep was disturbed by nightmares and insulin (to stimulate the appetite). Convalescent programs in the hospital were important in filling up the patient's time with constructive activity which was of interest to him. Included in the program were such activities as occupational therapy, sports and other recreational activities, lectures, and further training in the patient's military specialty.

HOMOSEXUALITY IN THE ARMED FORCES

In military life, the individual's contacts with members of the opposite sex are quite limited. For most persons this requires the forming of a new sexual adaptation. Direct sexual outlets were obtained by many men through masturbation and through nonmarital heterosexual contacts. Living in close contact with relatively large numbers of persons of the same sex was likely to arouse homosexual impulses even in those who had attained an adequate heterosexual adjustment in civilian life. Most servicemen handled this problem by sublimation through satisfying social contacts. In some individuals, however, homosexuality created a problem in their military adjustment. These fell into three groups: (1) latent homosexuals who were disturbed by the close contact with other members of their own sex; (2) individuals who indulged in overt homosexual practices while intoxicated; and (3) overt homosexuals who attempted to seduce others by making open propositions or through exhibitionism. In addition to these three groups, there was a large number of overt homosexuals who had attained a homosexual adjustment in civilian life and who were able to adjust adequately to military life. These men were able to control their sexual behavior adequately. Some idea of the extent of the problem of homosexuality can be gained from the following figures: In 1943, of 20,620 men in the army diagnosed as "constitutional psychopaths," 1625 were presumed to be homosexual (641). The author estimates, however, that for every homosexual who was detected, from five to ten remained undetected. As an example of how well some of these men were able to adjust to the army, the following study is of interest. Of 270 patients seen in one army hospital because of problems of homosexuality, there were ten master sergeants, six technical sergeants, and nineteen staff sergeants, while many others had lesser ratings (581).

CIVILIAN STRESSES IN WARTIME

In time of war, civilians also are subjected to new and increased environmental stress. Among these are separation from and loss of loved ones, overwork leading to fatigue, bombings, and general war tensions such as enemy propaganda, which is aimed at arousing fear and defeatist attitudes, and uncertainty as to the future. Although the war created new and increased pressures upon the individual and therefore precipitated psychopathological reactions, it did not, as in the case of military personnel, "cause" them. In other words, it served mostly to break down already tenuous adjustments. Some individuals appeared to adjust better under wartime conditions than they did during peacetime. This was due to several factors. People who had difficulty in making occupational adjustments now could find jobs and get occupational training. People directly or indirectly involved in the war effort could feel that they were doing a worth-while job and that their efforts were appreciated. Conflict over aggressive impulses could be lessened in that hostility could be directed toward the enemy and aggressive drives could be channeled into useful and constructive work.

CHILDREN IN WARTIME

War is likely to bring unusual stress situations into the lives of children. The stability of family life is seriously interfered with. The father is away from home, and the mother may go to work. If the serviceman father is not sent overseas, the family may move about the country trying to remain near him and may have to live in crowded, inadequate quarters. In areas where bombings occur, the children may be sent away from home. The separation from the family and from all familiar surroundings is difficult for the child. This can be mitigated if the child already knows the people with whom he will live or if the mother pays frequent visits to him. The effects of different types of handling of the separation can be seen in the following case descriptions of children brought to live at a nursery.

"Hetty, two years one month old, and Christine, seventeen months old, were both brought to stay while their mothers went to the hospital to be delivered of another baby."

Hetty was brought "as a day child more than two months before the expected birth. . . . [Her mother] helped the child through a period of adaptation to daily life shared with other children which was by no means easy. Hetty was shy, at times aggressive, withdrawn and often unresponsive. She slowly accustomed herself to the nursery. A week before the expected confinement she entered the house as a boarder, slept in the shelter with the other children whom she already knew well but was rewarded in day time by frequent visits from her mother. When her mother at last disappeared into the maternity hospital, Hetty was used to her new surroundings, felt at home and showed no ill effects of any kind.

"Christine, on the other hand, was brought two or three days previous to her mother's confinement and left at once and completely, though she had never before left her mother's side and had evidently been taken care of very well by her mother. She found herself unexpectedly in completely strange surroundings to which she reacted in a most bewildered way.

"For days she sat or stood around quietly or crying and would only at intervals say: 'Mum, Mum.'

"She did it in a surprisingly deep voice.

". . . She would sometimes stretch out her arms to visitors. She was at times content when she could sit on somebody's lap with her face averted. Probably she imagined herself in this position to be sitting on her mother's lap without being disturbed by the sight of a strange face."[7]

If the children remain in an area where bombing occurs, they surprisingly show no signs of traumatic shock reactions to the bombing, even when they are buried under debris. Anxieties do develop, however, which are relevant to their bombing experiences. There may be anxiety due to the realistic danger. This, however, is limited to the child's understanding of it. When the mother experiences intense anxiety, this is communicated to the child. This is particularly true of younger children. When the father is killed by a bomb, each bomb thereafter represents the bomb that killed the father. This is primarily a reaction to the father's death. In older children, there is fear of the arousal of their own recently repressed aggressive impulses. Where, in peacetime, the child feared punishment by ghosts, devils, bogy-men, etc., he now thinks of the air raid as punishment or fears that his protector (nurse) will be spirited away during the night (300).

SUGGESTED READINGS

Grinker and Spiegel's *Men Under Stress* (370) is dramatic reading. Kardiner and Spiegel's *War Stress and Neurotic Illness* (845) presents a broad approach. Freud and Burlingham's *War and Children* (300) is a readable and penetrating book on the effect of war on children. Menninger's *Psychiatry in a Troubled World* (641) gives a survey of the many psychiatric implications of war.

[7] A. Freud and D. T. Burlingham, *War and Children,* Medical War Books, New York, 1943, pp. 112-113.

XXXIII Manic-Depressive Reactions

CLASSIFICATION OF PSYCHOTIC REACTION TYPES

Phenomena classified in various psychotic reaction types may occur in one patient; sometimes neurotic and psychotic manifestations may be combined. It is important to realize that, like the neurotic, psychotic manifestations are motivated by catastrophic fears and are the individual's attempts to solve his conflicts and cope with the world as best he can. Extreme psychotic manifestations are in part, however, *actual* catastrophic breakdowns rather than just fear of breakdown; in part, that is, they express complete discouragement and giving up in the face of the problem.

In general, the following reaction types are differentiated: (1) the affective, or manic-depressive; (2) the schizophrenic; and (3) the organic. Some also include the paranoiac as a separate reaction type. Although ultimate proof is lacking, the affective and the schizophrenic are assumed to be chiefly psychogenic. In the organic reaction type the patient has a serious bodily condition which is caused by physical agents and which directly affects the functioning of the brain; the patient has a further psychological reaction to his organic difficulties. Thus, when the blood vessels in the brain harden, the patient is irritable and suffers from disturbed memory; he is particularly liable to irritation when he feels ashamed of forgetting something. In other words, his irritability is due not alone to changes in his brain; it may also be a defensive, hostile reaction toward someone before whom he feels ashamed of his loss of memory.

THE MANIC-DEPRESSIVE REACTION TYPE

Patients who react to severe stress with manic or depressive states often show characteristic personality traits during the time they are relatively normal (Reiss). Many of them are outgoing, hard-driving, and successful. Others are very conscientious in their habits and work with great accuracy (the "compulsive" type). Still others are worried, concerned, and anxious. Another large percentage is composed of individuals who vary between optimism, cheerfulness, and energy on the one hand, and discouragement, lassitude, and gloominess on the other. These latter people are called cyclothymic. Their swings of mood are based on conflicts and attempted solutions similar to those in the manic-depressive reaction itself. Kretschmer claims that in physical appearance the majority of manic-depressive patients are short, stocky people with thick necks (his "pyknic" type). Other psychiatrists, however, are inclined to doubt this. It should be realized that patients may develop manic-depressive reactions under stress, regardless of their personality or physique.

"Harvey Behring is an extreme case in point. He was a stout, florid man who gave the impression of great ability and power. His conversation immediately stamped him as a superior individual. When he was only thirty-three he had acquired nearly forty thousand dollars by his enormous activity, working nightly until one o'clock in the morning month after month. He became over-sanguine, invested all the money in one project, lost heart in it, became depressed, and lost all of his money.

"He recovered from this and started in business again on a small scale. A few years later the building which his business occupied was destroyed by fire and he was plunged into another depression, in which he remained a year. After that there occurred attack after attack, with and without provocation.

"His characteristic cycle would begin with a phase of prodigious activity in which he would exert himself to the utmost. His efforts were usually crowned with a good deal of success, and this success would only stimulate him to greater exertion. At the same time, however, his judgment would become impaired by an overdose of optimism and he would make wild plunges and risk large sums of money. Sometimes these speculations turned out well, but more often they turned out badly. Then he would be plunged into a depression in which he would be quite incapable of doing any work at all. He would wake up in the morning groaning, crying out for God to spare his soul, heaving long sighs, and bursting into tears when spoken to. This depression would pass and he would again work himself up to great enthusiasm and industry.

"In one of his depressed phases he shot himself."[1]

COURSE OF THE REACTION: GENERAL CHARACTERISTICS

1. Some patients suffer only from periods of depression; others manifest only periods of elation; still others show alternation between the two.

2. The manic-depressive reaction may develop gradually or suddenly. In typical instances the reaction terminates after about six months or a year, either spontaneously or in response to treatment.

3. Patients with manic-depressive reactions have essentially "normal" periods of several years' duration between attacks.

[1] K. Menninger, *The Human Mind,* Alfred A. Knopf, Inc., New York, 1937, p. 107.

4. Attacks of manic or depressive reaction often recur.
5. Manic-depressive reactions do not lead to a deterioration of the intellectual and emotional faculties of the individual.

DEPRESSIVE REACTIONS: GENERAL CHARACTERISTICS

The depressive reaction is usually characterized by three major symptoms.

Depression. The patient feels sad, discouraged, disheartened, and hopeless. This depression is continuous and is maintained even in a comic or humorous situation. In addition, the patient finds it difficult to take any interest in his surroundings.

Psychomotor Retardation. The patient is disinclined to engage in any activity; he has to exert an effort to do anything, and he works slowly. This is related to the next symptom.

Difficulty in Thinking. The patient's thought processes are considerably retarded; he has to make an effort to think or to solve problems.

These three symptoms lead to characteristic behavior. The patient is inclined to sit in the same place for long periods of time. His speech is slow and monotonous, his activities are lethargic, and it takes him much longer than usual to do tasks.

These major symptoms are frequently accompanied by others, among which are the following.

Delusions. The general thought content is characterized under all circumstances by ideas of utter worthlessness and guilt. The patient thinks little of himself, condemns himself, and feels guilty over misdemeanors which seem trivial to other people. In more severe cases the patient has delusions, particularly of sin and guilt. He accuses himself of having committed the unpardonable sin, of being an abomination before God and man. He may be convinced that he has cancer or syphilis and that he will infect the whole world. He considers the future absolutely hopeless and black. There may be fleeting and changeable "ideas of reference"; i.e., he may think that people are talking about him and are going to harm him. This last, however, is infrequent.

Hallucinations. The patient may hear voices which accuse him of having committed a crime or call him derogatory names. These phenomena also are infrequent.

Bodily Symptoms. As has been said, the patient's behavior is lethargic; his posture, whether sitting or standing, is stooped, and he is apt to drag his feet when he walks. The muscle tone is diminished. The eyes are lusterless; the facial expression is sad.

The common vegetative symptoms are: (1) Considerably diminished secretion of saliva. (2) Decrease in gastrointestinal activity, resulting in severe constipation and loss of appetite. The latter is present in every acute depression; because of it, the patient eats little and loses weight. The constipation may lead to secondary auto-intoxication. (3) Changes in blood pressure from high to low in elation or depression, respectively. (4) Cessation of menstruation at the onset of the reaction; its reappearance is often a sign of real improvement. (5) Sleeplessness, which in the depressive reaction is correlated with the patient's sadness and anxiety, and, in the manic reaction, with his continuous excitement.

VARIETIES OF DEPRESSIVE REACTIONS

All these symptoms may be shown by one patient, but most frequently they vary in intensity from one case to another, or some may be entirely absent. Thus, in some mild cases, the patient's depression may be more apparent to others than to the patient himself; or he may be depressed, but not retarded in his behavior, reactions, or thinking; or his depression may lead to considerable restlessness and agitation, such as wringing the hands. Depending on the degree and type of the symptoms, the following classes of depressive reactions are usually differentiated.

Mild (Masked) Form. The patient may be aware of and complain of a slight depression, but more usually his complaint concerns a physical discomfort, such as persistent vague headache, gastric disturbance with loss of appetite, bad taste in the mouth, constipation, blurred vision, irritability, fatigue, exhaustion, lassitude. It is difficult for him to work, and he does so with great effort. He cannot concentrate, and he cannot express himself easily. Sleep is disturbed and does not refresh him. Although he may completely repress his depression and sadness, the continuous presence of these symptoms and his general behavior enable the examiner to conclude that the patient is suffering from a general depressive reaction.

Patients with this type of reaction can usually be treated and brought to full recovery by the psychotherapist without hospitalization, although suicide must be guarded against in some cases.

Simple Retardation. In simple retardation the patient is depressed and lethargic; his facial expression is sad, and his eyes are dull. Questions and commands often have to be repeated, and it takes him a long time to respond to them. He has to be helped in such daily activities as getting dressed, eating, and going to the toilet. He feels worthless and guilty, but there is no disturbance of consciousness or of intellectual faculties. Patients of this type should be treated as invalids. They should be hospitalized when possible, although they can be treated at home if adequate care is available.

Acute Depression. The same symptoms appear in acute depression as in simple retardation, but are more marked. The patient sits alone, does not speak of his own accord, and is extremely slow in his responses. He accuses himself of frightful wrongdoings that will bring disaster to everyone and for which he will be imprisoned or executed. He thinks that his bowels are completely stopped up, that his heart is badly damaged, or that his brain is wasting away. He feels that his whole personality is changed, and everything around him seems unreal. He may have hallucinations, particularly in connection with sin and guilt, disease and poverty.

Depressive Stupor. The patient is utterly depressed; he does not speak and does not respond. He has to be fed because he will not eat voluntarily; his bladder and bowels have to be emptied artificially. His health is in great danger because of loss of weight and auto-intoxication. The heart action and circulation suffer, and infections may develop.

THE DANGERS FROM DEPRESSIVE REACTIONS

The patient with the mild form of depression may be unable to do his work and as a consequence may lose his job. This loss is a blow to his self-esteem. Lack of sympathy in his social environment and the accusation that he is pretending or indulging himself increase his irritability and his feeling of inadequacy and self-condemnation. Well-meant remarks like "Snap out of it" and "There's nothing to worry about" make him feel that no one realizes that he is sick or sympathizes with him. All this increases his discomfort and intensifies his symptoms. The danger of suicide is, in general, proportionate to the intensity of the depression, although it may be present even in relatively mild cases. In serious cases there is considerable danger from loss of weight, exhaustion, and auto-intoxication. However, most patients recover with adequate care.

PSYCHODYNAMICS OF DEPRESSIVE REACTIONS

It is frequently found that the accusations which the patient makes against himself have previously been directed by him toward someone close to him by whom he has been profoundly hurt (Freud). For example, a depressed woman may accuse herself of unfaithfulness, selfishness, and immorality; but careful investigation shows that she formerly made these accusations against her husband. The unspeakable crimes of which she accuses herself may really express her profound hostility toward her husband; in other words, they are the crimes she would have committed if she had carried her repressed impulses into action.

Depressed patients are unable to turn away from the people who hurt them because of their emotional dependence on them. The profound feeling of worthlessness is caused by their self-condemnation and their expectation of disapproval resulting from their hostility toward these indispensable individuals. Such a patient then feels not only disapproved of by this individual but also abandoned and rejected. His helplessness and suffering are increased by his desire to abase himself and suffer in order to expiate his hostility, show his helplessness, and thus obtain forgiveness, approval, and help. This constellation closely approximates for the patient the catastrophic situation of which he is afraid—namely, utter rejection and condemnation both by himself and by the persons on whom he depends. Because of these factors, his appreciation and evaluation of reality are altered.

The characteristics of the emotional pattern of the depressive phase thus are: (1) intense dependence on another individual; (2) strong hostility toward this individual, which the patient turns on himself; (3) intense self-condemnation, guilt, feeling of worthlessness, and expectation of disapproval and abandonment because of this hostility.

The psychodynamics and mechanism of suicide are essentially the same as those of depression: feeling of utter hopelessness as a result of failure and rejection, aggression turning in on the self, and self-punitive form of vengeance. In this respect, suicide might be considered the equivalent of murder—murder of the self. In addition to these, there may be three other determinants: destructive forces at the time of the act outweigh the positive clinging to life and the fear of death; death may represent a fantasy of release from suffering and even the attainment of bliss and immortality, at times through joining another deceased person; the patient identifies with a dead parent who died at a crucial period in the patient's development (1010, 1011).

Suicide is most common in psychotic depression, but also occurs in schizophrenia and in the neuroses. A suicidal trend represents a transient but recurrent danger.

TREATMENT OF DEPRESSIVE REACTIONS

The general treatment should be based on understanding; this is particularly important in mild or moderate cases. The patient should feel that the therapist realizes his suffering and wishes to help him. Encouragement is important, but it should be so given that the patient will not feel that his condition is being minimized. A measure of persistence, persuasion, and kind firmness is needed to persuade him, when feasible, to attend to his needs, to eat, to engage in some activity. Patients with suicidal tendencies must, of course, have constant but not too obvious supervision.

Adequate nourishment is essential. Severely depressed patients who are unable to eat have to be fed through a stomach tube. Constipation is corrected by cathartics and occasional enemas; if the patient is unable to void by himself, the bladder has to be emptied artificially. Sleeplessness is combated by hot baths and, in some cases, hypnotic drugs.

Occupational therapy is always valuable for patients capable of interesting themselves in something. The activity chosen by the patient varies; it may be something in which he has been interested before, or it may be entirely new—drawing or painting, carpentry, clay-modeling. Attending the occupational class and seeing others engaged in useful activities may in itself have a therapeutic effect.

Electric convulsive therapy is especially effective in the treatment of depressed patients. A relatively few "shocks" result in the lifting of the depression, thus making the patient amenable to psychotherapy. One difficulty in the use of ECT in these patients is that, following the course of "shock" treatments, the patient's mood may be elated and he may decide that he does not need psychotherapy. At times there is not much point to psychotherapy because psychotherapeutic investigation yields nothing substantial, either because the material is too deeply repressed or, possibly, because no significant events were responsible for the depression. In any type of case there is always a possibility of a recurrence.

More active psychotherapy, such as discussing his difficulties from the psychiatric point of view, should be begun only when the patient is strong enough to face his problems, conflicts, and frustrations. It is always safe to encourage him to talk about his mild difficulties; but the conversation should never lead him, when he is extremely depressed, to topics which for him are charged with serious conflict. Psychoanalytic treatment should not be undertaken until the patient is over his depression.

It is always desirable to consult with the patient's family, investigate their adjustments, help them with their difficulties, and advise them regarding their relationships with him during his normal periods. Only in this way can the situations and difficulties which depress the patient be either diminished or eliminated.

In mild cases of depression the use of benzedrine sulfate has proved to be of limited usefulness. Benzedrine, a derivative of ephedrine, has a stimulating effect on the psychomotor functions and on mood. In this way, depression may be lessened enough so that the psychiatrist may be able to make contact with the patient.

MANIC REACTIONS: GENERAL CHARACTERISTICS

Like the depressive reaction, the manic reaction is also characterized by three primary symptoms.

Elation. The patient is happy and has a general feeling of well-being. He evaluates himself highly and has an optimistic outlook, in which he expects everything he undertakes to turn out well. In one phase of elation, jocularity, the patient makes humorous remarks, laughs at them, and succeeds in making others laugh too; he enjoys punning.

> "There is absolutely nothing the matter. Everything is perfect, all is peace and love. I feel fine—perfect. Everything is hotsy-totsy now. My only complaint is Patsy isn't here. I have never been sick. I have always been good or else God couldn't have lifted me up. Now Adam made a mistake and he's doing time now. I never did. I was perfect and I see the light and love. He sent my mother and father down here as the best in order to have me. They were perfect when they had me—I've always been clean."[2]

[2] Wendell Muncie, *Psychobiology and Psychiatry,* Mosby, St. Louis, 1939.

Flight of Ideas. The patient's thoughts, as well as his speech and writing, jump from one topic to another without following a single course. The trend of thought is diverted to a subtopic, which in turn diverts it in still another direction. Distractibility is common; that is, the trend of thoughts may be diverted by an external event, such as a noise, the ringing of a bell, a picture on the wall.

Psychomotor Activity. The patient is always on the go, always busy. His activities are not merely aimless motor phenomena such as playing with a pencil or drumming with the fingers; they may have a definite purpose. For example, he will talk to other individuals, pick up a book and start to read aloud, try to persuade someone to do something, try to organize a party, invite people, write letters, make purchases, want to institute changes in the routine of the ward, etc.—all in rapid succession. The terms "pressure of activity" and "pressure of speech" are customarily used in connection with these phenomena.

Because of these three symptoms, the patient is over-talkative, is constantly on the go, engages in one activity after another, and displays a rather infectious gaiety.

A woman in a psychopathic hospital was walking around in the ward in a gay mood with a smile on her face. She stopped at one of the rooms, the door of which was open. In this room the psychiatrist was examining a patient, who kept repeating stereotyped phrases and stereotyped motions and would not answer the examiner's questions. After watching for a short time, the manic patient entered the room and said to the other patient in a cheerful, laughing manner: "Talk to him. Why don't you talk to him? The paragon of beautiful male specimen is trying to converse with you. Just look at her! Here is the paragon of beautiful male specimen talking to her and she won't answer."

Frequently, even relatively dull people become very entertaining and show a mastery of their language in the manic reaction. The above patient would never be able to coin the phrase "paragon of beautiful male specimen" when she was well.

Other symptoms are frequent in the manic reaction, among them the following:

Irritability When Thwarted. The patient becomes angry and abusive, to the point of shouting or even assault, if anyone crosses him, if his requests are not granted immediately, or if someone tries to show him that what he is doing is not right. He cannot brook contradiction or accept criticism. His thoughts, activities, and mood are unstable.

Suspiciousness. The patient may be suspicious of the actions and motivations of those around him, may assume that they want to do harm or that they have sexual designs.

Delusions. The patient's over-valuation of himself may reach the degree of grandiose delusions. He may consider himself extremely wealthy, a great political or military genius, or an emissary of God. The delusions in typical manic reactions are changeable and of short duration.

Hallucinations. Hallucinations are not common but, if present, are usually of the auditory type. The patient hears someone whom he loves say tender things to him, or he hears God talking. As a rule, the hallucinations do not have an obscene and derogatory content as in schizophrenia.

Physical Symptoms. The patient's facial expression is lively, either joyful or angry; his eyes shine. There is increased perspiration with the excessive activity, and the muscle tone is increased. Among the vegetative symptoms are rapid heart action, increased blood pressure, and, possibly, cessation of menstruation. Sleeplessness may result from the patient's excitement. Because of his constant activity, excitement, and sleeplessness, he may lose considerable weight. If his excitement reaches a delirious intensity, he may refuse to eat, he may lose considerable water through perspiration, and a toxic state may result.

VARIETIES OF MANIC REACTIONS

The patient may have all or only some of the symptoms, in varying degrees of intensity and in various combinations. He may be elated, flighty, and jocular, or irritable, angry, domineering, over-active, and talkative, with no obvious sign of elation. The only indication of elation may be the fact that he says he feels particularly well. Hallucination and delusion may accompany relatively moderate over-activity. In some patients the reaction is mild and remains essentially the same during the whole illness; in others it increases in intensity, hallucinations and delusions appearing at its height. The relative dominance of the elation or of the irritability and impulsive stubbornness may fluctuate during the course of the illness. Three varieties of manic reactions are usually differentiated.

Hypomania. The characteristic features are moderate elation, flightiness, and over-activity. The patient is particularly witty and entertaining—he is the life of the party. He may get into trouble because of extravagance, sexual promiscuity, or alcoholic indulgence, or, if his mood changes, because of his irritability, combativeness, and intolerance of criticism. The continuous activity and restlessness are the most constant symptom. Such a patient is difficult to treat unless hospitalized because the people around him are often reluctant or unable to realize that he is sick. He himself, as a rule, does not realize this; he insists on having his own way, disregards advice, and resents supervision.

Acute Mania. Acute mania may follow hypomania or it may appear in its full intensity, possibly after a short period of sleeplessness and irritability. The patient's excitement is intense, his flightiness and restlessness are at a high pitch. He considers himself superior to everyone, wants to manage everyone's affairs and to command and dominate everyone. The dominant mood fluctuates from gaiety to anger. The patient may break up the furniture and strike other patients or nurses. He loses his sense of shame, is obscene in his talk, exposes himself, and makes sexual advances toward those around him. He may also have delusions and hallucinations. His intellectual functions are not impaired, but his orientation for time, place, and person may be inadequate; even his consciousness may be cloudy. Because of the flight of ideas and his distractibility, his speech may become incoherent. The physical symptoms described in connection with hypomania may be intensified by the continuous excitement, loss of water, and lack of nourishment—the pulse rate may rise to 180. Such patients unquestionably require hospitalization.

Delirious Mania. Delirious mania may develop from hypomania and acute mania, or it may appear almost at the beginning of the manic reaction. The patient's symptoms are manifested so intensely that he is totally disoriented; his speech is incoherent, he is extremely restless, and his activities lack any apparent organization or goal. He may have vivid auditory and visual illusions and hallucinations. He lacks all insight and is entirely shameless in his behavior, appearance, and habits. The chances of exhaustion, self-intoxication, and infection by other diseases are great, and the loss of weight may be very rapid. Such patients, of course, must be treated in hospitals.

THE DANGERS FROM MANIC REACTIONS

In mild types of manic reactions, the patient is in danger of getting into trouble because of his reckless spending of money and mismanagement of his business, his indiscriminate conclusion of contracts, etc. He may be arrested on charges of felonious assault, misconduct, or immoral behavior, or be injured in a brawl. These dangers are also present in acute mania. Because of indiscriminate sexual behavior, the patient may acquire a venereal infection, or a woman may become pregnant without knowing who her partner was. In the acute and delirious reactions there is danger from physical exhaustion, intoxication, and infection by disease.

PSYCHODYNAMICS OF MANIC REACTIONS

The nature of the conflict and of the catastrophic fear in the manic reaction is probably the same as in the depressive reaction. The manic patient, however, arrives at a different solution and uses different means of coping with his difficulties and problems. He declares that his conflicts, his anxieties, his guilt, and his helplessness do not exist; he is stronger than any problem he faces, stronger than the individual who hurt him and threatened him with condemnation and abandonment. He considers himself remarkably capable instead of helpless. He is demanding instead of submissive. Instead of condemning himself, he fully approves of himself. Far from being abandoned by the world, he declares that the whole world is his. With tremendous effort and expenditure of energy he overrides his guilt, anxiety, and helplessness, and makes contact with the world, rushing from one object to another.

There is another factor in the hyperactivity as well as in the flight of ideas; i.e., the patient is constantly running away from his pain and discomfort, his conflict, guilt, and fear. He is escaping into his environment from his own conflicts; hence the manic reaction may in a sense be called a pathological outgoingness. In this whole process, the evaluation of reality in all its phases—the evaluation of the self and of social customs, and of the functions of the senses and ideas—is seriously altered. Overriding his anxieties and throwing off the yoke of his conscience make the patient joyous because he feels completely liberated; he discards his inhibitions and gets additional pleasure from gratifying "forbidden" and previously inhibited impulses.

Attention has been called to the fact that some of the physiological manifestations of manic-depressive reactions involve particularly the mouth functions (Abraham). As we have seen, the depressed patient does not want to eat; this is his reaction to his desire to destroy the individual who disappointed him. The situation in the patient with a manic reaction is reversed. He may eat ravenously, saying, in effect, that the whole world is his and he can have his fill of it.

At times the patient's hopes and expectations of a solution of his difficulties center in his relationship with another individual, such as a child or a lover. Upon being disappointed in or losing this individual, the patient may develop a manic reaction instead of becoming depressed. The manic reaction here represents an overriding of the feeling of loss and resentment and of all the conflicts which in the complete constellation represent a catastrophic situation for him. The delusions then assume a wish-fulfilling quality—that the child is alive or that the lover will marry the patient. This is not a simple wish-fulfilling fantasy; it is a fantasy to which the patient clings in order to escape the catastrophic situation and for which he has to alter his evaluation of reality. The following case illustrates this point. This is one of those rare instances in which the observer had the opportunity to see the patient before the development of the overt manic reaction and in which he was thoroughly familiar with the event to which the patient was reacting.

A woman of twenty-five was moderately depressed in connection with her difficulties with her family, her aspirations, and her station in life. This depression did not seriously interfere with her work or her everyday life. She met a man who was superior to her in intellect and who, as a way out of his emotional difficulties, was seeking contact with someone who would be unqualifiedly devoted to him. This man was under psychoanalytic treatment; against the analyst's advice, he proposed to her; she had fallen intensely in love with him.

As the day of their marriage approached, the man became panicky and antagonistic toward the woman; he wanted to break with her completely; not openly, but by such an aggravation of his symptoms that they would completely incapacitate him. The analyst felt forced, under these circumstances, to take a more active part in the situation, and he suggested that the man ask the woman to come to his office. It became obvious in the course of the conversation that her love for the man contained an element of pure admiration for a person whom she considered great and strong and on whom she could unqualifiedly depend.

The analyst told her that the man was in no condition to embark on a marriage, and that it would be best to postpone any decision in the matter since a hasty step might cause severe suffering to both. Although she had looked forward to marriage and had talked about it constantly to the man, she accepted the analyst's advice.

The next day, the woman became over-active and over-talkative and remained home from work. She saw the man that day, and volubly and happily discussed the coming marriage with him, and made plans to go to the country. When the analyst heard this story from the man, he asked him to bring the woman to his office. In a happy, elated mood, the woman told the analyst that she had come to his office with the man to be married there, and that they were going to the country. Her facial expression was blissful, her eyes were shining. While sitting in a chair across from the analyst's desk, she gazed intently into the distance and talked to herself. On direct questioning she said that she could hear her fiancé talking to her, and that she was conversing with him. She herself repeated both sides of the conversation. For example: She: "What did you say, darling?" He: "We are going to the country, darling." She: "Are we going to be married?" He: "Yes, sweetheart, we'll get married right away." The patient also heard him tell her how to comb her hair, what dress to wear, and what to eat.

In this instance the postponement of marriage was evaluated by the woman as a threatening catastrophe, depriving her of hoped-for help and dependence, and rescue from her state of helplessness and abandonment. She felt an undercurrent of resentment toward and conflict with her fiancé because of this blow. As a way out of her conflict and the threatening catastrophe, she developed this relatively manic reaction, which contained the wish-fulfilling delusion that they were being married immediately.

This patient did not lack insight entirely in this interview. As long as she was permitted to talk about her delusion and to hallucinate freely, she seemed happy. But when the psychiatrist asked her, "Are you feeling entirely well?" or "Don't you think you are disturbed?" an expression of alarm came over her face and she said, "Am I going mad? Am I hallucinating?" After the analyst told her that she was not well and that she needed rest and treatment, she became alarmed and had to lie down because she was faint. When he advised her to go back to her family, which she had just left, she was reluctant, but her fiancé prevailed on her to do so. Following the interview with the analyst, the woman lost her delusions and hallucinations; she remained tense and disturbed, but she was able to return to and continue her work. Under treatment by another psychiatrist she emerged from her condition without losing her job.

This case affords a rare type of observation. Because of the mild character of the reaction, the immediate treatment, and the understanding coöperation of everyone concerned, the condition could be controlled from the start. The degree of insight that this patient still showed is rare in fully developed reactions, but disturbing and contradictory flashes of insight can be observed in any case of relatively mild severity.

MIXED STATES

The variation in the predominant symptoms presented by different patients has been mentioned in connection with both the depressive and the manic reaction. In some instances the symptoms are mixed. These mixed states are particularly frequent when a manic reaction changes into a depressive reaction, or vice versa, without an intervening period of relative well-being. In "maniacal stupor," for example, the patient has a blissful expression; and, as he says later, he has flights of ideas and delusions but he does not speak or react to stimuli. Other patients may be depressed and have flights of ideas, or be depressed and agitated, over-active, irritable. Psychodynamically, such patients have not succeeded in adopting either form of solution for their conflicts but are employing conflicting measures.

TREATMENT OF MANIC REACTIONS

Mild cases may be treated at home if adequate understanding and supervision can be obtained. Unless these are provided, the patient may damage his self-interest or get into any of many difficulties. The handling of the manic patient requires a combination of understanding, kindness, patience, and firmness; but any attempt to "talk him out of his problems" has a bad effect. He should be given adequate nourishment and should be urged to eat and drink. Prolonged baths have a soothing effect. In relatively mild cases occupational therapy is valuable because it guides the patient's activity into some organized and constructive channel. The activity may be one which the patient already likes, or it may be new to him. Participating in a dramatic performance, for example, is helpful because it satisfies his desire and need for activity, and he is willing to accept constructive suggestions and criticisms for the sake of the organized group goal. In more serious conditions, but to some extent in mild ones also, hypnotics and continuous baths are necessary to quiet the patient; temporary restraint may also be required.

Electric convulsive therapy is almost as effective in the manic phase of manic-depressive psychosis as it is in the depressive phase. Intensive treatment (two or three treatments a day) may result in remission within two or three days (474). The treatment does not prevent relapses.

Discussion of the patient's difficulties, even if the conversation only touches on distressing topics, has no value in a reaction of any intensity. This type of therapy, however, is useful when the condition begins to subside or after it has ceased. Psychoanalysis can be used successfully only after the manic reaction has disappeared.

SUGGESTED READINGS

The treatment of the psychoses in this and following chapters should be compared with those in any standard textbook of psychiatry. For fundamental concepts, see Freud's paper on mourning and melancholia in his *Collected Papers* (304), *The Commonsense Psychiatry of Dr. Adolf Meyer* (646), Sullivan's *Conceptions of Modern Psychiatry* (913), and Schilder's *Introduction to a Psychoanalytic Psychiatry* (829). B. D. Lewin's *The Psychoanalysis of Elation,* Norton, New York, 1950, is an important contribution to the literature. All of these represent advanced reading.

XXXIV Schizophrenic Reactions

THE "SCHIZOID" PERSONALITY

The type of individual who, under adequate stress, most frequently develops a schizophrenic reaction is the so-called "shut-in" person. These people are disinclined to seek other individuals; they are bad mixers; when they do make friends, they do not form intimate or close friendships. They often have queer habits, are apt to behave in a silly manner and to consider themselves superior to others in a grandiose way. They often show a peculiar lack of appreciation and evaluation of other people's reactions, particularly in connection with social customs. This trait, together with an impulsive urge to make decisions without conscious emotions, may appear in situations which are of extreme importance for the patient, as when a man faced by a difficult situation says nothing to his wife or his close relatives and leaves home without much conscious emotion. Sometimes there is a continuous tenseness in the person who in general is inclined to be "shut in." When he is with other people his manner is intense, loud, and awkward, not in harmony with the emotional requirements of the situation. These same patients often have an odd way of thinking; for example, they may approach relatively simple problems in an involved philosophical way. There are other characteristics and varieties of "shut-in," or schizoid, personality. It should be remembered, however, that occasionally individuals develop schizophrenic reactions regardless of personality type.

NATURE OF SCHIZOPHRENIC REACTIONS

SYMPTOMS OF SCHIZOPHRENIC REACTIONS

The symptoms of schizophrenic reactions vary considerably, "queerness" of emotional, thought, and behavior processes being the most common feature. By "queerness" is meant the fact that the examiner and the normal individual find it difficult to feel themselves into the manifestations or to sympathize with them, whereas this is very easy in manic-depressive reactions. The symptoms may appear at any time of life, but most commonly they first appear between 15 and 25 years of age. The condition may persist, although with fluctuations, throughout the individual's life and often terminates in a complete deterioration of the intellectual and emotional faculties. However, any form of schizophrenic reaction may end in a social and occupational recovery.

The symptoms usually include: (1) An emotional dulling, with absence of adequate emotional response by the patient to either the situation or his own thoughts. If there is emotional excitement, it is rigid and preoccupied, without keen and adequate contact with the external world. (2) Bizarre thinking, which manifests itself in (3) delusions, preoccupation with curious inventions, plans, and mechanical devices. (4) Frequent obscene hallucinations. (5) Rigid behavior, with a silly fixed smile, stereotyped movements, negativism, or automatonlike behavior. (6) Radical alteration of speech, including the coining of new words, rambling, monosyllables, nonsensical utterances. These will now be discussed in detail.

Emotional Alterations. Alterations in emotional responses may be manifest in several ways. In emotional dulling, the patient does not consciously manifest or experience keen and adequate emotions. He is apathetic, dreamy, or indifferent, and does not seem to comprehend joy, sorrow, or fear. He may speak of a death or great disaster or of being a genius or a great inventor without any show of sorrow, excitement, or pleasure. There is "lack of contact" with people around him.

The patient's emotional responses, when they do occur, have more the nature of a general excitement than a specific quality of emotion. When the patient talks loudly and vehemently and is comparatively silent and preoccupied by turns, it is difficult to determine properly the quality of this emotional response. The most common response to be identified is fear, even amounting to panic, resulting from anticipated harm by persecutors. Here, too, however, the excitement is more in the foreground than the fear; at times it has a strong self-aggrandizing tone. Suspiciousness is another mode of behavior that the patient may both experience and show. But generally the emotions seem to be undifferentiated, to "run one into the other." It is easy to say of a normal person that he is afraid *or* joyous *or* angry; of the schizophrenic, one can say only that he is excited or emotional-in-general.

Bizarre Thinking. The patient may be preoccupied with his bodily processes, his thoughts being concerned with any organ in which he usually has some abnormal sensation. He has various explanations for these. If, for example, he has a feeling of discomfort in his spine, he may explain how masturbation or an infection in his nose is responsible for this complaint. He may be preoccupied with mechanical devices to cure this condition, or with a complicated drawing which graphically represents it. The perpetual motion machine has always held particular fascination for these patients. In all these thoughts and preoccupations such patients always deviate foolishly and persistently from the accepted thinking on such matters, nor can they be influenced concerning them.

Delusions. Ideas of reference and of influence and delusions of persecution and of grandeur are common in schizophrenic reactions.

Ideas of reference are present when the patient evaluates trivial occurrences as referring to him and implying something very significant. He may think that people are talking about him or laughing at him or dropping hints, or that they close the door in a certain way either to convey something to him or to express something in reference to him. If details are asked for, the patient's assumption is found to be entirely unsubstantiated, but he believes it just the same. Thus he may say that two persons who passed him said that he had an immoral character. Investigation shows that he did not actually hear this remark, that he never saw the two individuals before, that they were not even looking at him when they passed. Nevertheless, he remains unshaken in his belief.

Ideas of influence are manifest when the patient says that someone puts thoughts into his head, influences his actions, causes him discomfort and pain by influencing the functioning of his organs. Often this influence is assumed to be exerted by complicated machines operated by electricity or some other means; patients often describe the influence as "hypnotic."

In delusions of persecution, the patient attributes many of these phenomena just mentioned to his "enemies." One of the best means of securing information about delusions of persecution or ideas of reference or influence is to ask the patient if he has any enemies; this usually elicits a vivid account of at least one enemy, usually many. He may believe that "secret police" are after him, or attribute his troubles to a lawyer or a physician. He may believe that poisonous gas is being released in his room or that poison is being placed in his food. Such patients often think that they are being followed or that their enemies have immoral intentions.

Delusions of grandeur, in the form of mild statements indicating a belief in the possession of remarkable qualities, can almost always be elicited from patients suffering from schizophrenic reactions. At times such statements consist only of answers to this effect; the patients cannot name these qualities. Other patients, either spontaneously or on direct questioning, say that they can influence others, that they can send secret messages, that they are great thinkers or inventors who will be called up to assist in a national crisis, or that they are already serving in this capacity. They also claim to be of royal blood, or, depending on their sex, to be Napoleon or Jesus Christ or the Virgin Mary.

These statements are not accompanied by an adequate emotional response. There are fleeting disturbances in the patient—i.e., he is reluctant to answer, or evasive—but he does not evidence joy over his invention or great deed or wonderful quality.

These thoughts and convictions and experiences are not systematized or worked out consistently by the schizophrenic patient. Contradictory and fragmentary thoughts exist side by side. Thus the patient may accuse a lawyer or a relative of being responsible for his troubles, but be unable to give a systematized answer as to how or why. A woman may protest insistently against persecution by a certain man, but upon seeing him smile, say that his voice speaks of love, and announce her engagement to him. The patient may announce himself as the king of England and at the same time agree to work in the laundry. Contradictions of this sort, indicating conflicting attitudes, have often been referred to as ambivalence, implying rejection and acceptance, love and hatred, at the same time. It should be emphasized again, however, that, while the patient's ideas, thoughts, and experiences are largely incoherent, they persist in their vague form week after week and month after month.

Hallucinations. Hallucinations are most frequently of the auditory type. The patient may hear the voice of the same person or of several persons. This voice may belong to someone he knows, or he may attribute it to an unseen enemy or to secret police or to God. The content of the hallucinations varies, but in general it is of the following types: (1) Obscene words: The patient is called sexually immoral, a pervert, a street woman, etc. These hallucinations are particularly malignant and are most characteristic of schizophrenia. (2) Statements about what the patient is doing at the moment: "Now he is eating," "Now he takes the spoon." (3) Command: The voices tell the patient what to do. The commands may vary, and the patient may or may not execute them. Thus he may be commanded to throw furniture out of the window or hurl a stone into a show window or follow a woman and propose to her. (4) Messages from secret organizations or religious bodies or God: The contents are usually of the type, "You will redeem mankind," "Yea, we shall relish thee," "You are my prophet," etc.

Hallucinations of taste and smell are next in frequency. The patient says that the food has a curious taste and believes that there is poison or vermin in it. He smells a peculiar odor and attributes it to poisonous gases released in the room by his enemies. In hallucinations of touch and pain, the patient has unpleasant sensations in various organs and may be convinced that he has been sexually assaulted. The patient suffering from visual hallucinations may see objects change in shape, or see fiery crosses or God or the saints.

Changes in Behavior and Actions. The patient's posture is often rigid and constrained. His facial expression is vacant and lacks mobility. He does not look at the examiner while they are talking. A silly smile is extremely frequent in schizophrenia, as are also facial grimaces recurring in a stereotyped fashion, sniffing or snorting, short repeated coughs, spitting movements. Stereotyped movements are apparent in other parts of the body; these consist of rubbing the hands or legs, twisting the hair, etc. In waxy flexibility the patient's body retains whatever posture the examiner puts it in; thus the arm remains lifted for long periods of time without apparent fatigue. In negativism, the patient does not carry out commands, and he resists movement of any part of his body. Unchanging, and at times strained, posture may be maintained. The patient may lie motionless without eating or attending to his wants for long periods, even years. He may assume a peculiar posture—for example, the intrauterine position of the fetus—and retain it for a long time; if it is disturbed, he resumes it again. The patient may become actively absorbed in his hallucinations; he looks intently at one spot as if seeing something, listens intently to his "voices," moves his lips, or makes signs with his hands. He may make compulsive assaults on individuals whom he considers his persecutors, or make sexual attacks, or display exhibitionism.

Changes in Speech. Some change in the speech is always present in schizophrenia. At times it consists of a lack of proper inflections, leading to monotonous speech; less frequently, the speech becomes vehement, and the patient talks animatedly about his troubles. In evasiveness, the patient does not answer the question, but makes a statement about something else; for example, "How did you get along with your mother?" "I ate various things at home," or "My mother bought some furniture and it was spoiled." The speech may ramble; that is, the patient talks freely, but he does not follow the topic, and one sentence merges into another. In monosyllabic speech, he answers only yes or no; he may answer such questions as "What day is today?" but he does not respond spontaneously to such questions as "What are your complaints?" In mutism, the patient does not speak at all; in echolalia he repeats like an echo whatever the examiner says; for example, "What day is it today?" "Today." The statements may be incoherent. Even if they form clear sentences, they show no coherence and are often unconnected. The speech shows other remarkable alterations which are the result of the peculiar emotional and thought processes characteristic of schizophrenia. The sentence structure is often shattered to the point where a sentence consists of a sequence of apparently unconnected words: "The nail file on the wall, the radio said, a green came out on the wall, gosh." New words are coined. These neologisms often consist of the condensation of two or more words, and if the patient is willing he can explain them. Thus a patient who used the word "gacidcator" said that it was the name of a chemical he had invented to dry out gas in the acid in the stomach (gas, acid, desiccator). The patient may invent a complicated language, which can be deciphered with adequate analysis.

VARIETIES OF SCHIZOPHRENIC REACTIONS

Four varieties of schizophrenic reactions are usually differentiated. However, these should not be considered fixed, for one patient may have certain features of various reactions, or the dominant reaction may vary from one kind to another in any patient.

Simple Schizophrenic Reaction. The patient becomes disinterested and apathetic. He wants to be alone, neglects his work, and does not participate in any activities. He becomes dull emotionally and loses his ambition; depending on the environment, he may become a hobo. The patient may be somewhat irritable and moody; he is unable to sustain attention and may become evasive and monosyllabic in his conversation. He is apt to sit in the same place with no facial expression or a foolish smile. At this stage the patient is still oriented for place and time, and there is no serious intellectual impairment; if his condition receives attention, it may develop no further, and he may recover. In other cases the condition progresses, and, as the years pass, the patient becomes completely apathetic and deteriorates intellectually to the moronic level. In this type of schizophrenic reaction there are almost no hallucinations and no delusions.

Paranoid Schizophrenic Reaction. The dominant symptoms of the paranoid reaction are ideas of reference and influence, delusions of persecution and often of grandeur. There are usually vivid auditory hallucinations and often hallucinations of smell and taste.

The patient becomes moody, preoccupied, and suspicious. His life becomes disorganized; he does not continue his work; he gets into trouble with other individuals, whom he accuses of persecuting him. He may withdraw; he may want to stay in bed to avoid exposing himself to danger, and he may refuse to eat to escape being poisoned. He may commit a violent act, such as breaking up the furniture, at the command of a "voice." His speech may be voluble, excited, rambling, and even incoherent.

Patients of this type require hospitalization. The condition may fluctuate; that is, the patient may eat, speak, and behave better, and may recover, at least socially and occupationally. But there is no adequate insight; he remains evasive if asked about his illness, or he may deny that he has ever had hallucinations and delusions. Frequently, however, the condition continues throughout life and may end in a complete deterioration of the emotional and intellectual capacities.

Catatonic Schizophrenic Reaction. The catatonic reaction may be preceded by symptoms of simple or paranoid schizophrenic reactions, but in some cases it is present almost from the beginning. The symptoms are usually described as a fluctuation between depression, excitement, and stupor.

After a period of apathy or queer behavior the patient may sit idly in one position or remain in bed in a peculiar posture; he does not speak or eat, and does not react to painful stimuli. He either is incontinent as far as excreta are concerned, or retains them completely. The patient may lie with his eyes open, without blinking, for hours or days. There may also be waxy flexibility or negativism. This condition is called "stupor." The patient is not unconscious; he is able to notice everything that goes on around him even though he does not participate in it. If the patient is not in a condition of stupor, more moderate disturbances of initiative and responsiveness may be present. The patient then may sit idly, may be willing to go to the table if led, and to eat if the food is offered him. He may not answer questions, but he may make stereotyped irrelevant utterances, such as repeating, "I could not say, I could not say," or making up a list of unrelated names. Stereotyped actions may be prominent, together with mannerisms—the patient may make the same motions with his hands continuously, he may walk in the same peculiar way, there may be echopraxia (imitation of the actions of the examiner) and echolalia.

The patient's experiences in this stuporous condition are very vivid and often on a cosmic scale.

The patient sometimes suddenly emerges from the catatonic stuporous state with a violent, frenzied excitement. He may talk excitedly and incoherently, engage in excited activities, impulsively attack and attempt to kill another person, or mutilate himself or commit suicide.

After a paranoid period, a patient became stuporous. His family, particularly his mother, refused to send him to a hospital. After a few days of being in this stuporous state he suddenly got up, struck his mother unconscious with a chair, got dressed, turned on the gas, and left the house. His father came home in time, and the mother, although her skull was fractured, recovered. The patient himself, after other violent acts in the street, was taken to a psychopathic hospital by the police.

The catatonic excitement may last from a few hours to several days, after which the patient may lapse back into a stuporous state. In their excited state patients frequently have hallucinations, and the violent acts that they commit are often commanded by their "voices." They may also have delusions of persecution, and they often hear the voice of God.

The pupillary disturbances mentioned above and the cold, clammy, bluish extremities, nose, and ears are most common in this reaction.

The schizophrenic reaction type in which catatonic features predominate may end in social and occupational recovery even after many years of illness; but it may also end in an emotional and intellectual deterioration.

Hebephrenic Schizophrenic Reaction. It is customary to differentiate the hebephrenic reaction also, although most of its characteristic features are present in the other three types. The difference lies in greater emphasis on incoherence of thought, queer impulsive conduct, sudden weeping and laughter without adequate cause, and lively hallucinations. In addition, there are usually shallowness of affect, delusions of persecution or grandeur, catatonic features and mannerisms—all usually summed up under the term "hebephrenic silliness."

In addition to the four traditional types of schizophrenia or their mixtures, there are some less frequently seen varieties. One of them is an acute confusional state with narrowing of consciousness, some disorientation for space and time, auditory hallucinations, and delusions. The condition gives the impression of a dream state; hence it is called oneirophrenia. There is no perplexity, and visual hallucinations are in the minority. The patient may recover from this state in a few days or a week or may develop one of the classic types. In other less frequent varieties the patient may be predominantly depressed or manic or may show hysterical symptoms—e.g., paralysis of an extremity.

The following describes a predominantly hebephrenic patient:

"P. R., a young girl 20 years old, who had been employed as a nurse, was admitted in a restless, agitated state, but a few minutes later she was smiling and happy. . . .

". . . Her diffuseness and inconsequent talk can be gathered from the following:

" 'Who discovered America?' 'Well, I think it was a Murray. I had an old Aunt Sally who died and an old brother went to Hudson Bay.'

"She behaved in a disturbed, excitable way, . . . smashed several panes of glass. . . . She refused food, so that for a time it was necessary to tube-feed her. . . .

"She . . . explained that she had two voices; the one which was speaking she called her 'top voice,' and what she said with the 'top voice' was true; but there was a second voice, an 'under-voice,' which she apparently believed or felt was what her auditors at times heard replacing the true 'top voice.' Consequently we were getting false ideas by believing this second voice. She also expressed the idea that the doctors and nurses used her as a 'medium' to affect the others. . . .

"Her condition has become gradually worse . . . and her speech is incoherent. . . .

" 'Losh, I don't know what it is. You see—she says—I don't know, I'm sure. There's Cinderella. There is a much better play than that. "I don't know," I said. He is an awful idiot. Oh dear God, I'm so stupid. . . .'

"A sample of her letter-writing shows very well the incoherence and the tendency to repetition.

"Dear Sir,

"I have just had dinner. I ate my dinner the monkey and I feel better. change I. Nurse is always making the tea. Betsy's nurse.

"Wearing for a cup of
tea.
"Bathing patient.
"(Ogalvie).
"Your—
"I j g u.
"gins Druce,
"Yours
"sincerely,
"P. R. . . ."[1]

[1] D. K. Henderson and R. D. Gillespie, *A Textbook of Psychiatry*, Oxford University Press, London, 5th ed., 1940, p. 222.

PSYCHOLOGY OF SCHIZOPHRENIA; SCHIZOPHRENIC THINKING; A RESULT OF PROJECTIVE TEST PROCEDURES

We will now proceed to examine with projective tests the nature of schizophrenic reactions. Not all aspects of the schizophrenic's behavior in these tests will be discussed here, merely some typical trends.[2]

A schizophrenic patient saw, in card III of the Rorschach Test, a hen and a rooster. (The popular response to this card is the figures of two persons.) Explaining his response, the patient said that, because there was also red in the card, there being two figures meant something to him—namely, conflict. From this concept he moved to the idea of the opposition between male and female. From this idea he then moved to the idea of a hen and a rooster. And then, although the two figures show no differences that he could point out, he was convinced they represented hen and rooster. Let us now examine what kind of thinking processes took place. The patient started out with two perceptual (concrete) experiences, the red and the twoness. This he turned into an abstract concept: conflict. At the end of the process he went through the opposite process; he turned abstract notions—namely, conflict and maleness and femaleness—into concrete things—namely, a hen and a rooster. The process of symbolization is illustrated by his reacting with the idea of "conflict" to the redness of the card. We can further observe a disturbance in the process of relatedness. The patient reacted to the color red in the card. That percept was not incorporated into the picture of the hen and the rooster, but its effect was present and was taken as a reality. Thus relationships are established which clearly overstep logical boundaries. In this process, as well as in the whole sequence, we observe still another phenomenon—namely, an arbitrary reshuffling of relationships existing in objective reality. Thus the red, via the reaction mentioned, turns into reality at an entirely different place in the card, and the idea of conflict turns into concreteness and thus into reality in the notion of the hen and the rooster. Still another process is observable, that of condensation. The patient fuses the idea of conflict with the idea of the difference between the sexes.

Thus, in the example given, we have observed the following characteristics of schizophrenic thinking: making the concrete abstract; making the abstract concrete; condensation; establishing relationships where they do not exist; a strongly personal, subjective character of connections and sequences; symbolization; and the breaking down of the boundaries of reality. A brief example will show similar phenomena by the use of another test.

The patient is presented, in the Sorting Test, with a group of paired identical objects, although some of them differ in size; i.e., a spoon is paired with a spoon, a cigar with a cigar, a nail with a nail, etc. He is then asked, "Why do they all

[2] For the diagnostic use of these and other tests, the student is referred to the following books: S. Deri, *Introduction to the Szondi Test: Theory and Practice* (188); D. Rapaport, M. Gill, and R. Schafer, *Diagnostic Psychological Testing*, Vols. I and II (757); and R. Schafer, *The Clinical Application of Psychological Tests* (825).

The thought processes discussed in this section were observed clinically before the use of these tests, which, however, highlight them dramatically.

belong together?" The correct abstraction would be that they are "all pairs of similar objects." To be sure, this is frequently a difficult abstraction to make for the person tested, but now the schizophrenic patient's reply was that they were all "objects of pleasure."[3] The significant aspect of this reply is not that it is inadequate but the nature of the response and the nature of the error. For one thing, it is an over-abstraction, and, secondly, it is patently in clash with reality—e.g., the nails.

To be sure, these processes and some additional ones to be mentioned are present as tendencies in every person's psychic life, some of them most strikingly illustrated in dreams. They are also, within very definite conventional limitations, a part of normal waking life—e.g., green with envy. However, these processes dominate schizophrenic thinking, and they distort reality. Many investigators consider these features the primary disturbance of schizophrenia, together with some emotional features which they also consider primary. These emotional changes are dulling of affects (i.e., absence of sadness while talking over a tragic event), rigidity of affect (i.e., the patient's mood remains the same while talking about topics that usually have different emotional coloring), inappropriateness of affect (i.e., the patient talks with a smile about tragic events), and disunity of affects (i.e., the patient may weep and laugh at the same time). This last phenomenon is very close to what some consider one of the most characteristic and fundamental features of the affective life of schizophrenia—namely, ambivalence, implying by that the constant presence of opposing positive and negative attitudes.

These authors consider the more dramatic manifestations of schizophrenia, such as delusions and hallucinations, to be secondary results of these fundamental alterations. Thus, if a schizophrenic hears a parental voice accusing him of being a pervert, this is a result of his distortion of reality, the domination of his thinking by subjective attitudes, ambivalence (toward his sexual impulses), and the love and hate of his parents (98). Going a step further, some authors emphasize the loss of self-respect of the schizophrenic, from which they then assume that three developments may follow. (1) They drift into the psychosis, accepting easy modes of satisfaction and gradually withdrawing into a world of fantasy. (2) Some engage in delusional misinterpretation, striving to escape a sense of failure or guilt by refusing to admit defeat, and blame the world for their ills. (3) A reaction of panic at the vague sense of distress and failure may then result in stuporousness or agitation (434). This loss of self-respect is further intensified by a disturbed ability for empathy—namely, the difficulty of forming close emotional ties with others, the difficulty of being part of a group, an inadequate sense of social relationship. This would indicate self-centeredness. Self-

[3] From R. Schafer, *The Clinical Application of Psychological Tests: Diagnostic Summaries and Case Studies,* International Universities Press, New York, 1948, p. 201.

centeredness being more marked in children than in adults, it would indicate general psychological immaturity. These authors further point to some of the somatic phenomena observed in schizophrenics as a group and try to utilize them as a basis for etiological concepts. We will now proceed to discuss these observations and concepts.

PHYSICAL SYMPTOMS IN SCHIZOPHRENIA

A considerable amount of investigation has been done on the pathology of the function and anatomy of various organs of schizophrenic patients. Some investigators found changes in the anatomy of the various endocrine glands, in the brain tissue, and in the anatomy of the circulatory system (e.g., narrowness of the aorta) (564), but others were unable to find these changes with the same regularity or found them as frequently in other patients with organic psychoses who had had prolonged stays in mental hospitals (554). One difficulty in the problem of some investigations was that the secondary effects of prolonged or acute starvation, dehydration in sustained excitement, and inactivity, which are frequent occurrences in schizophrenics, lead to microscopic anatomical changes. As a result, some of the tissue changes found were due to these factors and not to the disease process. Similar problems arise in connection with certain physical symptoms. Patients are frequently undernourished, and they usually lose weight because of their disturbed appetite and reluctance or refusal to eat. The extremities and nose and ears may be bluish and cold and clammy. Pupillary reactions may be disturbed. Under normal circumstances, the pupils dilate in response to pain; in schizophrenia this reaction may be absent. In women, the menstrual flow may be decreased or disappear. These symptoms are also difficult to interpret as they may represent primary physical disturbances or may be psychogenically determined. Some investigations on the somatic functions in schizophrenic patients have been done under careful control, in that the findings were compared with those on "average normals" living under identical conditions. These investigations show that the schizophrenics as a group have a tendency to respond less adequately to a variety of stimulating agents—e.g., the administration of thyroid substance. Seventy-two schizophrenic patients and twenty-four normal controls were given 1 cc. of dilute adrenalin solution (0.05 mg.) intravenously. For the controls, the maximal rise of systolic blood pressure averaged 56 mm. of mercury as against 44 mm. in the patients. The pulse rates increased 16.3 and 13.6 beats as an average respectively. Pupils dilate in normal individuals in response to pain. In schizophrenics this reaction may be absent. Schizophrenics as a group have also shown disturbances in homeostasis—the tendency of the organism to maintain a constant level of functioning—as measured by the ability to maintain equal level of functioning under identical circumstances. Under basal conditions, the standard deviations of the means shown in Table 14 were found for some of the functions in the patients as compared with those of control subjects.

TABLE 14[4]

	Patients	Controls
Blood sugar	8.6	5.8
Arterial oxygen	2.64	1.50
Venous oxygen	3.06	1.80
Oxygen consumption	12.0	9.0
Systolic pressure	14.7	9.9
Diastolic pressure	12.4	8.7
Urine volume	1702	629

These authors then advance the construction that the schizophrenic psychosis represents an end-result of a generalized failure of adaptation that arises from defective evolution of the maturing processes. The failure is manifested in an intricate variety of ways but especially in defective homeostasis (somatic and psychic) and defective empathy, and the final, overall disintegration of the personality is manifested in the thinking, acting (behaving, reacting), and feeling of the patient. The accessory symptomatology, representing mainly reactions to the feeling of failure, can be regarded as a secondary adaptation to the difficulties arising out of the primary defect. Before evaluating this formulation of the schizophrenic reaction, we will approach the problem from a different angle.[5]

PSYCHODYNAMICS OF SCHIZOPHRENIA

Even though one of the most characteristic features of schizophrenic reactions is the alteration in emotions—the dulling or the unjustified excitement—it must not be assumed that the patient lacks an emotional life. It is more correct to say that his emotional reactions are so intense, so painful, and so fraught with danger that he represses them. This repression is so intense that it affects all his emotional processes in reference both to himself and to his environment. The world is so full of danger and pain for him

[4] Based on a table in R. G. Hoskins, *The Biology of Schizophrenia,* W. W. Norton & Co., New York, 1946, p. 158.

[5] Certain chemicals are capable of producing symptoms closely resembling those of schizophrenia. Synthetic mescaline, given intravenously in dosage of 0.4 to 0.6 gm., produces psychotic manifestations in normal individuals in a state of clear consciousness. Visual hallucinations, filled with condensations, symbolizations, and infantile wish-fulfilling fantasies, dominate the individual. Auditory hallucinations usually start as an idea, and then the concept is projected and heard from the outside. The individual has somatic sensations (of alteration or loss of parts of the body, electricity); paranoid, grandiose, or hypochondriacal delusions; misinterpretation of environmental situations; depersonalization experiences; disturbances of thought (incoherence, flight of ideas, blocking, etc.); ambivalence; negativism (418). The ultimate light such observations will shed on the psychoses is not as yet clear. The psychotic's reaction differs, nevertheless, from that of the "normal." The method may be used to bring out into the open for the period of the experiment a latent psychotic or neurotic process before and after treatment.

that he withdraws from it emotionally. Withdrawal from the world is particularly marked in catatonic stupor. The "senseless" laughter and weeping are his complicated attempts both to react and at the same time to refrain from reacting to something emotionally. At times, because he thereby turns something desperate into a joke, his laughter is supercilious and superior, not laughter at something humorous, at something he enjoys. Because of the anticipated rejection and the catastrophic nature of the disappointment, a schizophrenic is afraid to have warm feelings toward and form attachments to others. He is even afraid to show any positive emotions.

A schizophrenic patient under treatment would shyly smile and for a split second his rigid, catatonic facial expression would turn into a warm and grateful one when he felt that the therapist understood the hidden meaning of what he wanted to convey. As soon as he felt observed, his smile turned into an endless barrage of compulsive laughter. After accepting this without comment for more than a year of daily interviews, the therapist finally asked the patient whether his loud, compulsive laughter was due to a wish to hide the friendly smile and joy at being understood. He nodded, "Yes," quite seriously and indicated by his whole behavior that he understood. Not long after this, the compulsive laughter disappeared.

Another catatonic patient formulated the reason for the need to hide his feelings very clearly. The therapist was silently wandering around the grounds of the sanitarium with him. He was at that time on very good terms with the therapist. Suddenly he became frightened and tried to get away. The next day the therapist asked him about the reason for this behavior. "We run away from fear of another rebuff," was his immediate reply. "This is the clue to each and every one of our reactions."[6]

The vehement excitement occurs when the patient's pain, anxiety, and anger get the better of him. This is his reaction to conflicting experiences, from which he tries to escape by apathy and emotional blunting. Hence his excitement, too, lacks the essential quality of realness and contact with reality. Similar defensive measures, together with conflicting attitudes, are responsible for the fragmentation, the illogicality and inconsistency of his emotions. In all these phenomena the patient attempts to deprive his reactions of poignancy, of consistency, of meaning, because, if he did not, they would be catastrophic.

There is still another aspect to the psychodynamics of withdrawal. A patient always, to a varying degree, shows a definite self-centering of interest: "The world for me is full of danger and disappointment, pain and catastrophe. I will withdraw from all this and get consolation, pleasure, and safety from my own excellence." This attitude is particularly manifest in the patient's grandiose trends.

[6] F. Fromm-Reichmann, A preliminary note on the emotional significance of stereotypes in schizophrenics, *Bull. Forest Sanitarium,* 1942, 1, 17-21.

Several other processes can be identified in a schizophrenic reaction. The evaluation of reality, as regards both social customs and perceptions, is disturbed partly because of the phenomena just discussed; but in addition the patient seems to follow a formula which implies: "Reality does not matter; only what I desire matters." This results in the absence of shame and the disregard of restrictions common to normal human beings. These phenomena in themselves—exhibitionism, lack of sexual control—also represent the patient's attempts to derive gratification and strength from substitute sources. The delusions of grandeur necessitate an altering of reality, for otherwise they could not occur or serve their purpose.

Finally, these symptoms also represent a good deal of discouragement and feeling of defeat. This probably explains the frequent apathy

Some authors go a step further in their construction about the genetic dynamics of schizophrenia. They assume that a severe trauma occurs very early in the individual's life—namely, in early infancy—when the human being is particularly helpless and vulnerable. This trauma sensitizes the individual considerably more toward the frustrations of later life than do later traumatic experiences. What would be a minor trauma to an essentially healthy individual, or a moderate trauma to one suffering from psychoneurosis, becomes an unbearably painful experience to the potential schizophrenic. Once he reaches his limit of endurance, he escapes the unbearable reality of his present life by attempting to reëstablish the autistic, delusional world of the infant; but this is impossible because the content of his delusions and hallucinations is naturally colored by the experiences of his whole lifetime (323).

We will discuss the "constitutional," "somatogenic," and "psychogenic" theories of schizophrenia further in connection with recent developments and observations in the treatment of the disorder.

THERAPY OF SCHIZOPHRENIA

Somatic Treatment. The most important developments in the somatic treatment of schizophrenia are shock therapy and lobotomy, the latter more recently modified to topectomy. The details of these procedures and their possible modes of action have been discussed elsewhere. (See Chapter XIX.) One interpretation of their effectiveness is that they alter the somatic factors in the psychosis directly. The interpretation is prevalent that lobotomy and topectomy, when effective, eliminate the emotional distress arising out of the patient's orientation, much as the cutting of the nerve would eliminate the pain coming from a diseased part of the body. The elimination of the distressing affect may then cut the vicious circle of the patient's defending himself against his distress and getting into further difficulties through the nature of his defensive measures. Shock treatment, when effective, may also admit of such interpretation, except that the process would be more gradual and the connection between the brain centers would be reëstablished after the illness was remedied. The other interpretations of the effectiveness of shock treatment have been mentioned, and they do not exclude the possibility of a fundamental alteration of an organic process. The theories relating to the manner in which shock therapy is effective in curing schizophrenia are closely related to the theories dealing with the dynamics of schizophrenia. Those who take a basically organic approach to the illness will consider the organic changes occurring in shock treatment as crucial—as, for example, its effects on the autonomic nervous system and the alterations in brain metabolism. If, on the other hand, a psychodynamic viewpoint is held, the emotional changes resulting from the experience of shock and the effects of being nursed back to health from a helpless state will be considered the important ones. A further attempt at integrating the somatogenic and the psychogenic approach will be made after discussion of the psychotherapy of schizophrenia. It should be mentioned here that some workers use shock treatment mainly for the purpose of making the extremely anxious or suspicious patient less tense and thus accessible to psychotherapeutic procedures.

Psychotherapy. We will first discuss the briefer psychotherapy of schizophrenia.

Much can be accomplished if a schizoid personality is recognized early and given adequate attention. These people should be examined and the situations of stress to which they are reacting should be determined; the latter usually concern relationships with their own family. They should be encouraged to make contact with others of their age, to join clubs, to participate in activities.

Mild cases of schizophrenic reactions can be treated at home. Even though these patients are inclined to be withdrawn, are emotionally dull to some extent, are suspicious, and have mild ideas of reference, mild delusions of persecution, and even some hallucinations, they are often able to continue at work, particularly if they are employed by a friend or relative. Some emotional contact with the psychiatrist can be established in weekly or biweekly visits, each lasting about an hour, during which their complaints are discussed and suggestions are offered on how to spend their free time. It is useless to try to convince such a patient that his ideas or delusions are false, for he takes this as a sign of a lack of understanding or as an insult. The psychiatrist should talk with some members of the family in order to make them understand the patient's difficulties. The patient himself should not be relied upon, at least not in the beginning, for information as to the sources of his distress, because he has not strength enough to face his conflicts openly. Gross situations of stress should be ascertained from his family and corrected. Usually, after a few months of treatment, a patient loses his ideas of reference and delusions of persecution, stops hearing voices, and gains some insight and he attributes his previous ideas to an "upset."

More severe cases of schizophrenic reaction require hospitalization. Often the hospital acts first of all as a custodian; that is, the patients are cared for and are prevented from getting into trouble. Special cases necessitate special measures, such as permanent baths for excited patients. The more attention patients receive, the less frequently do they go into catatonic stupors, and the shorter the stupor is.

Occupational therapy is of value for patients who have improved sufficiently or are in a relatively mild phase. Some patients can do simple repetitious work well. Even if they are not able to leave the hospital, at least they feel useful and are happier.

There have been important developments in the application of psychoanalytic principles to the treatment of schizophrenics. The technique of the procedure, of course, had to be modified. The patient is allowed to behave much as he wishes, and any change in his actions or any of his utterances may be used for interpretation in place of the classic "free association," of which the psychotic patient is hardly capable. Thus the analysis of the psychotic patient has parallels with the analysis of children. The analyst may engage in activities jointly with the patient or even in an imitative manner. Thus, if the only thing the patient does is to jump up and down or to sit on the floor or to carry out certain repetitive movements, one way the therapist may succeed in establishing contact is by engaging in similar behavior. That way he may win the patient's trust by showing him that he is a person like him.

One formulation states that the analyst should not attempt to prove his understanding of the patient by giving interpretations, nor should he ask questions when he does not understand the patient, for he cannot know what trend of thought or hallucinations he may be interrupting. He should give evidence of understanding by responding cautiously with gestures or actions appropriate to the patient's communication—for example, by lighting his cigarette from the patient's cigarette instead of using a match when the patient seems to indicate the wish for friendship. Interpretations should come only after a protracted period of this type of handling (Fromm-Reichmann). The following is an illustration of the patient's response to this kind of handling.

"A very suspicious patient after two days of fear and confusion ushering in a real panic became stuporous for a month—mute, resistive to food and retaining excretions. In spite of this rather unpromising picture, I sat with him for an hour every day. The only sign of contact he gave to me or anyone was to indicate by gestures that he wanted me to stay; all that he said on two different days during this period was: 'Don't leave!'

"One morning after this I found him sitting naked and masturbating on the floor of his room which was spotted with urine and sputum, talking for the first time yet so softly that I could not understand him. I stepped closer to him but still could not hear him so I sat down on the floor close to him upon which he turned to me with genuine concern: 'You can't do that for me, you too will get involved.' After that he pulled a blanket around himself saying, 'Even though I have sunk as low as an animal, I still know how to behave in the presence of a lady.' Then he talked for several hours about his history and his problems.

"Finally I offered him a glass of milk. He accepted the offer and I went to get it. When I came back after a few moments his friendliness had changed to hostility and he threw the milk on me. Immediately he became distressed: 'How could I do that to you?' he asked in despair. It seemed as though the few minutes I was out of the room were sufficient time for him to feel that I had abandoned him.

"His confidence was regained by my showing that I did not mind the incident. And for eight months of daily interviews he continued to talk."[7]

Another approach, at present controversial, and based on psychoanalytic concepts, is characterized by the direct attempt to establish an immediate contact with the patient's emotional life. This approach will be illustrated by the following example:

The patient was a girl of twenty-one who was being seen for the first time by the therapist. She came into the room with an anxious and yet rigid facial expression, making repetitive, stereotype movements with her hands and her head. She began to talk incoherently. Various remarks and questions by the therapist about the patient's stereotypes and utterances produced no contact until the patient suddenly put her right hand in front of her mouth. Then the therapist quickly asked, "Why did you do that?" The patient replied, "To prevent bad odor from coming out." The therapist then said, "Where does the bad odor come from?" The patient pointed to her buttocks. The therapist then asked, "What is there?" The patient replied in an embarrassed manner, "My anus." The therapist then said, "What else is there?" The patient replied, "Nothing." The therapist said then, "What is in front?" The patient hesitated and then said, "Nothing." The therapist then became insistent and, raising his voice, said, "You know what is there; don't try to fool me." This raising of the voice and insistence on the issue at the moment, as will be seen, represented the wrong tack on the part of the therapist, but this very quickly became evident when the patient said, in a tremulous voice, "My father used to shout, but my mother had a gentle voice," thereby conveying to the therapist that he was being harsh. The therapist now quickly utilized this reaction of the patient and became very friendly and said, "Yes, Frances, you are telling me that I shouldn't shout at you, that I ought to be understanding and gentle. Come on, sit down here next to me." He had her sit down in the adjoining chair, patting her hands and saying, "Of course you can't answer my question any differently. That is your conviction now. You have no sex, or the back and the front are the same thing to you."[8]

[7] F. Fromm-Reichmann, Transference problems in schizophrenics, *Psychoanal. Quart.*, 1939, 8, 412-426.

[8] Author's direct observation of Dr. John Rosen's handling of a case.

This illustration, as well as the previous one with the more cautious approach, shows that all detailed aspects of the behavior and statements of the schizophrenic patient have a meaning for him which is accessible to the therapist, and that a close contact can be established between the therapist and the patient. It should be added, however, that at present there are no statistics available on the effectiveness of these methods of treatment, nor on the permanence of the results.

RÉSUMÉ AND FORMULATION OF SCHIZOPHRENIC REACTIONS

It has been stated in the foregoing that one approach to the problem stresses the constitutional-somatic basis in schizophrenia, derives from that some of the primary psychological manifestations—e.g., feeling of failure or disturbances of thinking—and then derives manifestations of full-blown psychosis from the reaction of the total personality to these primary physiological and psychological disturbances. The evidence in favor of this approach has been presented: relatively mild somatic disturbances of the schizophrenics as a group—e.g., defective homeostasis—and the effectiveness of somatic forms of treatment—e.g., shock treatment. We have presented the other approach, which states that the manifestations of schizophrenia have psychological meaning and are brought about by clear-cut psychodynamic processes. In its boldest form it states that the schizophrenic suffered a severe trauma in early infancy. As a result of this damage, he reacts to all frustrations, even of a relatively mild nature, as traumata of catastrophic intensity. He then goes through a variety of measures and maneuvers to protect himself and make life livable as he sees it and get the satisfaction of which he is capable. The most convincing evidence of this approach is presented by observation of patients who have undergone psychoanalytic treatment, modified to suit schizophrenic patients. What is now the possible relationship between these two approaches? As previously mentioned, some investigators are inclined to differentiate between a constitutional, and therefore primary somatic, type of schizophrenia, usually referred to as process schizophrenia, and another which represents a reaction to severe and shattering experience. This differentiation may be correct. A further possibility, however, is that the dividing line between these two assumed groups is not a sharp one but that they represent the extremes of a continuum. In a later section, evidence will be given that some patients show signs of a qualitatively psychotic nature, either on projective tests or on brief clinical examination or during more detailed psychoanalytic treatment, and develop full-blown psychoses only after an additional major trauma occurs. There is no doubt about the psychotic potential in these patients, although there would be no clear indication of it anywhere in their life history. Further evidence will be presented about other patients to show that, although they offer fairly definite evidence of symptoms of a psychotic nature, both on clinical examination and on projective tests, these symptoms disappear with adequate handling, and the patients, becoming capable of going through adequate analytic clarification of their symptoms and personality, remain essentially well through decades of subsequent life history. Thus one could say at present that, if one accepts the concept of a somatic-constitutional basis for schizophrenia, the patients in this respect range from a strong vulnerability to a near-normal hardiness. Proportionately to this relative potential, the severity of problems varies from those of daily existence, adaptation, and growing up to severe recurrent and shattering experiences.

PATIENTS WITH PSYCHONEUROTIC SYMPTOMS WITH A PSYCHOTIC POTENTIAL; PSYCHONEUROTICS WITH AN UNDERCURRENT OF PSYCHOTIC PROCESSES; PSYCHONEUROSES WITH PSYCHOTIC (OR PSYCHOTIC-LIKE) FEATURES

There are patients whose predominant symptoms are of a psychoneurotic or psychosomatic nature but in whom a set of examinations elicits features that are strongly suggestive of a psychotic process, mostly of the schizophrenic or schizoid type. In general, these patients fall into two groups.

PATIENTS WITH SOME OVERT PSYCHOTIC-LIKE SYMPTOMS

Symptoms that such a patient may show—along with attacks of anxiety of a psychoneurotic nature or obsessional thoughts, asthma, or peptic ulcer—are these: He may have little conscious desire to seek out the company of other people, or after a few hours or weeks of treatment he gives information that he has performed auto-fellatio several times in his life, or that he eats his semen after masturbating, that he follows women on the subways who attract him because of their large breasts or buttocks, staying on the train for an hour's ride beyond his destination. He may at times hear noises with suggestive meaning without their clearly being voices, or he may have attacks of anxiety with feelings of depersonalization, as if he did not exist or objects around him did not quite exist. He then may become preoccupied with the philosophical problem of whether, let us say, the house he lives in does or does not exist when he is not looking at it.

PATIENTS WITH PROJECTIVE TEST RESULTS SUGGESTIVE OF A PSYCHOTIC PROCESS

Another group of patients shows no clinical signs of a psychotic nature. They make good contact with the therapist, furnish relevant material in the course of the treatment, which can be interpreted to them, and respond to the interpretation with further material and improvement. Yet the projective tests show signs which are commonly encountered in psychoses.

As an example of this, a patient who clinically was not psychotic gave pure symbolic color responses, such as "blue indicates sky" and "green suggests envy," as his only color responses on the Rorschach, a type of response usually seen only in schizophrenic patients, which usually indicates affective blandness and uncontrolled outbursts of emotion. (See Appendix I.)

The majority of either type of patients are good subjects for psychotherapy, including psychoanalysis. The therapist, however, must be aware of the psychotic potential and must pay special attention to the following points: (1) The ultimate behavior of the environment may make or break the treatment. "Breaking" here means precipitating a psychotic reaction. (2) The interpretations have to be given cautiously at times, yet, at other times, when the patient is in definite need of help, without postponement. It should always be made clear to the patient that he has complete liberty to accept or to reject the interpretation offered. (3) The patient should have a choice of sitting in the chair, lying on the couch, or walking around in the room, and the therapist himself at times has to advise the patient to sit up. (4) In the early part of the treatment, the interpretations should deal mainly with the patient's current interpersonal problems, particularly his loneliness, fear of abandonment, feelings of humiliation, and anxieties in general. The appearance of the psychotic-like symptoms should be interpreted in the early part of the treatment also from this angle, and the situations in which they appeared should be pointed out to the patient together with the probable motivation—e.g., the philosophical preoccupation with evil following a disappointment the patient just suffered representing a feeling that life is frustrating and harsh. Illustrations of the favorable outcome of the handling of such cases will be given later. Here an illustration will be given showing a disastrous result because of the uncoöperative environment.

A girl of twenty-one, a college student, applied for psychoanalytic treatment because of asthma, from which she had been suffering since the age of five. Her asthmatic attacks were so severe two years earlier that she suffered a collapse of one of the lungs and had to stay in bed for six months. She had always been very ambitious in her studies, achieving superior marks. This was the only field of activity that gave her a feeling of worth, although not without an undercurrent of anticipation of ultimate failure. She had never been intimate with boys, although she had a strong longing for friends of both sexes. She had always felt rejected by her mother, considered her father unreasonable and domineering, and had always felt that her sister, three years her senior, was superior to her and was rejecting her. After continuous criticism and rebukes by her mother and father about her alleged envy of all children during her childhood, the asthmatic attacks were precipitated at the age of five after her mother caught her masturbating and humiliated her in the presence of the whole family. On the Rorschach Test she had very few color but many movement responses, several of which were of an unusual nature—for example, seeing a small white spot as a man running violently. These responses indicated a psychotic potential in the form of withdrawal, introversion, and projection. None of these indications of the tests was observable, however, in the patient's clinical responses. She formed good rapport in the treatment and started to improve. After six months, she was free from asthmatic attacks, for the first time since the age of five, for several weeks, began to think well of herself, started to go out with boys, and became assertive with her parents. After ten months of therapy the father began to deny the effectiveness of the treatment and told her that he would be willing to spend any amount of money on physical care but not for psychotherapy; she would have to stop treatment in two months. The patient's asthmatic attacks recurred, and gradually her other improvements were dissipated. The father promised, in an interview with the therapist, that he would reassure his daughter about the continuation of the treatment. He not only did not carry out his promise but repeated his previous threat to her—just the day before her college final examinations. Now the first psychotic-like reaction appeared. The patient called the therapist on the telephone and said that she knew now why she had difficulty in thinking and that she was going to announce to her parents that her masturbation at the age of five had ruined her mind. The therapist succeeded in pulling her out of this immediate reaction; she walked out in the middle of one of her final examinations, however. Soon after this, she made her first suicidal attempt by taking some sleeping pills. When the father came home from work next evening, the following conversation took place:

"Mother told me that you took sleeping pills last night."

"Yes, that is true."

"You took too much?"

"Yes, I took too much."

"You know I could have you arrested for attempting suicide."

Soon after this, the patient developed a severe eczema, which, together with the asthma, required hospitalization. She would have been willing to go to a psychiatric hospital, but the parents were against it because it would have been a blot on the name of the family. The psychiatric treatment was discontinued. After some improvement in a general hospital, the patient was discharged only to suffer a worse relapse at home. She then looked up in the library what the lethal dose of the hypnotic was and this time took enough to prove fatal.

PARANOIA

In a fully developed paranoiac reaction, the patient's delusions are unshakable. They are well systematized and, if the patient's first premise is granted, highly logical. The patient stubbornly defends them and usually is lively emotionally when they are discussed. His emotions are usually even in tone—he may feel bitter or mistrustful or superior or antagonistic. The delusions may center on any topic, such as some problem which may arise in anyone's life—e.g., marital infidelity or mistreatment. The patient with this type of delusion often succeeds in enlisting even highly intelligent friends and acquaintances on his side, and they may be willing, at least for a while, to assist him legally in his attempts to secure "justice." Closer examination, however, brings out the following evidences of a disturbance: (1) The patient, in the course of the conversation, is either suspicious and uncommunicative when the examiner talks on the topic, or unusually insistent in making and defending points. This becomes evident, of course, only after a period of discussion. (2) The patient is absolutely unwilling to consider any other possibility than the one he has in mind. (3) The evidence that the patient advances to justify his idea is often extremely slim and inconclusive.

A man who was jealous of his wife returned home from work one day and found that the dust was missing from one of the hooks on the clothes rack. He immediately concluded that a man's coat had been hanging there. From this he came to the conclusion that his wife had had a male visitor and had committed adultery.

FORMS OF PARANOIA

The development of the paranoiac delusion is gradual; at first there are only suspicions, but these become more and more numerous, more and more systematized and unshakable. The following forms of paranoia can be differentiated on the basis of the main theme of the delusion: (1) Paranoia of jealousy, the most common form. The case above is an example. (2) Persecutory paranoia, in which the patient is convinced that someone is attempting to thwart him, harm him, and induce others to do likewise. (3) Erotomania, in which the patient, usually a woman, is convinced that someone is making sexual advances toward her. She puts this interpretation on all types of actions, and she may feel persecuted by this person for rejecting his advances. (4) Litigious paranoia, a comparatively rare condition. The patient may actually have been slightly wronged or have been denied something to which he felt entitled, such as a license. However, he expends an enormous amount of effort in getting justice, and appeals to higher and higher authorities; his efforts and the emotions involved are far in excess of the significance of the matter.

In all these delusions, the circle of accused individuals widens and involves higher and higher authorities. The topic of the delusions does not always remain confined to everyday topics, and "queerer" aspects may enter into them. Thus a patient may accuse a physician of introducing germs into her sinuses when treating her, and at the same time of making sexual advances. Grandiose features, together with hallucinations, also occur.

PSYCHODYNAMICS OF PARANOIA

The most striking and consistent aspect of paranoia is projection. Reality is completely revalued on the basis of subjective reactions, but this alteration of reality has a unique aspect because, in contrast to schizophrenia, many other aspects of reality are retained. In fact, the sharp and consistent logic represents an attempt to prove the reality of the distortion. Furthermore, both the distortion of reality and the compensatory attempt to retain it are limited to a single theme and do not destroy the patient's general personality.

The formula for projection as stated by Freud is exemplified by the following: "I don't love him; I hate him; I don't hate him; he hates me." These "projections" are made in order to escape intolerable self-condemnation and feelings of worthlessness because of repressed homosexuality. There is always a strong element of defensive hostility in paranoia; the patient feels threatened and therefore becomes hostile and ready to attack. Because of this and because of his clear logic and ability to plan, the patient may be very dangerous; he may carry out a carefully planned attempt on his "persecutor's" life.

The catastrophic hurt in paranoia may vary, but usually has three elements: rejection, very low self-esteem, and injury.

Before the onset of the paranoiac reaction the patient has often succeeded in unconsciously satisfying a vital need, such as pride, aloofness, homosexuality, excessive erotic attachment. The paranoiac reaction develops over conflicts or threats.

TREATMENT

In the early stages of paranoia, careful interview therapy may be effective; the patient may lose his delusions and acquire insight into his sickness in the course of a few months. In more advanced cases, hospitalization is necessary; but here also a rapport between physician and patient is valuable. This can be established by the physician's discussing understandingly with the patient his delusions and his evidence for them, but without questioning or challenging them. After a period the physician raises some questions and suggests other possibilities. Eventually he attempts to convince the patient that his delusions are unfounded and wrong. This treatment, when accompanied by other institutional measures, such as occupational therapy and a sheltered environment, is sometimes effective. In some cases it is dangerous to discharge an advanced paranoiac patient as cured, for he may simulate improvement but commit murder after his discharge.

These therapeutic measures should, of course, always be attempted; but the prognosis for paranoia is not good.

CASE ILLUSTRATIONS OF THE PSYCHOSES

The following case histories of the members of one family will show that:

1. The reaction patterns may be either a "clear type" or a "mixture" of various psychotic and even neurotic types (Greenacre).

2. All the reaction patterns should be considered as the individual's responses to situations of stress and his attempts to cope with catastrophic expectations and conflicts.

3. Even if the occurrence of these reactions in the family is assumed to be suggestive of a hereditary predisposition, there still remains the question of the extent to which this is influenced by the parents' handling of the children. In any case, the breakdown is a response to situations of internal and external stress.

4. A patient with any form of manic-depressive or schizophrenic reaction may recover, at least in a social sense.

Several members of a family of Armenian extraction developed fairly severe psychopathological reactions. The mother suffered from manic-depressive reactions. The father was neurotic and had anxiety attacks. Of the four children in this family, the oldest had schizophrenic reactions with paranoid and catatonic features. Another had a mild schizoid reaction which could be treated at home. The third child had a compulsion neurosis with schizoid aspects. One daughter was free from serious disturbances.

The father, an engineer, was an active, enterprising man, conscientious in his work but very selfish and domineering at home. He had always earned enough to support his family, but he was stingy and dictatorial with his money as far as his family was concerned. For example, he insisted on giving his wife money from day to day instead of a weekly allowance. He sharply rebuked anyone who contradicted his views or opinions, often showing temper and raising his voice. He expected the utmost attention from his family when he had even mild ailments such as a cold or a cough; on such occasions he suffered attacks of anxiety. However, if other members of the family were ill, he would tell them not to give in to such weaknesses.

The mother, as a rule, was submissive to her husband; she never challenged any of his wishes or opinions, and tried to mediate between him and the children. She accepted, though with some inner rebellion, his reluctance to give her money and tried to save on every item. Her home was spotless, and she took good care of her children, but was inclined to worry about them. She submitted to physical intimacies reluctantly. She had periods of over-activity about every two or three years, when she would sleep little and talk excessively. She would be busy rearranging the furniture, and receiving and visiting friends. During such periods she was excitable, and frequent altercations occurred between her and her husband. In the excitement she or her husband would break things, the whole family would be in a turmoil, and the children would try to separate the parents by taking sides. Most of her attacks lasted about six or eight months.

She had a few periods of depression, which also lasted about six months but were less frequent than her periods of excitement. During such periods she looked sad and did her work with difficulty. She was inclined to sit all day, and she did little cleaning or cooking. She accused herself of being selfish, inconsiderate, and a sinner.

Her background was as follows: As a child in Armenia she had escaped several massacres. Her mother died when she was four years old, and her father remarried about a year later. Her stepmother made her do all the housework, always criticized her, and preferred her own children. The patient had her first attack of depression about the age of sixteen, before she was married. Her first period of excitement occurred about one year after her marriage, approximately a month following the birth of her first child. The patient's periods of depression were later determined chiefly by her anger at her husband, her feeling of helplessness, self-condemnation, and guilt, and her fear of abandonment. The nuclear emotional constellation was first developed in her relationship with her stepmother and was later further elaborated in her relationship with her husband. Her period of excitement was chiefly one of rebellion against her husband and of overriding her own conflicts, self-constraint, submissiveness, guilt, anxiety, and self-condemnation.

There were four children in the family; the age difference between the oldest and the youngest was twelve years. The oldest of the children, a girl, was thirty-five at the time of this report. She had developed a schizophrenic reaction with paranoid and catatonic features. During most of her life she had been inclined to keep to herself; she had few friends, and was sensitive and easily hurt. She did her school work moderately well, and was later steadily employed as a dressmaker. She derived some pleasure from her work and from books and movies, and she enjoyed the company of one of her sisters. When she was twenty-five years old, she became even more withdrawn and started to behave queerly. She would refuse to eat some articles of food at home, and she would stand at the window making grimaces; she would listen attentively as if someone were speaking to her, and she made apparently senseless remarks. She soon quit her job because she was convinced that her fellow workers were talking about her and whispering indecent and obscene words. She then said that she would not eat at home because the food was being poisoned. She later said that there were lice in her clothes and that they were creeping into her body. She refused to leave the house and sometimes locked herself into her room for long periods. On one occasion she became excited, broke some furniture, and threw it out of the window. She said that the voice had told her to do so. As a result, she was sent to a psychopathic hospital.

This patient had a "shut-in" personality all her life. The immediate situation of stress to which she responded concerned a man. Mostly at the persuasion of a friend, she started to go with a man who worked where she did. She liked his company and had thoughts of marriage, but never permitted any intimacy, not even a kiss. They quarreled, and she refused to go out with him again. He then became sarcastic and ostentatiously paid attention to other girls. All this coincided with one of her mother's periods of excitement and the resulting strife at home.

In the hospital she remained withdrawn and was occasionally excited. She was emotionally queer and unapproachable; her facial expression was unchanging, except for a recurring grimace and spitting motion. At times she refused to eat. She would not answer some questions, and gave evasive replies to others. When pressed for an answer, she sometimes became excited, and then she talked about lice and poison in the food and about voices calling her obscene names. On one occasion she struck another patient who she said was making remarks about her. She also spoke of the secret police being after her and said that they were sending out radio messages about her. Often she imagined that she was Queen Esther and that God was talking to her. At times she refused to eat and would sit alone without moving. She showed waxy flexibility.

She remained in the hospital for eight years. Her condition fluctuated, but she gradually improved in her behavior. She remained evasive when asked about her delusions, but was able to leave the hospital and for the two years since has been getting along well.

Another sister, who had been married for five years, became considerably concerned about herself when her sister was sent to the psychopathic hospital. About this time she developed the persistent thought that there were lice in her clothes or in the furniture and that they were getting into her skin. She often had an uncomfortable sensation in her skin and she made slight "brushing" movements as if to get rid of the lice. In contrast to her sister, she realized that this was only a thought, and she tried to get rid of it, but could not. She could not use such articles as combs or purses because of this thought. She became tense and distressed emotionally, made frequent mistakes in her work, and was afraid that she would go insane. She showed genuine concern about herself and was easily persuaded to seek help.

The patient's complaints were of the obsessional neurotic reaction type, but the nature of her thoughts closely resembled that found in schizophrenic reactions. Thus, repeatedly during treatment, she had reactions which were like mild delusions. For example, she once refrained from buying aspirin for a headache because she was convinced that the analyst would somehow get in touch with the druggist. In spite of this, careful psychoanalysis was possible with this patient. She recovered fully and has had no recurrence for six years.

Her sister's psychosis aroused this patient's fear that she too might suffer a breakdown. This fear was intensified by the fact that the father at first denied that the oldest daughter was sick. The patient resented this, and as a result had feelings of fear and retribution. In her difficulty she leaned on her husband for support. However, her husband, although tender and understanding in many respects and with many interests in common, was rather penurious and acted superior toward her. She responded to this with the feeling, "Not only does he not give me the help I need, but he even rejects me and humiliates me." Thus the patient was resentful and was again afraid of abandonment and retribution.

The next sister was essentially well. She was married and had two children at the time of the report.

The brother, a statistician, was twenty-three at the time of this report. He had begun to masturbate during puberty. He had some sexual thoughts about his sisters and about men, and he began to brood and to stay by himself more, but he did not break off friendships. When he was about eighteen, he began going out with a girl, but she put an end to this. Following this, his sexual thoughts about his sisters and about men increased; he considered himself degenerate and believed that people knew this and moved away from him in the train. Moreover, he thought that these troubles were the result of his masturbation, and he became preoccupied with various bodily sensations, and began to talk loudly and at great length on involved philosophical matters. He was dissatisfied with his job, but did nothing to improve his status. He himself did not want to go to a physician, but one of his sisters, who was aware of his changed behavior, persuaded him to consult a psychiatrist.

The particular problems with which this man was struggling were the pressure of his sexual urge, his relationship with women, and, to a lesser extent, his career. Contact with individuals and, even more, with the opposite sex involves considerable self-assertion and self-confidence, at least enough to enable one to bear disappointment and hardships. This was impossible for this patient. Furthermore, his emotional conflicts made him view the socially taboo sexual activity as dangerous and one in which he might inflict injury or be injured. His sexual thoughts about his sisters represented the reaching out of a helpless individual who could not look for satisfaction anywhere else. His homosexual thoughts, chiefly about his superiors in business, represented submissive reactions of a helpless person.

A reaction to one of the psychiatrist's comments illustrates the precarious state of the patient's adjustment, the caution and experience necessary in handling such patients, and the appearance of the manic response in the course of a predominantly schizophrenic reaction. After this man had shown considerable improvement, the psychiatrist said: "You have homosexual thoughts particularly in connection with your employer because you feel too much frightened, you lack self-confidence; you are really expressing by these thoughts: 'I want to submit to you without any reservation in order to have your good will.'" The next day the patient's mood was somewhat excited; he said that he felt remarkably well after the preceding day's session, and that for the first time in his life he had real self-confidence. He had decided, he said, that he would be submissive no longer, and that henceforth, when his employer asked him to do something objectionable, he would refuse. During this interview the patient talked animatedly and much more voluminously than usual. Obviously, he had reacted with a mild elation to the psychiatrist's remarks on the previous day, unconsciously following the formula: "The physician, who is all-powerful, said that I have the strength and that I can assert myself. I now have renewed powers in myself, and I can cope with any situation." The intensity of the elation based on this excess of self-confidence was due to the pressure of helplessness and fear behind it. The self-confidence, as it were, overrode the anxiety, and with it were freed the patient's anger, hostility, and aggression, which previously he had not dared to release. If this reaction had proceeded further, he would have developed an open psychosis. The psychiatrist, realizing this danger, told the patient that, although his increase in self-confidence was good, he was imprudent to try to do too much in a short time, and that he must avoid disagreements in the office. The patient calmed down after these remarks and returned the next day in a quiet state, yet with a definite increase in his well-being and self-confidence. This he maintained in the course of further treatment, and he made a satisfactory adjustment to the problems of his daily existence.

This patient would probably have developed a serious condition had he not had his sister's interest and advice and had he not come for treatment early.

SUGGESTED READINGS

Apart from the respective sections in the standard textbooks, for special aspects of schizophrenia we recommend Hanfmann and Kasanin's *Language and Thought in Schizophrenia* (383); Kalinowsky and Hoch's *Shock Treatment and Other Somatic Methods in Psychiatry* (474); and Rapaport, Gill, and Schafer (757) and Schafer (825) on test procedures. As additional reading in the psychological treatment of schizophrenia, the articles of Federn (261, 262) and Sullivan et al. (915) are recommended. Bellak gives a thorough survey of varying views in his book *Dementia Praecox* (57).

XXXV Organic (Chemogenic and Histogenic) Psychotic Reactions

The psychological phenomena in organic reactions are the results of a direct disturbance of the functioning of the brain and of the individual's reaction to this disturbance. Organic reactions may be acute or chronic. In many conditions both kinds are combined; that is, there is chronic disturbance with occasional acute periods. Senility and hardening of the arteries of the brain, for example, are accompanied by chronic changes with acute periods intervening. In other reactions there are only acute disturbances. Fever, as a rule, causes only acute disturbances. Periods of mental clarity may intervene in all organic reactions.

The causes of organic psychotic reactions are numerous. Among them are deterioration of the brain substance because of hardening of the arteries due to age; infections of the brain, such as syphilis or encephalitis; infections in other parts of the body which are accompanied by fever, such as pneumonia, inflammation of the joints, typhoid fever; toxic substances, such as alcohol, opium, illuminating gas, lead; growths on the brain; injury to the brain; vitamin and glandular deficiency.

The chief symptoms of organic reactions—the chronic in particular—are (1) impairment of intellectual functions: comprehension, orientation, memory for both recent and remote events, concentration; (2) emotional instability: general irritability, laughter and weeping without adequate cause; (3) changes in general conduct: carelessness in personal appearance, neglect of responsibilities, disturbance of morals. There are considerable individual variations, and one or another set of symptoms may predominate. The acute reaction resembles a delirium; the patient is disoriented, has illusions—i.e., misinterprets his perceptions—has difficulty in focusing his attention, hallucinates, and does not remember what has happened to him. He may be highly excited and have various emotions, particularly fear, or he may be emotionally dull. He cannot carry out certain functions or recognize objects adequately.

INFECTIOUS DISORDERS

GENERAL PARESIS (DEMENTIA PARALYTICA)

General paresis is caused by syphilitic damage to the brain tissue. However, it has been estimated that only about 2 percent of the people who contract syphilis ever develop general paresis. The condition appears from five to twenty-five years after the syphilitic infection, and, unless treated, usually leads to death within a year and a half after the first symptoms appear. General paresis manifests itself in mental and emotional deterioration and in physical and biochemical changes. The disease usually begins gradually; but in some cases convulsions are the first symptoms.

Mental Symptoms. The mental symptoms are as follows: There are alterations in character. The patient becomes careless in his work or disinterested in his family or his appearance, or he starts to drink or commit petty thefts or expose himself. These changes usually occur in the early stages of the disease, in contrast to those in arteriosclerosis. The patient shows changes in emotional reactions, such as irritability or over-sentimental behavior. There are disturbances in simple intellectual functions, such as memory and calculating. These likewise appear early and at first concern recent events. The patient forgets what he did even a few minutes earlier, and he makes mistakes in simple calculations, particularly if sustained effort is required. Lack of insight is present in some cases. Such patients are not aware of their condition, and do not realize that their habits have changed and that their functions are growing defective. Some patients, however, in the early stages of the disease are distressed by their disturbed memory, their declining efficiency, and their fatigability, and may seek medical advice in this connection.

As the condition progresses, other mental symptoms appear. The following classification is based on the predominance of one symptom over another; but the various groups are not sharply differentiated because the patient's symptoms may belong to one group at one time, and to another at a later time. (1) Dementia: The patient's intellectual faculties decline progressively. He is content with his lot; when asked how he feels, he may answer, "As well as a fish in water." If he is asked the names of the Presidents of the United States, he may answer blandly, "I was never interested in politics." Demented patients may have grandiose but not luxuriant delusions. For example, a patient may repeat for days, "I am the best carpenter in the universe." This type of patient finally becomes completely unable to take care of himself; he becomes disoriented for time and place. (2) Depression: The patients are despondent and anxious. They have delusional ideas, such as that their bowels are completely stopped up, that their heart has been removed, that they are dead, or that they have no pulse. The patients may be so depressed that they become mute and stuporous and attempt to mutilate themselves or to commit suicide. Such attempts are usually unsuccessful because their mental deterioration makes any but foolish attempts impossible. (3) Expansiveness: The expansive patient has a feeling of great well-being, over-values himself, and has grandiose delusions. For example, one patient said that he was two hundred years old and weighed four hundred pounds; that he had a head of gold, a hundred wives, and a thousand million boys and girls; that his urine was Rhine wine, his feces gold (Kraepelin). Such patients claim superhuman qualities and remarkable strength; they say that they are giants, that they "broke the bank at Monte Carlo," that they own five hundred houses in New York. Before they become obviously incapacitated, they may engage in commercial enterprises which ruin them financially. As they deteriorate more and more and become completely helpless, their grandiose ideas may disappear entirely or be manifest only by some phrase such as "millions of houses." (4) Agitation: Agitated patients are extremely restless and are engaged in some activity all the time. Their mood may be changeable—depressed or elated—and their thoughts may be grandiose or hypochondriacal or persecutory.

Physical Symptoms. In general paresis there are the following characteristic physical manifestations: (1) The pupils of the eyes do not react to light but may show the accommodation reaction. (2) The face has a characteristic appearance. The features are smoothed out, the expression is vacant, and the patient looks somewhat dissipated. This last is so characteristic that a correct diagnosis can sometimes be made simply by looking at the patient. (3) There are speech disturbances, particularly slurring. This becomes evident when the patient repeats certain test phrases, such as "medical electricity," "truly rural," "Methodist Episcopal," "round the rugged rock the ragged rascal ran." (4) When the patient writes, the lines are tremulous, and syllables are omitted or transposed. (5) In rare cases the optic nerve atrophies. This nerve can be seen by looking through the pupil of the eyes with a special instrument. Under normal circumstances the nerve appears as a yellow disk where it enters the eye; if it is atrophied, it is white. (6) If locomotor ataxia is associated with general paresis, there is an absence of tendon reflexes, such as the knee jerk.

Biochemical Symptoms. Various tests and analyses have been devised to determine the presence of biochemical symptoms. (1) The Wassermann test, a complicated procedure, can be done on the blood serum and the spinal fluid. The fluid is obtained by means of a hollow needle, which is inserted into the spinal canal between two lumbar vertebrae and through which about 5 or 10 cc. are withdrawn. In general paresis, the Wassermann test on the spinal fluid is positive in about 95 percent of the cases, and on the blood serum in about 100 percent. (2) The number of cells in the spinal fluid increases as the result of an irritation of the membranes lining the brain.

The number of cells is determined by putting freshly drawn spinal fluid into a special counting chamber, in which the cells are counted with a microscope. Normally, the spinal fluid contains up to 5 cells per cc.; more than 10 cells indicates an unquestionable increase. In general paresis, the increase may vary from 10 to 200 per cc. (3) An increase in the protein content of the spinal fluid is likewise due to inflammation of the membranes lining the brain. For this test, a saturated solution of ammonium sulphate is mixed with the spinal fluid. If the protein content has increased, the protein will precipitate, and the mixture will become cloudy within three minutes. (4) Another method of testing for biochemical symptoms is the colloidal gold reaction. A solution of gold chloride is mixed with varying concentrations of spinal fluid. The solution itself is colorless; a change in color gives a positive test. The changes consist of various mixtures of red and blue.

Psychodynamics. As has been said, some disturbances are attributable to the organic damage and some are due to the patient's reaction to this damage. The reaction itself may be correlated with the organic damage. For example, a patient may be irritated because of the organic damage, and he becomes more irritated when he makes mistakes (defensive hostility). The irritability which thus appears is more severe because of the organic damage.

In general paresis the most obvious damage is that to the memory. The patient reacts to this in various ways which are sometimes in harmony with his previous personality. The grandiose trends may partly represent an attempt to over-compensate for the failing functions and his consequent inferiority feelings. Depression may appear for similar reasons (damaged self-esteem). In other words, the patient who has previously felt worthless for many other reasons now feels even more worthless and self-condemnatory because of his failing function, and often evaluates this failure as a punishment or retribution for his previous sins and aggression or as a rejection by the world. In still other instances the pathological processes which have diminished the patient's judgment and inhibitions permit him to give freer rein to his previously inhibited impulses.

Treatment. Three great discoveries have made possible the successful treatment of paresis: (1) fever treatment, (2) treatment with arsenical compounds, and (3) penicillin.

Two methods are generally used to induce fever: infection with malaria, and short-wave apparatus.

In the malaria technique, blood obtained from a patient with malaria is injected either subcutaneously or directly into the blood stream of the paretic patient. Within from three days to four weeks, if the injection is subcutaneous, or from two to twenty days, if intravenous, the patient starts to have chills and fever; his temperature rises to about 104° F. After from eight to twelve such attacks, the attacks are terminated by giving him quinine sulphate. The improvement ordinarily is rapid, but in some cases it appears only after some months. A second malarial treatment is usually given about one year after the first.

Fever can also be induced by short-wave apparatus. The patient's temperature is raised to about 104° F. and is kept at that level for about six hours.

In arsenical treatment of paresis, an arsenical called tryparsamide is injected into the blood stream once a week for eight weeks. The patient then rests a few weeks, after which injections are resumed.

Penicillin is injected intramuscularly daily for from fourteen to twenty days. A total of about nine million units is given.

Statistical surveys show that the first two methods are about equally successful. From 30 to 35 percent of the patients undergo a complete remission of symptoms which for practical purposes can be called a cure; that is, they are able to live their normal daily life. Approximately another 30 to 35 percent improve but are unable to resume their former daily life. About 15 percent show no improvement, and about 10 percent die.

Two factors apparently are operative in the effectiveness of these two methods of treatment. The spirochetes are killed by the arsenical compound or by the high temperature incident to the fever. Certain defensive biochemical reactions are brought about by the fever or the compound which enable the patient to fight the infection better and to improve his general health. A combination of the two methods does not improve the chances of recovery to any extent.

Penicillin seems to be the most efficient way of killing the spirochete (the more modern term is *Treponema pallidum*). It entails the fewest complications, and some investigators maintain that it is superior to the other two in effectiveness (180).

The patient, a moderately successful businessman, forty-five years old, first went to a physician with a friend to get a certificate for injuries sustained in an accident. He had crashed into another car and suffered a minor contusion of his arm. This friend told the physician that the accident was the patient's fault, and said that he often had to pull the emergency brake because the patient was apt not to stop for a red light. The physician examined the patient carefully and found that his pupils did not react to light; he also noticed that his speech was slurred. The patient himself told the physician that his memory was not as good as it used to be, and that he made mistakes in his work. The physician took a blood sample for testing, and told him to return later for the report; but he never came back.

About a month later he got into more trouble. He called a taxi, went to a restaurant, and had the cab wait while he ate. He left a check in the restaurant instead of cash. He then had the cab driver take him to various places; he told the driver that he had many friends with a lot of money. After three hours of driving, the driver asked for his money. This angered the patient, and he struck the driver in the face. The latter called a policeman, and the patient was taken to jail, where he sang, told everyone about his rich friends, and said that his business was worth millions of dollars. The judge sent him to a hospital. He told everyone in the hospital that he felt excellent, better than ever before in his life, and told about his riches, that he had three hundred houses and about seventy children.

The blood and spinal fluid tests were positive. He was given the malaria treatment. After several attacks he began to improve; he became quieter, and lost his delusions. He was discharged from the hospital after two months, and has been working since.

(For a discussion of encephalitis, see Chapter XXI.)

DISORDERS DUE TO CHEMICAL POISONS AND DEFICIENCIES

ALCOHOLIC PSYCHOSES

Delirium Tremens. Delirium tremens occurs in people who have drunk excessively for a long time; it may also appear after a debauch, or after an injury or an infection. It is sometimes assumed to follow a sudden cessation of drinking, but this is questionable.

In some cases the delirium does not appear immediately. Before its onset, the patient is restless and unable to sleep, has nightmares, and is terrified by sounds or impressions, particularly in the dark. This may last several days. In other cases the delirium itself appears suddenly, and the patient is then disoriented for time and place.

The particular characteristics of this delirium are: (1) Vivid hallucinations, particularly of such animals as snakes and rats: The patient may see these animals or feel them crawling over him. Often such patients hallucinate while engaged in their regular occupation—driving a truck, gardening, etc. (2) Acute fear: The patient is terrified by the animals in his hallucinations. But in addition he may be in a state of acute terror. He may be afraid that something dreadful will happen to him, that he will be mutilated or killed. This terror may lead him to attempt suicide. (3) Extreme suggestibility as to sensory illusions: The patient, when requested, will read a blank piece of paper which is placed before him; if asked what he sees on the wall, he may say animals and try to catch them. (4) Misidentification: The patient may mistake a total stranger for one of his close friends.

The most striking symptom, which gives this condition its name, is coarse tremor of the hands, face, and tongue. The tongue is coated, and the breath is foul. The heart is rapid, and the patient perspires profusely.

The delirium usually lasts from three to six days. Although most patients recover, the delirium may terminate in death from exhaustion or heart failure (about 3 percent).

The Korsakoff Syndrome. The Korsakoff syndrome is most frequently encountered in chronic alcoholism, but it occasionally appears in other conditions, such as cerebral arteriosclerosis, lead poisoning, or chronic infections. The symptoms are as follows: (1) Impairment of memory for recent events: The patient cannot remember what he did a few hours earlier.

(2) Confabulation: If the patient is asked what he did during a period that he does not remember, he will make up a story—that he went to visit a friend or went to the country, etc. (3) Delirium with visual and auditory hallucinations: The patient may picture himself in his workshop at home engaged in some trivial occupation. Frequently patients know where they are and recognize people, but may be disoriented for time. (4) Emotional instability: The patient is at times friendly and cheerful, but at other times he is irritable and quarrelsome.

Among the physical symptoms are inflammation of the nerve trunks throughout the body (polyneuritis), areas of anesthesia in the skin, and paralysis—for example, wrist drop, in which the patient cannot raise his hand. The Korsakoff syndrome lasts a fairly long time, there often being no sign of improvement until after six or eight weeks. The syndrome may be permanent.

Chronic Alcoholism. In some individuals who have used alcohol excessively for many years, certain changes take place which are due to the toxic effect of the alcohol on the brain tissue. Chronic alcoholism is a combination of this toxic effect and of slow psychological deterioration.

The symptoms may vary, and they usually develop gradually. The following are characteristic: The patient is affable and charming on superficial contact but is apt to be abusive, rude, and inconsiderate to his family, friends, or business associates, and to neglect his responsibilities to them. He is likely to lie, particularly about his activities. He relates his good deeds, and tries to give the impression that he has lived up to high ideals. He makes a sentimental appeal to people for money to buy drinks with. If he works at all, his work is poor; he is unreliable and inefficient, and is likely to give up his job at a crucial time. His memory is impaired, particularly for recent events and for such matters as work he has to do. In more advanced stages, the patient may commit sexual crimes such as exhibition or assaults. Frequently these symptoms represent intensifications of the prealcoholic personality in reaction to impairment resulting from brain damage. It is difficult to know at times what part of the symptom picture is psychogenic and what part is due to the chronic effect of alcohol on the brain tissue. Even in the latter case, much of the pathology is reversible, and the patient can recover if he stops ingesting alcohol.

The physical symptoms are tremor, a "flat, ironed-out" face (characteristic facial expression), gastritis, cirrhosis of the liver, heart disease, nephritis, etc.

Treatment. Patients with acute psychotic reactions are best treated in a hospital. The patient with delirium tremens should be given a great deal of fluid in small amounts; sleep can be induced by means of a warm bath followed by a hypnotic.

The patient with alcoholic hallucinosis must be hospitalized because his acute state of fear and panic and the sudden cessation of alcohol make him unmanageable. He should be given good food and adequate amounts of liquids. Bromides may be used to quiet him and induce sleep.

PELLAGRA (VITAMIN-B DEFICIENCY)

This disorder is characterized by inflammation, accompanied by brown discoloration, of the skin of the back of the hands, inflammation of the mouth, diarrhea, and nervous and mental changes. The last are headache, dizziness, irritability, depression, and sleeplessness; in severer cases, anxiety, confusion, and delirium. The condition is due to deficiency of the vitamin-B group, particularly of nicotinic acid. It occurs at times endemically in the poor population—for example, in the southeastern United States—who live on a deficient diet. The treatment is administration of the vitamins.

CARBON-MONOXIDE POISONING

Carbon-monoxide poisoning occurs either accidentally or as an attempted suicide. Some patients first turn on the gas and then change their mind. The resultant symptoms can be acute and chronic. The immediate effects are headache and vomiting and, after prolonged exposure, delirium or coma, followed by death within a week or a dreamy mental state and recovery. The time of exposure necessary for disaster depends on the concentration of carbon monoxide. When a man has been exposed some hours to an atmosphere containing more than 0.02 percent carbon monoxide, symptoms of poisoning occur. If the exposure lasts long enough, the patient dies. The nerve cells of infants apparently are more susceptible than those of adults. It may happen that the mother either accidentally or with suicidal intentions gets exposed to the poison together with her infant; they are discovered; the mother recovers, and the infant dies. The chronic symptoms may be neurological, in the main, including paralyses, speech disturbances, and tremor. At times the symptoms are those of extrapyramidal injury, as in chronic encephalitis. The mental symptoms may be apathy, intellectual deterioration, disorientation for time, and confabulation.

A woman of thirty-five became depressed after a disappointment in her husband and attempted suicide by turning on the gas. She remained unconscious for about twenty-four hours after discovery. She had a rise in temperature and pain in the abdomen for the next few days. After a period of time she developed some stiffness and tremor in her extremities, with excessive salivation. She was apathetic and neglectful of her appearance, was disoriented for time, and had memory defects. She would confabulate about having visited relatives or having gone shopping the previous day or in the morning when she actually had not left the house. She did not remember her suicidal attempt and attributed her physical symptoms to having fallen or to having overworked.

The treatment of the acute poisoning is exposure to fresh air or oxygen, blood transfusion, and injection of hypertonic salt solution into the blood stream to reduce edema of the brain. Chronic symptoms can be handled only by custodial and nursing care.

ENDOCRINE DISORDERS

The psychopathology in endocrine disorders, like that in other primary bodily disorders, may be the direct result of the impaired brain functioning or the patient's reaction to his disorder, or both. We shall discuss here only the disturbances in which both factors are involved; and although three glands—the thyroid, the pancreas, and the pituitary—are particularly associated with such psychotic disturbances, we shall limit ourselves to the thyroid.

HYPOTHYROIDISM

Thyroid deficiency which appears in an adult hitherto normal in that respect is called myxedema. The characteristic mental symptoms are emotional dulling, decline in intelligence and in memory, and slowness of response, in both movement and speech. Among the physical symptoms are swelling and puffiness of the face; the swelling does not pit on pressure. The skin becomes coarse and dry, and the pulse slows to between forty and sixty per minute. There is sensitiveness to cold, and the basal metabolic rate drops sharply (—30 or lower). This last condition can be quickly remedied by the proper administration of thyroid extract.

An efficient worker in the street-cleaning department began to complain of slowness, fatigue, inability to work well, and loss of memory. On examination he was found to have a coarse skin; his face was swollen, dull, and stupid-looking; his speech was very slow. His basal metabolism was —36. Administration of desiccated thyroid raised his metabolism to normal within a month's time, and all his complaints disappeared. In such cases the thyroid usually has to be administered continuously.

HYPERTHYROIDISM

Since the causes and effects of a hyperactive thyroid have already been discussed, only severe psychotic reactions will be considered here. These are of two types: (1) The patient with a very severe toxicosis may become extremely restless and delirious. He may be partly or completely disoriented for time, place, and people. He may hallucinate, the hallucinations usually embodying great excitement and fear. This condition is due chiefly to the effects of the thyroid substance on the functioning of the brain; it disappears on the administration of iodine and partial removal of the thyroid gland. (2) In some instances the patient's reaction to severe emotional stress involves both hyperthyroidism and a psychotic reaction; in others the reaction to the initial stress is hyperthyroidism, additional stress eliciting psychotic symptoms.

The parents of a twenty-year-old girl had separated when she was one year of age. She lived in Haiti with her mother, and her father lived in the United States. She corresponded with her father but had not seen him for nineteen years. She came to visit him when she was twenty years old. Her father received her cordially, and she stayed at his apartment. He was popular with women, and several of them sometimes stayed at the apartment. The patient, who had keenly anticipated seeing her father, was deeply disappointed in him both morally and emotionally, for she had hoped to be the only object of his emotional interest during her visit.

The patient also had sexual fantasies about her father, and this made her feel guilty. In response to this situation of stress, she developed hyperthyroidism and went to a physician for treatment. Her father consulted the physician about her. She was much concerned about this visit because she hoped it would lead to different behavior on the part of her father. However, when he said merely, "Now, you see, there's nothing really the matter with you; you are not in any danger; you just have to take things easy," she considered this as the final rejection. Feeling that she had been betrayed by both her father and her physician, she grew depressed and self-accusatory, and sat by herself much of the time brooding. Her speech became rambling and partly incoherent. She was hospitalized and treated, and part of the thyroid gland was removed. Her thyroid symptoms disappeared, but her depression continued, though in a milder form. In about six months she recovered fully.

This patient's psychotic reaction was a response to the second and even more damaging disappointment, a situation of stress which arose when she was already in a debilitated physical and psychological condition.

HYPERINSULINISM (HYPOGLYCEMIA)

If the blood sugar falls below a certain level (from 60 to 40 mg. per 100 cc. of blood), confusion, dream states, and manic excitement may appear. Marked lowering of the blood sugar is usually due to an over-functioning of the pancreas caused by a benign tumor (adenoma). The operative removal of part of the gland cures the condition.

HEAD INJURIES

The reactions to be described in this section occur after severe head injuries. The psychological symptoms depend on the injury to the brain, which is usually but not always proportionate to the injury to the skull—a person may be killed by a blow to the head, but his skull may not be fractured. In most cases the injury to the brain is not direct; the force of the blow is transmitted through the skull to the brain.

The injury to the brain may cause small, "pinpoint" hemorrhages throughout the entire brain. In more severe injuries larger blood vessels may rupture, and the tissues may swell. All these effects may eventually disappear; but in some cases the nerve tissue is permanently destroyed, and scar tissue forms subsequently.

SYMPTOMS

The most common immediate effect of a severe blow to the head is a disturbance of consciousness. The victim may be only temporarily dazed, or he may remain completely unconscious for anywhere from a few minutes to several days. A relatively severe brain injury may cause only a slight disturbance of consciousness. The patient may suffer nausea, vomiting, headache, or dizziness in varying degrees. In some instances the patient becomes delirious on regaining consciousness. This condition may be of short duration or may last for several days or weeks. The patient is disoriented for time and place; he is restless, talks incoherently, may want to get dressed and return to work. He may have hallucinations.

A common sequel is the so-called "postconcussion syndrome," characterized by headaches, dizziness, irritability, cold and clammy extremities, and anxiety dreams. These symptoms often disappear in a few weeks.

The physical symptoms in brain injury depend on the extent of the damage. While the patient is unconscious, the breathing and pulse may be slow; the blood pressure may rise, and there may be a slight rise in temperature. In cases of more extended damage to the brain the pupils do not react.

The chronic symptoms, in general, can be classified as psychotic reactions and changes in personality.

The patient with a psychotic reaction may become apathetic and slow; he is often depressed and shows no initiative. People who knew him before his injury notice the change immediately. However, he may be oriented for time and place and answer questions correctly. This condition may disappear after several months. The patient usually has an amnesia for the accident, and there are often large gaps in his memory, which are gradually filled in if he improves.

Another form of psychotic reaction is characterized by over-activity, mild elation, and wittiness. The patient jokes and is very talkative; his stream of thought approximates a flight of ideas. He fills out his large gaps of memory with confabulations. His mood may be euphoric, in spite of such a serious noticeable injury as paralysis. This condition also may last several months and then disappear.

Changes in personality are often marked. In some instances such symptoms as headaches and dizziness persist; and the patient complains of fatigability and inability to concentrate. Together with this, he becomes markedly irritable, to the extent of sudden, almost impulsive violence. He may lose his ambition and initiative and become irregular in his work. His sense of beauty and his moral evaluations may slacken. Such patients tolerate alcohol very badly; their reaction to it is sometimes a terrific excitement, during which they commit acts of violence. These personality changes may persist without much change for several years. In some instances the change is progressive, and the patient deteriorates intellectually as well. However, the condition may clear up completely.

TREATMENT

During the acute period the patient must remain in bed; if he is unconscious, he must receive proper care and be given adequate fluids to prevent dehydration. The injection of caffeine has been recently recommended to reduce intracranial pressure. If the headache is severe, a lumbar puncture may be made. Sedatives and mild hypnotics may be necessary for a restless patient. The treatment of fracture of the skull is essentially the same, except that a longer period of rest is required. A depressed fracture, one in which part of the skull presses into the brain, requires surgery.

Psychotherapy is important after recovery because it allays the patient's fears, increases his desire to return to a regular mode of living, and prevents him from merging the problems arising from his accident with those connected with his everyday life. In other instances, however, the psychotherapy has another purpose: to make the patient who is reluctant to admit his helplessness realize his disability and go easy temporarily.

A man twenty-eight years old suffered a severe head injury when his car collided with another car. He was taken to a hospital and remained unconscious for two hours. An X-ray examination showed that his skull was fractured; the facial nerve on the right side was paralyzed, and he had difficulty in hearing with one ear; his spinal fluid was bloody. After being drowsy for several days, the patient became rather talkative. He obeyed instructions and stayed in bed, but had to be watched constantly because he would sit up and give everybody advice. He calmed down after several days except that he remained over-talkative. About a month later he grew even more talkative; flight of ideas and distractibility developed. He would talk about how well he felt, and say that he had planned a trip; then he would relate his experiences on one of his supposed trips and discuss the political policies of the various places he had visited. A few weeks later he began to talk of being secretly commissioned by the government to undertake various engineering projects to improve the condition of the country, and he described several visits to Washington which he had actually never made. He felt that he was in the best of health, although his face was still paralyzed from the accident. His condition remained essentially the same for about eight months, after which he gradually recovered, under ordinary medical treatment and discussions with a psychiatrist.

EPILEPSIES

FORMS OF EPILEPSY

In the severest form, called *grand mal,* the attack is often preceded by phenomena called aura: the patient sees flashes of light or smells an unpleasant odor or experiences an uncomfortable sensation in various parts of the body, or has visual hallucinations or muscular twitches or obsessive thoughts; he may start running. During the attack itself he loses consciousness, and his entire body begins to shake violently; his arms and legs thrash wildly about. During this attack the tongue is often bitten, there is foam on the mouth, and the face grows bluish. This violent thrashing, which is called the clonic phase, is often preceded by a contraction of the whole body; this is called the tonic phase. The patient remains unconscious for a while; he may regain consciousness for a short time, but he is drowsy and usually sleeps soundly for some time. When he recovers from the attack, he is often confused and acts in a half-conscious, automatic manner.

The attacks are not always as severe as this; for example, the patient may lose consciousness but have no convulsions, or the convulsions may not be general. In some instances, however, they may be extremely severe, the patient going from one attack to another without recovering consciousness; but usually there is an interval of anywhere from a day to a year between them. Sometimes the attacks occur at night while the patient is asleep. The patient has no memory of the attack, but usually remembers the aura. During the attack the pupils do not react to light, and there is a positive Babinski reflex. (Under normal circumstances, if the sole of the foot is stroked, all the toes flex; but if there is a temporary or permanent damage to the pyramidal tracts, the big toe extends instead of flexing, and the other toes may flex or extend.)

Petit mal, a less severe form of epilepsy, is characterized by a fleeting loss of consciousness, during which the patient may stand rigidly or keep doing what he was doing before the attack; he may drop things, turn pale, mumble, utter curious and irrelevant phrases, or make champing movements with his mouth. He has no memory of his actions.

In psychomotor epilepsy the patient carries out complex actions, such as sudden excited complaints of being mistreated and of everybody being against him, with anxiety, anger, and crying. There is no clear memory of the behavior.

In the epileptic fugue the patient suddenly stops what he has been doing and does something totally different. For example, he may steal something, leave his home at night clad only in his pajamas, and wander many miles away; when he recovers consciousness later, he has no idea how he got there.

In myoclonus epilepsy large muscle groups of the body exhibit gross paroxysmal twitching.

Another form of paroxysmal disorder which occurs in epilepsy is the so-called "psychic equivalent," also called epileptic furor. This may assume great importance, for it usually is characterized by great excitement, often with considerable anxiety and extremely violent behavior. A patient in this state may commit wholesale murder and know nothing about it, except possibly for a vague feeling that he has done something dreadful.

Other, more serious and lasting psychological disturbances occur in a prolonged psychotic state when there are hallucinations and delusions, particularly of a religious character. The patient may hear God talking to him; he may see a cross of fire, or pray most of the day. There may be stupor with ecstasy, during which the patient goes through intense religious experiences such as seeing God and all the angels. The patient may have a prolonged period of depression. This type of psychosis lacks the obscene characteristics which are almost invariably present in schizophrenia.

After many years of epileptic attacks, in spite of continued treatment, the patient may deteriorate intellectually; his memory may be violently disturbed and his judgment impaired.

It was formerly customary to include under epilepsy all disorders characterized by convulsions and attacks of psychological and motor disturbances; but, if this is done, the plural form, "epilepsies," should be used. A better procedure is to group these patients on the basis of the condition underlying their epilepsy. Convulsions may be caused by general paresis, hardening of the arteries of the brain (particularly if a hemorrhage occurs), or maldevelopment of the brain which results in idiocy or hydrocephalus. Patients with epileptic symptoms and these conditions are now customarily spoken of as having symptomatic epilepsy. The diagnosis is based on characteristic signs, such as the Wassermann test, mental changes, and neurological changes in general paresis. Another important group included under symptomatic epilepsy are patients with Jacksonian seizures. These seizures consist of attacks of muscular twitching which always start in the same place—the muscles of the face or of the hand, for example—while the patient is still conscious; the twitching then spreads over the entire body, and the patient loses consciousness. This condition is usually due to growths or pressure localized in the region of the motor area. A generalized convulsion which always starts with the same type of aura—for example, olfactory aura—may be due to brain tumors. After all forms of symptomatic epilepsies are eliminated, there remains a large group in whose brain no gross localized pathology can be found. This condition is called essential epilepsy (also idiopathic epilepsy), to indicate that the cause is not known. The discussion in this chapter concerns chiefly these patients. The genetic factors in the electroencephalographic findings in epilepsy have been discussed previously. (See Chapter X.)

PSYCHODYNAMICS OF EPILEPSY

The patient's general personality may be essentially normal, but in some cases characteristic alterations are observable before any attacks occur. In other instances they develop only after repeated attacks. Irritability is evident and is combined with destructiveness in younger age periods. The patient grows self-centered, selfish, and inconsiderate. He may grow especially susceptible to flattery and may boast childishly, with a shallow, at times sentimental and superficial interest in his environment. This interest is often religious.

The psychopathological processes which may occur in epilepsy can be divided into reactions arising out of continual and out of paroxysmal disturbances. The continual reactions represent hostile, aggressive, self-centered, self-magnifying attitudes and reactions of withdrawal as a consequence of the continual unlocalized organic disturbance. If this disturbance begins in infancy or, in severe cases, with frequently recurring attacks, it may lead to the development of the "epileptic character" described above and, in grave instances, to epileptic dementia.

The attacks (aura, convulsive attack, postconvulsive dream states, automatic acts, and *petit mal*) may have one or several of the following meanings: (1) Escape from an unbearable situation. (2) Engaging in a forbidden sexual activity. (3) State of anxiety: One patient's "automatic acts" consisted of lying on the side in a fetal position, preceded by an aura of epigastric "shuddering" or "trembling." This aura turned out to be a replica of a severe anxiety attack he had had just preceding the onset of his epilepsy during a period of serious conflict with his oppressive father (404). (4) Fantasy of an aggressive act, including murder: A patient would run away from his father in the preconvulsive state and then would worry after the attack whether he had actually killed his father (368). The most dramatic examples of the murderous epileptic experiences, of course, are those of epileptic furor in which the patient actually commits murder with complete amnesia. (5) Suicide: A patient, whose attacks started after he saw his mother hang herself, usually, either as an automatic act or in a postconvulsive state, hangs his head and sticks out his tongue. (6) Experience of destruction and rebirth: A patient in a postepileptic confusional state had the feeling that she must die, but this dying was to be the beginning of a new life. She prayed and heard religious songs—everything fitted the notion of the destruction of the world. This destruction was to take place in her. The next morning she felt like a new person and experienced a strong urge for activity (829).

TREATMENT

The majority of patients suffering from epileptic attacks can be treated outside of hospitals. There is still no entirely satisfactory treatment for epilepsy, but with certain methods the patient may be freed from attacks for many years and enabled to pursue his regular occupation.

The medicinal treatment consists of the administration of phenobarbital and/or dilantin in *grand mal,* tridion in *petit mal* and myoclonic epilepsy, and tridion or dilantin in psychomotor epilepsy. Drug therapy is best combined with psychotherapy.

The most favorable report on the effects of psychotherapy concerns twenty-two ambulatory cases who suffered from *petit mal,* automatic acts, or *grand mal.* The report stated that the patients were either cured or considerably benefited as regards attacks and personality disturbances (894). Such quite uniformly favorable results have not been reported by other authors.

In another study, thirty-one patients with essential or symptomatic (post-traumatic or encephalitic) epilepsy were carefully analyzed as to the effect of psychotherapy. The therapy included one or several of these forms: improving the attitude of the environment toward the patient; putting the patient into a new, improved social situation; having regular psychiatric interviews; and psychoanalysis. Drug therapy was continued in varying amounts. There was marked improvement as to frequency of attacks and personality disturbances in 67 percent of the cases, slight improvement in 10 percent, and no benefit in 23 percent (165).

Exceptionally severe cases require treatment in a psychopathic hospital. This is true if a prolonged psychotic episode occurs or if the personality changes, with irritability or a tendency to violence predominating. Special colonies for epileptics, such as Craig Colony in New York State, are of great value. The patients there live in healthful open surroundings and are under the supervision of individuals who know how to handle them.

The patient's convulsions began in association with her engagement, became aggravated by her marriage, and were most severe during her pregnancy. They decreased rapidly when she lived apart from her husband, were intensified again by his visits, and decreased markedly after her separation and divorce. Dreams and free associations indicated a persistent back-to-mother trend throughout, and the transference to the analyst was clearly of the dependent ("mother-libido") variety. Improvement was probably due to a combination of (1) transference, (2) catharsis (the emergence into consciousness of repressed and suppressed material), and (3) environmental alterations.[1]

BRAIN TUMORS

Brain tumors are new growths which appear in various parts of the brain. This growth may vary in nature and localization. For example, it may be a cyst—i.e., a round sac filled with fluid—which grows very gradually. This

[1] Based on a case presentation in K. A. Menninger, Psychoanalytic study of a case of organic epilepsy, *Psychoanal. Rev.,* 1926, **13,** 187-199.

type of tumor may damage the nerve tissue through pressure. The new growths may consist of cells which grow quickly and invade and infiltrate the surrounding tissue. The gliomas are of this type. This tumor is similar to cancer in its behavior.

PHYSICAL SYMPTOMS

The physical symptoms of brain tumor depend on two factors: the size of the tumor and its location. The general symptoms are headaches, vomiting, and slow pulse. The optic nerve may be swollen in one or both eyes where it enters the eye. All these general symptoms are due to increased intracranial pressure, the pressure sometimes being four times as high as is normal.

Local symptoms are produced by irritation or, more frequently, by damage to a particular part of the brain. These symptoms are numerous because of the extremely complex structure of the brain. Among them are paralysis; changes in the muscle, tendon, or skin reflexes; and disturbances in sense perception. If any of the nerve centers or the nerve paths leading to these centers are damaged, a loss of function results.

PSYCHOLOGICAL SYMPTOMS

The psychological symptoms may also be either general or local. The general symptoms may be due to disturbances not of the whole brain, but of certain parts of it, particularly the frontal lobe, the diencephalon, or the basal ganglia; but these symptoms are called general because the disturbances are often due to increased intracranial pressure as a whole. The general symptoms are apathy and disinterestedness, confusion and perplexity. The patient's consciousness may be deeply disturbed.

Considerable research has been done on localizing psychological signs. For example, Schuster found that emotional symptoms are more likely to appear if the tumor is localized on the left or dominant side of the brain (probably in right-handed people).

Gibbs analyzed 1545 records of patients who either were operated on or had died and been autopsied. Among his findings on hallucinations are the following: Visual hallucinations are most common if the tumor is located in the temporal or occipital lobe or in the thalamus. "Lilliputian" hallucinations are frequent in temporal lobe tumors; the patient sees small figures which he usually knows are not real. The temporal lobe is not a visual center, but some visual pathways go through it; and it is the irritation of these pathways that is responsible for the hallucinations.

Olfactory hallucinations (of smell) are most common when the tumor is localized in the temporal lobe or in the thalamus. The patient may smell peculiar odors, such as rubber burning, when there is no external cause for them. These hallucinations are produced by irritation of the olfactory areas.

Gustatory hallucinations (of taste) are produced by tumors in the basal ganglia and the thalamus. The patient may taste something bad—he may have a metallic taste or taste vinegar for no reason.

Jocularity is most common when the tumor is located in the thalamus or the striate body. The patient is witty, puns, and makes jokes, when he obviously is seriously ill. The jocularity may approximate the euphoria, elation, and flight of ideas found in manic reactions.

Irritability is most common when tumors involve the striate body on the left side of the brain.

Auditory hallucinations are extremely rare.

In some cases the mental symptoms may appear long before any convincing local symptoms appear. This is particularly likely when the tumor is in the frontal lobe because it may not extend back far enough to damage the motor area. It is also likely when the tumor is localized in the corpus callosum, the structure which connects the two hemispheres.

DIAGNOSIS AND TREATMENT

As a rule, brain tumors can be diagnosed. Ventriculography is one of the important diagnostic methods. The fluid is withdrawn from the ventricles of the brain; they are then filled with air, and X-ray pictures are taken. Any displacement, obstruction, or distortion in the shape of the ventricles indicates the presence and location of a tumor.

Electroencephalography is valuable in determining the location of a tumor, for there are changes in the electric waves if a tumor is present. For example, if electrodes are placed on the right side of the head of a patient who has a tumor in the middle of the left hemisphere, there will be no changes; but if the electrodes are placed on the left side of the head, changes will be observed.

Some brain tumors can be treated by an operation, in which the brain is exposed and the tumor removed. The patient may fully recover, depending on the size and location of the growth and whether any part of the brain had to be removed with the tumor. In other cases the patient has no recurrence of the tumor but is left with a residual symptom, such as partial paralysis. Certain types of tumors may recur after several years. Some tumors cannot be removed, and the patient dies within a short time.

A mechanic, twenty-five years old, grew very dull mentally. His reactions slowed, and his facial expression became dull and stupid. He was unable to grasp simple matters. For example, when he expected an out-of-town visitor, he would ask how the guest would travel and how long he would stay; he was unable to figure out where the visitor would sleep. He became more and more forgetful, even forgetting where he put his tools. He failed to complete jobs and, when criticized for it, did not know what he had done wrong. A mental examination showed that he had memory disturbances and slight intellectual impairment. His physical examination showed neither general nor local symptoms of brain tumor, but the encephalogram showed partial obliteration of the ventricles. On the basis of this, a tumor in both frontal lobes was diagnosed. It was removed surgically, the patient recovered fully and has been well for ten years.

SUGGESTED READINGS

Of the standard textbooks, Henderson and Gillespie (402) and Thorpe and Katz (930) are fairly detailed in their coverage of organic psychoses. For an approach to the psychological aspects, see Hollos and Ferenczi (426) and Schilder (829).

W. Penfield and K. Kristiansen's *Epileptic Seizure Patterns,* Thoms, Springfield, Ill., 1951, is a comprehensive work in its field.

PART VII

Syndromes in Old Age

XXXVI Problems of Aging and Reactions to Circumscribed Deficiencies

PROBLEMS OF THE AGING INDIVIDUAL

SOCIAL, INTERPERSONAL, AND FAMILY PROBLEMS

The older individual is confronted with becoming more self-sufficient as regards his family relations. The children have left home and want to live their own independent lives; if they do not, then there are problems with the in-laws. Brothers and sisters may be living in other countries or other cities.

The habits and interests of older people, as well as their abilities, have become more restricted, and there is a tendency for older people to be more comfortable in each other's company. This, however, represents a definite restriction of contact, which becomes difficult for some older people.

The cultural and individual status in both of these respects plays an important role. In groups where there is a tendency to patriarchal and/or matriarchal relationship in the family, contact with the children continues in the form of weekly visits, and the general respect accorded to the individual as parent or grandparent more than compensates for the diminution of contact. Among the Greeks, special respect was accorded to the "elders." On the other hand, in certain Eskimo tribes, older people are put on the ice floes to perish. Also, in certain occupational groups—for instance, artists or scientists—the tendency for limitation of social contact is less.

The problem of sexual limitations is different. Up to a certain point, in Western culture and also in most cultures, the man's opportunities increase with age, and the the woman's get restricted. Social custom raises no serious objections to a man's age as long as the man is older and as long as the woman has reached maturity. The children of the older man may object temporarily to his marrying a much younger woman, but the opposition is not insurmountable. There is no legal bias, but there is a strong social bias in the other direction—namely, against the woman's being older; thus this burden of adjustment becomes heavier on the woman.

Some of the economic problems also are based on bias against older people in some industrial situations, whereas at other times they are based on a physiological impairment of reaction time. Frequently employers reject people on the basis of age and not on the basis of lack of ability. If rejection is based simply on bias, it would be equivalent to a similar problem at any age, with the difference that it represents a much severer blow to the individual's confidence.

PROBLEMS BASED ON REACTIONS TO PHYSIOLOGICAL CHANGES

"Aging" is a universal process. The diminution of the elasticity of the skin, of the lens in the eye, and of the blood vessels is observable in all individuals (171). Yet there are individual differences in degree in such gross organic alterations. Psychologically, the individual differences are even greater, and in the emotional life of the individual aging may be absent. It is very important to realize this point in the approach to certain psychiatric and psychosomatic manifestations in people of sixty and seventy years of age. Individuals of that age may be more elastic than many individuals at any age in their lives. They may branch out successfully into a new creative field of endeavor.

The deterioration quotient,[1] as measured on the Wechsler-Bellevue Scale, has been found to decline in the average population from 97.9 at the age of 22.5 to 74.8 at the age of 57.5. Of the various subtests, Information, Comprehension, Object Assembly, and Vocabulary hold up with age, whereas Digit Span, Arithmetical Reasoning, Digit Symbol, Block Design, and Similarities show conspicuous age decline. (See Appendix I for a discussion of the Wechsler-Bellevue Scale.) Further, there is a lengthening of the reaction time, which is the largest factor in the decline of the scores mentioned, along with a decrease in the individual's power and endurance, at least in sustained vigorous activity.

In some important respects the aging process starts, on an average, at about the age of 21, although the effects of aging may still be outweighed in importance by experience. These considerations explain why the average age of highest performance in such sports as tennis, boxing, baseball, football, and ice hockey falls into the mid-twenties and almost invariably the champion is dethroned by a younger man. It is very instructive, however, that, if the previous champion does not retire but keeps competing for a number of years, he simply moves into the second place and then, for a number of years, into the third place. Thus, in the all-round picture, the

[1] This score is obtained by dividing the sum of those subtest scores which show definite decline with age by the sum of those which show little or no decline with age.

aging process, for a long time, is of relatively little disadvantage. In other fields, which we might call creative thinking—philosophy, medicine, music, politics, physics, fiction writing—it has been estimated that individuals as an average do their most important work in the late thirties or forties. The variations in these fields are very considerable. Michelangelo, for example, painted *The Last Judgment* at the age of seventy. In the light of all these considerations, the chronological period at which aging is of significance varies with the individual and his life situation. In a large segment of the city population, particularly the industrial population, this period may be somewhere between forty and fifty. In the farming population it is later. This age is also important because of the increase in the incidence of the various pathological conditions to be discussed below.

The appearance of the menopause in women also falls into this period. It should be mentioned, however, that the decline in sexual responsiveness and potency is not definite and may hardly occur until a much later period.

In the American male population studied by Kinsey et al. (494), the mean frequency of orgasm gradually declines from a peak of 3.0 per week in the age group 26-30 to 2.2 per week in the age group 56-60. The percentage of the population studied which was impotent rises from 0.1 percent at age 20 to 27.0 percent at age 70. The authors cite the case of a Negro of eighty-eight who was having regular intercourse with his wife of ninety.

SYNDROMES

The disturbances of aging have two dynamic factors: (1) the direct effects of the physiological disturbance, and (2) the individual's reactions to these disturbances. The direct effects of the physiological disturbance, of course, are quite different if they have taken place in the brain itself. As regards the individual's reactions, they may intensify the process—e.g., raise his blood pressure because of hostility and anxiety in a hypertensive disease—or produce additional symptoms. The individual's reactions are based on a blow to his self-esteem or on the feeling that a long-cherished hope for relief of a life situation is now irrevocably shattered. Thus a woman may have had serious conflicts with her husband and have planned for ten years to leave him but repeatedly postponed doing so; now, after menopause has set in and after she has developed a heart ailment, she feels that she can never carry out this plan.

PSYCHONEUROSES AND FUNCTIONAL PSYCHOSES

The most common reaction is depression. This may be of the psychoneurotic or of the psychotic type.

Involutional Melancholia. Severe depressive reactions which occur during the involutional period in people who have never previously had a psychotic episode are best grouped under involutional melancholia. The characteristic symptoms are as follows.

Depression with Agitation and Anxiety but Without Retardation. These patients are not retarded or slow in their thinking or responses, but they may be difficult to converse with. They feel depressed and worthless, are self-accusatory, and give the appearance of great misery. They are extremely anxious and expect something dreadful to be done to them. Similar thoughts are frequent in severe depressions at any time of life; but in the involutional period they are accompanied by great anxiety. In talking with the psychiatrist, the patient may at first want to say something; but he becomes anxious and agitated, wrings his hands, says nothing or gives an evasive answer, or just says that everything is lost, or asks, "Are they going to hurt me?" or repeats continually, "Oh, my God!"

Feeling of Unreality. The patient has the distressing feeling that neither he nor anything around him is quite real. He recognizes objects and can name them accurately, but he feels a peculiar distance between himself and them. According to him, both his perceptions and his feelings lack something.

Hypochondriacal or Nihilistic Delusions. These patients may say that they have changed; that their tongues are gone, their brains are going; that they are all dried up; that they suffer from cancer or syphilis; that their relatives are dead.

They may also have feelings of unworthiness, suspicions, and delusions of sin, guilt, and persecution. A particularly good example of the statements made by this type of patient is the following:

> "The beauty of the earth and the glory of the sky do not now exist; the seasons are not the seasons of yesteryear; the flowers, the trees and the birds are not raised in the glory of old time; people display only repulsiveness, deceit and all forms of wickedness. All, all is gone; those days are bygone splendor, and things can never be changed; body, soul and spirit have been altered until I have become a weariness to myself. . . . The beautiful furniture; the beautiful needlework—clean and beautiful people—think of them all, all buried: these things are literally under the earth. That is all over; all is gone, absolutely, and here am I. I wish I had never seen the world, and now I have ruined it."[2]

The physical symptoms during the period of depression are in general the same as those present in the depressive reaction, except for the additional symptoms, particularly those of the menopause, characteristic of the period of involution.

Psychodynamically, the general features of involutional melancholia are like those of depression. There is, however, an additional factor in that the

[2] D. K. Henderson and R. D. Gillespie, *A Textbook of Psychiatry*, Oxford University Press, London, 5th ed., 1940, pp. 184-185.

feeling of inadequacy and worthlessness is based on physiological decline and all that this means to the patient. Thus the woman may consider that all her attractiveness disappears with menopause. Her attractiveness may in itself have had for her a very significant supporting and reinforcing value against all sorts of feelings of helplessness and expectations of rejection. With this supportive aspect gone, she considers herself worthless, helpless, and about to be rejected. Any difficulties in her relationship with other individuals become tremendous dangers. The presence of strong hypochondriacal and nihilistic delusions is probably due to the involutional background, for they present an exaggeration of actual physiological decline. The patient may evaluate this decline in itself as a threat and retribution and injury on the part of those on whom she is dependent and toward whom she is hostile; this explains the strong anxiety.

The treatment of involutional melancholia is essentially like that of other depressive reactions, with, in addition, administration of the lacking hormone.

PSYCHOSOMATIC DISORDERS AND REACTIONS TO CIRCUMSCRIBED DISTURBANCES

The two groups of disorders are discussed together because in many of them it is a moot question to what extent the psychogenic factor plays a role in the primary causation, although it is certain that reactions to life situations aggravate the disturbance.

Menopausal Reactions. Menopause is characterized by cessation of menstruation and not infrequently by the appearance of hot flushes with excessive perspiration, dizziness, headaches, irritability, and depression. The hot flushes and the excessive perspiration are very likely due, not to diminished estrogenic sex hormone, but to excess of anterior pituitary hormone. Sexual receptivity and orgastic ability are retained in the healthy woman after menopause. The psychological symptoms are the result of a combination of direct effects of the endocrine imbalance and of the individual's reaction to these changes. The endocrine changes represent a double threat: (1) distressing, uncontrollable bodily symptoms, and (2) aging and the final loss of fulfillment of lifelong desires. The administration of ovarian follicular hormone is largely effective in removing the physical symptoms. Additional psychotherapy eliminates psychological symptoms also.

In the majority of cases, decline of sexual function in the male is very gradual and causes no serious disturbance, although in some instances depression occurs. The decline in function can be remedied by the injection of testosterone.

Disturbances of the Eyes. The two most common eye diseases of aging are glaucoma and cataract. Cataract consists of a clouding of the crystalline lens of the eye, which is entirely a primary histogenic (somatic) disorder, but the difficulty in vision may become fused with anxieties from various sources in the form of fear of blindness. Glaucoma is an increase in the intraocular pressure. In this disorder, reactions to life situations play an important role, and it may occur at a younger age (early thirties) also. Irritability may be a marked symptom in both disorders. Both glaucoma and cataract, as a rule, require operative treatment. Both may require psychotherapy to help the patient adjust to his changed function and, in glaucoma, to prevent aggravation of the process (166).

Disturbances of the Respiratory Apparatus. The respiratory apparatus may show chronic bronchitis and emphysema in old age. The difficulty in breathing and the cough resulting from these sources fuse with similar symptoms arising out of anxiety or frustrated hostility.

Disturbances of the Digestive System. The digestive system is very frequently involved in the psychosomatic reactions but only occasionally becomes a dominant seat of the psychosomatic pathology of aging. When it does, it is apt to be connected with the fear of cancer, and it then colors anxiety reactions in this special way. In fact, the whole anxiety reaction may be precipitated by the news that someone else in the family or among the patient's friends has developed or died of cancer.

Disturbances of the Auditory System. Diminution of hearing is almost universal in advanced age. Some of the disturbances may be comparatively severe and may be accompanied by ringing in the ear (732). Some individuals react to this defect badly and become irritable and suspicious, as if they felt constantly humiliated and as if they suspected that people were talking about them. This usually represents a reaction to their own hostility. In some instances the reaction to disturbances of the auditory apparatus can be very severe. The disturbance may represent the first bodily defect in the patient's life which is incurable even if not severe.

Disturbances of the Circulatory System. The disturbances of the circulatory system may represent a continuation of essential hypertension which arose at an earlier period, or it may represent new pathology of the type that more frequently occurs with aging. The two types of disturbance fuse in so far as essential hypertension, after many years' duration, is accompanied by irreversible changes in the vascular system and may show complications of heart failure, cerebral hemorrhage (apoplexy), and hardening of the arteries (arteriosclerosis). All of these disorders, as well as coronary disease of the heart, cause greater incapacity if they are aggravated by reactions to life situations.

A man of sixty-one was referred by his physician for psychiatric treatment. The patient had a variety of vascular symptoms. He had arterial hypertension, with blood pressure fluctuating between 170/90 and 210/110. Four years before applying for psychiatric treatment he had had an occlusion of one of the branches of the coronary artery. After that he had suffered from an attack of precordial pain. At times he had mild congestive failure of the heart. He had to take digitalis continually and carried nitroglycerine with him all the time after he started to work again. He worked on half time with very little endurance, and discontinued all spontaneous activity such as writing articles, giving speeches, or conducting meetings. He was an educator of note.

Since his first attack of coronary thrombosis he had been afraid of dying, was very anxious, and continually asked his physician for reassurance but never felt secure for more than half an hour after he got it.

The analysis of this man was truly remarkable. Intellectually, as it turned out, he showed no gross aging, regained his active mind, to everybody's surprise, and engaged in active writing again. Very briefly, the psychological story was this: In the beginning of the analysis he had dreams in which he was in the synagogue on the Day of Atonement; he had to leave the synagogue, and saw his friend dead on the street; he was in search of a place, wandered aimlessly, and could not find it; nobody would recognize him or pay attention to him. The guilt and the feeling of abandonment, of "excommunication," was quite obvious in these dreams. Later he had dreams in which he attacked people who hurt him violently, and murdered them by choking them to death.

When he was a child, the oldest of six siblings, his father had been quite strict and was very abusive to his mother. The patient was deeply hurt by this; when he was about ten years old, he got up on a chair, shook his fist in his father's face, and said, "You can't talk to my mother like that." After he got married, at the age of twenty-three, he was profoundly hurt by his wife's frigidity. She never refused him sexually, but, he said, "she didn't respond. She lay there like a piece of wood. I used to feel terribly hurt and desperate. She told me, 'What do you want of me? It doesn't mean anything.' But I felt deeply wounded. Sometimes at night I would look at her and get so angry that I wanted to choke her." The patient later hoped that by finding another woman he would have consolation. When another woman fell in love with him, he felt that she was a "redeeming angel." However, when he had opportunity to have sex relations with the woman, he postponed them, and never saw her again. Similar developments occurred with three other women. Between the successive appearances of these women the patient felt lonely. He would stand on the street corner at times and invite a prostitute to sit with him in a restaurant and talk with him, and then would pay the woman for the time. The patient's ability to work and his interest in his work declined, particularly after his wife became suspicious about the last of the women for whom he had felt a sentimental attachment.

The patient's resentment toward his wife in the course of the marriage at first was conscious. Even at the time the problem about it was its terrific intensity and its murderous quality. His wife's "coldness" represented to him rejection, a threat to his manliness, a statement of his worthlessness. His self-evaluation was disturbed, beginning with his clashes with his father in his childhood. The betrayal by the woman (his mother) whom he had risen to defend against his father was deadly. His wife's frigidity represented to him such a betrayal. His guilt over his hostility and over his attempt to get the recognition and love from other women was intense. This continuous conflict unquestionably intensified the results of the aging process and aggravated his vascular disease. Even after the coronary accident occurred, he was restored to almost full bloom of life at the advanced age of sixty-one, through psychoanalysis. He even resumed sex relations with his wife after abstaining from such activity for a year and a half.

ORGANIC PSYCHOTIC REACTIONS

Arteriosclerotic-Senile Reactions. With advancing age the brain substance and its functioning usually deteriorate. Although a certain degree of intellectual and emotional decline is just as normal as the wrinkling of the skin, this decline may be more marked and certain additional symptoms may appear. These symptoms are due to (1) damage of the brain tissue itself, which is usually made worse by the hardening of its arteries and the consequent defective blood supply; (2) the individual's reactions to the damaged functions. The condition is often initiated by a stroke.

In arteriosclerosis of the brain after the age of forty the following symptoms are common: (1) Disturbed memory, particularly for recent events. The person who used to remember everything well cannot remember where he put his keys or his glasses; a businessman who formerly remembered figures very well has to ask three or four times for them. (2) Difficulty in sustaining effort. The patient at first works actively at a task, then seems to tire, begins to make mistakes, and wanders away from it. (3) Emotional instability and irritability. These emotional traits may be manifest on many occasions, but they are particularly marked when the patient makes a mistake. There may be frequent outbursts of laughter or weeping without cause.

When arteriosclerosis occurs at a comparatively early age, attention to appearance, the desire to behave properly, moral values, and interest remain present for a relatively long time.

Simple Senile Deterioration. Senile deterioration appears after the age of sixty. The chronic condition is marked by the following symptoms: The individual's range of interest grows smaller; he becomes self-centered and loses interest in other people, even his family. His thinking slows up, and he is inclined to be stubborn about his opinions and ways of existence, and he may be irritable. He tells the same stories over and over and spends most of his time in reminiscences. His memory becomes worse, particularly for recent events—he may even forget that someone in his immediate family has died recently. The failure to remember past events may be so complete that the patient will finally say that he is one day old. Patients with this condition frequently hide things—money or such useless articles as pencils or newspapers. Their orientation as to place is impaired; they often wander around the hospital wards asking where their beds are. They are also disoriented for time, having no knowledge of the year, season, month, or day. As the condition proceeds, other symptoms frequently appear, such as paranoid attitudes and delusions. Patients accuse others, frequently close relatives, of being their enemies, and for this reason they often change their wills and disinherit their children. They often accuse others of stealing articles. More marked paranoid delusions, together with hallucinations, may appear. These patients will say that policemen are after them or that people are making immoral remarks about them. Their emotional states may likewise be seriously disturbed. They may be depressed, or grow extremely anxious and panicky in anticipation of something terrible such as being burned to death or cut to pieces. They may become very restless and be unable to sleep, wandering about day and night. They may become indecent, expose themselves, make sexual assaults on children. They may grow violent, particularly those who are jealous and paranoid. Chronic senile deterioration may have acute phases in which periods of delirium occur.

The physical symptoms are those of old age. Speech is slow, the handwriting shaky. The patients become incontinent and soil themselves. Some physical symptoms, such as convulsions, stroke, loss of speech, are caused by a sudden disturbance in the circulation of the brain, but these symptoms may be only temporary.

Patients with simple senile deterioration can be taken care of at home, as can also the patients with delirium except during the delirious period. Patients with lively hallucinations and delusions should be hospitalized because they are dangerous both to themselves and to those around them. Sleeplessness can often be combated by baths or hot drinks before retiring, but sometimes sedatives are required.

A man of seventy-five wandered away from home. He asked a policeman where he was, and the officer took him to a hospital. The patient's wife died while he was in the hospital, and his son came to take him to her funeral. Later, when the patient was visiting a friend, he talked of his wife as if she were alive, and he talked about his experiences in the Spanish-American War, saying what a great hero he had been. He wandered away from home again and was taken to the hospital. He was completely disoriented as to both time and place. He was delirious and hallucinated himself as being in a workshop; at other times he became panicky because he saw an imaginary fire break out. He had no control over his bladder and bowels. He died in about three months.

Two relatively rare disorders are similar in manifestation to the arteriosclerotic-senile reactions, but show different histopathology or age of onset. They are Alzheimer's disease and Pick's disease. In both there may be intellectual deterioration, loss of interest and apathy, and foolish behavior, and, depending on the individual's previous personality, irritability, euphoria, and depression, at times with ideas of reference, suspicion, or delusions of persecution. The neurological symptoms not infrequently are aphasia (inability to name objects), agraphia (inability to write), apraxia (inability to use objects adequately), and epileptiform seizures. The pathology in Alzheimer's disease is a replacement of brain cells by neurofibrillar tangles arranged in baskets. On air encephalograms one finds enlarged ventricles.

The condition has been called presenile dementia. In Pick's disease there is a circumscribed atrophy of certain portions of the cerebral cortex, particularly the frontal and temporal lobes. Microscopically, the nerve cells in the cerebral cortex become swollen or disappear and are replaced by neuroglia (the nonfunctioning supportive cells of the brain).

TREATMENT OF SYNDROMES

It is very important, in treating and advising older patients, to determine to what extent their difficulties have to do with the aging process. Frequently it has very little to do with it, at least psychologically, and a man may get his first anxiety attack at the age of sixty in response to a life situation which could have occurred just as well thirty years earlier. The psychotherapy of such an individual differs in no way from that of a younger person. The results of the therapy can be just as good as at any age.

As regards problems connected with the aging process, it is helpful to break up habitual rigidity. One may insist that they eat in different restaurants, go to different vacation places, and read different newspapers and books. On the other side of the ledger, the therapist may help the older individual meet other people of his age—e.g., in clubs or church groups.

As regards occupational problems, men whose speed has declined so that they cannot work on the assembly line can learn crafts such as watch-repairing or engraving, or they may be transferred from the assembly line to a part of the plant where speed is not of paramount importance. It may be very important to loosen up and relieve the paralyzing feeling of defeatism and hopelessness over situations that in part arise out of family problems.

A woman of fifty-five, who was divorced, had three children. One of them was married but did not want her mother to live in the house with her. Another was about to get married. The mother was depressed and had made one suicidal gesture; therefore the third daughter was afraid to live alone with her. This daughter moved out and lived with her sister. The therapist saw not only the patient but also the children. The therapist considered it ill-advised for the daughter to move back in with the mother. The mother was angry about this but took measures to adjust herself in a more constructive way. She sold her house, went to live with a friend in another city, and got a job as a receptionist, the kind of work she had done before she was married.

If there is a decline in some of the functions—e.g., hearing—an artificial aid is, naturally, to be used. It may require psychotherapeutic measures to have the individual accept such aids. Similarly, it may require psychotherapeutic measures to have the individual accept limitations arising out of a pathological process or aging in general. He may consider it a blow to his self-esteem and may be trying, in a defiant, hostile, irritable manner, to follow his old occupations and social pursuits. This, however, is not always an easy matter, and therapy may fail. While some patients will accept the suggestions of learning a new trade and developing new hobbies after they have retired, others will decline to do this. Similarly, they may refuse to resign themselves to an organic failing. It is impressive, however, how many older people with problems of the type mentioned accept at least a partial solution. It should also be mentioned that some of them are happiest when they spend their remaining years in a well-conducted home for the aged.

SUGGESTED READINGS

Kaplan's book *Mental Disorders in Later Life* (841) gives a comprehensive presentation of the psychiatric problems. Lawton's *Aging Successfully* (529) and *New Goals for Old Age* (528) discuss the problems and their management in a practical and constructive manner.

Glossary[1]

Abulia: Diminution or loss of initiative and decisiveness; inability to make a decision.

Adaptation, adjustment: The sum total of the individual's reactions to the needs of his life situations; the preferred form for these reactions. (See *Life style.*)

Agitation: A restless, anxious, worried frame of mind, with motor manifestations (e.g., wringing the hands).

Agoraphobia: A morbid fear of open places.

Allergy: A reaction to eating, inhaling, or touching proteins which elicits certain symptoms (hay fever, asthma, hives, etc.).

Ambivalence: Contradictory attitudes (particularly love and hate) toward the same person or thing.

Ameliorative device: A psychological process which aims at relieving psychic distress.

Amentia: Feeble-mindedness. A mental state (psychotic reaction) characterized by apathy, disorientation, and impaired consciousness.

Amnesia: Inability consciously to recall events or personal identity.

Anesthesia: Loss of sensation, particularly touch, heat, pain, or cold.

Anorexia: Loss of appetite or ability to eat.

Anxiety, neurotic: Fear in the absence of actual danger.

Anxiety hysteria: A psychoneurotic reaction characterized by attacks of fear in response to situations of stress. Phobias are usually included.

Anxiety neurosis: A condition characterized by attacks or physiological signs of anxiety (e.g., palpitation), originally thought to be caused by ungratified sexual excitement. A colloquial term for any condition characterized by attacks of anxiety.

Apathy: Absence of emotional interest.

Aphasia: Impairment in the ability to use or understand language caused by a disturbance in certain parts of the brain.

Astasia-abasia: Inability to stand or walk, the patient having normal control of the legs while sitting or lying.

Asthma: A disease characterized by difficulty in breathing.

Ataxia: Disturbance of muscular coördination.

[1] For definitions of terms not included in this list, see L. E. Hinsie and J. Shatzky, *Psychiatric Dictionary,* Oxford University Press, 1940.

Atrophy: A wasting away of organ or tissue, particularly muscle.
Aura: Sensory experiences preceding epileptic seizures, such as seeing lights.
Automatic writing: Writing without full conscious control.
Autonomic nervous system: That part of the nervous system that regulates involuntary bodily functions.
Babinski reflex: Extension of the great toe (instead of normal flexion) when the sole of the foot is stroked.
Basic anxiety: The feeling of helplessness in a potentially hostile world.
Behaviorism: A system of psychology based exclusively on objectively observable phenomena.
Benign: Relatively mild, in contrast to malignant.
Blocking: Retardation of the flow of thought or associations to the point of stoppage.
Castration fear: A constellation of conscious and unconscious ideas centered in the fear of genital injury, including mutilation.
Catalepsy: A condition characterized by lack of response to stimuli, and by waxy rigidity of the limbs.
Catastrophic breakdown: A reaction to stress which entails incapacity in an indispensable psychological function and is accompanied by intense suffering.
Catastrophic fear: Anticipation of situations which imply destructive and unbearable distress and panic.
Catatonia: A condition in schizophrenic reactions, characterized by stupor, waxy flexibility, and periods of excitement.
Catharsis: The emotional discharge which occurs when a repressed traumatic experience is recalled and which is followed by relief; used sometimes also for sudden conscious realization of any repression.
Central nervous system: The brain and the spinal cord.
Character: The sum total of the individual's relatively permanent modes of behavior, attitudes, reaction patterns, and methods of coping with problems.
Character neurosis (neurotic character): Disturbances in character with or without symptoms.
Chorea: A disease of the nervous system characterized by involuntary muscular movements.
Chronic: Pertaining to a condition which progresses slowly and is long continued, or reaches this phase after an acute beginning.
Claustrophobia: A morbid fear of enclosed places.
Clinical methods: Methods of investigation, except laboratory and experimental procedures, which imply direct contact with and observation of the patient.
Coma: A state of profound unconsciousness characterized by absence of reflexes and the loss of nearly all bodily defense reactions (nonresponsiveness to pricks or to obstruction of breathing).
Compensation: The individual's attempt to make up for an undesirable trait and the consequent discomfort by emphasizing or exaggerating a desirable trait.
Complex: An affectively (emotionally) charged constellation of ideas.
Compromise formation: The process, conscious or unconscious or both, leading to the formation of symptoms and patterns of behavior which attempt to satisfy opposing needs.

Compulsion: The impulse to perform usually harmless and apparently senseless acts which the individual's judgment opposes and he wants to resist; also the performance of such acts.

Compulsion or obsessional neurosis: A psychoneurotic reaction characterized chiefly by compulsions and obsessional thoughts which seriously impair the individual's functioning.

Confabulation: The making up of stories and the readiness to give fluent but false answers to questions.

Conflict: A clash between conscious or unconscious impulses and needs.

Constellation: A pattern or syndrome of connected or correlated motives, impulses, ideas, and emotions.

Conversion hysteria: A psychoneurotic reaction in response to stress, characterized by a localized disturbance in bodily function but with no anatomical damage.

Coping: The individual's emotional and physical functioning in attempting to solve problems.

Coping reaction: Methods and devices used to avoid distress and to reach goals which are charged with fear and conflict.

Cretin: A feeble-minded individual whose condition is caused by a congenital deficiency of the thyroid gland.

Cultural conflicts: Conflicts engendered in the individual by opposing cultural demands and norms.

Cyclothymic: Temperamental make-up characterized by the alternation of optimism, cheerfulness, and planfulness, with sadness, pessimism, and worry.

Defense mechanisms: Psychological reaction patterns for avoiding psychic distress and danger.

Defensive hostility: The tendency, conscious or unconscious or both, to hurt or attack someone who is feared; this serves as a defense against him.

Delirium: A mental state characterized by disorientation, difficulty in perception, and excitement, accompanied by illusions and hallucinations.

Delusion: An abnormal conscious belief which the individual defends in spite of reality or its logical absurdity.

Dementia: Mental deterioration; loss of intellectual capacities.

Dementia paralytica: See *Paresis.*

Dementia praecox: A term formerly used to denote a group of mental disorders which appear between the ages of fifteen and thirty and end in dementia. The term has been replaced by "schizophrenia."

Depression: A prolonged mood of extreme sadness accompanied by decrease in initiative, difficulty in thinking, and self-debasing ideas.

Deprivation: The inability to satisfy a need or desire because of external obstacles. Some authors use the term synonymously with "frustration"; others restrict the latter to cases where psychological threat results from the deprivation. (See *Frustration.*)

Dipsomania: Periodic uncontrollable desire for and indulgence in alcohol.

Disorientation: Confusion or uncertainty concerning time, place, or people.

Displacement: The substitution of an object, circumstance, mode of expression, or body organ for the expression of an impulse, emotional reaction, or the function of another organ.

Dissociation: A condition in which the different mental processes lose their usual modifying influence upon one another.

Dominance feeling: A synonym for self-esteem.

Drive: A persistent or recurrent urge (motivation) to characteristic patterns of behavior. (See *Instinct.*)

Drive to power: An intense and persistent search for means which will enable the individual to control others. The drive is at least partly unconscious, is motivated by fear, and aims at safety and self-esteem.

Dynamic psychology: The approach to psychological phenomena which emphasizes the subjective experience of drivenness, the observable persistent striving, often unconscious, in certain directions and for certain goals in spite of obstacles. It emphasizes motivation, the integral interrelation between various psychological states, and the underlying (unconscious) meaning or purpose of any psychological state or bodily symptom.

Dystrophy: Faulty growth.

Echolalia: A symptom, usually in schizophrenic reactions, in which the patient echoes anything said to him.

Echopraxia: A condition in which the patient repeats mechanically the gestures and actions of another person.

Ego: The self. That part of the mental apparatus which controls conscious perception, thought, feeling, and behavior, and which attempts to guide the adjustment to external and internal reality.

Ego psychology: Aspects of psychoanalytic investigation and theory which emphasize the significance of anxiety, defense mechanisms, and character.

Elation: A strong feeling of cheerfulness, well-being, and satisfaction with oneself, often accompanied by an optimistic outlook and great energy.

Electrocardiography: A method of recording, by means of a special apparatus, the electrical changes caused by the contraction of the heart muscle.

Electroencephalography: A method of recording the electrical activity of the brain.

Encephalitis: Inflammation of the brain.

Encephalogram: An X-ray photograph of the brain made after the fluid in the ventricles has been withdrawn and replaced by air.

Enuresis: Involuntary discharge of urine; bed-wetting.

Epilepsy: A group of diseases characterized by generalized convulsions or loss of consciousness or both.

Erogenous zones: Sensitive regions of the body whose stimulation gives rise to erotic excitement.

Etiology: The source or origin of a symptom or disease.

Euphoria: A feeling of marked well-being and of satisfaction with oneself and the world in general.

Exhibitionism: A sexual perversion, in which display of the genitals affords the maximal erotic pleasure. Also an excessive desire, conscious or unconscious, to display oneself in order to be looked at or admired.

Exophthalmic goiter: A condition characterized by bulging of the eyes, overfunctioning and enlargement of the thyroid gland, rapid pulse, restlessness, increased basal metabolism.

Expiation process: A psychological process and behavior by which the individual unconsciously seeks forgiveness for an impulse or an act.

Fantasy: A vivid and prolonged imaginary activity, usually fictitious in nature, which either is satisfying to the individual or is evoked by a strong emotion.

Fetishism: Predominant sexual interest in an inanimate object.

Free association: The spontaneous reporting of every thought as it becomes conscious, with a minimum of rational or ethical criticism.

Frigidity: Any impairment of the woman's ability to reach sexual gratification.

Frustration: A serious or threatening nongratification of needs and desires because of environmental or intrapsychic obstacles. (See *Deprivation.*)

Frustration tolerance: The ability to experience deprivation or frustration without psychological disturbances.

Fugue: A period of "dissociation" (split consciousness) during which the individual is engaged in a complicated act away from his usual environment; he remembers nothing subsequently.

Functional psychoses: Mental disorders whose cause is primarily psychological rather than an anatomical or toxic damage to the nervous system.

Genetic: Pertaining to the origin, history, or development of anything.

Gestalt: Configuration. Any constantly observable pattern of functioning (action, sense perception, emotional reaction) whose parts are integrated into a whole.

Globus hystericus: A distressing and prolonged feeling of a "lump in the throat," often with choking sensations; correlated with partly unconscious emotional stress.

Goal object: That person or thing toward which, consciously or unconsciously, the drives or pleasure-seeking impulses are directed.

Gonad: A sexual gland; a testicle or ovary.

Grandiosity: Abnormal over-evaluation of the self.

Gratification: The act and experience of satisfying a bodily or psychological need.

Graves' disease: See *Exophthalmic goiter.*

Gyri: The convolutions of the brain.

Hallucination: An abnormal sensory experience that has no real and external stimulus.

Heredity: Traits, tendencies, and reaction patterns which are transmitted by the germ plasm.

Heterosexuality: Sexual interest in the opposite sex.

Homosexuality: Erotic relationship with an individual of one's own sex.

Hydrocephaly: An abnormal accumulation of fluid in the skull, often accompanied by enlargement of the head and mental defect.

Hyperemia: A superabundance of blood in circulation in any part of the body.

Hyperkinetic: Pertaining to excessive general motor activity.

Hyperthyroidism: Over-abundant secretion from the thyroid gland.

Hypnoanalysis: A therapeutic technique which combines some psychoanalytical techniques with hypnosis.

Hypnosis: A mental state called a trance, which is characterized primarily by extreme responsiveness to suggestions.

Hypochondria: A neurotic reaction whose most conspicuous symptom is preoccupation with morbid sensations in various organs.

Hypomania: The mildest form of the manic phase of manic-depressive psychosis.

Hysteria: A term applied to diverse neurotic reactions by various writers. The syndromes are organic dysfunctions with no anatomical pathology: attacks of anxiety and phobia, amnesia, and double personality. Most frequently the term is used to characterize physical symptoms which have psychological rather than organic causes.

Identification: The process by which real or imagined characteristics of one person are reproduced in the personality of another by unconscious or partly unconscious mechanisms.

Idiomotor tendency: The tendency to react, without reasoning, to a stimulus, either overt or implied, when the attention is concentrated elsewhere.

Idiot: A feeble-minded person whose IQ is less than 25.

Imbecile: A person whose IQ is between 25 and 50.

Inadequacy: A conscious and unconscious disturbance of self-evaluation or self-esteem.

Incoherence: Disconnected and unrelated thoughts, utterances, or actions.

Inferiority complex: The constellation of ideas and feelings which centers in a conscious or unconscious self-evaluation in terms of inadequacy; the attitudes and reactions deriving from this, including (according to some writers) compensatory measures.

Inhibition, neurotic: The impairment or cessation of a function as the result of conflicts.

Insanity: Any psychological disorder, other than feeble-mindedness, which legally constitutes a person irresponsible and thereby warrants his commitment to an institution. The medical term is "psychosis" or "mental disease."

Insecurity: The evaluation of the environment and of other people as rejecting, threatening, dangerous, or hostile, leading to feelings of rejection or isolation.

Instinct: A term given various meanings by different authors: an inborn bodily need which is gratified in a predetermined manner; any psychological reaction the tendency to which is inborn.

Integration: The process or result of establishing relations between parts and welding them into a functional whole.

Intelligence quotient: The mental age obtained by the Binet or other standard intelligence tests, divided by the chronological age, multiplied by 100 to eliminate decimals.

Kleptomania: Compulsive stealing.

Lesion: A visible damage or abnormality in an organ.

Libido: The term used by Freud to denote either the life force, the drive for any activity, or the drive for pleasure.

Life style: The characteristic manner of perceiving, reacting to, and solving the problems of life.

Macrocephaly: A pathological condition characterized by an abnormal enlargement of the head.

Maladjusted individual: A person who is inadequately adjusted to, and therefore unable to cope adequately with, reality and his own needs; a person whose vital needs clash with reality. The term "maladjusted" is used variously to refer to any psychological disturbance, or to mild disturbances, particularly of behavior.

Manic-depressive psychosis: A psychotic reaction characterized by prolonged periods of excitement etc. (mania), or by periods of depression, or by both.

Masochism: A sexual perversion characterized by the need to experience pain in order to attain the maximal erotic satisfaction; conscious or unconscious desires to experience physical or psychological pain.

Megalomania: A psychotic condition characterized by delusions of grandeur.

Melancholia: Serious depression occurring during involution (40-60 years); the depressive phase of manic-depressive psychosis.

Menopause: Permanent cessation of menstruation in the course of aging.

Mental conflict: The condition resulting when desires, needs, or impulses which are partly or completely incompatible are present simultaneously.

Mental hygiene: Therapeutic techniques for preventing or relieving mental and emotional disturbances before they become severe and incapacitating.

Microcephaly: A pathological condition characterized by an abnormally small cranium.

Migraine: Periodic attacks of severe headache, usually on only one side.

Mongolism: A form of feeble-mindedness characterized by many body disturbances, particularly by slanting eyes.

Moron: A person whose IQ is between 50 and 70.

Multiple personality: A character abnormality which causes an individual, in reacting to stress or conflict, to assume an entirely different personality and identity. This indicates that there are two or more fairly distinct, autonomous, and mutually exclusive mental integrations within the individual.

Mutism: Lack of speech, either because of reluctance to speak, as during a psychotic reaction, or because of failure of the speech function to develop.

Myxedema: A disease caused by adult hypothyroidism, resulting in increased weight, retardation of mental processes and action, and usually mental deficiency.

Narcissism: Love of self. In an abnormal reaction to stress, as in schizophrenia, this may reach the point of self-aggrandizement. The individual's selfish preoccupation with his pleasure-seeking impulses.

Negativism: Marked resistance; the tendency to do the opposite of what one is requested to do.

Neurasthenia: A psychoneurotic reaction characterized by sensations of fatigue; there are often also constipation and a feeling of pressure on the head.

Neurosis: Any psychological disturbance or symptom, or both. A psychological disturbance arising as a reaction to stress, but with no serious disturbance in the evaluation of reality (in contrast to psychosis); in this sense the term is synonymous with "psychoneurosis."

Neurosyphilis: Syphilis of the nervous system.

Neurotic character: See *Character neurosis.*

Nihilistic delusion: The delusion that the patient himself, any organ of his body, or the world does not exist or is dead.

Obsession: A persistently recurring and distressing thought upon which attention must be focused, even though it is adequately evaluated by the intellect and opposed by the will.

Obsessional neurosis: See *Compulsion or obsessional neurosis.*

Occipital: Pertaining to the back of the head.

Oedipus complex: Sexual attachment to the parent of the opposite sex and hostility toward the other parent.

Organic disease: A condition in which the abnormality of a tissue or organ can be inferred or demonstrated.

Orientation: Knowledge of time, place, and person; one's perspective of himself both as an individual and in relation to others.

Over-compensation: The development of excessively positive character traits and reaction patterns in an attempt to overcome feelings of inadequacy.

Overprotection: An attitude and course of action by which one person tries to guard another from extremely trivial risks, particularly characteristic of some mother-child relationships.

Overt: Objectively observable.

Paranoia: A psychotic reaction characterized by systematized and unshakable delusions.

Paresis: An organic psychotic reaction caused by syphilis of the brain; also called dementia paralytica.

Parkinsonian syndrome: A pathological condition caused by damage to certain groups of cells in the brain tissue, and manifested by muscular rigidity, coarse trembling, stooped posture, and masklike expression.

Pathogenic: Causing disease or disturbance.

Pathological: Abnormal; indicating the presence of disease or structural damage.

Peptic ulcer: A "wound" of the inner lining of the stomach or the duodenum, caused by the action of a gastric juice upon a portion of this lining whose nutrition has been interfered with in some way.

Perseveration: The involuntary tendency to continue a response even if the stimulus has ceased or is altered; continued interest in an unsolved problem.

Personality: The integrated expression of the characteristic needs, goals, reaction patterns, and modes of handling situations.

Phobia: A neurotic reaction characterized by intense fear arising in special situations.

Play technique: A therapeutic method which uses toys and play to encourage and enable the child to express his conscious and unconscious emotional attitudes and conflicts in the presence of the therapist.

Prestige suggestion: Direct suggestion which depends for its effect upon the personality, reputation, and past success of the one who makes it.

Prognosis: Prediction of the probable outcome of an illness.

Projection: Ascribing to other persons modes of behavior which in reality are unconscious wishes or character traits of the individual himself.

Projective methods: Investigation techniques in which, by reacting to an unstructured or loosely structured situation, the subject reveals (projects) his fantasies, needs, attitudes, and conflicts.

Psychasthenia: Literally, psychic or mental exhaustion. A psychoneurotic syndrome characterized by obsessions, compulsions, doubts, scruples (Janet). This classification is not used in this book.

Psyche: The human mind; the sum total of psychological processes.

Psychiatry: The branch of medicine which treats psychological illness and the mental aspects of organic disease.

Psychoanalysis: A psychological method of study and treatment which includes frequent interviews, free association, and dream analysis, and the interpretation to the patient of his reactions to daily events and to the analysis. The data, concepts, and theories resulting from the use of this method.

Psychogenic: Caused by psychological factors.

Psychoneurosis: A disturbance of psychological or physiological functions, or both, which arises as a reaction to external or internal stress, but does not seriously alter the evaluation of sensory or social reality. The term is used in this book synonymously with "neurosis," although some differentiate between them in various ways.

Psychopathology: More serious psychological disturbances; the study of these disturbances.

Psychosis: A disturbance in mental and emotional behavior, usually to an extent incompatible with social adjustment, and often accompanied by delusions and hallucinations. Disturbance of relation with, or perception of, reality.

Psychosomatic: Pertaining to the interrelations between bodily and psychological phenomena.

Psychotherapy: Treatment by psychological methods.

Pyromania: A morbid and usually compulsive tendency to start fires.

Rapport: An attitude of mutual trust, confidence, openness, and dependence between two individuals.

Rationalization: The process of "manufacturing" rational explanations for attitudes or acts to avoid the distress resulting from acknowledging their true motivations.

Reaction formation: The excessive development of the opposite of a repressed attitude which is disapproved of by the individual.

Regression: A method of reacting to difficulties in which adequate response patterns are relinquished in favor of the reaction patterns of childhood.

Rejection: Such attitudes and behavior, partly unconscious, toward another person as lead him to believe that he is not loved and valued as an individual.

Release: The freeing of blocked impulses; this is followed by relief of distress.

Repetition compulsion: The tendency to repeat reaction patterns regardless of whether they are pleasurable or painful.

Repression: The rejection and shutting out of the awareness of a reaction pattern (thought, feeling, impulse, memory) in order to avoid distress.

Resistance: Largely unconscious reluctance on the part of the patient to relinquish his existing mode of coping with situations.

Sadism: A sexual perversion characterized by the need to inflict physical pain in order to attain the maximal erotic gratification; a conscious or unconscious tendency to derive pleasure from hurting others.

Schizoid character: A personality type characterized by seclusiveness, lack of adequate emotional attachment, diminished initiative, and preoccupation with fantasies.

Schizophrenia: A psychotic reaction characterized by absence of emotional attachment and of the experience and expression of normal emotions, by extreme preoccupation, by unreal ideas, and by bizarre delusions, hallucinations, and behavior.

Security: The evaluation of the environment as essentially helpful and friendly, leading to a feeling of safety and acceptance.

Security system: The sum total of the attitudes and reaction patterns by which the individual maintains his safety and self-evaluation of worth and allays his expectation of potentially catastrophic distress.

Self-aggandizement: A conscious or unconscious need or desire to over-estimate oneself. The reaction patterns which result from this.

Self-esteem: The self-evaluation of an individual; his estimate of worth, adequacy, strength, or power. Many near-synonyms are used by various writers—dominance-feeling, ascendance-submission, feeling of superiority or inferiority, self-regard, ego-strength, self-evaluation.

Self-evaluation: Evaluation of the self as regards strength, comparative performance or moral status.

Somatic: Pertaining to the body.

Somatopsychic: Pertaining to both the body and the mind.

Somnambulism: A trancelike state in a period of sleep during which the individual carries out a complex activity which he does not remember later.

Stereotypy: Continued repetition of apparently senseless syllables, words, or movements.

Stomach ulcer: See *Peptic ulcer.*

Sublimation: The process of consciously gratifying unconscious sexual or aggressive impulses, in work, play, or art.

Submissive attitudes: Conscious or unconscious tendencies to obey or submit to another person which are motivated by fear of the other person and by desire for his protection.

Suggestibility: A permanent or temporary trait which makes a person receptive to the ideas, requests, and demands of others.

Suggestion: A request or command, overt or implied, with which the individual complies without logical reasoning (e.g., in hypnosis). A psychotherapeutic technique by which symptoms are cured by direct or implied authoritative assurance that they will disappear.

Symbol: The representation of an intended act, thought, or emotion by means of a substitute act or thought which has some parallel features. Also, anything which represents something else, as the word representing the object.

Syndrome, or *symptom complex:* A group of symptoms often found together and characteristic of a particular disorder or disease; by extension, any group of characteristics which can be integrated into a whole.

Tic: A periodic involuntary contraction of any muscle group, the resulting motion resembling an organized action, such as turning the head or licking the lips.

Trance: A sleeplike state in which the range of consciousness is narrowed and voluntary movements are suspended.

Transference: The sum total of the patient's attitudes toward the psychoanalyst which develop during the treatment, spring from the patient's fears, vital needs, and memory patterns, and are essentially nonlogical in nature. The patient "transfers" those attitudes onto the therapist.

Traumatic: Pertaining to or resulting from injury; pertaining to any event which creates a significant psychological disturbance.

Traumatic neurosis: A psychoneurotic reaction to physical injury or threat of death. "Shell shock" is the best-known form.

Traumatic psychosis: A psychotic reaction resulting from brain injury.

Unconscious (referring to psychological processes): Inaccessible to consciousness by effort of voluntary attention.

Urticaria: Hives; itching red weals or eruptions over the entire body. They may disappear in a few hours, and new ones may appear.

Ventriculography: A diagnostic procedure involving the injection of air into the ventricles of the brain after the withdrawal of fluid. Following this, X-ray photographs are taken. The procedure is used chiefly for the diagnosis of brain tumors.

Verbigeration: A senseless or prolonged repetition of words or phrases.

Vicious circle: A series of psychological reactions which have the unconscious purpose of relieving stress, but which, because of their nature, lead to a renewal of the stress.

Waxy flexibility: A peculiar pliable rigidity of the muscle. Any part of the patient's body can be put into various positions which can be retained for a long time without any apparent fatigue.

Appendix I — Test Procedures: Projective Methods of Examination

The most important methods of examining the individual and arriving at a diagnosis are the interview and observation, supplemented by information obtained from the patient's relatives and friends and from laboratory tests. One of the methods frequently used can be called the questionnaire method. In questionnaires, the subject or patient is presented with a set of standardized questions which he is asked to answer. Frequently these methods present questions to which the answer is "Yes" or "No." They are also frequently self-administering and hence are called paper-and-pencil tests. One such questionnaire, the Cornell Index, will be described below. (See also 392 and 393.)

In the so-called projective methods of studying personality, the subject is confronted with a loosely structured test situation and asked to organize it. The term "loosely structured" implies that the nature of the objects or their interrelation in the situation is not strictly defined; on the contrary, the subject is free to handle and interpret them in any way he wishes. This process and its results are called "organization."

Furthermore, test situations have to be looked upon as situations of mild stress to which the individual reacts not only verbally but also with autonomic responses. Normal subjects without color shock on the Rorschach experiment (see p. 586) react with a lowering of palmar skin resistance (PGR) when the ink blots are presented and while giving their responses. However, a group of subjects with color shock, indicating difficulty in handling strong affects, showed greater psychogalvanic responses than a normal group under the same circumstances (778).

It is instructive to contrast projective methods with the method followed in intelligence tests. In the latter, the subject is confronted with a test situation which he is expected to handle in only one way, the "correct" way. The test situation is potentially structured. As Frank phrases it: "The standardized tests offer procedures for rating the individuals in terms of their socialization and how nearly they approximate to the acceptance and the use of culturally described patterns of belief, action, and speech." In projective methods of examination, we "induce the individual to reveal his way of organizing experience by giving him a field (objects, materials, experiences) with relatively little structure and cultural patterning so that the personality can project upon the plastic field his way of seeing life, his meanings, significances, patterns, and especially his feelings. Thus we elicit a projection of the individual personality's *private world*."[1] Hence these methods are often called "projective" methods.

The use of the term "projective method of testing" has been considerably expanded in recent years. It includes also a use of strictly structured tests—e.g., of intelligence tests—in which the examiner applies slants or points of view that the subject is not aware of and which aim at elucidating his emotional life.

THE CORNELL INDEX

The Cornell Index is a questionnaire consisting, in its shorter form (N3) of 62, and in its longer form (N2) of 101, items. Some items are devoted to crucial symptomatology—for example, "Did you ever have a nervous breakdown?" and "Do you suffer badly from frequent loose bowel movements?" These are called "stop questions" because anyone answering them in the positive should be "stopped" for neuropsychiatric appraisal. The remainder of the questions have less serious implications, such as "Do you often have difficulty in falling asleep or staying asleep?" In this group a certain number of answers suggestive of difficulties in adjustment is the indication for psychiatric disturbance. The questions are answered by drawing a circle around either the "Yes" or the "No" after each.

The test can be used for three different purposes: (1) For singling out from a group individuals who should, on the basis of the test results, be examined for psychiatric or psychosomatic disturbances. For this purpose, the test is used as a quantitative instrument. The criteria for earmarking the individual are a certain number of positive items. (2) As a preparation for the interview. The discussion with the patient starts with some of the positive items appearing on the test. (3) To make sure that certain aspects of personality disturbance have been checked.

THE RORSCHACH TEST

The Procedure. The "unstructured" material in this test consists of a series of ten cards. On each one of these cards there appears a form which does not represent any definite object. These forms are commonly referred to as *ink blots.* Some are gray-black; others contain colors in addition. They were originally obtained by Rorschach by dropping ink on a sheet of paper, which was then folded in the middle and pressed together, thus giving the ink drop an accidental symmetrical shape. The same ink blots are used in all the tests and are shown in the same sequence. Of the many originally used, the final ones were selected by Rorschach in many tests as the ones that best bring out variable responses. As the ink blots are shown, the subject is asked: "What might this be?" At the end of the test the examiner goes over his responses with him, attempting by apparently naïve questions to discover what qualities in the blots (colors, form, shading) he used in arriving at his concept.

Scoring. The test is scored on the basis of the evaluation of each response and

[1] L. K. Frank, Projective methods for the study of personality, *J. Psychol.,* 1939, **8,** 394-403.

then on the relative percentage of various types of response in the total number of responses.

For instance, one subject describes Card 2 as two clowns with red hats playing pat-a-cake. Another subject sees an Indian arrowhead where the first one saw the hands of the clowns. How are such responses evaluated? What is the significance of the relative frequency of one type of response and of another? This has been arrived at *empirically*. It has been found, for example, that active, outgoing individuals have a different percentage of certain types of response than rigidly repressed ones. Schizophrenics give different responses from manic-depressives. Therefore we might say roughly that the various types of response represent various tendencies in the subject.

1. The first aspect of the response to be considered is what "space" in the ink blot the subject chooses for interpretation; in other words, whether the response relates to the ink blot as a whole (W), to a frequently considered and obvious detail (D), or to a small and rarely seen detail (Dd). In the above examples, the first (two clowns) is a whole response; the second (arrowhead), an obvious detail.

W represents the generalizing tendencies, D represents the sense for the obvious, and Dd represents the interest partly in the minute and partly in the extravagant and queer.

2. Another aspect is the content—animals, human figures, objects, landscapes, plants, anatomical content, formless geological and geographical content, blood, cloud, etc. In the above examples the first response is a human, the second an object, response. Roughly, the more variegated the content, the wider are the subject's interests and education. The human responses indicate an interest in fellow humans; if, however, there are more parts than complete human figures in the test record, this usually indicates that the subject is an anxious person whose interest in human beings is rather an anxious preoccupation. Anatomical answers may be indicative of bodily preoccupation.

3. The third aspect is the way the subject integrates the chosen space and chosen content. This integration can be achieved in the following ways:

(a) The form of the chosen space determines the integration and thus the content of the interpretation (F). Such a form response may be "good" (+) or "bad" (—). It is good if the content seen by the subject is in harmony with the form on the card; thus the arrowhead response above is a (good) form response. It has been found that the higher the percentage of form responses the greater the subject's control over his emotions; that if the form percentage is too high, the presence of repression is indicated. The percentage of good responses in all the form responses (F+%) has been found to represent the subject's intelligence level; there is a fair interrelation between this measure and the IQ. The intelligence level, however, is not determined solely on the basis of this percentage, for the number and quality of whole responses, of movement responses, of original responses (see below), the variety of content, etc., are all significant.

(b) A response is termed a movement response when in addition to the form a kinesthetic impression contributes to the integration, as, for example, two clowns *playing* pat-a-cake. The significance of movement responses can be roughly described as indicating reactiveness to inner stimuli, and hence rich inner emotional life, spontaneity, creativity, natural endowment. The movements may be human, as in the example just cited. Such responses indicate mature inner feelings. Movements of animals may indicate more elementary instinctual drives; movements of inanimate objects, unassimilated chaotic drives.

(c) The responses in which bright colors appear as the integrative agent are called color responses (C). Sometimes they appear with and in harmony with forms; sometimes they have the leading role and suggest the forms to the subject; and sometimes they appear independently, producing formless responses and becoming the sole determiners of the content attributed to the chosen space. These color responses represent the emotionality (affectivity) of the subject, particularly in response to external stimuli. In the first illustration the color red ("red hats") played a role, in good harmony with the form, in determining the subject's response. Where the colors only accompany the form (as in this example), they are indicative of an adaptive affectivity; where they determine the form ("flowers," "flames," etc.), they are usually indicative of unstable affectivity, of an uneven emotional discharge; where they appear independently (blood, lawn, sea), they are indicative of uncontrolled, impulsive, violent affectivity, of paroxysmal emotional discharges.

(d) When shadings of gray and black ("chiaroscuro") are the integrative agent, anxiety is indicated. Here again these light and dark effects appear—as did colors—in varied relations to forms, indicating more or less controlled or uncontrolled anxieties. In the best possible harmony with forms they are indicative of anxious, cautious, unfree adaptation.

(e) Other characteristics of the responses can be determined and evaluated. Thus responses which are frequently given by various subjects (P, popular) or responses which are rare and therefore original can be indicative of the subject's common sense or his originality respectively.

Interpretation. After all the responses have been obtained, each one is evaluated. Thus the response "two clowns with red hats playing pat-a-cake" is tabulated W M FC H meaning that the whole blot is used by the subject (W), that the figure is in motion (M), that color is used in conjunction with form for the hats (FC), and that the content is human (H). The second response (Indian arrowhead) is tabulated D F obj.—that is, a detail (D), determined only by the form of the blot (F), in content an object (obj.). After each response is thus tabulated, the whole responses, movement responses, form responses, etc., are added up, and their percentages of the total determined and compared with previously established norms. It should be emphasized again that no single response nor even the *absolute* sum of any one type of response determines the interpretation; it is their relationships to each other in the total number of responses.

Two persons give five movement responses. One has ten responses using color and very little pure F; the other has much F and almost no color. The first subject is probably an active, spontaneous, social individual (unless other evidence in the test contradicts this impression), whereas the second is likely to be a repressed introvert. An accurate view of the personality structure depends upon insight into the *interplay* of different forces, not upon an enumeration of traits. The skilled Rorschach expert not only must know all the subtle implications of the test (of which only the most obvious have been mentioned), but must be an experienced clinician as well. The test is useless in the hands of an untrained examiner, but yields surprisingly detailed and accurate information about the personality structure when administered by an experienced tester. However, the test still awaits validation by the techniques most in favor with experimental psychologists.

THE THEMATIC APPERCEPTION TEST

Procedure. The test material consists of three series of ten photographs each, each of which represents an independent scene. The pictures are presented to the subject with the following instructions: "This is a test of your creative imagination. I shall show you a picture and I want you to make up a plot or story for which it might be used as an illustration. What is the relation of the individuals in the picture? What has happened to them? What are their present thoughts and feelings? What will be the outcome?"[2]

The pictures in the standardized Thematic Apperception Test were developed for adults. They give valuable information on children and adolescents also. There have been some special cards developed for the purpose of testing children (58), using animals in the pictures.

The following is an example of a response in an adult subject:

> A student who was working for a Ph.D. in science had, as a child and adolescent, gone through poverty and pogroms, with his mother in Russia. "Recollections of those persecutions," he stated, "still prey on my mind: dead bodies with torn limbs dragged in heaps to the cemetery; my uncle forced to dig his own grave before my eyes; my aunt shot in cold blood at my hand; bombs thrown a few feet before me."[3] His father had immigrated to America when the subject was six months old. There were frequent quarrels with the father after they came to America, in which he always took his mother's part. Recently his mother has been sick. He has been depressed lately.
>
> Picture No. 13 shows, on the floor against the couch, the huddled form of a boy with his head bowed on his right arm. Beside him on the floor is an object which resembles a revolver. The subject interpreted this as follows:
>
> " 'Some great trouble has occurred. Someone he loved has shot herself. Probably it is his mother. She may have done it out of poverty. He, being fairly grown up, sees the misery of it all and would like to shoot himself. But he is young and braces up after a while. For some time he lives in misery—the first few months thinking of death.'
>
> "Here, the possible death of the mother appears as one determinant of his present pessimism. The story is one variety of a large class of complex themas—the Tragic Love Thema."[4]

Scoring. The hypothesis underlying Murray's scoring system is that the subject in making up his story projects into the strivings of the main figure (figure of identification) his own strivings, which Murray designates as "needs"; the other figures, objects, and facts are also results of projection and represent the forces

[2] H. A. Murray, *Explorations in Personality,* Oxford University Press, New York, 1938, p. 532.

[3] *Ibid.,* p. 535.

[4] *Ibid.,* p. 536.

confronting the subject. Murray calls the latter "press" (e.g., "mother" in the above quotation).

Interpretation. The predominance of needs and presses as obtained by scoring is considered to represent the predominant trends of the subject and of the presses he feels himself exposed to. The interpretation can be restricted to describing these tendencies and their relative order of dominance, or psychological knowledge can be used to draw out further conclusions from the coexistence of such factors, thus leading to personality description and even to formal psychiatric diagnosis.

GRAPHOLOGY (HANDWRITING ANALYSIS)

The subject is requested to write, in his accustomed way, anything he desires, preferably using pen and ink. He should write enough to cover about three-fourths of a sheet of paper 8½ by 11 inches. Past writing samples—e.g., letters—are a very useful addition.

Concepts Underlying the Analysis. Handwriting is considered the result of "expressive movements" which are integrally related to the patient's total personality. Changes in environment, in emotional patterns, and in personality structure result in changes in motor activity. These result in alterations of concentration and release of muscular tension and in the quality of the handwriting. Variations in writing are indicative of variability of personality structure.

Method of Analysis. The writing sample is inspected as a whole to determine the "form level." This is determined, in the main, on the basis of the aesthetic balance and originality of the form of the sample. This requires a considerable degree of experience and judgment on the part of the examiner. After the form level has been determined, the sample is analyzed for various characteristics. By and large, a positive or negative value is assigned to each characteristic, depending on the form level, the nature of the interrelationship of the respective characteristics, and their meaningfulness in constructing a total personality picture; for example, speed of writing may be interpreted as "agility" in one case and as "haste" in another. If the form level is good, the tendency is to interpret speed as agility; if the form level is bad, one is inclined to interpret it as haste. The following are some of the main characteristics of handwriting and their corresponding psychological significance.

Regularity, in a favorable sense, may mean good integrative control; in a poor sense it may mean excessive control. Irregularity, in a good sense, may mean adequate integration and allowance for emotional reactions; in a poor sense, the tendency to be ruled by irrational emotion.

Size of the letters relates to the nature of the self-image. Large size may mean pride, independence, and generosity or conceit, arrogance, and self-aggrandizement.

Pressure of line relates to energy output. High pressure may imply a great deal of energy or obstinacy; low pressure, adaptability or lack of energy.

Relationship of upper, middle, and lower zones is indicative of the relationship of conscience, integration and adaptation, and impulse. (The middle zone is the area covered in writing letters of average size, such as *a*; the upper zone includes extensions above, as in *h*; the lower zone, extensions below, as in *y*.

Slant indicates the relation of the self to the social environment. Rightward slant may mean dominance of social feelings or lack of control and restraint; perpendicular writing may mean dominance of intellect or lack of empathy; leftward slant may mean introspectiveness or self-consciousness.

By way of illustration, the handwriting of an obsessive-compulsive person may have the following characteristics: regularity, smallness, high pressure, total leftwardness.

FIGURE-DRAWING ANALYSIS

Personality analysis based on the drawing of the human figure (Machover [598]) grew out of the Goodenough Drawing of a Man, given for the measurement of mental maturity and intelligence. The subject is asked to draw the figure of a person. When he has finished his drawing, he is asked to draw the figure of a woman if he has drawn a man or that of a man if he has drawn a woman. He is then asked to describe what sort of persons the people he has drawn might be.

The drawing of a person is roughly equivalent to the placing of oneself in the environment. A paper of conventional size, 8½ by 11 inches, constitutes the "environment." As a result of experiences with his own body and the bodies of other individuals, as well as of his reactions to them, each individual evolves a "body image" (830). Based on this image, he constructs in this test figures whose graphic attributes have been largely determined, consciously and unconsciously, by his own needs, values, frustrations, and aspirations.

The analysis of the psychological implications of the figures drawn is done from the viewpoints of both content and structure. All parts of the body, as well as the facial expression, the postural one of the figure, and details of clothing, constitute the content for analysis. Size of the figure, placement on the page, pressure of line, stance, background, exactness, degree of completion and detailing, symmetry, midline emphasis, perspective, proportions, shading, reinforcements, and erasures of line are some of the structural features considered.

Each part of the body has some special significance for interpretation. Some examples are discussed here. The treatment of the head and facial features may be expressive of social needs and responsiveness, intellectual aspirations, rational control or fantasy life. The hair refers more to the sensual needs and, perhaps in a more direct way, the sexual vitality of the individual. The chest, shoulders, and muscular development in the male figure may be stressed as an expression of physical brawn. In the female figure, these areas are more related to oral dependency problems, close identification with the mother, and the general reaction to the development of the breasts. In the hands, organs involved in prehension, manipulation of and contact with objects, people, and oneself, we find indications of the subject's aspiration level, efficiency, aggressivity, feelings of confidence concerning contacts, and guilt or conflict centering in interpersonal and sexual relations.

Bilateral symmetry, when stressed to the extent of producing rigid effects, signifies an obsessive-compulsive system of control, usually associated with repression, over-intellectualization, and emotional distance. Midline emphasis, with either a row of buttons or just a central axis, may indicate the feeling of inadequacy or body preoccupation, at times to the point of hypochondriasis. Undue emphasis on joints offers evidence of pathological somatic concentration, while surface display of internal organs is generally correlated with somatic delusions. The body showing through clothing may be an extreme expression of body consciousness, often with voyeuristic and exhibitionistic trends. Transparencies, in general, are indicative of childish concrete thinking, resulting, behaviorally, in poor judgment. When one occurs in a particular area, it may be an indication of conflict about the function of that area. Conflicts may also be expressed through erasures, reinforcement of lines, and shading. The size of the figures may give clues to the degree of real self-esteem and the general expansiveness of the individual. Comparison of the male and female figures of a set of drawings indicates attitudes toward the opposite sex, toward parental figures and authority. Whether the self or the opposite sex is drawn first is also related to the problem of identification and role acceptance.

WORD-ASSOCIATION TESTS

Procedure. A standard list of words is read to the subject one word at a time, and he is asked to respond with the first word that comes to his mind upon hearing the stimulus word. The procedure has a long history (see 472, 492, and 791). Several standard word lists are in use which have been built up on the basis of various principles. They vary as to length. One that is considered most useful at present consists of sixty words (757). (The current discussion is based on this list.)

These lists consist of words and phrases which relate to emotional aspects of a person's life, such as "love," "suicide," "girl friend," "bowel movement." Interspersed with these "traumatic" terms, relatively innocuous words, such as "chair" and "hat," are usually included. After the list is gone through, it is read through a second time, and this time the subject is asked to respond to each word with the same word that he gave the first time. The examiner records the reaction time to each response on both the first reading and the recall, along with the responses. Then follows an inquiry during which the patient is questioned as to any unusual responses which may have occurred and as to responses on which there was a delayed reaction time. The inquiry is directed toward ascertaining whether any ideas occurred to the patient before he gave his response and to revealing the connections between the stimulus word and the response.

Interpretation. The examiner notes those stimulus words to which deviant responses are given, the nature and the content of the deviations, those words on which delay took place, and those where there was incorrect recall. Rapaport (757) has classified *associative disturbances* into two main types: (1) *close reactions,* including such responses as definitions, naming an attribute of the stimulus word ("house"—"white"), clang associations, etc.; and (2) *distant reactions,* where little or no connection is evident between the stimulus word and the response, or where only an arbitrary or idiosyncratic connection exists: for example, "dance"—"eat (people sometimes eat at dances)," "house"—"empty."

The interpretation is based upon the type of association disturbance that occurs, the number of deviant responses, and the content of the stimulus words that lead to disturbance. In general, it is found that the greater the number of disturbed reactions which are present, the more serious the illness, although this is not always so, for even a person who is quite severely ill may retain certain functions relatively intact. The type of associative disorder which is found on the test gives the examiner a clue to the patient's thought processes. Thus the occurrence of many distant responses, where the relationship to the stimulus words can be seen only upon inquiry that reveals rather arbitrary and highly personal links between them, the examiner may conclude that a severe associative disturbance exists and that the patient's thinking is dominated by autistic ideas with little reference to objective reality. This type of thought disorder is characteristic of schizophrenic thinking (see discussion of schizophrenic thinking in Chapter XXXIV). On the other hand, the occurrence of many close responses together with many delayed reaction times would suggest a slowing down of thought processes, together with rigidity in thinking, where the subject is unable to get away from the immediate connotation of the original idea. This type of thinking would suggest a depressive picture. When disturbance is shown in reaction to several words relating to the same emotional sphere, it can be concluded that the patient experiences difficulties in situations which evoke ideas relative to this area. For example, if the subject gives deviant or delayed associations to the words "fight," "cut," and "gun," it is well to assume that he has difficulty in handling his aggressive impulses and in dealing with situations which arouse aggressive and hostile feelings in him. Similarly, if deviant responses are given to such terms as "girl friend" and "intercourse," it is likely that serious sexual conflict is present. In addition to the types of interpretations already mentioned, it is possible in some cases to carry the test interpretation further. When patients give a good deal of material in response to inquiry, it may be possible to make some statements as to their fantasy life and attitudes. At other times, however, although it is possible to name those areas in which disturbance exists—and from that an experienced clinician can glean a great deal—little can be said about the nature of these disturbances or how the patient handles the difficulties.

THE SZONDI TEST[5]

Procedure. The test consists of forty-eight photographs, representing various types of mental patients, grouped into six sets, each set consisting of eight photographs: a homosexual, a sadist, an epileptic, a hysteric, a catatonic schizophrenic, a paranoid schizophrenic, a manic-depressive depressive, and a manic-depressive manic.

The subject is presented one set of pictures and asked to pick out the two he likes and the two he dislikes the most. This procedure is repeated with the five other sets consecutively, finally resulting in a choice of twelve liked and twelve disliked pictures. These choices are recorded graphically on a scoring sheet. The test must be administered six or more times, with at least one day of interval between successive administrations, in order to be able to give a valid clinical interpretation of the personality.

Interpretation. There is no satisfactory theory for the effective working of the test, and some of the ideas advanced at times are rather esoteric. The forty-eight photographs, which represent extreme manifestations in facial expression of eight

[5] The following discussion is based on S. K. Deri's description of the Szondi Test in O. K. Buros, *The Third Mental Measurements Yearbook,* Rutgers Univ. Press, New Brunswick, N.J., 1949.

mental disorders, evoke responses in the subject's likes and dislikes, for they represent tendencies present to a greater or lesser extent in all of us. Depending on the state of tension in each of the eight "basic" psychological needs, the pictures representing the corresponding needs will be chosen in various proportions. To make it more concrete: more pictures of sadists will be chosen by a person whose aggression is pent up than by somebody who is able to find ways to discharge his aggression.

Whether a particular type of picture is chosen as liked or disliked depends upon the person's conscious or unconscious attitude toward the particular need in question. To continue our example: the person whose aggression is dammed up and ready to be discharged as open aggression will choose a great number of pictures of sadists as *liked,* while somebody whose aggression is dammed up but strongly repressed will choose the same number of pictures of sadists as *disliked.* The psychological meaning of the choices in the remaining seven categories has to be interpreted according to the same dynamic principle but varying in the specific content of the needs represented by the various categories.

As in all projective techniques, configurational patterns of the global profile have greater diagnostic value than the single factors.

THE SORTING TEST

Procedure. The Sorting Test (360) consists of thirty-three objects that are common in everyday experience. Included are a knife, a fork, a spoon, a toy knife, a toy fork, a toy spoon, a cigarette, a cigar, a matchbook, etc. In the first part of the test the examiner presents one of these items—for example, the fork—to the subject and asks him to put with this everything that belongs with it. When the subject has done so, the examiner asks, "Why do they all belong together?" In the second part the examiner sorts a group of items (one such group consists of a pipe, a cigar, a cigarette, an imitation cigar, an imitation cigarette, and a matchbook) and then asks the subject to state why they all belong together.

Scoring. In Part I the subject's sortings are scored according to adequacy and to concept span (how much the subject's concept includes). If the sorting is relevant to the sample object and segregates a group of objects from the rest of the test materials in a well-defined manner, it is considered an adequate sorting and given a "plus" (+) score. When sortings are irrelevant to the sample objects, they are considered inadequate and given a "minus" (—) score. When the subject includes objects in his sorting which are unrelated to the sample object, his sortings are considered "loose" and scored L. If, however, he omits objects which are related to the sample object, the sorting is considered "narrow" and scored N. In both Part I and Part II the subject's definitions of the sortings are scored as to adequacy of verbalization and as to the conceptual level. A verbalization is considered adequate if it covers correctly the group sorted, and it is given a plus score; it is considered inadequate if it does not (for example, if the subject defines the silverware as being "metal," the definition is considered inadequate as there are several other metal objects and this definition misses the essential relationship among the objects in the given sorting) and is given a minus score. The conceptual level of the definition can perhaps best be discussed by means of an example. If the subject defines a sorting containing the knife, fork, and spoon and the toy knife, fork, and spoon as "silverware," his definition is on an abstract-conceptual level and would be scored *CD* (conceptual definition); if he says, "They are all used for eating," he defines them in terms of function, and his response is given the score *FD* (functional definition); if his response is that "they are all found on a table," it is a concrete definition, as it describes the objects in terms of their concrete relationship to other objects, and it is given the score *C*; the subject's definition may be so broad and generalized that it could include many objects not contained in the sorting, as in the response "They are all manufactured articles," which is considered a syncretistic definition and scored *Syn*; if he makes up a story in which the objects in the sorting play a part (perhaps about a mother and child who sit down to eat together), this is a fabulated definition *(Fab)*; his definition would be a symbolic one (scored *Symb*) if he were to say that "the large silverware represents an adult and the small silverware represents a child." Still one other type of definition occurs. This is where the subject sees no overall relationship among the objects, but relates one object to a second one, this second object to a third, etc. This is a chain definition *(Ch)*. (See 757.)

Projective Interpretation. The Sorting Test is aimed primarily at eliciting one aspect of the subject's thought processes—namely, ability to make abstractions. However, as with almost any other psychological test (aside from paper-and-pencil tests), the experienced clinician can learn much about the subject's adaptive techniques through careful observation and recording of his test behavior. The person who is careful to make sure he has included all the related objects in his sorting or who debates whether a particular object strictly belongs with the others in the sorting can be expected to handle life situations quite differently from the person who impulsively picks out the first few objects he sees that he considers related and then considers his sorting complete. As an individual's thought processes are an expression of his total personality, the more formal aspects of the test interpretation (based directly on scoring) are also useful. The test is most useful as a psychiatric diagnostic instrument in those disorders where disturbances of thought processes are likely to be most prominent, such as the psychoses. A schizophrenic, whose reality-testing is seriously impaired and for whom reality boundaries are apt to break down (see the discussion in Chapter XXXIV), can be expected to give many loose and syncretistic sortings. An extreme example of this sort of thinking is seen in the schizophrenic patient who sorted all the test objects together and explained, "They all relate to my own needs."

THE WECHSLER-BELLEVUE INTELLIGENCE SCALE

Procedure. The Wechsler-Bellevue test of adult intelligence consists of eleven subtests divided into verbal and performance scales. The verbal subtests include an Information Test, containing questions concerning general information; a Comprehension Test, designed to test the subject's judgment (with such items as "What should you do if while sitting in the movies you were the first person to discover a fire?"); an Arithmetic Test, with arithmetical problems requiring the subject to select the necessary arithmetical procedures and to carry them out orally; a Digit Span Test, in which the subject is asked to repeat a series of numbers after the examiner has read them off; a Similarities Test, where the subject is asked to state how two named things—e.g., an orange and a banana—are alike; and a Vocabulary Test. The performance tests consist of a Picture Arrangement Test, in which the subject is asked to arrange a series of pictures in such a way that they tell a story; an Object Assembly Test, consisting of jigsaw puzzles, which when put together make up specific objects—e.g., a face; a Picture Completion Test, in which the subject is shown a series of pictures and asked to state what is missing in each one; a Block Design Test, where the subject is asked to reproduce designs with colored blocks; and a Digit Symbol Test, where each number is assigned a symbol and the subject is asked to write the symbol below each number with a key in front of him.

Scoring. The *raw score* for each subtest is obtained by adding up the credits for each item. This raw score is then translated into an *equated score.* The equated scores are so arranged that the mean score (of the standardization population) for each subtest is equal to the mean score of every other subtest and that the range of scores for each of the subtests is the same. Thus the subject's achievement on any subtest can be compared with his achievement on the others. These equated scores are totaled to obtain the subject's *total score,* from which his IQ is obtained. In addition to this *Total IQ,* a *Performance IQ* and a *Verbal IQ* can be obtained.

Projective Interpretation. Although this test is used primarily for ascertaining intelligence level, many clinicians use it also as a projective test of personality. This latter use is based upon the idea that anything an individual does in some way reflects his total personality and that a person's intellectual functioning and thinking processes are intimately bound up with his personality make-up. Frequently, much can be discerned about the subject's personality make-up by comparing his various equated subtest scores with each other. For example, if intellectual activity plays a large role in a person's life, he will tend to do better on the verbal subtests than on the performance subtests. On the other hand, if a person expresses himself more readily through externalized activity than through intellectual activity, he will tend to do better on the performance subtests. In a similar manner, variations in scores on the individual subtests have been found to have significance (957, 757). An example of this can be seen in the case of a schizophrenic patient who obtains a high Information score, reflecting his intellectualizing trends and his ability to acquire and retain facts, and who at the same time obtains a markedly lower score on the Comprehension subtest, reflecting his impaired judgment. Each subtest has been found to tap certain functions primarily, and to be predominantly sensitive to certain disturbed personality factors—e.g., anxiety, tension, depressed mood. Thus the Information Test is, to a large extent, a test of memory; the Similarities Test is primarily a test of abstract thinking; those tests involving motor coördination easily reflect the impairing effects of tension; and those where speed is a factor reflect psychomotor retardation as seen in depressed states (see Rapaport). Qualitative observations of the subject's test performance (757, 825) also reveal whether he usually considers all aspects of a problem before deciding on a solution or tends impulsively to jump to conclusions, to give responses without adequate forethought. Some people may go so far in their pondering about all the possibilities involved in a particular item and are so unwilling to reject any of them as unimportant that they are unable to reach any solution or, at best, are only able to respond by giving several alternatives. Careful attention is also given to the quality of the patient's verbalization, whether it is frequently careless and inexact or careful, whether it is simple or complicated to the point of pedantry, whether it is in any way peculiar, reflecting disorganized thinking. An example of this last type of verbalization is the neologistic response of a schizophrenic patient to the Comprehension item "Why does land in the city cost more than land in the country?" His answer was, "Because of the communicable fixilities." From this sort of test analysis both psychiatric diagnoses and personality descriptions can be formulated.

EVALUATION OF PROJECTIVE METHODS

The significance and usefulness of projective methods can be summarized as follows:

"1. Apparently random reactions of the human individual are strictly determined by his personality make-up. The Rorschach Test, for example, illustrates how even an apparently indifferent type of activity, such as a seemingly unemotional perception, is deeply influenced by the individual's emotional life.

"2. Projective methods can be of great diagnostic significance. The random reactions are elicited and recorded in well-controlled experimental situations and can therefore be classified and compared with such personality trends of the individual as can be established by talking with and observing him. The projective methods are the more useful for diagnostic purposes, the less familiar the stimulus is, the more it calls for a free organizing activity (reaction) of the subject, and the more it elicits responses which have classifiable characteristics that allow for immediate comparison with records obtained from other individuals."[6]

In this sense the best-standardized test is the Rorschach Test. Its possible accuracy can be spectacularly demonstrated if it is given "blindly"—that is, if someone administers the test and someone else interprets it. The latter can often give a very accurate diagnosis and a surprisingly good description of the subject's personality traits. The test can also be used as a sort of gauge of how far the treatment of a patient has progressed.

SUGGESTED READINGS

Buros' *The Third Mental Measurements Yearbook* gives a very thorough survey of personality inventory tests (questionnaires) as well as projective methods. A comprehensive account of various tests is given in Rosenzweig and Kogan's *Psychodiagnosis* (803). The books of Rapaport, Gill, and Schafer (757) and Schafer (825) are indispensable for the advanced student. Murray's *Explorations in Personality* is a classical experimental and clinical work. Standard books on the individual tests are Wechsler (957), Sonnemann (879), Deri (188), Rorschach (789), Machover (598), Goldstein and Scheerer (360), and Klopfer and Kelley, *The Rorschach Technique.*

[6] D. Rapaport, Principles underlying projective techniques, *Character and Personality,* 1942, 3, 213-219.

Appendix II The Magnitude of the Problem of Mental Disease: Statistical Data

The magnitude of the problem of mental disease is best indicated by statistics on the size of the populations of state psychopathic hospitals. (See also Landis and Page, *Modern Society and Mental Disease* [523].) "It should be clearly recognized, however, that statistics of mental patients in hospitals do not directly measure the prevalence of mental disease either in the country as a whole or in the various states. Many persons having nervous and mental diseases never receive hospital treatment. The hospital cases probably cover most of the severe cases of mental disease, but fail to cover many cases of milder type."[1] Actually, the loss in health

TABLE 15. Patients in State, Veterans', County, City, and Private Hospitals for Mental Disease in the U.S.A. at the Beginning of the Year, 1937 to 1947[2]

Year	Total Number on Books	In Hospital	In Family Care[a]	In Other Extramural Care
1947	610,252	533,003	2,051	75,198
1946	592,268	518,672	2,165	71,431
1945	581,096	510,661	2,309	68,126
1944	572,251	501,751	2,213	68,287
1943	567,423	498,828	2,038	66,557
1942	556,476	490,448	2,137	63,891
1941	542,477	480,741	1,175	60,561
1940	527,399	468,924	974	57,501
1939	514,712	459,258	1,316	54,138
1938	499,919	444,989	1,366	53,564
1937	484,237	431,990	603	51,644

[a] State hospitals only.

[1] *Patients in Hospitals for Mental Disease, 1937,* U.S. Department of Commerce, Washington, 1939.

[2] Based on tables in *Patients in Mental Institutions, 1946,* U.S. Department of Commerce, Washington, 1948; *Patients in Mental Institutions, 1947,* and *Administrative Statistics for Public Mental Hospitals, 1947, Mental Health Statistics: Current Reports,* Federal Security Agency, Washington, September, 1949. The publications are obtainable on request from the Bureau of the Census, Washington, D.C.

and social economy is greater than is indicated by the figures. Furthermore, it should be recognized that only very severe cases of psychoneurotic reactions reach psychopathic hospitals; most of them are treated outside of institutions. Table 15 indicates the total mental-hospital population in various years. Table 16 indicates the number of first admissions in 1946 to various mental hospitals.

TABLE 16. First Admissions to State, Veterans', County, City, and Private Hospitals for Mental Disease, by Mental Disorder, for the U.S.A.: 1946[3]

Mental Disorder	Number
Total	145,203
With psychosis	120,761
General paresis	*6,021*
With other forms of syphilis of the CNS	837
With epidemic encephalitis	197
With other infectious disease	335
Alcoholic	*5,713*
Due to drugs and other exogenous poisons	622
Traumatic	633
With cerebral arteriosclerosis	*15,665*
With other disturbances of the circulation	905
With convulsive disorders	1,617
Senile	*13,543*
Involutional psychosis	6,888
Due to other metabolic, etc., diseases	887
Due to new growth	223
With organic changes of the nervous system	1,226
Psychoneuroses	11,677
Manic-depressive	*12,078*
Dementia praecox (schizophrenia)	*29,753*
Paranoia and paranoid conditions	1,757
With psychopathic personality	1,240
With mental deficiency	2,837
Other, undiagnosed, and unknown	6,107
Without psychosis	18,847
Epilepsy	1,497
Mental deficiency	1,437
Alcoholism	*9,541*
Drug addiction	954
Personality disorders due to epidemic encephalitis	84
Psychopathic personality	1,586
Primary behavior disorders	622
Other, unclassified, and unknown	3,126
Mental disorder not reported	5,595

[3] Based on a table in *Patients in Mental Institutions, 1946,* U.S. Department of Commerce, Washington, 1948.

Bibliography

1. Abeles, M., and Schilder, P., Psychogenic loss of personal identity, *Arch. Neurol. Psychiat.*, 1935, **34**, 587-604.
2. Abraham, K., *Selected Papers on Psychoanalysis,* Hogarth, London, 1927.
3. Abrahamsen, D., *Crime and the Human Mind,* Columbia Univ. Press, New York, 1944.
4. Abramson, H. A., *Psychodynamics and the Allergic Patient,* Bruce, St. Paul and Minneapolis, 1948.
5. Ackerly, S., Rebellion and its relation to delinquency and neurosis in 60 adolescents, *Amer. J. Orthopsychiat.*, 1933, **3**, 147-160.
6. Ackerman, N. W., Constructive and destructive tendencies in children: An experimental study, *Amer. J. Orthopsychiat.*, 1938, **8**, 265-285.
7. Ackerman, N. W., and Jahoda, M., The dynamic basis of anti-Semitic attitudes, *Psychoanal. Quart.*, 1948, **17**, 240-260.
8. Adelson, E. T., Sugar, C., and Wortis, S. B., A sociopsychiatric study of twenty-five young offenders, *Amer. J. Psychiat.*, 1949, **105**, 619-622.
9. Adler, Alexandra, *Guiding Human Misfits,* Macmillan, New York, 1938.
10. Adler, Alfred, *Neurotic Constitution,* Moffat, Yard, New York, 1917.
11. Adler, Alfred, *Study of Organ Inferiority and Its Psychical Compensation,* Nerv. & Ment. Dis. Pub., Washington, 1917.
12. Adler, Alfred, *The Practice and Theory of Individual Psychology,* Harcourt, Brace, New York, 1924.
13. Adler, Alfred, *The Education of Children,* Greenberg, New York, 1930.
14. Adler, Alfred, *Social Interest: A Challenge to Mankind,* Faber & Faber, London, 1938.
15. Adler, M. H., and Secunda, L., An indirect technique to induce hypnosis, *J. Nerv. Ment. Dis.*, 1947, **106**, 190-193.
16. Adorm, T., Frenkel-Brunswick, E., Levinson, D., and Sanford, R. N., *The Authoritarian Personality,* Harper, New York, 1950.
17. Aichhorn, A., *Wayward Youth,* Viking, New York, 1935.
18. Albert, K., Hoch, P., and Waelsch, H., Preliminary report on the effect of glutamic acid administration in mentally retarded subjects, *J. Nerv. Ment. Dis.*, 1946, **104**, 263-274.
19. Alexander, F., Emotional factors in essential hypertension, *Psychosom. Med.*, 1939, **1**, 173-179.

20. Alexander, F., *The Medical Value of Psychoanalysis,* Norton, New York, rev. ed., 1950.
21. Alexander, F., French, T. M., and others, *Psychoanalytic Therapy,* Ronald, New York, 1946.
22. Alexander, F., and French, T. M., *Studies in Psychosomatic Medicine,* Ronald, New York, 1948.
23. Alexander, F., and Portis, S. A., A psychosomatic study of hypoglycaemic fatigue, *Psychosom. Med.,* 1944, **6,** 191-205.
24. Alexander, F. G., The influence of psychologic factors upon gastro-intestinal disturbances: A symposium, *Psychoanal. Quart.,* 1934, **3,** 501-588.
25. Alexander, F. G., and Healy, W., *Roots of Crime,* Knopf, New York, 1935.
26. Allen, F. H., *Psychotherapy with Children,* Norton, New York, 1942.
27. Allers, R., *The Successful Error: A Critical Study of Freudian Psychoanalysis,* Sheed & Ward, New York, 1940.
28. Allport, G. W., Bruner, J. S., and Jandorf, E. M., Personality under social catastrophe: Ninety life-histories of the Nazi revolution, in Kluckhohn, C., and Murray, H. A., *Personality in Nature, Society, and Culture,* Knopf, New York, 1948.
29. Alschuler, R. H., and Hattwick, La B. A., *Painting and Personality,* 2 vols., Univ. of Chicago Press, Chicago, 1947.
30. Anderson, O. D., and Liddell, H. S., Observations on experimental neurosis in sheep, *Arch. Neurol. Psychiat.,* 1935, **34,** 330-354.
31. Anderson, O. D., and Parmenter, R., A long-term study of the experimental neurosis in the sheep and dog with nine case histories, *Psychosom. Med. Monog.,* 1941, **2,** Nos. 3 and 4.
32. Anderson, O. D., Parmenter, R., and Liddell, H. S., Some cardiovascular manifestations of the experimental neurosis in sheep, *Psychosom. Med.,* 1939, **1,** 93-100.
33. Angyal, A., *Foundations for a Science of Personality,* Commonwealth Fund, New York, 1941.
34. Angyal, A., The holistic approach in psychiatry, *Amer. J. Psychiat.,* 1948, **105,** 178-182.
35. Anthonisen, N. L., Aggression and anxiety in the determination and nature of manic attacks, *Arch. Neurol. Psychiat.,* 1937, **38,** 71-89.
36. Apfelberg, B., Sugar, C., and Pfeffer, A. Z., A psychiatric study of 250 sex offenders, *Amer. J. Psychiat.,* 1944, **100,** 762-770.
37. Appel, M. H., Aggressive behavior of nursery school children and adult procedures in dealing with such behavior, *J. Exp. Educ.,* 1942, **11,** 185-199.
38. Arlow, J. A., Identification mechanisms in coronary occlusion, *Psychosom. Med.,* 1945, **7,** 195-209.
39. Axline, V. M., *Play Therapy,* Houghton Mifflin, Boston, 1947.
40. Baird, P. S., Jr., Biochemical component of the manic-depressive psychosis, *J. Nerv. Ment. Dis.,* 1944, **99,** 359-366.
41. Bak, R. C., Masochism in paranoia, *Psychoanal. Quart.,* 1946, **15,** 285-301.
42. Baker, L. E., The pupillary response conditioned to subliminal auditory stimuli, *Psychol. Monog.,* 1938, **50,** No. 3.

43. Bakwin, R. M., and Bakwin, H., *Psychologic Care During Infancy and Childhood,* Appleton-Century, New York, 1942.
44. Barach, A., Continued arrest of lung movement, *Amer. Rev. Tuberc.,* 1941, **43**, 56-90.
45. Barach, A. L., and Kagan, J., Mental function and oxygen tension, *Psychosom. Med.,* 1940, **2**, 53-67.
46. Barker, R. G., Dembo, T., Lewin, K., and Wright, M. E., Experimental studies of frustration in young children, in Newcomb, T. M., Hartley, E. L., and others, *Readings in Social Psychology,* Holt, New York, 1947.
47. Barker, W., Studies on epilepsy: The petit mal attack, *Psychosom. Med.,* 1948, **10**, 73-94.
48. Barker, W., Personality pattern, situational stress, and symptoms of narcolepsy, *Psychosom. Med.,* 1948, **10**, 193-202.
49. Barry, H., Jr., A study of bereavement: An approach to problems in mental disease, *Amer. J. Orthopsychiat.,* 1939, **9**, 355-360.
50. Bartemeier, L. H., Concerning the psychogenesis of convulsive disorders, *Psychoanal. Quart.,* 1943, **12**, 330-337.
51. Baruch, D. W., and Miller, H., Interview group psychotherapy with allergy patients, in Slavson, S. R., *The Practice of Group Therapy,* Internat. Univ. Press, New York, 1947.
52. Bateson, G., and Mead, M., *Balinese Character: A Photographic Analysis,* Special Publications, N.Y. Acad. Sci., New York, 1942.
53. Baudouin, C., *Suggestion and Auto-Suggestion,* Dodd, Mead, New York, 1921.
54. Beach, F. A., *Hormones and Behavior,* Hoeber, New York, 1948.
55. Beers, C. W., *A Mind That Found Itself,* Longmans, Green, New York, 1908.
56. Bell, S., A preliminary study of the emotion of love between the sexes, *Amer. J. Psychol.,* 1902, **13**, 325-354.
57. Bellak, L., *Dementia Praecox,* Grune & Stratton, New York, 1948.
58. Bellak, L., and Bellak, S. S., *Children's Apperception Test (C.A.T.),* C. P. S. Co., New York, 1949.
59. Belo, J., The Balinese temper, in Haring, D. G., *Personal Character and Cultural Milieu,* Syracuse Univ. Press, Syracuse, N.Y., rev. ed., 1949.
60. Bender, L., Behavior problems in Negro children, *Psychiatry,* 1939, **2**, 213-228.
61. Bender, L., The psychology of children suffering from organic disturbances of the cerebellum, *Amer. J. Orthopsychiat.,* 1940, **10**, 287-292.
62. Bender, L., Childhood schizophrenia, *Nerv. Child,* 1942, **1**, 138-140.
63. Bender, L., Organic brain conditions producing behavior disturbances: A clinical survey of encephalitis, burn encephalopathy and the traumatic states, in Lewis, N. D. C., and Pacella, B. L., *Modern Trends in Child Psychiatry,* Internat. Univ. Press, New York, 1945.
64. Bender, L., *Instructions for the Use of Visual Motor Gestalt Test (and Test Forms),* Amer. Orthopsychiat. Assoc., New York, 1946.
65. Bender, L., Childhood schizophrenia: Clinical study of 100 schizophrenic children, *Amer. J. Orthopsychiat.,* 1947, **17**, 40-55.
66. Bender, L., Psychopathic behavior disorders in children, in Lindner, R. M.,

and Seliger, R. V., *Handbook of Correctional Psychology,* Philosophical Library, New York, 1947.

67. Bender, L., Psychological principles of the visual motor Gestalt test, *Trans. N.Y., Acad. Sci.,* Series II, 1949, **2,** 164-170.
68. Bender, L., Psychological problems of children with organic brain disease, *Amer. J. Orthopsychiat.,* 1949, **19,** 404-415.
69. Bender, L., A visual motor Gestalt test and its clinical use, *Research Monog.,* No. 8, Amer. Orthopsychiat. Assoc., 1949.
70. Bender, L., *Child Psychiatric Techniques,* Thomas, Springfield, Ill., 1951.
71. Bender, L., Keiser, S., and Schilder, P., Studies in aggressiveness, *Genet. Psychol. Monog.,* 1936, **18,** 357-564.
72. Bender, L., and Lipkowitz, H. H., Hallucinations in children, *Amer. J. Orthopsychiat.,* 1940, **10,** 471-490.
73. Bender, L., and Silver, A., Body image problems of the brain damaged child, *J. Soc. Issues,* 1948, **4,** 84-89.
74. Bender, L., and Woltmann, A., The use of puppet shows as a psychotherapeutic method for behavior problems in children, *Amer. J. Orthopsychiat.,* 1936, **6,** 341-354.
75. Bender, L., and Woltmann, A., The use of plastic material as psychiatric approach to emotional problems in children, *Amer. J. Orthopsychiat.,* 1937, **7,** 283-300.
76. Bender, L., and Yarnell, H., An observation nursery, *Amer. J. Psychiat.,* 1941, **97,** 1158-1174.
77. Benedek, T., and Rubenstein, B. B., The sexual cycle in women: The relation between ovarian function and psychodynamic processes, *Psychosom. Med. Monog.,* 1942, **3,** Nos. 1 and 2.
78. Benedict, R., *Patterns of Culture,* Houghton Mifflin, Boston, 1934.
79. Benedict, R., Continuities and discontinuities in cultural conditioning, *Psychiatry,* 1938, **1,** 161-167.
80. Benussi, V., quoted by Woodworth, R. S., *Experimental Psychology,* Holt, New York, 1938.
81. Bergler, E., *The Basic Neurosis: Oral Regression and Psychic Masochism,* Grune & Stratton, New York, 1949.
82. Bergman, P., and Escalona, S. K., Unusual sensitiveness in very young children, in *The Psychoanalytic Study of the Child,* Vols. III/IV, Internat. Univ. Press, New York, 1949.
83. Berle, B. B., Emotional factors and tuberculosis, *Psychosom. Med.,* 1948, **10,** 366-373.
84. Berliner, B., On some psychodynamics of masochism, *Psychoanal. Quart.,* 1947, **16,** 459-471.
85. Bernard, V., Psychodynamics of unmarried motherhood in early adolescence, *Nerv. Child,* 1944, **4,** 26-45.
86. Bernfeld, S., *Psychologie des Säuglings,* Springer, Vienna, 1925.
87. Bernheim, H., *Suggestive Therapeutics,* Putnam, New York, 1883.
88. Betlheim, W., and Hartmann, H., Über Fehlerreactionen bei der Korsakoffschen Psychose, *Archiv f. Psychiatrie,* 1924-1925, **72,** 275-286.

89. Bettelheim, B., Individual and mass behavior in extreme situations, in Newcomb, T. M., Hartley, E. L., and others, *Readings in Social Psychology,* Holt, New York, 1947.

90. Biber, B., Murphy, L. B., and others, *Child Life in School,* Dutton, New York, 1942.

91. Bieber, I., and Tarachow, S., Autonomic symptoms in psychoneurotics, *Psychosom. Med.,* 1941, **3,** 253-262.

92. Billings, E. G., *A Handbook of Elementary Psychobiology and Psychiatry,* Macmillan, New York, 1939.

93. Binger, C., *The Doctor's Job,* Norton, New York, 1945.

94. Binger, C. A. L., Ackerman, N. W., Cohn, A. E., Schroeder, H. A., and Steele, J. M., Personality in arterial hypertension, *Psychosom. Med. Monog.,* No. 8, 1945.

95. Birch, H. G., and Clark, G., Hormonal modification of social behavior: II. The effects of sex-hormone administration on the social dominance status of the female-castrate chimpanzee, *Psychosom. Med.,* 1946, **8,** 320-331.

96. Blanchard, P., Psychoanalytic contributions to the problem of reading disabilities, in *The Psychoanalytic Study of the Child,* Vol. II, Internat. Univ. Press, New York, 1946.

97. Blanton, S., and Blanton, M., *For Stutterers,* Appleton-Century, New York, 1936.

98. Bleuler, E., *Textbook of Psychiatry,* Macmillan, New York, 1924.

99. Bloomberg, W., Effects of benzedrine in altering mental and emotional processes, in *The Inter-Relationship of Mind and Body,* Williams & Wilkins, Baltimore, 1939.

100. Blos, P., *The Adolescent Personality,* Appleton-Century, New York, 1941.

101. Blos, P., Psychological counseling of college students, *Amer. J. Orthopsychiat.,* 1946, **16,** 571-580.

102. Bochner, R., and Halpern, F., *The Clinical Application of the Rorschach Test,* Grune & Stratton, New York, 2nd ed., 1945.

103. Bolles, M. M., Metzger, H. F., and Pitts, M. W., Early home background and personality adjustment, *Amer. J. Orthopsychiat.,* 1941, **11,** 530-535.

104. Bonaparte, M., Passivity, masochism and femininity, *Int. J. Psychoanal.,* 1935, **16,** 325-333.

105. Bond, E. D., Continued follow-up results in shock therapy and control cases, *Amer. J. Psychiat.,* 1941, **97,** 1024-1028.

106. Bond, E. D., Insulin shock therapy after seven years, *Amer. J. Psychiat.,* 1944, **101,** 62-63.

107. Bond, E. D., and Appel, K. E., *The Treatment of Behavior Disorders Following Encephalitis,* Commonwealth Fund, New York, 1931.

108. Bond, E. D., and Braceland, F. Y., Prognosis in mental disease, *Amer. J. Psychiat.,* 1937, **94,** 263-274.

109. Bond, E. D., and Rivers, T. S., Further follow-up results in insulin shock therapy, *Amer. J. Psychiat.,* 1942, **99,** 201-202.

110. Booth, G., Organ function and form perception, *Psychosom. Med.,* 1946, **8,** 367-385.

111. Bornstein, B., The analysis of a phobic child: Some problems of theory and technique in child analysis, in *The Psychoanalytic Study of the Child,* Vols. III/IV, Internat. Univ. Press, New York, 1949.
112. Bowen, M., Children with problems: Nursery technic for school-age patients, *Amer. J. Nurs.,* 1942, **42,** 1262-1268.
113. Bowlby, J., *Forty-four Juvenile Thieves: Their Characters and Home-Life,* Bailliere, Tindall and Cox, London, 1946.
114. Bowman, K. M., Miller, E. R., Dailey, M. E., Simon, A., Frankel, B., and Lowe, G. W., Thyroid function in mental disease measured with radioactive iodine, I^{131}, *Amer. J. Psychiat.,* 1950, **106,** 561-572.
115. Bowman, K. M., and Simon, A., Studies in electronarcosis therapy: I. Clinical evaluation, *Amer. J. Psychiat.,* 1948, **105,** 15-27.
116. Braceland, F. J., Meduna, L. J., and Vaichuliz, J. A., Delayed action of insulin in schizophrenia, *Amer. J. Psychiat.,* 1945, **102,** 108-110.
117. Bram, I., Psychosomatic obesity: With comments on 924 cases, *Med. Rec.,* 1944, **157,** 673-676.
118. Brenman, M., and Gill, M. M., *Hypnotherapy: A Survey of the Literature,* Internat. Univ. Press, New York, 1947.
119. Brenman, M., and Knight, R. P., Hypnotherapy for mental illness in the aged: Hysterical psychosis in a 71-year-old woman, *Bull. Menninger Clinic,* 1943, **7,** 188-198.
120. Brenner, C., Friedman, A. F., and Carter, S., Psychologic factors in chronic headache, *Psychosom. Med.,* 1949, **11,** 53-56.
121. Breuer, J., and Freud, S., *Studies in Hysteria,* Nerv. & Ment. Dis. Pub., Washington, 1936.
122. Brickner, R. M., *The Intellectual Functions of the Frontal Lobes,* Macmillan, New York, 1936.
123. Brill, A. A., The concept of psychic suicide, *Int. J. Psychoanal.,* 1939, **20,** 246-251.
124. Brodman, K., *Men at Work: The Supervisor and His People,* Cloud, Chicago, 1947.
125. Brodman, K., Mittelmann, B., and Wolff, H. G., Psychologic aspects of convalescence: XX, *J. Amer. Med. Assoc.,* 1945, **129,** 179-187.
126. Brody, M. W., Neurotic manifestations of the voice, *Psychoanal. Quart.,* 1943, **12,** 371-380.
127. Bromberg, W., *Crime and the Mind: An Outline of Psychiatric Criminology,* Lippincott, Philadelphia, 1948.
128. Brosin, H. W., Panic states and their treatment, *Amer. J. Psychiat.,* 1943, **100,** 54-61.
129. Brown, E. A., and Goitein, P. L., The meaning of asthma, *Psychoanal. Rev.,* 1944, **31,** 209-306.
130. Brown, J. F., *The Psychodynamics of Abnormal Behavior,* McGraw-Hill, New York, 1940.
131. Bruch, H., Physiologic and psychologic interrelationships in diabetes in children, *Psychosom. Med.,* 1949, **11,** 200-210.
132. Bruch, H., and Cottington, F., Diary of a psychotic child, *Nerv. Child,* 1942, **1,** 232-249.

133. Bullard, D. M., The application of psychoanalytic psychiatry to the psychoses, *Psychoanal. Rev.*, 1939, **26**, 526-534.
134. Bullard, D. M., Experiences in the psychoanalytic treatment of psychotics, *Psychoanal. Quart.*, 1940, **9**, 493-504.
135. Bunker, H. A., The treatment of general paralysis by inoculation with malaria, *J. Amer. Med. Assoc.*, 1925, **84**, 563-568.
136. Burgum, M., Constructive values associated with rejection, *Amer. J. Orthopsychiat.*, 1942, **12**, 424-486.
137. Burlingame, C. C., Psychiatry in industry, *Amer. J. Psychiat.*, 1947, **103**, 549-552.
138. Burrow, T., *The Neurosis of Man: An Introduction to a Science of Human Behavior*, Routledge & Kegan Paul, London, 1949.
139. Burstine, M. S., The psychosomatic aspects of dental problems, *J. Amer. Dent. Assoc.*, 1946, **33**, 862-871.
140. Burton, A., and Harris, R. E., *Case Histories in Clinical and Abnormal Psychology*, Harper, New York, 1947.
141. Buxbaum, E., The role of detective stories in a child analysis, *Psychoanal. Quart.*, 1941, **10**, 373-381.
142. Bychowski, G., The preschizophrenic ego, *Psychoanal. Quart.*, 1947, **16**, 225-233.
143. Cabot, P. S. de Q., *Juvenile Delinquency*, Wilson, New York, 1946.
144. Cameron, D. E., Observations on the patterns of anxiety, *Amer. J. Psychiat.*, 1944, **101**, 36-41.
145. Cameron, N., A study of thinking in senile deterioration and schizophrenic disorganization, *Amer. J. Psychol.*, 1938, **51**, 650-665.
146. Cameron, N., Deterioration and repression in schizophrenic thinking, *J. Abnorm. Soc. Psychol.*, 1939, **34**, 265-270.
147. Cameron, N., *The Psychology of Behavior Disorders: A Biosocial Interpretation*, Houghton Mifflin, Boston, 1947.
148. Campbell, A. A., Factors associated with attitudes towards Jews, in Newcomb, T. M., Hartley, E. L., and others, *Readings in Social Psychology*, Holt, New York, 1947.
149. Cannon, W. B., *The Wisdom of the Body*, Norton, New York, 1932.
150. Cannon, W. B., *Bodily Changes in Pain, Hunger, Fear and Rage*, Appleton-Century, New York, 2nd ed., 1936.
151. Cantor, N. F., *Dynamics of Learning*, Foster, Buffalo, 1946.
152. Carmichael, L., *Manual of Child Psychology*, Wiley, New York, 1946.
153. Carpenter, J., and Eisenberg, P., Some relations between family background and personality, J. Psychol., 1938, **6**, 115-136.
154. Cason, H., Conditioned pupillary reactions, *J. Exp. Psychol.*, 1922, **5**, 108-146.
155. Cason, H., The symptoms of the psychopath, *Publ. Hlth. Rep.*, 1946, **61**, 1833-1868.
156. Cattell, R. B., The diagnosis and classification of neurotic states: A reinterpretation of Eysenck's factors, *J. Nerv. Ment. Dis.*, 1945, **102**, 576-589.
157. Chamberlain, H. E., Neurotic personalities and education, *Smith Coll. Stud. Soc. Wk.*, 1941, **11**, 179-190.

158. Chassel, J., Individual counseling of college students, *J. Consult. Psychol.*, 1940, **4**, 205-209.

159. Chisholm, G. B., Psychological adjustment of soldiers to army and civilian life, *Amer. J. Psychiat.*, 1944, **101**, 300-302.

160. Claremont, C. A., Normalization of the child-adult relationship, *Brit. J. Educ. Psychol.*, 1944, **14**, 35-43.

161. Clark, G., and Birch, H. G., Hormonal modifications of social behavior: I. The effect of sex-hormone administration on the social status of a male-castrate chimpanzee, *Psychosom. Med.*, 1945, **7**, 321-329.

162. Clark, L. P., Clinical studies in epilepsy, *Psychiat. Bull.*, 1916, **9**, 60-103.

163. Cleckley, H., *The Mask of Sanity: An Attempt to Reinterpret the So-Called Psychopathic Personality*, Mosby, St. Louis, 1941.

164. Clifton, E., and Hollis, F., *Child Therapy: A Casework Symposium*, Family Serv. Assoc. of Amer., New York, 1948.

165. Cobb, S., Psychiatric approach to the treatment of epilepsy, *Amer. J. Psychiat.*, 1940, **96**, 1009-1021.

166. Cobb, S., *Borderlands of Psychiatry*, Harvard Univ. Press, Cambridge, Mass., 1948.

167. Conrad, A., The psychiatric study of hyperthyroid patients, *J. Nerv. Ment. Dis.*, 1934, **79**, 505-656.

168. Conrad, H. S., Vocational interests and job orientation, *Appl. Psychol. Monog.*, No. 2, Amer. Assoc. Appl. Psychol., 1944.

169. Coriat, I. H., *Stammering*, Nerv. & Ment. Dis. Pub., Washington, 1927.

170. Corn-Becker, F., Welch, L., and Fisichelli, V., Conditioning factors underlying hypnosis, *J. Abnorm. Soc. Psychol.*, 1949, **44**, 212-222.

171. Cowdry, E. V., *Problems of Aging*, Williams & Wilkins, Baltimore, 2nd ed., 1942.

172. Crookshank, F. G., Individual psychology, medicine, and the bases of science, *Individual Psychology Pamphlets*, No. 3a, Daniel, London, 1933.

173. Crowley, M. R., Psychoanalytic literature on drug addiction and alcoholism, *Psychoanal. Rev.*, 1939, **26**, 39-54.

174. Culpin, M., Mode of onset of the neuroses in war, in Miller, E., *The Neuroses in War*, Macmillan, New York, 1942.

175. Dai, B., Some problems of personality development among Negro children, in Kluckhohn, C., and Murray, H. A., *Personality in Nature, Society, and Culture*, Knopf, New York, 1948.

176. Daniels, G. E., Neuroses associated with the gastro-intestinal tract, *Amer. J. Psychiat.*, 1934, **91**, 529-540.

177. Daniels, G. E., Present trends in the evaluation of psychic factors in diabetes mellitus: A critical review of experimental, general medical and psychiatric literature of the last five years, *Psychosom. Med.*, 1939, **1**, 527-552.

178. Daniels, G. E., Treatment of case of ulcerative colitis associated with hysterical depression, *Psychosom. Med.*, 1940, **2**, 276-285.

179. Darling, H. F., Shock treatment in psychopathic personality, *J. Nerv. Ment. Dis.*, 1945, **101**, 247-255.

180. Dattner, B., Treatment of neurosyphilis with penicillin alone, *Amer. J. Syphilis, Gonorrhea, Ven. Dis.*, 1948, **32**, 399-403.

181. Davis, A., and Dollard, J., *Children of Bondage: The Personality Development of Negro Youth in the Urban South,* Amer. Council on Educ., Washington, 1940.
182. Davis, K., Extreme social isolation of a child, *Amer. J. Sociol.,* 1940, **45,** 554-565.
183. Davis, W. A., and Havighurst, R. J., *Father of the Man: How Your Child Gets His Personality,* Houghton Mifflin, Boston, 1947.
184. Davison, C., Psychological and psychodynamic aspects of disturbances in the sleep mechanism, *Psychoanal. Quart.,* 1945, **14,** 478-497.
185. Dayton, N. A., *New Facts on Mental Disorders: Study of 89,190 Cases,* Thomas, Springfield, Ill., 1940.
186. DeJong, R. N., Further observations on the use of tridione in the control of psychomotor attacks, *Amer. J. Psychiat.,* 1946, **103,** 162-164.
187. Dennyssen, J. A., and Watterson, D. J., On the mechanism of cardiazol convulsion, *J. Ment. Sci.,* 1936, **85,** 1002.
188. Deri, S., *Introduction to the Szondi Test: Theory and Practice,* Grune & Stratton, New York, 1949.
189. Deri, S. K., The Szondi Test, in Buros, O. K., *The Third Mental Measurements Yearbook,* Rutgers Univ. Press, New Brunswick, N.J., 1949.
190. Dershimer, F. W., Psychiatry in industry, *Amer. J. Psychiat.,* 1946, **103,** 145-148.
191. Despert, J. L., Psychopathology of stuttering, *Amer. J. Psychiat.,* 1943, **99,** 881-885.
192. Despert, J. L., Stuttering: A clinical study, *Amer. J. Orthopsychiat.,* 1943, **13,** 517-524.
193. Despert, J. L., Emotional factors in some young children's colds, *Med. Clin. N. Amer.,* 1944, **28,** 603-614.
194. Despert, J. L., Psychosomatic study of fifty stuttering children: I. Social, physical, and psychiatric findings, *Amer. J. Orthopsychiat.,* 1946, **16,** 100-113.
195. Despert, J. L., Dreams of children of preschool age, in *The Psychoanalytic Study of the Child,* Vols. III/IV, Internat. Univ. Press, New York, 1949.
196. Despert, J. L., and Pierce, H. O., The relation of emotional adjustment to intellectual function, *Genet. Psychol. Monog.,* 1946, **34,** 3-56.
197. Deutsch, A., *The Mentally Ill in America: A History of Their Care and Treatment from Colonial Times,* Columbia Univ. Press, New York, 1946.
198. Deutsch, F., Gehäuftes Auftreten von Morbus Basedowi, *Med. Klin.,* 1923, **19,** 678-681.
199. Deutsch, F., Emotions and respiratory mechanism: Hypnotic experiments, *Wiener Kl. Woch.,* 1925, **38,** 1127-1130.
200. Deutsch, F., The choice of organ in organ neuroses, *Int. J. Psychoanal.,* 1939, **20,** 252-262.
201. Deutsch, F., The associative anamnesis, *Psychoanal. Quart.,* 1939, **8,** 354-381.
202. Deutsch, F., Analysis of postural behavior, *Psychoanal. Quart.,* 1947, **16,** 195-213.
203. Deutsch, F., The production of somatic disease by emotional disturbance, in *The Inter-Relationship of Mind and Body,* Williams & Wilkins, Baltimore, 1939.

204. Deutsch, F., and Kauf, E., Über die Ursachen der Kreislaufstörungen bei den Herzneurosen, *Ztsch. f. d. ges. Exper. Med.*, 1923, 34, 71-81.

205. Deutsch, F., and Nadell, R., Psychosomatic aspects of dermatology with special consideration of allergic phenomena, *Nerv. Child*, 1946, **5**, 339-364.

206. Deutsch, H., Zur Psychologie der manisch-depressiven Zustände, insbesondere der chronischen Hypomanie, *Int. Zeit. f. Psychoanal.*, 1933, **19**, 358-370.

207. Deutsch, H., *The Psychology of Women*, Vol. I, Grune & Stratton, New York, 1944.

208. Devereux, G., Institutionalized homosexuality of the Mohave Indians, *Hum. Biol.*, 1937, **9**, 498-527.

209. Dickinson, R. L., and Beam, L., *One Thousand Marriages*, Williams & Wilkins, Baltimore, 1932.

210. Dicks, G. H., and Childers, A. T., The social transformation of a boy who had lived his first fourteen years as a girl: A case history, *Amer. J. Orthopsychiat.*, 1934, 4, 508-517.

211. Diethelm, O., *Treatment in Psychiatry*, Thomas, Springfield, Ill., 2nd ed., 1950.

212. Diethelm, O., and Simmons, D. J., Electroencephalographic changes associated with psychopathic personalities, *Arch. Neurol. Psychiat.*, 1946, 55, 410-413.

213. Dollard, J., *Criteria for the Life History—With Analysis of Six Notable Documents*, Yale Univ. Press, New Haven, 1935.

214. Dollard, J., *Caste and Class in a Southern Town*, Yale Univ. Press, New Haven, 1937.

215. Dollard, J., Hostility and fear in social life, *Social Forces*, 1938, **17**, 15-29.

216. Dollard, J., Doob., L., Miller, N., Mowrer, O., and Sears, R., *Frustration and Aggression*, Yale Univ. Press, New Haven, 1939.

217. Doob, L. W., and Sears, R. R., Factors determining substitute behavior and the overt expression of aggression, *J. Abnorm. Soc. Psychol.*, 1939, **34**, 293-313.

218. Doshay, L. J., Male sex delinquency and community responsibilities, in Lewis, N. D. C., and Pacella, B. L., *Modern Trends in Child Psychiatry*, Internat. Univ. Press, New York, 1945.

219. Doswald, D. C., and Kreibich, K., Zur Frage der posthypnotischen Hauptphänomene, *Monatshefte f. prakt. Dermat.*, 1906, **43**, 634-640.

220. Draper, G., Constitution and disease, in *Nelson Loose-Leaf Living Medicine*, Vol. VII, Chap. XVI.

221. Dreikurs, R., *Challenge of Parenthood*, Duell, Sloan, & Pearce, New York, 1948.

222. Du Bois, C., *The People of Alor*, Univ. of Minnesota Press, Minneapolis, 1944.

223. Dunbar, H. F., Psychoanalytic notes relating to syndromes of asthma and hay fever, *Psychoanal. Quart.*, 1938, **7**, 25-68.

224. Dunbar, H. F., *Psychosomatic Diagnosis*, Hoeber, New York, 1943.

225. Dunbar, H. F., Rheumatic disease, with special reference to psychosomatic diagnosis and treatment, *Psychosom. Med.*, 1944, **6**, 206-210.

226. Dunbar, H. F., *Emotions and Bodily Changes,* Columbia Univ. Press, New York, 3rd ed., 1946.

227. Dunham, H. W., Sociological aspects of mental disorders in later life, in Kaplan, O. J., *Mental Disorders in Later Life,* Stanford Univ. Press, Stanford, Calif., 1945.

228. Dunn, W. H., Emotional factors in neurocirculatory asthenia, *Psychosom. Med.,* 1942, **4,** 333-354.

229. Dunton, W. R., Jr., *Prescribing Occupational Therapy,* Thomas, Springfield, Ill., 2nd ed., 1945.

230. Dworkin, S., Baxt, J. O., and Dworkin, E., Behavioral disturbances in conditioned cats, *Psychosom. Med.,* 1942, **4,** 75-81.

231. Ehrenwald, J., *Telepathy and Medical Psychology,* Norton, New York, 1948.

232. Eisenberg, P., Factors related to feelings of dominance, *J. Consult. Psychol.,* 1937, **1,** 89-92.

233. Eisenberg, P., Judging expressive movement: I. Judgments of sex and dominance-feeling from handwriting samples of dominant and non-dominant men and women, *J. Appl. Psychol.,* 1938, **22,** 468-480.

234. Eisenberg, P., and Lazarsfeld, P., The psychological effects of unemployment, *Psychol. Bull.,* 1938, **35,** 358-390.

235. Eisenberg, P., and Zalowitz, E., Judging expressive movement: III. Judgments of dominance feeling from phonograph records of voice, *J. Appl. Psychol.,* 1938, **22,** 620-631.

236. Eisenbud, J., A method for investigating the effect of repression on the somatic expression of emotion in vegetative functions, *Psychosom. Med.,* 1939, **1,** 376-387.

237. Eisenbud, J., Telepathy and problems of psychoanalysis, *Psychoanal. Quart.,* 1946, **15,** 32-87.

238. Eisendorfer, A., The clinical significance of the single parent relationship in women, *Psychoanal. Quart.,* 1943, **12,** 223-239.

239. Eisenson, J., *Psychology of Speech,* Crofts, New York, 1938.

240. Eissler, R. S., Riots: Observations in a home for delinquent girls, in *The Psychoanalytic Study of the Child,* Vols. III/IV, Internat. Univ. Press, New York, 1949.

241. Ellis, A., Telepathy and psychoanalysis: A critique of recent findings, *Psychiat. Quart.,* 1947, **21,** 607-659.

242. Engel, G. L., Ferris, E. B., and Logan, M., Hyperventilation: Analysis of clinical symptomatology, *Ann. Int. Med.,* 1947, **27,** 683-704.

243. English, O. S., and Pearson, G. H. J., *Emotional Problems of Living: Avoiding the Neurotic Pattern,* Norton, New York, 1945.

244. Ephron, H. S., Moral judgment in therapy, *Amer. J. Orthopsychiat.,* 1939, **9,** 339-347.

245. Erickson, M. H., The experimental demonstration of unconscious mentation by automatic writing, *Psychoanal. Quart.,* 1937, **6,** 513-529.

246. Erickson, M. H., A study of clinical and experimental findings on hypnotic deafness, *J. Gen. Psychol.,* 1938, **19,** 151-167.

247. Erickson, M. H., An experimental investigation of the possible anti-social use of hypnosis, *Psychiatry,* 1939, **2,** 391-414.

248. Erickson, M. H., Experimental demonstrations of the psychopathology of everyday life, *Psychoanal. Quart.,* 1939, **8,** 338-353.

249. Erickson, M. H., Hypnotic investigation of psychosomatic phenomena: I. Psychosomatic interrelationships studied by experimental hypnosis, *Psychosom. Med.,* 1943, **5,** 51-58.

250. Erickson, M. H., and Hill, L. B., Unconscious mental activity in hypnosis: Psychoanalytic implications, *Psychoanal. Quart.,* 1944, **13,** 60-78.

251. Erickson, M. H., and Kubie, L. S., Use of automatic drawing in interpretation and relief of a state of acute obsessional depression, *Psychoanal. Quart.,* 1938, **7,** 443-453.

252. Erickson, M. H., and Kubie, L. S., The permanent relief of an obsessional phobia by means of communications with an unsuspected dual personality, *Psychoanal. Quart.,* 1939, **8,** 471-509.

253. Erikson, E. H., Observations on Sioux education, *J. Psychol.,* 1939, **7,** 101-156.

254. Erikson, E. H., Studies in the interpretation of play: I. Clinical observation of play disruption in young children, *Genet. Psychol. Monog.,* 1940, **22,** 557-669.

255. Escalona, S. K., Feeding disturbances in very young children, *Amer. J. Orthopsychiat.,* 1945, **15,** 76-80.

256. Eysenck, H. J., and others, *Dimensions of Personality,* Kegan Paul, Trench, Trubner, London, 1947.

257. Fairbairn, J. S., Eccles, W. M., and others, Individual psychology and psychosomatic disorders (II), *Individual Psychology Pamphlets,* No. 9, Daniel, London, 1935.

258. Farber, L. H., and Fisher, C., An experimental approach to dream psychology through use of hypnosis, *Psychoanal. Quart.,* 1943, **12,** 202-216.

259. Faris, R. E. L., and Dunham, H. W., *Mental Disorders in Urban Areas,* Univ. of Chicago Press, Chicago, 1939.

260. Faulkner, W. B., Jr., Objective oesophageal changes due to psychic factors, *Amer. J. Medic. Sci.,* 1940, **200,** 796-803.

261. Federn, P., Principles of psychotherapy in latent schizophrenia, *Amer. J. Psychother.,* 1947, **1,** 129-144.

262. Federn, P., Mental hygiene of the psychotic ego, *Amer. J. Psychother.,* 1949, **3,** 356-371.

263. Feldman, S. S., Mannerisms of speech, *Psychoanal. Quart.,* 1948, **17,** 356-367.

264. Feldman, Y., and Van Ophuijsen, J. H. W., The case of Miriam Kohn, in *Primary Behavior Disorder in Children: Two Case Studies,* Family Serv. Assoc. of Amer., New York, 1945.

265. Felix, R. H., An appraisal of the personality types of the addict, *Amer. J. Psychiat.,* 1944, **100,** 462-467.

266. Fenichel, O., Problems of psychoanalytic technique, Parts 1-4, *Psychoanal. Quart.,* 1939, **8,** Nos. 1-4.

267. Fenichel, O., *The Psychoanalytic Theory of Neurosis,* Norton, New York, 1945.

268. Ferenczi, S., *Contributions to Psychoanalysis,* Badger, Boston, 1916.
269. Ferenczi, S., *Further Contributions to the Theory and Technique of Psychoanalysis,* Hogarth, London, 1926.
270. Ferenczi, S., and Rank, O., *The Development of Psychoanalysis,* Nerv. & Ment. Dis. Pub., Washington, 1925.
271. Ferguson, M., Weber, H., Woodcock, O. H., Bevan-Brown, F. H., and Young, J. C., Awareness and the neuroses of the declining years, *Individual Psychology Pamphlets,* No. 14, Daniel, London, 1936.
272. Finesinger, J. E., Effect of pleasant and unpleasant ideas on respiration in psychoneurotic patients, *Arch. Neurol. Psychiat.,* 1939, **42,** 425-490.
273. Finesinger, J. E., and Cobb, S., A contrast between the electroencephalograms of 100 psychoneurotic patients and those of 500 normal adults, *Amer. J. Psychiat.,* 1945, **101,** 443-448.
274. Fisher, C., and Joseph, E. D., Fugue with awareness of loss of personal identity, *Psychoanal. Quart.,* 1949, **18,** 480-493.
275. Fite, M. D., Aggressive behavior in young children and children's attitudes toward aggression, *Genet. Psychol. Monog.,* 1940, **22,** 151-319.
276. Flanagan, D., The influence of emotional inhibition on learning and recall, unpublished Master's Thesis, Univ. of Chicago, 1930 (quoted by Sears [843]).
277. Flugel, J. C., *The Psychoanalytic Study of the Family,* Internat. Psychoanal. Press, London, 1921.
278. Foerster, O., Symptomatologie der Erkrankungen des Grosshirns, Morotische Felder und Bahnen, in Bumke and Foerster, *Handbuch der Neurologie,* 1936, **6,** 1-448.
279. Foley, J. P., The criterion of abnormality, *J. Abnorm. Soc. Psychol.,* 1935, **30,** 279-291.
280. Ford, F. R., *Diseases of the Nervous System in Infancy, Childhood and Adolescence,* Thomas, Springfield, Ill., 1937.
281. Frank, J. D., Psychotherapeutic aspects of symptomatic treatment, *Amer. J. Psychiat.,* 1946, **103,** 21-25.
282. Frank, L. K., Projective methods for the study of personality, *J. Psychol.,* 1939, **8,** 389-413.
283. Frank, L. K., *Society as the Patient,* Rutgers Univ. Press, New Brunswick, N.J., 1948.
284. Frank, R. L., The influence of unrecognized difficulties, *Psychoanal. Quart.,* 1948, **17,** 84-96.
285. Fredericksen, N., The effects of frustration on negativistic behavior of young children, *J. Genet. Psychol.,* 1942, **61,** 203-226.
286. Freedman, B., Psychosocial repression and social rationalization, *Amer. J. Orthopsychiat.,* 1939, **9,** 109-123.
287. Freeman, F. N., Holzinger, J. J., and Mitchell, B. C., The influence of environment on the intelligence, school achievement, and conduct of foster children, in *The Twenty-Seventh Yearbook, Nat. Soc. for Study of Educ.,* 1928.
288. Freeman, G. L., The effect of inhibited micturition upon interrupted and completed acts of unrelated origin, *J. Gen. Psychol.,* 1938, **29,** 277-283.

289. Freeman, G. L., Postural tensions and the conflict situation, *Psychol. Rev.*, 1939, **46**, 226-240.

290. Freeman, W., and Watts, J. W., *Psychosurgery,* Thomas, Springfield, Ill., 1942.

291. Fremont-Smith, F., The physiological basis of aggression, *Child Study,* 1939, **15**, 234-235.

292. Fremont-Smith, F., The influence of emotional factors upon physiological and pathological processes, *Bull. N.Y. Acad. Med.*, 1939, **15**, 560-569.

293. French, T. M., Reality and the unconscious, *Psychoanal. Quart.*, 1937, **6**, 23-61.

294. French, T. M., Ego analysis as a guide to therapy, *Psychoanal. Quart.*, 1945, **14**, 336-349.

295. French, T. M., and Alexander, F., Psychogenic bronchial asthma, Parts I & II, *Psychosom. Med. Monog.*, Vol. I, No. 4, 1941, Vol. II, No. 1, 1941.

296. Frenkel-Brunswik, E., Levinson, D. J., and Sanford, R. N., The anti-democratic personality, in Newcomb, T. M., Hartley, E. L., and others, *Readings in Social Psychology,* Holt, New York, 1947.

297. Freud, A., *Introduction to the Technic of Child Analysis,* Nerv. & Ment. Dis. Pub., Washington, 1928.

298. Freud, A., *The Ego and the Mechanisms of Defense,* Hogarth, London, 1937.

299. Freud, A., The psychoanalytic study of infantile feeding disturbances, in *The Psychoanalytic Study of the Child,* Vol. II, Internat. Univ. Press, New York, 1946.

300. Freud, A., and Burlingham, D. T., *War and Children,* Medical War Books, New York, 1943.

301. Freud, S., Analysis of a phobia of a five-year-old boy (1909), in Freud, S., *Collected Papers,* Vol. III, Hogarth, London, 1946.

302. Freud, S., *Group Psychology and the Analysis of the Ego,* Boni & Liveright, New York, 1922.

303. Freud, S., *Beyond the Pleasure Principle,* Internat. Univ. Press, London, 1922.

304. Freud, S., *Collected Papers,* Vols. I-IV, Internat. Psychoanal. Press, London, 1924. (Contains Freud's most significant papers and case histories up to 1918 in English translation.)

305. Freud, S., *The Ego and the Id,* Hogarth, London, 1927.

306. Freud, S., *The Future of an Illusion,* Woolf, London, 1928.

307. Freud, S., *Civilization and Its Discontents,* Hogarth, London, 1930.

308. Freud, S., *New Introductory Lectures on Psychoanalysis,* Norton, New York, 1933.

309. Freud, S., *Gesammelte Schriften,* Vols. I-XII, Int. Z. Psychoanal., Leipzig, Vienna, Zurich, 1934. (Contains all of Freud's work in German up to the year 1934.)

310. Freud, S., *A General Introduction to Psychoanalysis,* Liveright, New York, 1935.

311. Freud, S., *The Problem of Anxiety,* Norton, New York, 1936.

312. Freud, S., Analysis terminable and interminable, *Int. J. Psychoanal.*, 1937, **18**, 373-405.

313. Freud, S., *The Basic Writings of Sigmund Freud,* Modern Library, New York, 1938. (Includes *The Interpretation of Dreams, The History of the Psychoanalytic Movement, The Psychopathology of Everyday Life, Three Contributions to the Theory of Sex, Totem and Taboo,* and *Wit and Its Relation to the Unconscious.*)

314. Friedlander, D., Personality development of twenty-seven children who later became psychotic, *J. Abnorm. Soc. Psychol.,* 1945, **40,** 330-335.

315. Friedlander, K., *The Psycho-Analytical Approach to Juvenile Delinquency: Theory, Case-Studies, Treatment,* Internat. Univ. Press, New York, 1947.

316. Friedman, M., and Kasanin, J. S., Hypertension in only one of identical twins: Report of a case, with consideration of psychosomatic factors, *Arch. Intern. Med.,* 1943, **72,** 767-774.

317. Fries, M. E., Interrelationship of physical, mental and emotional life of a child from birth to four years of age, *Amer. J. Dis. of Children,* 1935, **49,** 1546-1563.

318. Fries, M. E., Psychosomatic relationships between mother and child, *Psychosom. Med.,* 1944, **6,** 157-162.

319. Fries, M. E., Research in problems of infancy and childhood (by Malcove), in *The Psychoanalytic Study of the Child,* Vol. I, Internat. Univ. Press, New York, 1945.

320. Fries, M. E., Brokaw, K., and Murray, V. G., The formation of character as observed in the Well Baby Clinic, *Amer. J. Dis. of Children,* 1935, **49,** 28-42.

321. Fromm, E., *Escape from Freedom,* Farrar & Rinehart, 1941.

322. Fromm, E., *Man for Himself,* Rinehart, 1947.

323. Fromm-Reichmann, F., Transference problems in schizophrenics, *Psychoanal. Quart.,* 1939, **8,** 412-426.

324. Fromm-Reichmann, F., A preliminary note on the emotional significance of stereotypes in schizophrenia, *Bull. Forest Sanitarium,* 1942, **1,** 17-21.

325. Frosch, J., Impastato, D., Ottenheimer, L., and Wortis, S. B., Some reactions seen after electric shock treatment, *Amer. J. Psychiat.,* 1945, **102,** 311-315.

326. Fry, C. C., *Mental Health in College,* Commonwealth Fund, New York, 1942.

327. Fulton, J. F., *Physiology of the Nervous System,* Oxford Univ. Press, London, 2nd ed., 1943.

328. Funkenstein, D. H., Greenblatt, M., and Solomon, H. C., Psychophysiological study of mentally ill patients, *Amer. J. Psychiat.,* 1949, **106,** 16-28.

329. Furneaux, W. D., The prediction of susceptibility to hypnosis, *J. Personality,* 1946, **14,** 281-294.

330. Gantt, W. H., *Experimental Basis for Neurotic Behavior: Origin and Development of Artificially Produced Disturbances of Behavior in Dogs,* Hoeber, New York, 1944.

331. Garma, A., The genesis of reality testing, *Psychoanal. Quart.,* 1946, **15,** 161-174.

332. Gates, A., *The Improvement of Reading,* Macmillan, New York, 2nd ed., 1936.

333. Gates, A., The role of personality maladjustment in reading disability, *J. Genet. Psychol.,* 1941, **59,** 77-84.

334. Geleerd, E. R., A contribution to the problem of psychoses in childhood, in *The Psychoanalytic Study of the Child,* Vol. II, Internat. Univ. Press, New York, 1946.

335. Geleerd, E. R., The psychoanalysis of a psychotic child, in *The Psychoanalytic Study of the Child,* Vols. III/IV, Internat. Univ. Press, New York, 1949.

336. Geleerd, E. R., Hacker, F. J., and Rapaport, D., Contribution to the study of amnesia and allied conditions, *Psychoanal. Quart.,* 1945, **14,** 199-220.

337. Gellender, B., A study of overinhibited and unsocialized-aggressive children: Part III. The later adjustment of overinhibited children, *Smith Coll. Stud. Soc. Wk.,* 1944, **15,** 135-136.

338. Gellhorn, E., *Autonomic Regulations: Their Significance for Physiology, Psychology and Neuropsychiatry,* Interscience Pub., New York, 1943.

339. Gelperin, J., Spontaneous remissions in schizophrenia, *J. Amer. Med. Assoc.,* 1939, **112,** 2393-2395.

340. Gerard, M., Enuresis: A study in etiology, *Amer. J. Orthopsychiat.,* 1939, **9,** 48-58.

341. Gesell, A., and Amatruda, C. S., *Developmental Diagnosis,* Hoeber, New York, 2nd ed., 1947.

342. Gesell, A., and Ilg, F. L., *Infant and Child in the Culture of Today,* Harper, New York, 1943.

343. Gibbs, F. A., and Gibbs, E. L., *Atlas of Electroencephalography,* Cummings, Cambridge, Mass., 1941.

344. Gill, M. M., and Brenman, M., Treatment of a case of anxiety hysteria by an hypnotic technique employing psychoanalytic principles, *Bull. Menninger Clin.,* 1943, **7,** 163-171.

345. Gill, M. M., and Menninger, K., Techniques of hypnoanalysis: A case report, *Bull. Menninger Clin.,* 1946, **10,** 110-126.

346. Ginsburg, S. W., What unemployment does to people: A study in adjustment to crisis, *Amer. J. Psychiat.,* 1942, **99,** 439-446.

347. Girden, E., Cerebral mechanisms in conditioning under curare, *Amer. J. Psychol.,* 1940, **53,** 397-406.

348. Gitelson, M. (chairman), Ross, H., Erikson, E. H., Allen, F., Blanchard, P., Lippman, S. H., Gerard, M., and Lowrey, L. G., Section on play therapy, *Amer. J. Orthopsychiat.,* 1938, **8,** 499-524.

349. Glauber, I. P., Observations on a primary form of anhedonia, *Psychoanal. Quart.,* 1949, **18,** 67-78.

350. Glover, E., The psycho-analysis of affects, *Int. J. Psychoanal.,* 1939, **20,** 299-307.

351. Glover, E., Fenichel, O., Strachey, J., Bergler, E., Nunberg, H., and Bibring, E., Symposium on the theory of the therapeutic results of psychoanalysis, *Int. J. Psychoanal.,* 1937, **18,** 125-189.

352. Glueck, B., A study of 608 admissions to Sing Sing Prison, *Ment. Hyg.,* 1918, **2,** 85-151.

353. Glueck, S., and Glueck, E. T., *One Thousand Juvenile Delinquents,* Harvard Univ. Press, Cambridge, Mass., 1934.

354. Goldfarb, W., The effects of early institutional care on adolescent personality, *J. Exp. Educ.,* 1943, **12,** 106-129.

355. Goldfarb, W., Psychological privation in infancy and subsequent adjustment, *Amer. J. Orthopsychiat.*, 1945, **15**, 247-255.

356. Goldman, G. S., A case of compulsive handwashing, *Psychoanal. Quart.*, 1938, **7**, 96-121.

357. Goldstein, K., *The Organism,* American Book Co., New York, 1939.

358. Goldstein, K., *Aftereffects of Brain Injuries in War,* Grune & Stratton, New York, 1942.

359. Goldstein, K., *Language and Language Disturbances: Aphasic Symptom Complexes and Their Significance for Medicine and Theory of Language,* Grune & Stratton, New York, 1948.

360. Goldstein, K., and Scheerer, M., Abstract and concrete behavior, *Psychol. Monog.*, No. 239, 1941.

361. Goodenough, F. L., *Measurement of Intelligence by Drawings,* World Book Co., Yonkers, N. Y., 1926.

362. Gould, R., Review of "Frustration and Aggression," *Amer. Anthrop.*, 1940, **42**, 350-353.

363. Grace, W. J., Seton, P. H., Wolf, S., and Wolff, H. G., Studies of the human colon: I. Variations in concentration of lysozyme with life situation and emotional state, *Amer. J. Med. Sci.*, 1949, **217**, 241-251.

364. Gralnick, A., A seven year survey of insulin treatment in schizophrenia, *Amer. J. Psychiat.*, 1945, **101**, 449-452.

365. Gramlich, F. W., A psychological study of stress in service, *J. Gen. Psychol.* 1949, **41**, 273-296.

366. Greenacre, P., The predisposition to anxiety, *Psychoanal. Quart.*, 1941, **10**. 66-94.

367. Greenacre, P., Pathological weeping, *Psychoanal. Quart.*, 1945, **14**, 62-75.

368. Greenson, R. R., On genuine epilepsy, *Psychoanal. Quart.*, 1944, **13**. 139-159.

369. Gressel, G. C., Shobe, F. O., Saslow, G., DuBois, P. H., and Schroeder, H. A., Personality factors in arterial hypertension, *J. Amer. Med. Assoc.*, 1949, **140**, 265-271.

370. Grinker, R. R., and Spiegel, J. P., *Men Under Stress,* Blakiston, Philadelphia, 1945.

371. Grossman, M., Sequels of acute epidemic encephalitis, *J. Amer. Med. Assoc.*, 1922, **78**, 959-961.

372. Grotjahn, M., Laughter in dreams, *Psychoanal. Quart.*, 1945, **14**, 221-227.

373. Gutheil, E., *The Language of the Dream,* Macmillan, New York, 1939.

374. Guthrie, E. R., *The Psychology of Human Conflict,* Harper, New York, 1938.

375. Haggard, E. A., Psychological causes and results of stress, in *Human Factors in Undersea Warfare,* Nat. Res. Council, 1949.

376. Halliday, J. L., *Psychosocial Medicine: A Study of the Sick Society,* Norton, New York, 1948.

377. Hallowell, A. I., The child, the savage, and human experience, in Haring, D. G., *Personal Character and Cultural Milieu,* Syracuse Univ. Press, Syracuse, N.Y., rev. ed., 1949.

378. Hallowell, A. I., The social function of anxiety in primitive society, in

Haring, D. G., *Personal Character and Cultural Milieu,* Syracuse Univ. Press, Syracuse, N.Y., rev. ed., 1949.

379. Halverson, H. M., Infant sucking and tensional behavior, *J. Genet. Psychol.,* 1938, **53,** 365-430.

380. Halverson, H. M., Genital and sphincter behavior of the male infant, *J. Genet. Psychol.,* 1940, **56,** 95-137.

381. Hamilton, G., *Theory and Practice of Social Case Work,* Columbia Univ. Press, New York, 1940.

382. Hamilton, G., *Psychotherapy in Child Guidance,* Columbia Univ. Press, New York, 1947.

383. Hanfmann, E., and Kasanin, J., *Conceptual Thinking in Schizophrenia,* Nerv. & Ment. Dis. Monog., New York, 1942.

384. Haring, D. G., *Personal Character and Cultural Milieu,* Syracuse Univ. Press, Syracuse, N.Y., rev. ed., 1949.

385. Harlan, S. C., The influence of reward, punishment and incentives for recovery in treatment of psychoneurosis, *J. Crim. Psychopathol.,* 1944, **5,** 787-794.

386. Harms, E., *Handbook of Child Guidance,* Child Care Pub., New York, 1947.

387. Harris, N. G., *Modern Trends in Psychological Medicine,* Hoeber, New York, 1948.

388. Harris, S., Clinical types of hyperinsulinism: A report of cases, *Amer. J. Digest. Dis. and Nutr.,* 1934, **1,** 562-569.

389. Harrower-Erickson, M. R., and Steiner, M. E., *Large Scale Rorschach Techniques,* Thomas, Springfield, Ill., 1944.

390. Hartley, E., *Problems in Prejudice,* King's Crown Press, New York, 1946.

391. Hartmann, H., Kris, E., and Loewenstein, R. M., Notes on the theory of aggression, in *The Psychoanalytic Study of the Child,* Vols. III/IV, Internat. Univ. Press, New York, 1949.

392. Hathaway, S. R., and McKinley, J. C., A multiphasic personality schedule (Minnesota): I. Construction of the schedule, *J. Psychol.,* 1940, **10,** 249-254.

393. Hathaway, S. R., and McKinley, J. C., *Manual for the Minnesota Multiphasic Personality Inventory,* Psychol. Corp., New York, 2nd ed., 1943.

394. Hauptmann, A., Studies of finger capillaries in neurosis, epilepsy and migraine, *J. Nerv. Ment. Dis.,* 1945, **101,** 387-389.

395. Havighurst, R. J., and Taba, H., *Adolescent Character and Personality,* Wiley, New York, 1949.

396. Hayward, E. P., Types of female castration reaction, *Psychoanal. Quart.,* 1943, **12,** 45-66.

397. Healy, W., and Bronner, A. F., *Treatment and What Happened Afterward,* Judge Baker Guidance Center, Boston, 1939.

398. Heath, C. W., Brouha, L., Gregory, L. W., Seltzer, C. C., Wells, F. L., and Woods, W. L., *What People Are—A Study of Normal Young Men,* Harvard Univ. Press, Cambridge, Mass., 1945.

399. Heath, R. G., and Pool, J. L., Treatment of psychoses with bilateral ablation of a focal area of the frontal cortex, *Psychosom. Med.,* 1948, **10,** 254-256.

400. Heilig, R., and Hoff, H., Über psychogene Entstehung des Herpes labialis, *Med. Klin.,* 1928, **24,** 1472.

401. Helson, H., and Quantius, L., Changes in skin temperature following intense stimulation, *J. Exp. Psychol.*, 1934, **17**, 20-35.

402. Henderson, D. K., and Gillespie, R. D., *A Textbook of Psychiatry*, Oxford Univ. Press, London, 6th ed., 1944.

403. Hendrick, I., *Facts and Theories of Psychoanalysis*, Knopf, New York, 2nd ed., 1939.

404. Hendrick, I., Psychoanalytic observations on the aurae of two cases with convulsions, *Psychosom. Med.*, 1940, **2**, 43-52.

405. Henry, G. W., *Sex Variants*, 2 vols., Hoeber, New York, 1941.

406. Hermann, I., The use of the term "active" in the definition of masculinity, *Int. J. Psychoanal.*, 1935, **16**, 219-222.

407. Herman, M., London, J., and Wortis, S. B., Mental changes in patients with subdural hematoma, *J. Amer. Med. Assoc.*, 1944, **125**, 113-116.

408. Heuser, K. D., The psychopathic personality: The Rorschach patterns of 28 cases, *Amer. J. Psychiat.*, 1946, **103**, 105-112.

409. Hilgard, E. R., *Theories of Learning*, Appleton-Century-Crofts, New York, 1948.

410. Hilgard, E. R., and Marquis, D. G., *Conditioning and Learning*, Appleton-Century, New York, 1940.

411. Hill, L. B., A psychoanalytic observation on essential hypertension, *Psychoanal. Rev.*, 1935, **22**, 60-64.

412. Hill, L. B., The use of hostility as defense, *Psychoanal. Quart.*, 1938, **7**, 254-264.

413. Hinkle, L. E., Jr., and Wolf, S., Experimental study of life situations, emotions, and the occurrence of acidosis in a juvenile diabetic, *Amer. J. Med. Sci.*, 1949, **217**, 130-135.

414. Hinsie, L. E., *The Person in the Body: An Introduction to Psychosomatic Medicine*, Norton, New York, 1945.

415. Hinsie, L. E., and Shatzky, J., *Psychiatric Dictionary*, Oxford Univ. Press, New York, 1940.

416. Hitschmann, E., and Bergler, E., *Frigidity in Women: Its Characteristics and Treatment*, Nerv. & Ment. Dis. Pub., Washington, 1936.

417. Hoch, P. H., Theoretical aspects of frontal lobotomy and similar brain operations, *Amer. J. Psychiat.*, 1949, **106**, 448-453.

418. Hoch, P. H., Experimentally produced abnormal mental states, *Digest Neurol. Psychiat.*, 1950, **18**, 154-155.

419. Hoch, P. H., and Knight, R. P., *Epilepsy*, Grune & Stratton, New York, 1947.

420. Hoch, P. H., Kubis, J. F., and Rouke, F. L., Psychogalvanometric investigations in psychoses and other abnormal mental states, *Psychosom. Med.*, 1944, **6**, 237-242.

421. Hoch, P. H., and Zubin, J., *Psychosexual Development in Health and Disease*, Grune & Stratton, New York, 1949.

422. Hoffer, W., Mouth, hand, and ego-integration, in *The Psychoanalytic Study of the Child*, Vols. III/IV, Internat. Univ. Press, New York, 1949.

423. Holden, W. H., Effect of civilization as evidenced by lack of hypertension and coronary occlusion in primitive people, *Proc. 8th Amer. Sci. Congr.*, 1942, Part 2, 309-312.

424. Hollingshead, A. de B., *Elmtown's Youth: The Impact of Social Classes on Adolescents,* Wiley, New York, 1949.

425. Hollitscher, W., On the concepts of psychological health and illness, *Int. J. Psychoan.,* 1943, **24,** 125-140.

426. Hollos, I., and Ferenczi, S., *Psychoanalysis and the Psychic Disorders of General Paresis,* Nerv. & Ment. Dis. Pub., Washington, 1925.

427. Holmes, T. H., Goodell, H., Wolf, S., and Wolff, G. H., *The Nose: An Experimental Study of Reactions Within the Nose in Human Subjects During Varying Life Experiences,* Thomas, Springfield, Ill., 1950.

428. Holt, L. E., and McIntosh, R., *Diseases of Infancy and Childhood,* Appleton-Century, 11th ed., 1939.

429. Homburger-Erikson, E., Configurations in play—clinical notes, *Psychoanal, Quart.,* 1937, **6,** 139-214.

430. Horney, K., The denial of the vagina, *Int. J. Psychoanal.,* 1933, **25,** 694-704.

431. Horney, K., *The Neurotic Personality of Our Time,* Norton, New York, 1937.

432. Horney, K., *Our Inner Conflicts,* Norton, New York, 1945.

433. Horsley, J. S., *Narco-Analysis,* Milford, London, 1943.

434. Hoskins, R. G., *The Biology of Schizophrenia,* Norton, New York, 1946.

435. Hovland, C. I., and Sears, R. R., Minor studies of aggression: VI. Correlation of lynchings and economic indices, *J. Psychol.,* 1940, **9,** 301-310.

436. Hudgins, C. V., Conditioning and voluntary control of the pupillary light reflex, *J. Gen. Psychol.,* 1933, **8,** 2-51.

437. Hull, C. L., *Hypnosis and Suggestibility,* Appleton-Century, New York, 1933.

438. Hull, C. L., *Principles of Behavior,* Appleton-Century, New York, 1943.

439. Hunt, J. McV., *Personality and the Behavior Disorders: A Handbook Based on Experimental and Clinical Research,* 2 vols., Ronald, New York, 1944.

440. Hunt, J. McV., and Willoughby, R. R., The effect of frustration on hoarding in rats, *Psychosom. Med.,* 1939, **1,** 309-319.

441. Hunt, W. A., Wittson, C. L., Harris, H. I., Solomon, P., and Jackson, M. M., Psychometric procedures in the detection of the neuropsychiatrically unfit, *U.S. Naval Med. Bull.,* 1943, **41,** 471-480.

442. Huschka, M., A study of training in voluntary control of urination in a group of problem children, *Psychosom. Med.,* 1943, **5,** 254-265.

443. Huschka, M., and McKnight, W., Psychiatric observation in well-baby clinic, *Psychosom. Med.,* 1943, **5,** 42-50.

444. Huston, P. E., and Shakow, D., Learning capacity in schizophrenia, *Amer. J. Psychiat.,* 1949, **105,** 881-888.

445. Hutton, L., Weber, H., and Wolfe, B., Individual psychology and the child (II), *Individual Psychology Pamphlets,* No. 8, Daniel, London, 1935.

446. Hyde, R. W., and Chisholm, R. M., Studies in medical sociology: III. The relation of mental disorders to race and nationality, *New Engl. J. Med.,* 1944, **231,** 612-618.

447. Hyde, R. W., and Kingsley, L. V., Studies in medical sociology: I. The relation of mental disorders to the community socioeconomic level, *New Engl. J. Med.,* 1944, **231,** 543-548.

448. Hyde, R. W., and Kingsley, L. V., Studies in medical sociology: II. The

relation of mental disorders to population density, *New Engl. J. Med.*, 1944, **231**, 571-577.

449. Isaacs, S., *Social Development in Young Children*, Routledge, London, 1933.
450. Itard, J., *The Wild Boy of Aveyron*, Appleton-Century, New York, 1932.
451. Jacobsen, C. F., A study of cerebral function in learning: The frontal lobes, *J. Comp. Neurol.*, 1931, **52**, 271-340.
452. Jacobsen, C. F., Wolfe, J. B., and Jackson, T. A., An experimental analysis of the functions of the frontal association areas in primates, *J. Nerv. Ment. Dis.*, 1935, **82**, 1-14.
453. Jacobson, E., *Progressive Relaxation*, Univ. of Chicago Press, Chicago, 2nd ed., 1938.
454. Jacobson, E., A case of sterility, *Psychoanal. Quart.*, 1946, **15**, 330-350.
455. Janet, P., *The Major Symptoms of Hysteria*, Macmillan, New York, 2nd ed., 1920.
456. Janet, P., *Principles of Psychotherapy*, Macmillan, New York, 1924.
457. Janet, P., *Psychological Healing*, Allen & Unwin, London, 1926.
458. Jekels, L., Zur Psychologie des Mitleids, *Imago*, 1930, **16**, 5-22.
459. Jelliffe, S. E., Sketches in psychosomatic medicine, *Nerv. Ment. Dis. Monog.*, No. 65, 1939.
460. Jelliffe, S. E., and Evans, E., Psychotherapy and tuberculosis, *Amer. Rev. Tuberc.*, 1919, **3**, 417-432.
461. Jennings, D., Perforated peptic ulcer, *Lancet*, 1940, **239**, 395-444.
462. John, M., Group treatment with particular reference to group projection methods, *Amer. J. Psychiat.*, 1944, **101**, 292-299.
463. Johnson, A., Shapiro, L. B., and Alexander, F., Preliminary report on rheumatoid arthritis, *Psychosom. Med.*, 1947, **9**, 295-300.
464. Johnson, W., *People in Quandaries*, Harper, New York, 1946.
465. Jolliffe, N., Effects of vitamin deficiency on mental and emotional processes, in *The Inter-Relationship of Mind and Body*, Williams & Wilkins, Baltimore, 1939.
466. Jones, E., *Papers on Psychoanalysis*, Williams & Wilkins, Baltimore, 2nd ed., 1948.
467. Jones, H. E., The adolescent growth study: VI. The analysis of voice records, *J. Consult. Psychol.*, 1942, **6**, 255-256.
468. Jones, M., Group psychotherapy, *Brit. Med. J.*, 1942, Part 2, 276-278.
469. Joseph, E. D., Peck, S. M., and Kaufman, M. R., Psychological study of neurodermatitis with a case report, *J. Mt. Sinai Hospit.*, 1949, **15**, 360-366.
470. Jost, H., Some physiological changes during frustration, *Child Developm.* 1941, **12**, 9-15.
471. Jung, C. G., *Psychology of the Unconscious*, Moffat, Yard, New York, 1916.
472. Jung, C. G., *Studies in Word Associations*, Heinemann, London, 1919.
473. Jung, C. G., *Psychological Types or the Psychology of Individuation*, Harcourt, Brace, New York, 1923.
474. Kalinowsky, L. B., and Hoch, P. H., *Shock Treatments and Other Somatic Procedures in Psychiatry*, Grune & Stratton, New York, 1946.
475. Kallmann, F. J., The genetic theory of schizophrenia, *Amer. J. Psychiat.*, 1946, **103**, 309-322.

476. Kallmann, F. J., The genetic theory of schizophrenia, in Kluckhohn, C., and Murray, H. A., *Personality in Nature, Society, and Culture,* Knopf, New York, 1948.

477. Kamiat, A. H., *Social Forces in Personality Stunting,* Sci-Art, Cambridge, Mass., 1939.

478. Kanner, L., Irrelevant and metaphorical language in early infantile autism, *Amer. J. Psychiat.,* 1946, **103,** 242-246.

479. Kanner, L., *Child Psychiatry,* Thomas, Springfield, Ill., 2nd ed., 1948.

480. Kanner, L., Problems of nosology and psychodynamics of early infantile autism, *Amer. J. Orthopsychiat.,* 1949, **19,** 416-426.

481. Kaplan, O. J., *Mental Disorders in Later Life,* Stanford Univ. Press, Stanford, Calif., 1945.

482. Kardiner, A., *The Bio-Analysis of the Epileptic Reaction,* Psychoanal. Quart. Press, Albany, 1932.

483. Kardiner, A., *The Individual and His Society,* Columbia Univ. Press, New York, 1939.

484. Kardiner, A., and others, *The Psychological Frontiers of Society,* Columbia Univ. Press, New York, 1945.

485. Kardiner, A., and Spiegel, H., *War Stress and Neurotic Illness,* Hoeber, New York, 1947.

486. Kasanin, J. S., *Language and Thought in Schizophrenia,* Univ. of California Press, Berkeley, 1944.

487. Katan, A., Experience with enuretics, in *The Psychoanalytic Study of the Child,* Vol. II, Internat. Univ. Press, New York, 1946.

488. Katan, M., The understanding of schizophrenic speech, *Int. J. Psychoanal.,* 1939, **20,** 353-362.

489. Kaufman, M. R., and Beaton, L. E., A psychiatric treatment program in combat, *Bull. Menninger Clin.,* 1947, **11,** 1-14.

490. Kempf, E., *The Autonomic Functions and the Personality,* Nerv. & Ment. Dis. Pub., Washington, 1918.

491. Kennard, M. A., Inheritance of electroencephalogram patterns in children with behavior disorders, *Psychosom. Med.,* 1949, **11,** 151-157.

492. Kent, G. H., and Rosanoff, A. J., A study of association in insanity, *Amer. J. Insanity,* 1910, **47,** Nos. 1-2.

493. Kerr, W. J., Dalton, J. W., and Gliebe, P. A., Some physical phenomena associated with anxiety states and their relationship to hyperventilation, *Ann. Int. Med.,* 1937, **2,** 961-992.

494. Kinsey, A. C., Pomeroy, W. B., and Martin, C. E., *Sexual Behavior in the Human Male,* Saunders, Philadelphia, 1948.

495. Klapman, J. W., Didactic group psychotherapy with psychotic patients, in Slavson, S. R., *The Practice of Group Therapy,* Internat. Univ. Press, New York, 1947.

496. Klein, D. B., *Mental Hygiene: The Psychology of Personal Adjustment,* Holt, New York, 1944.

497. Klein, E., Psychoanalytic aspects of school problems, in *The Psychoanalytic Study of the Child,* Vols. III/IV, Internat. Univ. Press, New York, 1949.

498. Klein, H. R., A personality study of one hundred unselected patients attending a gastrointestinal clinic, *Amer. J. Psychiat.*, 1948, **104**, 433-439.
499. Klein, H. R., and Horwitz, A., Psychosexual factors in the paranoid phenomena, *Amer. J. Psychiat.*, 1949, **105**, 697-701.
500. Klein, M., *The Psycho-Analysis of Children*, Hogarth, London, 2nd ed., 1937.
501. Klein, M., *Contributions to Psycho-Analysis: 1921-1945*, Hogarth, London, 1948.
502. Klein, M., and Riviere, J., *Love, Hate and Reparation*, Hogarth, London, 1938.
503. Klineberg, O., Negro intelligence and urban residence, in Newcomb, T. M., Hartley, E. L., and others, *Readings in Social Psychology*, Holt, New York, 1947.
504. Kluckhohn, C., *Mirror for Man*, Whittlesey House, New York, 1949.
505. Kluckhohn, C., and Murray, H. A., *Personality in Nature, Society, and Culture*, Knopf, New York, 1948.
506. Knight, R. P., Introjection, projection, and identification, *Psychoanal. Quart.*, 1940, **9**, 334-341.
507. Knight, R. P., Evaluation of the results of psychoanalytic therapy, *Amer. J. Psychiat.*, 1941, **98**, 434-446.
508. Knopf, O., Preliminary report on personality studies in thirty migraine patients, *J. Nerv. Ment. Dis.*, 1935, **82**, 270-285.
509. Knott, J. R., and Gottlieb, J. S., The electroencephalogram in psychopathic personality, *Psychosom. Med.*, 1943, **5**, 139-142.
510. Koch, H. L., The influence of some affective factors in recall, *J. Gen. Psychol.*, 1930, **4**, 171-190.
511. Korzybski, A., *Science and Sanity*, Internat. Non-Aristotelian Library, Lancaster, Pa., 1941.
512. Kraepelin, E., and Lange, J., *Psychiatrie*, Barth, Leipzig, 9th ed., 1927.
513. Kraines, S. H., Brief psychotherapy, *Ment. Hyg.*, 1943, **27**, 70-79.
514. Krech, D., and Crutchfield, R. S., *Theory and Problems of Social Psychology*, McGraw-Hill, New York, 1948.
515. Kroeber, A. L., *Anthropology: Race, Language, Culture, Psychology, Prehistory*, Harcourt, Brace, New York, rev. ed., 1948.
516. Kroll, S., Concealment of facts in psychoanalysis, *Amer. J. Psychother.*, 1947, **1**, 145-154.
517. Kubie, L. S., *Practical and Theoretical Aspects of Psychoanalysis*, Internat. Univ. Press, New York, 1950.
518. Kubie, L. S., and Margolin, S., The process of hypnotism and the nature of the hypnotic state, *Amer. J. Psychiat.*, 1944, **100**, 611-622.
519. Kubie, L. S., and Margolin, S., The therapeutic role of drugs in the process of repression, dissociation and synthesis, *Psychosom. Med.*, 1945, **7**, 147-151.
520. Landes, R., The abnormal among the Ojibwa Indians, *J. Abnorm. Soc. Psychol.*, 1938, **33**, 14-33.
521. Landis, C., and Bolles, M. M., *Textbook of Abnormal Psychology*, Macmillan, New York, 1946.

522. Landis, C., and Hunt, W. A., *The Startle Pattern,* Farrar & Rinehart, New York, 1939.

523. Landis, C., and Page, J. D., *Modern Society and Mental Disease,* Farrar & Rinehart, New York, 1938.

524. Langdon-Brown, W., Crookshank, F. G., Young, J. C., Gordon, G., and Bevan-Brown, C. M., Anorexia nervosa, *Individual Psychology Pamphlets,* No. 2, Daniel, London, 1933.

525. Langdon-Brown, W., Woodcock, O. H., Young, J. C., Pearson, S. V., Ray, M. B., Robb, M., and Crookshank, F. G., Individual psychology and psychosomatic disorders (I), *Individual Psychology Pamphlets,* No. 4, Daniel, London, 1933.

526. Langford, W. S., Anxiety attacks in children, *Amer. J. Orthopsychiat.,* 1937, **7,** 210-218.

527. Lasswell, H. D., *Psychopathology and Politics,* Univ. of Chicago Press, Chicago, 1930.

528. Lawton, G., *New Goals for Old Age,* Columbia Univ. Press, New York, 1943.

529. Lawton, G., *Aging Successfully,* Columbia Univ. Press, New York, 1946.

530. Lazarsfeld, P., An unemployed village, *Character and Pers.,* 1932, **1,** 147-151.

531. Leavitt, H. C., Bronchial asthma in functional psychoses, *Psychosom. Med.,* 1943, **5,** 39-41.

532. Lecky, P., *Self-Consistency: A Theory of Personality,* Island Press, New York, 1945.

533. Leeper, R., *Psychology of Personality,* Edwards, Ann Arbor, 1946.

534. Lehrman, P. R., Some unconscious determinants in homicide, *Psychiat. Quart.,* 1939, **13,** 605-621.

535. Lemere, F., Voegtlin, W. L., Broz, W. R., O'Hallaren, P., and Tupper, W. T., Conditioned reflex treatment of chronic alcoholism: A review of six years' experience of this treatment of 1,526 patients, *J. Amer. Med. Assoc.,* 1942, **120,** 269-271.

536. Lennox, W. G., Two new drugs in epilepsy therapy, *Amer. J. Psychiat.,* 1946, **103,** 159-161.

537. Lennox, W. G., The genetics of epilepsy, *Amer. J. Psychiat.,* 1947, **103,** 457-462.

538. Lennox, W. G., Gibbs, E. L., and Gibbs, F. A., Inheritance of cerebral dysrhythmia and epilepsy, *Arch. Neurol. Psychiat.,* 1940, **44,** 1155-1183.

539. Levine, A. J., *Current Psychologies: A Critical Analysis,* Sci-Art, Cambridge, Mass., 1940.

540. Levine, M., *Psychotherapy in Medical Practice,* Macmillan, New York, 1942.

541. Levy, D. M., Fingersucking and accessory movements in early infancy: An etiologic study, *Amer. J. Psychiat.,* 1928, **85,** 881-918.

542. Levy, D. M., Use of play technic as experimental procedure, *Amer. J. Orthopsychiat.,* 1933, **3,** 266-275.

543. Levy, D. M., Experiments on the sucking reflex and social behavior of dogs, *Amer. J. Orthopsychiat.,* 1934, **4,** 203-224.

544. Levy, D. M., Studies in sibling rivalry, *Res. Monog.,* No. 2, Amer. Orthopsychiat. Assoc., 1937.

545. Levy, D. M., Primary affect hunger, *Amer. J. Psychiat.,* 1937, **94,** 643-652.

546. Levy, D. M., On instinct-satiation: An experiment on pecking behavior of chickens, *J. Gen. Psychol.*, 1938, **18**, 327-348.
547. Levy, D. M., Release therapy, *Amer. J. Orthopsychiat.*, 1939, **9**, 713-736.
548. Levy, D. M., Sibling rivalry studies in children of primitive groups, *Amer. J. Orthopsychiat.*, 1939, **9**, 205-215.
549. Levy, D. M., *Maternal Overprotection,* Columbia Univ. Press, New York, 1943.
550. Levy, D. M., Anti-Nazis: Criteria of differentiation, *Psychiatry,* 1948, **11**, 125-167.
551. Levy, J., Relationship therapy, *Amer. J. Orthopsychiat.*, 1938, **8**, 64-67.
552. Levy, J., and Munroe, R., *The Happy Family,* Knopf, New York, 1938.
553. Levy, N. A., *Personality Disturbances in Combat Fliers,* Josiah Macy, Jr. Fdn., New York, 1945.
554. Lewin, B. D., A study of the endocrine organs in the psychoses, *Amer. J. Psychiat.*, 1927, **85**, 391-458.
555. Lewin, B. D., Analysis and structure of a transient hypomania, *Psychoanal. Quart.*, 1932, **1**, 43-58.
556. Lewin, B. D., Sleep, the mouth, and the dream screen, *Psychoanal. Quart.*, 1946, **15**, 419-434.
557. Lewin, B. D., The nature of reality, the meaning of nothing, with an addendum on concentration, *Psychoanal. Quart.*, 1948, **17**, 524-526.
558. Lewin, K., *Dynamic Theory of Personality,* McGraw-Hill, New York, 1935.
559. Lewin, K., *Principles of Topological Psychology,* McGraw-Hill, New York, 1936.
560. Lewin, K., Psychoanalysis and topographical psychology, *Bull. Menninger Clin.*, 1937, **1**, 202-212.
561. Lewin, K., *Resolving Social Conflicts,* Harper, New York, 1948.
562. Lewin, K., Lippitt, R., and White, R. K., Patterns of aggressive behavior in experimentally created "social climates," *J. Soc. Psychol.*, 1939, **10**, 271-299.
563. Lewis, J. H., and Sarbin, T. R., Studies in psychosomatics: The influence of hypnotic responses on gastric hunger contractions, *Psychol. Bull.*, 1942, **39**, 596-597.
564. Lewis, N. D. C., *Constitutional Factors in Dementia Praecox,* Nerv. & Ment. Dis. Pub., Washington, 1923.
565. Lewis, N. D. C., *A Short History of Psychiatric Achievement: With a Forecast for the Future,* Norton, New York, 1941.
566. Lewis, N. D. C., and Pacella, B. L., *Modern Trends in Child Psychiatry,* Internat. Univ. Press, New York, 1945.
567. Lhamon, W. T., Relation between finger volume changes, brain activity, and psychopathologic reactions, *Psychosom. Med.*, 1949, **11**, 113-118.
568. Liddell, H. S., Nervous strain in domesticated animals and man, *Cornell Veterinarian,* 1936, **26**, 107-112.
569. Liddell, H. S., The experimental neurosis and the problem of mental disorder, *Amer. J. Psychiat.*, 1938, **94**, 1035-1041.
570. Liddell, H. S., Symposium—Second colloquia on psychodynamics and experimental medicine: The alteration of instinctual processes through the influence of conditioned reflexes, *Psychosom. Med.*, 1942, **4**, 390-395.

571. Lidz, T., Emotional factors in hyperthyroidism, *Psychosom. Med.*, 1949, **11**, 2-8.
572. Lietch, E. M., and Escalona, S., The reactions of infants to stress, in *The Psychoanalytic Study of the Child*, Vols. III/IV, Internat. Univ. Press, New York, 1949.
573. Lincoln, S. J., *The Dream in Primitive Cultures*, Williams & Wilkins, Baltimore, 1937.
574. Lindemann, E., Symptomatology and management of acute grief, *Amer. J. Psychiat.*, 1944, **101**, 141-148.
575. Lindemann, E., Social science in relation to medicine and some of its recent contributions, *Cincinnati J. Med.*, 1949, **30**, 475-481.
576. Lindner, R. M., The equivalents of matricide, *Psychoanal. Quart.*, 1948, **17**, 453-470.
577. Linton, R., *The Cultural Background of Personality*, Appleton-Century, New York, 1945.
578. Lipkin, M., and Sharp, L. I., Psychosomatic medicine: Some notes on its implication in diagnosis and treatment, *Ann. Int. Med.*, 1944, **20**, 760-767.
579. Lippmann, H., Neurotic delinquent, *Amer. J. Orthopsychiat.*, 1937, **7**, 114-121.
580. Liss, E. (chairman), Bartley, S. H., Cole, E. M., Gates, A. I., Donahue, E. K., and Berens, C., Learning as a psychosomatic problem, Round Table, 1946, *Amer. J. Orthopsychiat.*, 1947, **17**, 381-403.
581. Loeser, L. H., Sexual psychopath in the military services, *Amer. J. Psychiat.*, 1945, **102**, 92-101.
582. Lorand, S., Dynamics and therapy of depressive states, *Psychoanal. Rev.*, 1937, **24**, 337-349.
583. Lorand, S., *Psychoanalysis Today*, Internat. Univ. Press, New York, 2nd ed., 1944.
584. Lorand, S., *Technique of Psychoanalytic Therapy*, Internat. Univ. Press, New York, 1946.
585. Lourie, R. S., Barrera, S. E., and Strongin, E. I., Autonomic nervous system function in children with behavior problems as measured by the parotid secretory rate, *Amer. J. Psychiat.*, 1942, **99**, 419-425.
586. Louttit, C. M., *Clinical Psychology of Children's Behavior Problems*, Harper, New York, 2nd ed., 1947.
587. Low, A. A., *Group Psychotherapy: A Record of Class Interviews with Patients Suffering from Mental and Nervous Ailments*, Recovery, Chicago, 1943.
588. Lowenstein, P., and Svendson, M., Experimental modification of behavior of shy and withdrawn children, *Amer. J. Orthopsychiat.*, 1938, **8**, 639-653.
589. Lowrey, L. G., *Psychiatry for Social Workers*, Columbia Univ. Press, New York, 1946.
590. Löwy, I., Stupidity as exemption, *Int. J. Individ. Psychol.*, 1935, **1**, 102-110.
591. Luria, A. L., *Nature of Human Conflict*, Liveright, New York, 1932.
592. Lynn, J. G., and Lynn, D. R., Face-hand laterality in relation to personality, *J. Abnorm. Soc. Psychol.*, 1938, **32**, 291-322.

593. MacDonald, M. W., Criminally aggressive behavior in passive, effeminate boys, *Amer. J. Orthopsychiat.*, 1938, **8**, 70-78.
594. MacKinnon, D. W., and Henle, M., *Experimental Studies in Psychodynamics: A Laboratory Manual,* Harvard Univ. Press, Cambridge, Mass., 1948.
595. McDermott, N. T., and Cobb, S., A psychiatric survey of fifty cases of bronchial asthma, *Psychosom. Med.*, 1939, **1**, 203-244.
596. McDougall, W., *Outline of Abnormal Psychology,* Scribner, New York, 1926.
597. McGranahan, D. V., A critical and experimental study of repression, *J. Abnorm. Soc. Psychol.*, 1940, **35**, 212-225.
598. Machover, K., *Personality Projection in the Drawing of the Human Figure,* Thomas, Springfield, Ill., 1949.
599. Machover, S., *Cultural and Racial Variations in Patterns of Intellect,* Bureau of Pub., Teachers College, Columbia Univ., New York, 1943.
600. Mahl, G. F., Chronic fear and gastric secretion of HCl in dogs, *Psychosom. Med.*, 1949, **11**, 30-44.
601. Mahler, M. S., Child analysis, in Lewis, N. D. C., and Pacella, B. L., *Modern Trends in Child Psychiatry,* Internat. Univ. Press, New York, 1945.
602. Mahler, M. S., and Rangell, L., A psychosomatic study of *maladie des tics* (Gilles de la Tourette's Disease), *Psychiat. Quart.*, 1943, **17**, 579-603.
603. Mahler-Schoenberger, M., Pseudoimbecility: A magic cap of invisibility, *Psychoanal. Quart.*, 1942, **11**, 149-164.
604. Maier, N. R. F., *Studies of Abnormal Behavior in the Rat,* Harper, New York, 1939.
605. Maier, N. R. F., *Psychology in Industry,* Houghton Mifflin, Boston, 1946.
606. Maier, N. R. F., *Frustration: The Study of Behavior Without a Goal,* McGraw-Hill, New York, 1949.
607. Mairet, P., *A.B.C. of Adler's Psychology,* Kegan Paul, London, 1928.
608. Malamud, W., and Sands, S. L., A revision of the psychiatric rating scale, *Amer. J. Psychiat.*, 1947, **104**, 231-237.
609. Malamud, W., Sands, S. L., Malamud, I. T., and Powers, P. J. P., The involutional psychoses: A socio-psychiatric follow-up study, *Amer. J. Psychiat.*, 1949, **105**, 567-572.
610. Malinowski, B., *Sex and Repression in Savage Society,* Harcourt, Brace, New York, 1927.
611. Malinowski, B., *The Sexual Life of Savages,* Liveright, New York, 1929.
612. Malzberg, B., *Social and Biological Aspects of Mental Disease,* State Hospitals Press, Utica, N.Y., 1940.
613. Marcus, G., *Some Aspects of Relief in Family Case Work,* based on a study made for the Charity Organization Society of New York, 1929.
614. Marcussen, R. M., and Wolff, H. G., A formulation of the dynamics of the migraine attack, *Psychosom. Med.*, 1949, **11**, 251-256.
615. Martland, H. S., The pathology of acute and chronic alcoholism, in *Alcohol and Man,* Macmillan, New York, 1935.
616. Maslow, A. H., The role of dominance in the social and sexual behavior of infrahuman primates: III. A theory of sexual behavior, *J. Genet. Psychol.*, 1936, **48**, 310-338.

617. Maslow, A. H., Personality and culture patterns, in Stagner, R., *Psychology of Personality,* McGraw-Hill, New York, 1937.
618. Maslow, A. H., Dominance, personality and social behavior in women, *J. Soc. Psychol.,* 1939, **10,** 3-39.
619. Maslow, A. H., The dynamics of psychological security-insecurity, *Character and Pers.,* 1942, **10,** 331-344.
620. Maslow, A. H., Self-esteem (dominance-feeling) and sexuality in women, *J. Soc. Psychol.,* 1942, **16,** 259-294.
621. Maslow, A. H., Conflict, frustration and threat, *J. Abnorm. Soc. Psychol.,* 1943, **38,** 81-86.
622. Maslow, A. H., A dynamic theory of motivation, *Psychol. Rev.,* 1943, **50,** 370-396.
623. Maslow, A. H., "Higher" and lower needs, *J. Psychol.,* 1948, **25,** 433-436.
624. Maslow, A. H., Some theoretical consequences of basic need-gratification, *J. Personality,* 1948, **16,** 402-416.
625. Maslow, A. H., The expressive component of behavior, *Psychol. Rev.,* 1949, **56,** 261-272.
626. Maslow, A. H., Self-actualizing people: A study in psychological health, *Personality-Symposium,* No. 1, 1950, 11-34.
627. Masserman, J. H., Psychobiological dynamisms in behavior, *Psychiatry,* 1942, **5,** 341-348.
628. Masserman, J. H., *Behavior and Neurosis,* Univ. of Chicago Press, Chicago, 1943.
629. Masserman, J. H., *Principles of Dynamic Psychiatry,* Saunders, Philadelphia, 1946.
630. Masserman, J. H., and Yum, K. S., An analysis of the influence of alcohol on experimental neuroses in cats, *Psychosom. Med.,* 1946, **8,** 36-52.
631. Max, L. W., Conditioned reaction technique: A case study, *Psychol. Bull.,* 1935, **32,** 734.
632. Max, L. W., Experimental study of the motor theory of consciousness: Action-current responses in the deaf, dreaming, awakening, kinesthetic imagery and abstract thinking, *J. Comp. Psychol.,* 1937, **24,** 301-344.
633. Mayo, E., *The Human Problems of an Industrial Civilization,* Macmillan, New York, 2nd ed., 1946.
634. Mead, M., *Competition and Cooperation Among Primitive Peoples,* McGraw-Hill, New York, 1937.
635. Mead, M., *From the South Seas: Studies of Adolescence and Sex in Primitive Societies,* Morrow, New York, 1939.
636. Meerloo, J. A. M., *Patterns of Panic,* Internat. Univ. Press, New York, 1950.
637. Menninger, K. A., Psychoanalytic study of a case of organic epilepsy, *Psychoanal. Rev.,* 1926, **13,** 187-199.
638. Menninger, K. A., *Man Against Himself,* Harcourt, Brace, New York, 1938.
639. Menninger, K. A., *The Human Mind,* Knopf, New York, 3rd ed., 1945.
640. Menninger, W. C., *Juvenile Paresis,* Williams & Wilkins, Baltimore, 1936.
641. Menninger, W. C., *Psychiatry in a Troubled World,* Macmillan, New York, 1948.

642. Menzies, R., Conditioned vasomotor responses in human subjects, *J. Psychol.*, 1937, 4, 75-120.

643. Meyer, A., An attempt at analysis of neurotic constitution, *Amer. J. Psychol.*, 1903, **14**, 90-103.

644. Meyer, A., Problems of mental reaction types, mental cases, and disease, *Psychol. Bull.*, 1908, **5**, 245-261.

645. Meyer, A., Objective psychology and psychobiology, *J. Amer. Med. Assoc.*, 1915, **65**, 860-863.

646. Meyer, A., *The Commonsense Psychiatry of Dr. Adolf Meyer*, McGraw-Hill, New York, 1948.

647. Meyer, A., Bollmeier, L. N., and Alexander, F., Correlation between emotions and carbohydrate metabolism in two cases of diabetes mellitus, *Psychosom. Med.*, 1945, **7**, 335-341.

648. Michaels, J. J., The relationship of anti-social traits to the electroencephalogram in children with behavior disorder, *Psychosom. Med.*, 1945, **7**, 41-44.

649. Miles, W. R., Psychological effects of alcohol in man, in *Alcohol and Man*, Macmillan, New York, 1935.

650. Miller, E., Wilson, A. T. M., and Wittkower, E., Clinical case studies and their relationships, including the psychosomatic disorders, in Miller, E., *The Neuroses in War*, Macmillan, New York, 1942.

651. Miller, H., and Baruch, D. W., Studies of children with allergic manifestations, *Psychosom. Med.*, 1948, **10**, 275-278.

652. Miller, J. G., *Unconsciousness*, Wiley, New York, 1942.

653. Miller, M. L., A psychological study of a case of eczema and a case of neurodermatitis, *Psychosom. Med.*, 1942, 4, 82-93.

654. Miller, M. L., Psychodynamic mechanisms in neurodermatitis, *Psychosom. Med.*, 1948, **10**, 309-318.

655. Miller, M. L., and McLean, H. V., The status of the emotions in palpitation and extrasystoles with a note on "effort syndrome," *Psychoanal. Quart.*, 1941, **10**, 545-560.

656. Millet, J. A. P., and Mosse, E. P., On certain psychological aspects of electroshock therapy, *Psychosom. Med.*, 1944, **6**, 226-236.

657. Mira, E., Myokinetic psychodiagnosis: A new technique of exploring the conative trends of personality, *Proc. Royal Soc. Med.*, 1940, **33**, 173-194.

658. Mittelmann, B., Allergic pruritus—neurotic excoriations, *J. Allergy*, 1933, 4, 141-145.

659. Mittelmann, B., Psychogenic factors and psychotherapy in hyperthyreosis and rapid heart imbalance, *J. Nerv. Ment. Dis.*, 1933, **77**, 465-488.

660. Mittelmann, B., Juvenile adiposogenital dystrophy: Neurological and psychopathological aspects: Results of organotherapy and psychotherapy, *Endocrinology*, 1938, **23**, 637-655.

661. Mittelmann, B., Euphoric reactions in the course of psychoanalytic treatment, *Psychoanal. Rev.*, 1940, **27**, 27-44.

662. Mittelmann, B., Complementary neurotic reactions in intimate relationships, *Psychoanal. Quart*, 1944, **13**, 479-491.

663. Mittelmann, B., Psychoanalytic observations on dreams and psychosomatic

reactions in response to hypnotics and anaesthetics, *Psychoanal. Quart.*, 1945, **14**, 498-510.

664. Mittelmann, B., Psychosomatic medicine and the older patient, in Kaplan, O. J., *Mental Disorders in Later Life*, Stanford Univ. Press, Stanford, Calif., 1945.
665. Mittelmann, B., Psychosomatics, in Harriman, P. L., *Encyclopedia of Psychology*, Philosophical Library, New York, 1946.
666. Mittelmann, B., Psychoanalytic observations on skin disorders, *Bull. Menninger Clin.*, 1947, **11**, 169-176.
667. Mittelmann, B., Psychopathology of epilepsy, in Hoch, P. H., and Knight, R. P., *Epilepsy*, Grune & Stratton, New York, 1947.
668. Mittelmann, B., The concurrent analysis of married couples, *Psychoanal. Quart.*, 1948, **17**, 182-197.
669. Mittelmann, B., Ego functions and dreams, *Psychoanal. Quart.*, 1949, **18**, 434-448.
670. Mittelmann, B., Briefer psychotherapy in psychosomatic disorders of children and adolescents, *Nerv. Child*, 1949, **8**, 291-310.
671. Mittelmann, B., Brodman, K., Weider, A., Wechsler, D., and Wolff, H. G., The Cornell Indices and the Cornell Word Form, *Ann. N.Y. Acad. Sci.*, 1946, **46**, 573-591.
672. Mittelmann, B., Weider, A., Brodman, K., Wechsler, D., and Wolff, H. G., Personality and psychosomatic disturbances in patients on medical and surgical wards: A survey of 450 admissions, *Psychosom. Med.*, 1945, **7**, 220-223.
673. Mittelmann, B., Weider, A., Vonachen, H. A., Kronenberger, M., Weider, N., Brodman, K., and Wolff, H. G., Detection and management of personality and psychosomatic disorders among industrial personnel, *Psychosom. Med.*, 1945, **7**, 359-367.
674. Mittelmann, B., and Wolff, H. G., Affective states and skin temperature: Experimental study of subjects with "cold hands" and Raynaud's Syndrome, *Psychosom. Med.*, 1939, **1**, 271-292.
675. Mittelmann, B., and Wolff, H. G., Emotions and gastroduodenal function: Experimental studies on patients with gastritis, duodenitis and peptic ulcer, *Psychosom. Med.*, 1942, **4**, 5-61.
676. Mittelmann, B., and Wolff, H. G., Emotions and skin temperature: Observations on patients during psychotherapeutic (psychoanalytic) interviews, *Psychosom. Med.*, 1943, **5**, 211-231.
677. Moloney, J. C., On Oriental stoicism, *Amer. J. Psychiat.*, 1946, **103**, 60-64.
678. Monroe, M., *Children Who Cannot Read*, Univ. of Chicago Press, Chicago, 1932.
679. Moreno, J. L., *Who Shall Survive?* Nerv. & Ment. Dis. Pub., Washington, 1934.
680. Moreno, J. L., *Psychodrama*, Vol. I, Beacon House, New York, 1946.
681. Morgan, C. T., *Physiological Psychology*, McGraw-Hill, New York, 1943.
682. Morgan, C. T., and Morgan, J. D., Auditory induction of an abnormal pattern of behavior in rats, *J. Comp. Psychol.*, 1939, **27**, 505-508.
683. Morgan, J. J. B., and Lovell, G. D., *The Psychology of Abnormal People*, Longmans, Green, New York, 3rd ed., 1948.

684. Morgan, L. D., Alterations in the hypothalamus in mental deficiency, *Psychosom. Med.,* 1939, **1,** 496-507.
685. Morlan, G. K., The statistical concept of normal: A criticism, *J. Gen. Psychol.,* 1948, **38,** 51-56.
686. Moses, L., Psychodynamic and electroencephalographic factors in duodenal ulcer, *Psychosom. Med.,* 1946, **8,** 405-410.
687. Moses, P. J., The study of personality from records of the voice, *J. Consult. Psychol.,* 1942, **6,** 257-261.
688. Mosse, E. P., Painting-analysis in the treatment of neuroses, *Psychoanal. Rev.,* 1940, **27,** 65-82.
689. Mosse, E. P., Electroshock and personality structure, *J. Nerv. Ment. Dis.,* 1946, **104,** 296-302.
690. Moulton, R., A psychosomatic study of anorexia nervosa, *Psychosom. Med.,* 1942, **4,** 62-74.
691. Moulton, R., The psychosomatic implications of pseudocyesis, *Psychosom. Med.,* 1942, **4,** 376-389.
692. Mowrer, O. H., An experimental analogue of "regression" with incidental observations on "reaction-formation," *J. Abnorm. Soc. Psychol.,* 1940, **35,** 56-87.
693. Mowrer, O. H., Learning theory and the neurotic paradox, *Amer. J. Orthopsychiat.,* 1948, **18,** 571-609.
694. Mowrer, O. H., What is normal behavior, in Pennington, L., and Berg, I., *An Introduction to Clinical Psychology,* Ronald, New York, 1948.
695. Mowrer, O. H., and Mowrer, W. M., Enuresis—A method for its study and treatment, *Amer. J. Orthopsychiat.,* 1938, **8,** 436-457.
696. Mowrer, O. H., and Ullman, A. D., Time as a determinant in integrative learning, *Psychol. Rev.,* 1945, **52,** 61-90.
697. Muench, G. A., A follow-up of mental defectives after 18 years, *J. Abnorm. Soc. Psychol.,* 1944, **39,** 407-418.
698. Muncie, W., *Psychobiology and Psychiatry,* Mosby, St. Louis, 2nd ed., 1948.
699. Munroe, R. L., Prediction of the adjustment and academic performance of college students by a modification of the Rorschach Method, *Appl. Psychol. Monog,* No. 7, Amer. Assoc. Appl. Psychol., 1945.
700. Munroe, R. L., *Trends and Schools in Psychoanalysis,* Dryden, New York (in press).
701. Murdock, G. P., *Social Structure,* Macmillan, New York, 1949.
702. Murphy, G., *Personality: A Biosocial Approach to Origins and Structure,* Harper, New York, 1947.
703. Murphy, G., Murphy, L. B., and Newcomb, T., *Experimental Social Psychology,* Harper, New York, rev. ed., 1937.
704. Murphy, L. B., *Social Behavior and Child Personality: An Exploratory Study of Some Roots of Sympathy,* Columbia Univ. Press, New York, 1937.
705. Murray, H. A., and others, *Explorations in Personality,* Oxford Univ. Press, New York, 1938.
706. Myerson, A., The relationship of hereditary factors to mental processes, in *The Inter-Relationship of Mind and Body,* Williams & Wilkins, Baltimore, 1939.

707. Myerson, A., Scrutiny, social anxiety, and inner turmoil in relationship to schizophrenia, *Amer. J. Psychiat.*, 1948, **105**, 401-409.
708. Naumburg, M., Studies of the "free" art expression of behavior problem children and adolescents as a means of diagnosis and therapy, *Nerv. Ment. Dis. Monog.*, No. 71, 1947.
709. Needles, W., A statistical study of 100 neuropsychiatric casualties from the Normandy campaign, *Amer. J. Psychiat.*, 1945, **102**, 214-221.
710. Newcomb, T. M., Hartley, E. L., and others, *Readings in Social Psychology*, Holt, New York, 1947.
711. Newman, F. B., The adolescent in social groups: Studies in the observation of personality, *Appl. Psychol. Monog.*, No. 9, Amer. Psychol. Assoc., 1946.
712. Nunberg, H., Practice and theory of psychoanalysis, *Nerv. Ment. Dis. Monog.*, No. 74, 1948.
713. Obermayer, M. E., and Greenson, R. R., Treatment by suggestion of verrucae planae of the face, *Psychosom. Med.*, 1949, **11**, 163-164.
714. Oberndorf, P. C., Constant elements in psychotherapy, *Psychoanal. Quart.*, 1946, **15**, 435-449.
715. Oberndorf, P. C., On retaining the sense of reality in states of depersonalization, *Int. J. Psychoanal.*, 1939, **20**, 137-147.
716. O'Kelly, L. I., *Introduction to Psychopathology*, Prentice-Hall, New York, 1949.
717. O'Kelly, L. I., and Steckle, L., A note on long-enduring emotional responses in the rat, *J. Psychol.*, 1939, **8**, 125-131.
718. Olden, C., Headline intelligence, in *The Psychoanalytic Study of the Child*, Vol. II, Internat. Univ. Press, New York, 1946.
719. Orr, D. W., A psychoanalytic study of a fraternal twin, *Psychoanal. Quart.*, 1941, **10**, 284-296.
720. O'Shea, H. E., Problems in college student adjustment service. *J. Consult. Psychol.*, 1940, **4**, 210-215.
721. Overholser, W., and Richmond, W. V., *Handbook of Psychiatry*, Lippincott, Philadelphia, 1947.
722. Pacella, B., Piotrowski, Z., and Lewis, N. D. C., The effects of electric convulsive therapy on certain personality traits in psychiatric patients, *Amer. J. Psychiat.*, 1947, **104**, 83-91.
723. Page, J. D., *Abnormal Psychology*, McGraw-Hill, New York, 1947.
724. Pavlov, I. P., *Conditioned Reflexes*, Oxford Univ. Press, New York, 1927.
725. Pavlov, I. P., *Lectures on Conditioned Reflex*, International Pub., New York, 1928.
726. Pearson, G. H. J., *Emotional Disorders of Children: A Case Book of Child Psychiatry*, Norton, New York, 1949.
727. Pederson-Krag, G., Telepathy and repression, *Psychoanal. Quart.*, 1947, **16**, 61-68.
728. Penrose, L. A., *Mental Defect*, Farrar & Rinehart, New York, 1934.
729. Perls, F. S., Theory and technique of personality integration, *Amer. J. Psychother.*, 1948, **2**, 565-586.
730. Perlstein, M. A., Tridione therapy, *Amer. J. Psychiat.*, 1947, **104**, 247-253.

731. Pfeffer, A. Z., Friedman, E. D., and Wortis, S. B., Cerebral lesion resulting in spatial disorientation, *Amer. J. Psychiat.*, 1946, **103**, 72-75.

732. Phillips, W. C., *Diseases of the Ear, Nose, and Throat,* Davis, Philadelphia, 1927.

733. Piaget, J., *The Language and Thought of the Child,* Kegan Paul, Trench, Trubner, London, 1926.

734. Piaget, J., *Judgment and Reasoning in the Child,* Harcourt, Brace, New York, 1928.

735. Piaget, J., *The Child's Conception of the World,* Harcourt, Brace, New York, 1929.

736. Plant, J., *Personality and the Cultural Pattern,* Commonwealth Fund, New York, 1937.

737. Pollock, H., Malzberg, B., and Fuller, R., *Hereditary and Environmental Factors in the Causation of Manic Depressive Psychoses and Dementia Praecox,* State Hospital, Utica, N. Y., 1939.

738. Posner, B. A., Selfishness, guilt feelings and social distance, unpublished Master's Thesis, Univ. of Iowa, 1940 (quoted by Sears [843]).

739. Powdermaker, H., The channeling of Negro aggression by the cultural process, in Kluckhohn, C., and Murray, H. A., *Personality in Nature, Society, and Culture,* Knopf, New York, 1948.

740. Prague, G., The psychiatrist's roles with his patients, *Amer. J. Psychiat.*, 1938, **95**, 135-147.

741. Prescott, D. A., *Emotions and the Educative Process,* American Council on Education, Washington, 1938.

742. Preston, G. H., *Psychiatry for the Curious,* Farrar & Rinehart, New York, 1940.

743. Price, J. C., and Putnam, T. J., The effect of intrafamily discord on the prognosis of epilepsy, *Amer. J. Psychiat.*, 1944, **100**, 593-598.

744. Prince, M., *Clinical and Experimental Studies in Personality* (A. A. Roback, ed.), Sci-Art, Cambridge, Mass., 2nd ed., 1938.

745. Rado, S., The problem of melancholia, *Int. J. Psychoanal.*, 1928, **9**, 420-438.

746. Rado, S., The psychoanalysis of pharmacothymia (drug addiction): I. The clinical picture, *Psychoanal. Quart.*, 1933, **2**, 1-23.

747. Rado, S., Developments in the psychoanalytic conception and treatment of the neuroses, *Psychoanal. Quart.*, 1939, **8**, 427-437.

748. Rado, S., Examination of the concept of bisexuality, *Psychosom. Med.*, 1940, **2**, 459-467.

749. Rado, S., Mind, unconscious mind, and brain, *Psychosom. Med.*, 1949, **11**, 165-168.

750. Rahman, L., Richardson, H. B., and Ripley, H. S., Anorexia nervosa, *Psychosom. Med.*, 1939, **1**, 335-365.

751. Raimy, V. R., The self-concept as a factor in counseling and personality organization, Ph.D. Thesis, Ohio State Univ., 1943.

752. Rank, B., Putnam, M. C., and Rochlin, G., The significance of the "emotional climate" in early feeding difficulties, *Psychosom. Med.*, 1948, **10**, 279-283.

753. Rank, O., *The Trauma of Birth,* Harcourt, Brace, New York, 1929.

754. Rank, O., *Will Therapy* and *Truth and Reality,* Knopf, New York, 1947.

755. Rapaport, D., Principles underlying projective techniques, *Character and Pers.,* 1942, 3, 213-219.

756. Rapaport, D., *Emotions and Memory* (Menninger Clin. Monog. Series, No. 2), Williams & Wilkins, Baltimore, 1942.

757. Rapaport, D., Gill, M., and Schafer, R., *Diagnostic Psychological Testing,* 2 vols., Year Book Pub., Chicago, 1945.

758. Rathbone, J. L., *Relaxation,* Columbia Univ. Press, New York, 1943.

759. Redl, F., The psychology of gang formation and the treatment of delinquents, in *The Psychoanalytic Study of the Child,* Vol. I, Internat. Univ. Press, New York, 1945.

760. Reich, A., A contribution to the psychoanalysis of extreme submissiveness in women, *Psychoanal. Quart.,* 1940, **9,** 470-480.

761. Reich, W., *Character-Analysis,* Orgone Institute Press, New York, 3rd ed., 1949.

762. Reider, N., Remarks on mechanisms in non-analytic psychotherapy, *Dis. Nerv. Syst.,* 1944, **5,** 22-25.

763. Reik, T., *Masochism in Modern Man,* Farrar, Strauss, New York, 1941.

764. Reik, T., *Listening with the Third Ear,* Farrar, Strauss, New York, 1948.

765. Rennie, T. A. C., and Howard, J. E., Hypoglycemia and tension-depression, *Psychosom. Med.,* 1942, **4,** 273-282.

766. Rennie, T. A. C., and Woodward, L. E., *Mental Health in Modern Society,* Commonwealth Fund, New York, 1948.

767. Res. Pub. Assoc. Nerv. Ment. Dis., *Epilepsy,* Williams & Wilkins, Baltimore, 1947.

768. Rhine, J. B., *The Reach of the Mind,* Sloane, New York, 1947.

769. Ribble, M. A., The significance of infantile sucking for the psychic development of the individual, *J. Nerv. Ment. Dis.,* 1939, **90,** 455-463.

770. Ribble, M. A., *The Rights of Infants,* Columbia Univ. Press, New York, 1943.

771. Richter, C. P., Biology of drives, *Psychosom. Med.,* 1941, **3,** 105-110.

772. Riesman, D., *This New Man, the American,* Yale Univ. Press, New Haven, 1950.

773. Riesman, D., The themes of work and play in the structure of Freud's thought, *Psychiatry,* 1950, **13,** 1-16.

774. Rinkel, M., Greenblatt, M., Coon, G. P., and Solomon, H. C., The effect of bilateral frontal lobotomy upon the autonomic nervous system, *Amer. J. Psychiat.,* 1947, **104,** 81-82.

775. Robbins, S. B., Significance of infantile nutritional disturbances in alcoholism, *Psychoanal. Rev.,* 1935, **22,** 53-59.

776. Robbins, S. B., Neurotic disturbances in work, *Psychiatry,* 1939, **2,** 333-342.

777. Robinson, V., *Supervision in Social Case Work,* Univ. of North Carolina Press, Chapel Hill, 1936.

778. Rockwell, F. V., Welch, L., Kubis, J., and Fisichelli, V., Changes in palmar skin resistance during the Rorschach Test: II. The effect of repetition with color removed, *Monthly Rev. Psychiat. Neurol.,* 1948, **116,** 321-345.

779. Roe, A., Painting and personality, *Rorsch. Res. Exch.,* 1946, **10,** 86-100.

780. Roe, A., Psychological examinations of eminent biologists, *J. Consult. Psychol.*, 1949, **13**, 225-246.
781. Roe, A., and Burks, B., Adult adjustment of foster children of alcoholic and psychotic parentage and the influence of the foster home, *Memoirs, Section on Alc. Stud., Yale Univ.*, No. 3, 1945.
782. Roethlisberger, F. J., and Dickson, W. J., *Management and the Worker*, Harvard Univ. Press, Cambridge, Mass., 1939.
783. Rogers, C. R., *Counseling and Psychotherapy*, Houghton Mifflin, Boston, 1942.
784. Rogers, K. H., *Vocational Guidance*, Big Brother Movement, Toronto, 1943.
785. Rogers, K. H., *Street Gangs in Toronto*, Ryerson Press, Toronto, 1945.
786. Roheim, G., *Psychoanalysis and the Social Sciences*, Internat. Univ. Press, New York; Vol. I, 1947; Vol. II, 1950.
787. Romano, J., and Coon, G. P., Physiologic and psychologic studies in spontaneous hypoglycemia, *Psychosom. Med.*, 1942, **4**, 283-300.
788. Romano, J., and Engel, G. L., Physiologic and psychologic considerations of delirium, *Med. Clin. N. Amer.*, 1944, **28**, 629-638.
789. Rorschach, H., *Psychodiagnostics*, Grune & Stratton, New York, 1942.
790. Rorschach, H., and Oberholzer, E., The application of the interpretation of form to psychoanalysis, *J. Nerv. Ment. Dis.*, 1924, **60**, 225-248.
791. Rosanoff, A. J., *Manual of Psychiatry and Mental Hygiene*, Wiley, New York, 7th ed., 1938.
792. Rosanoff, A. J., Handy, L. A., and Plesset, J. R., Mental disorders in triplets, *Amer. J. Psychiat.*, 1939, **95**, 1139-1142.
793. Rose, J. A., Eating inhibitions in children in relation to anorexia nervosa, *Psychosom. Med.*, 1943, **5**, 117-124.
794. Rosen, H., and Lidz, T., Emotional factors in the precipitation of recurrent diabetic acidosis, *Psychosom. Med.*, 1949, **11**, 211-215.
795. Rosen, J. N., A method of resolving acute catatonic excitement, *Psychiat. Quart.*, 1946, **20**, 183-198.
796. Rosen, J. N., The treatment of schizophrenic psychosis by direct analytic therapy, *Psychiat. Quart.*, 1947, **21**, 3-37.
797. Rosenbaum, M., Psychosomatic factors in pruritus, *Psychosom. Med.*, 1945, **7**, 52-57.
798. Rosenberg, R., Heredity in the functional psychoses, *Amer. J. Psychiat.*, 1944, **101**, 157-165.
799. Rosenberg, S. J., and Lambert, R. H., Analysis of certain factors in histories of two hundred soldiers discharged from the army for neuropsychiatric disabilities, *Amer. J. Psychiat.*, 1942, **99**, 164-167.
800. Rosenzweig, S., A test for types of reaction to frustration, *Amer. J. Orthopsychiat.*, 1935, **5**, 395-403.
801. Rosenzweig, S., Frustration as an experimental problem, *Character and Pers.*, 1938, **7**, 126-128.
802. Rosenzweig, S., Need-persistive and ego-defensive reactions to frustration as demonstrated by an experiment on repression, *Psychol. Rev.*, 1941, **48**, 347-349.
803. Rosenzweig, S., and Kogan, K. L., *Psychodiagnosis: An Introduction to*

Tests in the Clinical Practice of Psychodynamics, Grune & Stratton, New York, 1949.

804. Rosenzweig, S., and Mason, G., An experimental study of memory in relation to the theory of repression, *Brit. J. Psychol.*, 1934, **24**, 247-265.

805. Ross, D. W., and McNaughton, F. L., Objective personality studies in migraine by means of the Rorschach Method, *Psychosom. Med.*, 1945, **7**, 73-79.

806. Rothschild, D., and Sharp, M. L., The origin of senile psychoses: Neuropathologic factors and factors of a more personal nature, *Dis. Nerv. Syst.*, 1941, **2**, 49-54.

807. Rowe, A. W., and Lawrence, H. C., The male and female gonads, *Endocrinology*, 1928, **12**, 591-662.

808. Rowland, L. W., Will hypnotized persons try to harm themselves or others? *J. Abnorm. Soc. Psychol.*, 1939, **34**, 114-117.

809. Rowntree, L. G., Psychosomatic disorders as revealed by thirteen million examinations of Selective Service registrants, *Psychosom. Med.*, 1945, **7**, 27-30.

810. Rubin, S., and Bowman, K. M., Electroencephalographic and personality correlates in peptic ulcer, *Psychosom. Med.*, 1942, **4**, 309-318.

811. Rubin, S., and Moses, L., Electroencephalographic studies in asthma with some personality correlates, *Psychosom. Med.*, 1944, **6**, 31-39.

812. Ruesch, J., Social technique, social status, and social change in illness, in Kluckhohn, C., and Murray, H. A., *Personality in Nature, Society, and Culture*, Knopf, New York, 1948.

813. Ruesch, J., and others, Chronic disease and psychological invalidism, *Psychosom. Med. Monog.*, No. 9, 1946.

814. Sachs, W., *Black Anger* (now *Black Hamlet*), Little, Brown, Boston, 1947.

815. Sakel, M., The methodical use of hypoglycemia in the treatment of psychosis, *Amer. J. Psychiat.*, 1937, **94**, 111-129.

816. Salter, A., *What Is Hypnosis: Studies in Auto- and Hetero-Conditioning*, Richard R. Smith, New York, 1944.

817. Sanders, J. J., An experimental demonstration of regression in the rat, *J. Exp. Psychol.*, 1937, **21**, 493-510.

818. Sapirstein, M. R., The effect of anxiety on human after-discharges, *Psychosom. Med.*, 1948, **10**, 145-155.

819. Saul, L. J., Psychogenic factors in the etiology of the common cold and related symptoms, *Int. J. Psychoanal.*, 1938, **19**, 451-470.

820. Saul, L. J., Hostility in cases of essential hypertension, *Psychosom. Med.*, 1939, **1**, 153-216.

821. Saul, L. J., Some observations on the relations of emotions and allergy, *Psychosom. Med.*, 1941, **3**, 66-71.

822. Saul, L. J., Davis, H., and Davis, P. A., Correlations between electroencephalograms and psychological organization of the individual, *Trans. Amer. Neurol. Assoc.*, Vol. 63, 1937.

823. Saul, L. J., Davis, H., and Davis, P. A., Psychological correlations with the electroencephalogram, *Psychosom. Med.*, 1949, **11**, 361-376.

824. Schachtel, A. H., and Levi, M. B., Character structure of day nursery children in wartime as seen through the Rorschach, *Amer. J. Orthopsychiat.*, 1945, **15**, 213-222.

825. Schafer, R., *The Clinical Application of Psychological Tests: Diagnostic Summaries and Case Studies,* Internat. Univ. Press, New York, 1948.
826. Schaffner, B., *Father Land: A Study of Authoritarianism in the German Family,* Columbia Univ. Press, New York, 1948.
827. Scheerer, M., Rothman, E., and Goldstein, K., *A Case of "Idiot Savant": An Experimental Study of Personality Organization,* Psychol. Monog., No. 269, Amer. Psychol. Assoc., Washington, 1945.
828. Scheinfeld, A., *You and Heredity,* Lippincott, Philadelphia, 1939.
829. Schilder, P. F., *Introduction to a Psychoanalytic Psychiatry,* Nerv. & Ment. Dis. Pub., Washington, 1928.
830. Schilder, P. F., *The Image and Appearance of the Human Body,* Psyche Monog., Kegan Paul, London, 1935.
831. Schilder, P. F., *Psychotherapy,* Norton, New York, 1938.
832. Schilder, P. F., The social neurosis, *Psychoanal. Rev.,* 1938, **25**, 1-19.
833. Schilder, P. F., The psychogenesis of alcoholism, *Quart. J. Stud. Alcohol,* 1941, **2**, 277-292.
834. Schilder, P. F., *Goals and Desires of Man,* Columbia Univ. Press, New York, 1942.
835. Schilder, P. F., and Kauders, O., *Hypnosis,* Nerv. & Ment. Dis. Pub., Washington, 1927.
836. Schilder, P. F., and Wechsler, D., What do children know about the interior of the body? *Int. J. Psychoanal.,* 1935, **16**, 355-360.
837. Schmideberg, M., After the analysis, *Psychoanal. Quart.,* 1938, **7**, 122-143.
838. Schmideberg, M., On querulance, *Psychoanal. Quart.,* 1946, **15**, 472-502.
839. Schneck, J. M., A military offense produced by hypnosis, *J. Nerv. Ment. Dis.,* 1947, **106**, 186-189.
840. Schrotter, K., Experimentelle Träume, *Zentralblatt f. Psychoanalyse,* 1912, **2**, 638-646.
841. Scott, W. C. M., On the intense affects encountered in treating a severe manic-depressive disorder, *Int. J. Psychoanal.,* 1947, **28**, 139-144.
842. Sears, R. R., Experimental studies of projection: I. Attribution of traits, *J. Soc. Psychol.,* 1936, **7**, 151-163.
843. Sears, R. R., *Survey of Objective Studies of Psychoanalytic Concepts,* Bull. No. 51, Soc. Sci. Research Council, New York, 1943.
844. Sears, R. R., and Sears, P., Minor studies of aggression: V. Strength of frustration-reaction as a function of strength of drive, *J. Psychol.,* 1940, **9**, 297-300.
845. Seelman, K., A case of seeming feeblemindedness and its treatment in the elementary school, *Int. J. Individ. Psychol.,* 1935, **1**, 100-108.
846. Selinsky, H., Psychological study of the migrainous syndrome, *Bull. N.Y. Acad. Med.,* 1939, **15**, 757-763.
847. Seltzer, C. C., Body disproportions and dominant personality traits, *Psychosom. Med.,* 1946, **8**, 75-97.
848. Senn, M. J. E., Emotions and symptoms in pediatric practice, *Advances in Pediat.,* 1948, **3**, 69-89.
849. Senn, M. J. E., Focal points in child development, *Wis. Med. J.,* 1948, **47**, 195-198.
850. Seward, G. H., *Sex and the Social Order,* McGraw-Hill, New York, 1946.

851. Shaffer, L. F., *The Psychology of Adjustment,* Houghton Mifflin, Boston, 1936.

852. Shakow, D., The nature of deterioration in schizophrenic conditions, *Nerv. Ment. Dis. Monog.,* No. 70, 1946.

853. Shands, H. C., and Finesinger, J. E., Lymphocytes in the psychoneuroses: Preliminary observations, *Amer. J. Psychiat.,* 1948, **105**, 277-285.

854. Sharp, I. L., The treatment of acute alcoholism by the general practitioner, *Westchester Med. Bull.,* 1946, **14**, 199-802.

855. Sharpe, E. F., *Dream Analysis: A Practical Handbook in Psychoanalysis,* Norton, New York, 1938.

856. Shaw, C. R., and McKay, H. D., *Juvenile Delinquency and Urban Areas,* Univ. of Chicago Press, Chicago, 1942.

857. Sheldon, W. H., Constitutional factors in personality, in Hunt, J. McV., *Personality and the Behavior Disorders,* Vol. I, Ronald, New York, 1944.

858. Sheldon, W. H., and Stevens, S. S., *The Varieties of Temperament,* Harper, New York, 1942.

859. Sheldon, W. H., Stevens, S. S., and Tucker, W. B., *The Varieties of Human Physique,* Harper, New York, 1940.

860. Sherman, M., and Henry, T., *Hollow Folk,* Crowell, New York, 1933.

861. Shipley, W. C., and Kant, F., The insulin-shock and metrazol treatments of schizophrenia, with emphasis on psychological aspects, *Psychol. Bull.,* 1940, **37**, 259-284.

862. Shirley, M., A behavior syndrome characterizing prematurely born children, *Child Developm.,* 1939, **10**, 115-128.

863. Silverberg, W. V., The factor of omnipotence in neurosis, *Psychiatry,* 1949, **12**, 387-398.

864. Simmel, E., Alcoholism and addiction, *Psychoanal. Quart.,* 1948, **17**, 6-31.

865. Simons, D. J., and Diethelm, O., Electroencephalographic studies of psychopathic personalities, *Arch. Neurol. Psychiat.,* 1946, **55**, 619-626.

866. Singer, G. H., The influence of sudden oppression on a racial minority, *J. Soc. Psychol.,* 1939, **10**, 127-145.

867. Skodak, M., and Skeels, H. M., A follow-up study of children in adoptive homes, *J. Genet. Psychol.,* 1945, **66**, 21-58.

868. Slater, E., Neurosis and sexuality, *J. Neurol. Psychiat.,* 1945, **8**, 12-14.

869. Slavson, S. R., *The Practice of Group Therapy,* Internat. Univ. Press, New York, 1947.

870. Small, S. M., and Milhorat, A. T., Anorexia nervosa: Metabolism and its relation to psychopathologic reactions, *Amer. J. Psychiat.,* 1944, **100**, 681-685.

871. Smith, G. M., A phobia originating before the age of three cured with aid of hypnotic recall, *Character and Pers.,* 1936, **5**, 331-337.

872. Smith, H. W., The renal circulation, Harvey Lectures, Series 35, 1938.

873. Snidecor, J. C., Why the Indian does not stutter, *Quart. J. Speech,* 1947, **33**, 493-495.

874. Snowden, E. N., Mass psychotherapy, *Lancet,* 1940, **239**, 769-770.

875. Snygg, D., and Combs, A. W., *Individual Behavior: A New Frame of Reference for Psychology,* Harper, New York, 1949.

876. Solomon, C. I., Brown, W. T., and Deutscher, M., Electroencephalography in behavior problem children, *Amer. J. Psychiat.*, 1944, **101**, 51-61.
877. Solomon, H. C., and Yakovlev, P. I., *Manual of Military Neuropsychiatry,* Saunders, Philadelphia, 1944.
878. Solomon, J., Active play therapy, *Amer. J. Orthopsychiat.*, 1938, **8**, 479-498.
879. Sonnemann, U., *Handwriting Analysis as a Psychodiagnostic Tool: A Study in General and Clinical Graphology,* Grune & Stratton, New York, 1950.
880. Sontag, L. W., The purpose and fate of a skin disorder, *Psychosom. Med.*, 1945, **7**, 306-310.
881. Sperling, M., Psychoanalytic study of ulcerative colitis in children. *Psychoanal. Quart.*, 1946, **15**, 302-329.
882. Sperling, M., Analysis of a case of recurrent ulcer of the leg, in *The Psychoanalytic Study of the Child,* Vols. III/IV, Internat. Univ. Press, New York, 1949.
883. Spiegel, H., Shor, J., and Fishman, S., An hypnotic ablation technique for the study of personality development, *Psychosom. Med.*, 1945, **7**, 273-278.
884. Spitz, R. A., The importance of the mother-child relationship during the first year of life: A synopsis in five sketches, *Ment. Hlth. Today,* 1948, **7**, 7-13.
885. Spitz, R. A., Hospitalism: An inquiry into the genesis of psychiatric conditions in early childhood, in *The Psychoanalytic Study of the Child,* Vol. I, Internat. Univ. Press, New York, 1945.
886. Spitz, R. A., Anaclitic depression: An inquiry into the genesis of psychiatric conditions in early childhood, II, in *The Psychoanalytic Study of the Child,* Vol. II, Internat. Univ. Press, New York, 1946.
887. Spitz, R. A., Hospitalism: A follow-up report, in *The Psychoanalytic Study of the Child,* Vol. II, Internat. Univ. Press, New York, 1946.
888. Spitz, R. A., Emotional growth in the first year, *Child Study,* 1947, **24**, 68-70.
889. Spitz, R. A., and Wolf, K. M., Autoerotism: Some empirical findings and hypotheses on three of its manifestations in the first year of life, in *The Psychoanalytic Study of the Child,* Vols. III/IV, Internat. Univ. Press, New York, 1949.
890. Spock, B., *The Common Sense Book of Baby and Child Care,* Duell, Sloan & Pearce, New York, 1946.
891. Squier, R., and Dunbar, F., Emotional factors in the course of pregnancy, *Psychosom. Med.*, 1946, **8**, 161-175.
892. Stagner, R., *Psychology of Personality,* McGraw-Hill, New York, 2nd ed., 1948.
893. Steinberg, A., Pastor, N., Winheld, E. B., Segal, H. I., Shechter, F. R., and Colton, N. H., Psychoendocrine relationships in pseudocyesis, *Psychosom. Med.*, 1946, **8**, 176-179.
894. Stekel, W., Der epileptische Symptomenkomplex und seine Behandlung, *Fortschr. Sexualwiss. Psychoanal.*, 1924, **1**, 17-22.
895. Stekel, W., *Technique of Analytical Psychotherapy,* Norton, New York, 1940.
896. Stephen, K., Aggression in early childhood, *Brit. J. Med. Psychol.*, 1939, **18**, 178-188.
897. Sterba, E., Analysis of psychogenic constipation in a two-year-old, in *The*

Psychoanalytic Study of the Child, Vols. III/IV, Internat. Univ. Press, New York, 1949.

898. Sterba, R., Dreams and acting out, *Psychoanal. Quart.,* 1946, **15,** 175-179.
899. Stern, A., Psychoanalytic therapy in the borderline neuroses, *Psychoanal. Quart.,* 1945, **14,** 190-198.
900. Stern, E. M., and Hamilton, S. W., *Mental Illness: A Guide for the Family,* Commonwealth Fund, New York, 1942.
901. Stern, E. S., The psychopathology of manic-depressive disorder and involutional melancholia, *Brit. J. Med. Psychol.,* 1944, **20,** 20-32.
902. Stevenson, G. H., International psychiatry in the postwar world, *Amer. J. Psychiat.,* 1944, **100,** 529-532.
903. Stevenson, I. P., Duncan, C. H., Wolf, S., Ripley, H. S., and Wolff, H. G., Life situations, emotions, and extrasystoles, *Psychosom. Med.,* 1949 **11,** 257-272.
904. Stewart, D. N., and Winser, D. M. de R., Incidence of perforated peptic ulcer: Effect of heavy air-raids, *Lancet,* 1942, **242,** 259-260.
905. Stone, C. P., *Case Histories in Abnormal Psychology,* Stanford Univ. Press, Stanford, Calif., 1943.
906. Straub, L. R., Ripley, H. S., and Wolf, S., Disturbances of bladder function associated with emotional states, *J. Amer. Med. Assoc.,* 1949, **141,** 1139-1143.
907. Strauss, A. A., and Lehtinen, L. E., *Psychopathology and Education of the Brain-Injured Child.* Grune & Stratton, New York, 1947.
908. Strauss, H., Rahm, W. E., Jr., and Barrera, S. E., Children with psychiatric disorders: I. Electroencephalographic studies, *Psychosom. Med.,* 1940, **2,** 34-42.
909. Strecker, E. A., and Appel, K. E., *Psychiatry in Modern Warfare,* Macmillan, New York, 1945.
910. Strecker, E. A., Ebaugh, F. G., and Ewalt, J. R., *Practical Clinical Psychiatry,* Blakiston, Philadelphia, 6th ed., 1947.
911. Sullivan, A., Ulcerative colitis and personality, *Amer. J. Psychiat.,* 1938, **95,** 407-420.
912. Sullivan, H. S., The modified psychoanalytic treatment of schizophrenia, *Amer. J. Psychiat.,* 1931, **87,** 519-540.
913. Sullivan, H. S., *Conceptions of Modern Psychiatry,* Wm. Alanson White Fdn., Washington, 1947.
914. Sullivan, H. S., *The Meaning of Anxiety in Psychiatry and in Life,* Wm. Alanson White Fdn., Washington, 1948.
915. Sullivan, H. S., Staveren, H., Tower, S. S., and Cohen, R. A., *Therapeutic Investigations in Schizophrenia,* Wm. Alanson White Fdn., Washington, 1947.
916. Sulzberger, M. B., and Wolf, J., The treatment of warts by suggestion, *Med. Rev.,* 1934, **140,** 552-556.
917. Sutich, A., The growth experience and the growth-centered attitude, *J. Psychol.,* 1949, **28,** 293-301.
918. Symonds, P. M., *The Psychology of Parent-Child Relationships,* Appleton-Century, New York, 1939.
919. Symonds, P. M., *The Dynamics of Human Adjustment,* Appleton-Century, New York, 1946.

920. Symonds, P. M., *The Dynamics of Parent-Child Relationships,* Columbia Univ. Press, New York, 1949.

921. Taft, J., *The Dynamics of Therapy in a Controlled Relationship,* Macmillan, New York, 1937.

922. Tait, J. W., Race prejudice and personality, *School,* 1946, **34,** 795-798.

923. Terman, L. M., Miles, C. C., and others, *Sex and Personality,* McGraw-Hill, New York, 1937.

924. Terman, L. M., and Oden, M. H., *The Gifted Child Grows Up,* Stanford Univ. Press, Stanford, Calif., 1947.

925. Theron, P. A., Peripheral vasomotor reactions as indices of basic emotional tension and lability, *Psychosom. Med.,* 1948, **10,** 335-346.

926. Thomas, G., Psychic factors in rheumatoid arthritis, *Amer. J. Psychiat.,* 1936, **93,** 693-710.

927. Thomas, G. W., Group psychotherapy: A review of the recent literature, *Psychosom. Med.,* 1943, **5,** 166-180.

928. Thompson, C., Identification with the enemy and loss of the sense of self, *Psychoanal. Quart.,* 1940, **9,** 37-50.

929. Thompson, C., *Psychoanalysis: Evolution and Development,* Hermitage, New York, 1950.

930. Thorpe, L. P., and Katz, B., *The Psychology of Abnormal Behavior: A Dynamic Approach,* Ronald, New York, 1948.

931. Thunberg, T., The barospirator: A new machine for producing artificial respiration, *Skandinav. Arch. f. Physiol.,* 1926, **48,** 80-93.

932. Tiebout, H. M., Therapeutic mechanisms of Alcoholics Anonymous, *Amer. J. Psychiat.,* 1944, **100,** 468-473.

933. Tietz, E. B., Thompson, G. N., Van Harreveld, A., and Wiersma, C. A. G., Electronarcosis—A therapy in schizophrenia, *Amer. J. Psychiat.,* 1945, **101,** 821-823.

934. Tolman, E. C., *Drives Toward War,* Appleton-Century, New York, 1942.

935. Tolman, R. S., Differences between two groups of adult criminals, *Genet. Psychol. Monog.,* 1938, **20,** 353-455.

936. Tomkins, S. S., *The Thematic Apperception Test: The Theory and Technique of Interpretation,* Grune & Stratton, New York, 1947.

937. Torrance, P., The influence of the broken home on adolescent adjustment, *J. Educ. Sociol.,* 1945, **18,** 359-364.

938. Treuting, T. F., and Ripley, H. S., Life situations, emotions, and bronchial asthma, *J. Nerv. Ment. Dis.,* 1948, **108,** 380-398.

939. Tulchin, S. H., *Intelligence and Crime: A Study of Penitentiary and Reformatory Offenders,* Univ. of Chicago Press, Chicago, 1939.

940. Ullman, M., Herpes simplex and second degree burns induced under hypnosis, *Amer. J. Psychiat.,* 1947, **103,** 828-830.

941. Van der Merwe, A. B., The diagnostic value of peripheral vasomotor reactions in the psychoneuroses, *Psychosom. Med.,* 1948, **10,** 347-354.

942. Van Paassen, P., *Days of Our Years,* Hillman-Curl, New York, 1939.

943. Veblen, T., *The Theory of the Leisure Class,* Macmillan, New York, 1899.

944. Vogel, V. H., Ilbell, H., and Chapman, K. W., Present status of narcotic addiction: With particular reference to medical indications and compara-

tive addiction liability of the newer and older analgesic drugs, *J. Amer. Med. Assoc.*, 1948, **138**, 1019-1026.

945. Vollmer, H., Treatment of warts by suggestion, *Psychosom. Med.*, 1946, **8**, 138-142.

946. Von Meduna, L., and Friedman, E., The convulsive-irritative therapy of the psychoses, *J. Amer. Med. Assoc.*, 1939, **112**, 501-509.

947. Wälder, R., The psychoanalytic theory of play, *Psychoanal. Quart.*, 1933, **2**, 208-224.

948. Wall, J. H., The psychiatric problem of suicide, *Amer. J. Psychiat.*, 1944, **101**, 404-406.

949. Wall, J. H., and Allen, E. B., Results of hospital treatment of alcoholism, *Amer. J. Psychiat.*, 1944, **100**, 474-479.

950. Waller, J. V., Kaufman, M. R., and Deutsch, F., Anorexia nervosa: A psychosomatic entity, *Psychosom. Med.*, 1940, **2**, 3-16.

951. Waller, W., *The Family: A Dynamic Interpretation,* Dryden, New York, 1938.

952. Warner, W. L., Meeker, M., and Eells, K., *Social Class in America,* Sci. Res. Assoc., Chicago, 1949.

953. Warner, W. L., Havighurst, R. J., and Loeb, M. B., *Who Shall Be Educated?* Harper, New York, 1944.

954. Watson, J. B., *Behaviorism,* Norton, New York, rev. ed., 1930.

955. Watson, G., Areas of agreement in psychotherapy, *Amer. J. Orthopsychiat.*, 1949, **10**, 698-710.

956. Watson, J., Psychotherapy for the poor: A state-city cooperative enterprise in the field of mental hygiene, *Ment. Hyg.*, 1939, **23**, 558-566.

957. Wechsler, D., *The Measurement of Adult Intelligence,* Williams & Wilkins, Baltimore, 3rd ed., 1944.

958. Wechsler, D., and Harkoff, R., The clinical measurement of anxiety, *Psychiat. Quart.*, 1945, **19**, 618-635.

959. Weiss, E., Projection, extrajection and objectivation, *Psychoanal. Quart.*, 1947, **16**, 357-377.

960. Weiss, E., and English, O. S., *Psychosomatic Medicine: The Clinical Application of Psychopathology to General Medical Problems,* Saunders, Philadelphia, 1943.

961. Welch, L., The space and time of induced hypnotic dreams, *J. Psychol.*, 1936, **1**, 171-178.

962. Welch, L., and Kubis, J., The effects of anxiety on the conditioning rate and stability of the PGR, *J. Psychol.*, 1947, **23**, 83-91.

963. Wells, W. R., Hypnotizability versus suggestibility, *J. Abnorm. Soc. Psychol.*, 1931, **25**, 436-449.

964. Wells, W. R., Extent and duration of post-hypnotic amnesia, *J. Psychol.*, 1940, **9**, 137-151.

965. Wells, W. R., Ability to resist artificially induced dissociation, *J. Abnorm. Soc. Psychol.*, 1940, **35**, 261-272.

966. Wells, W. R., Experiments in the hypnotic production of crime, *J. Psychol.*, 1941, **11**, 63-102.

967. Wembridge, E. H., *Life Among the Lowbrows,* Houghton Mifflin, Boston, 1931.

968. Werner, H., *Comparative Psychology of Mental Development,* Follett, Chicago, 2nd ed., 1948.
969. Wertham, F., *Dark Legend: A Study in Murder,* Duell, Sloan & Pearce, New York, 1941.
970. Wexberg, E., *The Psychology of Sex,* Farrar & Rinehart, New York, 1931.
971. Wexberg, L. E., Outpatient treatment of alcoholics, *Amer. J. Psychiat.,* 1948, **104,** 569-572.
972. White, B. V., Cobb, S., and Jones, C. M., Mucous colitis—A psychological and medical study of sixty cases, *Psychosom. Med. Monog.,* 1940, **1,** No. 1.
973. White, R. W., *The Abnormal Personality,* Ronald, New York, 1948.
974. Whitehorn, J. C., The concepts of "meaning" and "cause" in psychodynamics, *Amer. J. Psychiat.,* 1947, **104,** 289-292.
975. Whitehorn, J. C., Kaufman, M. R., and Thomas, J. M., Heart rate in relation to emotional disturbances, *Arch. Neurol. Psychiat.,* 1935, **33,** 712-731.
976. Whyte, W. F., *Street Corner Society,* Univ. of Chicago Press, Chicago, 1943.
977. Wickes, F. G., *The Inner World of Man,* Holt, New York, 1948.
978. Williams, G. W., The effect of hypnosis on muscular fatigue, *J. Abnorm. Soc. Psychol.,* 1929, **24,** 318-329.
979. Wilson, G. W., A study of structural and instinctual conflicts in cases of hay fever, *Psychosom. Med.,* 1941, **3,** 51-65.
980. Witmer, H. L., *Psychiatric Interviews with Children,* Commonwealth Fund, New York, 1946.
981. Wittels, F., *Freud and His Time,* Liveright, New York, 1931.
982. Wittels, F., Phantom formation in a case of epilepsy, *Psychoanal. Quart.,* 1940, **9,** 98-107.
983. Wittkower, E., and Wilson, A. T. M., Dysmenorrhea and sterility: Personality studies, *Brit. Med. J.,* 1940, Part II, 586-590.
984. Wolberg, L. R., *Hypoanalysis,* Grune & Stratton, New York, 1945.
985. Wolberg, L. R., Hypnotic experiments in psychosomatic medicine, *Psychosom. Med.,* 1947, **9,** 337-342.
986. Wolberg, L. R., *Medical Hypnosis,* Grune & Stratton, New York, 1948.
987. Wolf, G. A., Jr., and Wolff, H. G., Studies on the nature of certain symptoms associated with cardiovascular disorders, *Psychosom. Med.,* 1946, **8,** 293-319.
988. Wolf, K. M., Evacuation of children in wartime: A survey of the literature, with bibliography, in *The Psychoanalytic Study of the Child,* Vol. I, Internat. Univ. Press, New York, 1945.
989. Wolf, S., and Almy, T. P., Experimental observations on cardiospasm in man, *Gastroenterology,* 1949, **13,** 401-421.
990. Wolf, S., and Wolff, H. G., Evidence on the genesis of peptic ulcer in man, *J. Amer. Med. Assoc.,* 1942, **120,** 670-675.
991. Wolf, S., and Wolff, H. G., *Human Gastric Function: An Experimental Study of a Man and His Stomach,* Oxford Univ. Press, New York, 2nd ed., 1947.
992. Wolff, H. G., Personality features and reactions of subject with migraine, *Arch. Neurol. Psychiat.,* 1937, **37,** 895-921.
993. Wolff, W., *The Expression of Personality: Experimental Depth Psychology,* Harper, New York, 1943.

994. Wolff, W., *The Personality of the Preschool Child,* Grune & Stratton, New York, 1946.
995. Wolff, W., *Diagrams of the Unconscious,* Grune & Stratton, New York, 1948.
996. Woodward, L. E., and Rennie, T. A. C., *Jobs and the Man,* Thomas, Springfield, Ill., 1945.
997. Woodworth, R. S., *Contemporary Schools of Psychology,* Ronald, New York, 2nd ed., 1948.
998. Wortis, S. B., Some aspects of military neuropsychiatry, *Trans. N.Y. Acad. Sci.,* 1945, Series II, Vol. 7, 167-180.
999. Wortis, S. B., Discussion of the symposium on acute and chronic alcoholism, *Westchester Med. Bull.,* 1946, **14,** 802-803.
1000. Wortis, S. B., Bender, M. B., and Teuber, H.-L., The significance of the phenomenon of extinction, *J. Nerv. Ment. Dis.,* 1948, **107,** 382-387.
1001. Wright, B., Altruism in children and the perceived conduct of others, *J. Abnorm. Soc. Psychol.,* 1942, **37,** 218-233.
1002. Yarnell, H., Fire-setting in children, *Amer. J. Orthopsychiat.,* 1940, **10,** 272-286.
1003. Yates, D. H., An association-set method in psychotherapy, *Psychol. Bull.,* 1939, **36,** 506.
1004. Yates, D. H., Relaxation in psychotherapy, *J. Gen. Psychol.,* 1946, **34,** 213-237.
1005. Young, K., Contribution of psychiatry to the study of group conflict, in *Social Conflict,* Univ. of Chicago Press, Chicago, 1931.
1006. Zeigarnik, B., Über das Behalten von erledigten und unerledigten Handlungen, *Psychol. Forsch.,* 1927, **9,** 1-85.
1007. Zilboorg, G., The dynamics of the schizophrenic reactions related to pregnancy and childbirth, *Amer. J. Psychiat.,* 1929, **8,** 733-767.
1008. Zilboorg, G., Anxiety without affect, *Psychoanal. Quart.,* 1933, **2,** 48-67.
1009. Zilboorg, G., Some sidelights on the psychology of murder, *J. Nerv. Ment. Dis.,* 1935, **81,** 442-444.
1010. Zilboorg, G., Differential diagnostic types of suicide, *Arch. Neurol. Psychiat.,* 1936, **35,** 270-291.
1011. Zilboorg, G., Considerations on suicide, with particular reference to that of the young, *Amer. J. Orthopsychiat.,* 1937, **7,** 15-31.
1012. Zilboorg, G., *Mind, Medicine, and Man,* Harcourt, Brace, New York, 1943.
1013. Zilboorg, G., and Henry, G. W., *A History of Medical Psychology,* Norton, New York, 1941.
1014. Zimmerman, F. T., Burgemeister, B. E., and Putnam, T. J., The effect of glutamic acid upon the mental and physical growth of Mongols, *Amer. J. Psychiat.,* 1949, **105,** 661-668.
1015. Zweig, S., *Mental Healers: Mesmer, Eddy, Freud,* Viking, New York, 1932.

INDEXES

Author Index

Subject Index